THE
FLEMISH SCHOOL

circa 1600 – *circa* 1900

NATIONAL GALLERY CATALOGUES

THE
FLEMISH SCHOOL

circa 1600 – *circa* 1900

BY

GREGORY MARTIN

A new edition of the *Illustrated General Catalogue* of the National Gallery Collection will be published in 1986 and also at that time the first of a new series of detailed catalogues, with illustrations en suite, dealing with the Dutch School, which will eventually cover the whole Collection. Meanwhile three of the existing schools catalogues have been reprinted, *The Earlier Italian Schools* by Martin Davies (1961), *The Flemish School* by Gregory Martin (1970), and *The Seventeenth and Eighteenth Century Italian Schools* by Michael Levey (1971). Each has been reissued without alteration to the text, but a list of paintings of the relevant school acquired since publication of the catalogue is added as an appendix. For further details about these paintings the reader is referred to the *Illustrated General Catalogue* and to the editions of the *National Gallery Report*, where fuller entries for acquisitions are supplied.

Published by order of the Trustees
National Gallery Publications
The National Gallery
London

© The National Gallery 1970
Reprinted 1986

ISBN 0 901791 02 4

Printed and bound in Great Britain by
William Clowes Limited, Beccles and London

Front Cover
Rubens 1577–1640, *A Roman Triumph* (detail)

FOREWORD

THIS CATALOGUE includes all the pictures in the National Gallery executed between *circa* 1600–*circa* 1900 by, or to be associated with, artists born or active in the southern Netherlands. For the sake of convenience—although many of the artists were in fact Flemings by birth—the volume has been called the catalogue of the Flemish School.

Many scholars have kindly given me their help, and they are thanked in the relevant place in the text. But some special acknowledgment must be made here: to Mr. Neil MacLaren for making available to me his notes and draft entries on the great majority of the pictures included in this catalogue; to the heirs of the late Dr. Ludwig Burchard and the authorities of the City of Antwerp for giving me permission, for exceptional reasons, to study the Burchard papers and notes on pictures by, or thought to be by, Rubens and van Dyck in the National Gallery (and I must thank Mr. Carl van der Velde of the Rubenianum for his help in this task); and to the staff of the Rijksbureau voor Kunsthistorische Documentatie—in particular Dr. J. Nieuwstraten—for much help and information especially concerning sales. Messrs. Christie, Manson and Woods have kindly given me frequent access to their sale records, which has also been of great help. I have very much benefited from discussions with, and information on particular points given by, Mr. Michael Jaffé, Mr. Oliver Millar, and Dr. Hans Vlieghe. The task of cataloguing the XIX-century pictures was made much easier by Mr. Ronald Alley of the Tate Gallery, who kindly made available his draft entries.

So far as the National Gallery is concerned, I must thank the members of the Conservation and Photographic Departments—the latter for taking many technical photographs, and Miss Reid and Miss Forward (notably the latter) for typing a great many of the entries. Miss Joyce Plesters of the Scientific Department has given me much advice especially on the supports used by Rubens, and has also analysed the grounds prepared for him; she has contributed appendices, which contain her findings and diagrams of the supports. Mr. Cecil Gould kindly read a good many of the page proofs. Finally, I must acknowledge a considerable debt of gratitude to Mr. Michael Levey who has helped me in innumerable ways—great and small.

Gregory Martin

This volume is one of a series produced under the editorship hitherto of the Keeper, but now of the Director, to replace the catalogue of 1929.

EXPLANATIONS

Abbreviations: Several abbreviations have been used; Burchard Documentation refers to the papers of the late Dr. Ludwig Burchard at the Rubenianum, Antwerp; the *Repertoire des Catalogues des Ventes*, 1938–64, 3 vols., by, or published under the direction of, Frits Lugt, is referred to as Lugt. Other abbreviations, fairly commonly used, are: B.I. for British Institution; coll. for collection; exh. for exhibited; R.A. for Royal Academy; R.K.D. for the Rijksbureau voor Kunsthistorische Documentatie, The Hague; Thieme Becker for Dr. U. Thieme & Dr. F. Becker *et alia, Allgemeines Lexikon der bildenden Künstler* etc., 1907–1950, 37 vols.; Witt Library for the Witt Library at the Courtauld Institute, London.

Engravings: Prints listed under this heading follow the direction of the painting, unless otherwise stated.

Measurements: All the paintings, except one, have been re-measured; measurements are given in inches and then metres; height precedes width.

Names: As far as possible names are spelt in the form most commonly used by the person concerned, or by contemporaries or near contemporaries.

Hendrick van BALEN I
1575 (?)–1632

Figure painter. Active in Antwerp. Born of parents living in Antwerp[1]; no baptismal record has been traced; however, in 1618 he stated that he was 43 years old.[2] Van Mander states that he was taught (in Antwerp) by Adam van Noort[3]; he was received as a master in the Antwerp guild of S. Luke in the year 1592/3.[4] He then probably visited Italy.[5] Frequently mentioned in the records of the guild of S. Luke, Antwerp, from 1602.[6] Married Margaretha Briers, 1605, by whom he had eleven children, three of his sons becoming painters.[7] Dean of the guild of S. Luke in 1609[8] and Dean of the guild of Romanists in 1613.[9] He had many pupils, among whom was van Dyck (*q.v.*). He died on 17 July, 1632.[10]

His portrait by van Dyck was engraved for the *Iconography*; a later state of the print is inscribed: '. . . Pictor Antv: Humanarum Figurum Vetustatis Cultor'.[11]

Among those who collaborated with him were Joos de Momper II and Jan Brueghel I and II.[12]

REFERENCES: *General:* I. Jost, *Netherlands Yearbook for the History of Art*, 1963, pp. 83 ff.

In text: (1) See Th. van Lerius, *Biographies d'Artistes Anversois*, 1881, II, pp. 234–7. (2) See F. J. van den Branden, *Geschiedenis der Antwerpsche Schilderschool*, 1883, p. 374, note 1. Van Lerius, *op. cit.*, p. 237 and note 1, is sceptical about the reliability of this statement and believes that he was born in 1573. (3) See *Le Livre des Peintres de Carel van Mander . . . (1604)*, translated with notes by H. Hymans, 1885, II, pp. 288–90, and pp. 292–4. Van Balen is not listed as a pupil in the records of the Antwerp guild of S. Luke; see also Jost, *op. cit.*, pp. 85–7. (4) See Ph. Rombouts and Th. van Lerius, *De Liggeren* etc., [1864–1876], I, p. 371. (5) See Jost, *loc. cit.*; he may well have worked in Rome as he was later to join the guild of Romanists in Antwerp, see above. (6) See Rombouts and van Lerius, *op. cit.*, pp. 420 ff. (7) See van den Branden, *op. cit.*, p. 465. (8) See Rombouts and van Lerius, *op. cit.*, pp. 446 and 452. (9) *Ibid.*, p. 371, note 1. (10) See van den Branden, *op. cit.*, p. 466. (11) See Fr. Wibiral, *L'Iconographie d'Antoine van Dyck*, 1877, p. 84, no. 42 (III). (12) See the account book of Jan Brueghel II in J. Denucé, *Letters and Documents concerning Jan Bruegel I and II*, 1934, pp. 141 ff.; and Jost, *op. cit.*, pp. 93–95.

Hendrick van BALEN I and a follower of
Jan BRUEGHEL I

659 PAN PURSUING SYRINX

Pan grabs only bull-rushes as Syrinx flees into the river Ladon. Copper, $9\frac{13}{16} \times 7\frac{5}{8}$ (0·25 × 0·194).

9

In fairly good condition. There is probably some strengthening of the darks; pointed evidence of Pan's excitement has been painted over. Yellow varnish.

The subject is taken from Ovid's *Metamorphoses*, I, 698 ff.[1]

Several attributions have been made concerning the authorship of no. 659; it was first catalogued at the Gallery as by J. Rottenhammer and J. Brueghel I[2]; then as by Jan Brueghel I and II[3]. The 1958 *Summary Catalogue* ascribed it merely to the Seventeenth Century Flemish School.

No. 659 is clearly the work of collaboration between two hands, the one being responsible for the figures and the other for the landscape and foliage. The figures bear no resemblance to the style of Jan Brueghel II, and are not delicate or brilliant enough to be by Rottenhammer, although they are accepted as his by Peltzer.[4] They seem clearly to be in the style of Hendrick van Balen I, and are probably by him as Jost has also suggested.[5] The landscape and foliage is executed in a manner closely reminiscent of Jan Brueghel I. The varnish and strengthening of the darks may well obscure the handling, which, however, does not seem to be of sufficient quality to be accepted as Brueghel's work. It is possible that it is the work of Jan Brueghel II (1601–1678); but it seems best to ascribe it here to a follower of the father.

There are few dated works by Hendrick van Balen I, and thus a definition or chronology of his œuvre is problematic. Jost has dated no. 659 between 1605–1608,[6] which may be too early.

No. 659 was probably inspired by the print of *Pan and Syrinx* designed by Hendrick Goltzius[7] (in which the figures face in the other direction), although no attempt was made to imitate the foreshortening of Syrinx's left leg or Pan's agile leap. The same print also probably inspired Rubens' rendering, in collaboration with Jan Brueghel I, of *Pan and Syrinx*, which has been acceptably dated *ca.* 1615.[8] And in spite of the evident knowledge displayed in no. 659 of the print, the fact that the position of Syrinx's arms is closer to the Rubens than to the print, may indicate that no. 659 was executed after *ca.* 1615.

COPY: Anon. sale, Christie's, 7 June, 1968 (170), panel, 11 × 8½ (0·28 × 0·216).

PROVENANCE: Perhaps in some or all of the following sales: Jan François d'Orvielle sale, Amsterdam, 15 July, 1705 (27) sold for 145 glds.[9]; Jacomo de Wit sale, Antwerp, 15 ff. May, 1741 (95), sold for 105 glds.[10]; Pieter de Klok sale, Amsterdam, 22 April, 1744 (44)[11]; Comte de Merle sale, Paillet (Paris), 1 ff. March, 1784 (45) bt. by Chariot for 580–19 livres.[12] Purchased with rest of the Edmond Beaucousin collection, 1860; lent, through the Arts Council, to the Laing Art Gallery, Newcastle-upon-Tyne, 1951–56, and to Cannon Hall, Barnsley, 1958–63.

REPRODUCTION: *National Gallery Illustrations, Continental Schools* (*excluding Italian*), 1950, p. 37, bottom.

REFERENCES: *In text:* (1) For the subject, see, for instance, M. Davies, *National Gallery Catalogues, The French School*, 1957 (2nd ed.), under Boucher no. 1090. (2) See the National Gallery catalogues from 1860–1906. (3) See the National Gallery catalogues from 1911–1929. (4) See R. A. Peltzer, *Jahrbuch der Kunsthistorischen Sammlungen des allerhöchsten Kaiserhaus*, 1916, p. 345. (5) See I.

Jost, *Netherlands Yearbook for the History of Art*, 1963, pp. 115–117. She records, note 97, Terlinden's rejection of Frimmel's attribution of no. 659 to Hendrick de Clerck. (6) *Loc. cit.* (7) See A. Bartsch, *Le Peintre Graveur* etc., 1803, III, p. 105, no. 18. (8) Private collection; see M. Jaffé, in *Studies in Renaissance and Baroque Art presented to Anthony Blunt*, 1967, p. 100 and fig. 5. (9) See G. Hoet, *Catalogus* etc., 1752, I, p. 82: 'Pan en Seringa, van dezelve [= van Balen and J. Brueghel I], 't landschap van Bruegel'. (10) See G. Hoet, *Catalogus* etc., 1752, II, p. 39: 'Een stukje verbeeldende den Sater Pan en Seringa door H. an Baalen, in een seer schoon Landschap van den Fluweelen Bruegel, h. 10d., br. 7d.' (11) See Hoet, *op. cit.*, p. 133: 'Pan in Seringa, door dezelven als boven [= Rottenhammer & J. Brueghel I] h. 10d. br. 7½d.' (12) As by J. Rottenhammer & J. Brueghel I; copper, 9 pouces 4 l. × 7 pouces (= *ca.* 9⅞ × 7½). For the buyer and price, see the marked catalogue in the Rijksmuseum Print Room Library.

Adriaen BROUWER
1606 (?)–1638

Genre and landscape painter. The record of his baptism has not been traced; according to Bullart, he was born at Oudenaarde and died at Antwerp aged 32.[1] The record of his burial is dated 1 February, 1638.[2] The first certain record of him is in Amsterdam in 1626. The following year he is described as the 'Constrijken en wijtberoemden Jongman Adriaen Brouwer, Schilder van Haarlem'. It is thought that he was in the northern Netherlands by 1620/21 and that he was a pupil of Frans Hals at Haarlem. He became a master in the Antwerp guild of S. Luke in the year 1631/2.[3] In 1633 he was confined in the Kasteel at Antwerp. His work was admired by Rubens.[4]

His portrait by van Dyck was engraved by Schelte à Bolswert for the *Iconography;* a subsequent state of the print is inscribed: 'Adrianus Brouwer Gryllorum Pictor Antverpiæ Natione Flander'.[5]

REFERENCE: *General:* Wilhelm von Bode, *Adriaen Brouwer*, 1924, pp. 12–25, from which the above is taken unless otherwise stated.

In text: (1) See Isaac Bullart, *Académie des Sciences et des Arts* etc., II, 1682, pp. 488–9. (2) See Ph. Rombouts & Th. van Lerius, *De Liggeren* etc., [1864–76], II, p. 22, note 2. (3) *Ibid.*, p. 22. (4) 17 paintings by Brouwer were in Rubens' collection for sale in Antwerp after his death, see J. Denucé, *The Antwerp Art Galleries, Inventories of the Art-Collections in Antwerp* etc., 1932, p. 68. (5) See Fr. Wibiral, *L'Iconographie d'Antoine van Dyck*, 1877, p. 73, no. 21.

Style of BROUWER

2569 FOUR PEASANTS IN A CELLAR

Outside men are working a bale on a pulley, attached to a house.

Oil on wood, *ca.* 10⅞ × 8¹¹⁄₁₆ (0·277 × 0·22).

The support is set in an oak tray, 11¹⁵⁄₁₆ × 9 (0·30 × 0·229).

In fairly poor condition. There is a good deal of wearing and not quite so much retouching. Damage to the peasant on the left is retouched. Cleaned, 1960.

No. 2569 was catalogued as by Brouwer from 1911–1929. The *Summary Catalogue* of 1958 ascribed it to him. The quality of execution is in fact poor. No. 2569 seems to be no more than executed in the style of Brouwer, as Knuttel[1] suggests.

PROVENANCE: Bought by George Salting for £180 after 1900[2]; exh. *The Collection of Pictures and Drawings of the late George Salting*, Agnew's, 1910 (69); George Salting Bequest, 1910; lent to the Leeds City Art Gallery, 1934; and, through the Arts Council, to the Glynn Vivian Art Gallery, Swansea, 1952–4, and the Municipal Art Gallery and Museum, Wolverhampton, 1958–60.

REPRODUCTION: *National Gallery Illustrations, Continental Schools (excluding Italian)*, 1950, p. 36, top.

REFERENCES: *In text:* (1) See G. Knuttel, *Adriaen Brouwer* etc., 1962, p. 92, note 2; Knuttel and previous National Gallery catalogues counted only three peasants in the interior; there is a fourth, however, in the background. As Knuttel pointed out, the peasant on the right is related to that in the picture by Brouwer in the Wallace Collection (no. 211). (2) Salting notebooks in the National Gallery library; the 1929 N.G. catalogue stated that Salting acquired no. 2569 'apparently' in 1904.

JAN BRUEGHEL I
1568–1625

Painter of landscapes and figures (on a small scale), and of flowers. Born in Brussels, the son of Pieter Bruegel the Elder, but active for the most of his career in Antwerp, where he died. No baptismal record has been traced; the year of his birth is taken from the inscription on his tombstone in the S. Joriskerk, Antwerp.[1] According to van Mander,[2] he was taught painting in tempera by his maternal grandmother, Meyken Verhulst (still alive in 1580), and oil painting by the Antwerp artist Peeter Goetkint († 1583).[3] Van Mander also states that he then went to Cologne, and thence to Italy. He was in Naples in June 1590,[4] and in Rome from *ca.* 1592–4[5]; there he came into contact with Cardinal Federigo Borromeo,[6] who was to remain a lifelong friend and admirer.[7] For a few months until the end of May 1596[8] he was a member of the household of the Cardinal—now Archbishop of Milan. Travelled in the Netherlands in the summer of 1596, and settled in Antwerp in September of the same year[9]; received (listed as a 'meesterssone') in the Antwerp guild of S. Luke, 1597,[10] in the Antwerp guild of Romanists in 1599,[11] and as poorter (bourgeois) of Antwerp in 1601,[12] when he was made co-Dean of the guild of S. Luke.[13] From at least 1606 he worked for the Governors of the Netherlands, which involved staying in Brussels when required.[14] Inscriptions on drawings show that he made other journeys from Antwerp: to Prague in 1604 and Spa in 1612.[15] He married twice, in 1599 and 1605, having two children by his first marriage and eight by his second.[16] He died from dysentery (?) on 13 January, 1625.[17]

There are signed and dated works for many years of his career.[18] He often worked in (not necessarily direct) collaboration with other artists, namely for instance: J. de Momper II,[19] H. van Balen I,[20] Peeter Neeffs I and H. van Steenwyck II (*q.v.*), executing the figures, flowers, or landscapes. He also collaborated with Rubens,[21] whose friend he was.[22]

His portrait was etched by van Dyck for the *Iconography*; a subsequent state of the print was inscribed: ' . . . Antverpiæ Pictor Florum et Ruralium Prospectum . . .'.[23]

Various spellings of his surname occur—a common variant being 'Breugel'[24]; he seems normally to have signed himself 'Brueghel'.[25]

REFERENCES : *In text:* (1) See Th. van Lerius, *Catalogue du Musée d'Anvers*, 1874, [3rd ed.], pp. 305 and 314; for the inscription, see, for instance, M. de Maeyer, *Albrecht en Isabella en de Schilderkunst*, 1955, p. 149, footnote 1. (2) See *Le Livre des Peintres de Carel van Mander* etc., translated and annotated by H. Hymans, 1884, I, p. 304. (3) See van Lerius, *op. cit.*, p. 305. (4) See M. Vaes, *Bulletin de l'Institut historique belge de Rome*, 1926, (6), p. 170. (5) For the most recent discussion of relevant drawings and inscriptions, see M. Winner, *Jahrbuch der Berliner Museen*, 1961, pp. 191–195. (6) See Vaes, *op. cit.*, pp. 170–173. (7) See G. Crivelli, *Giovanni Brueghel*, 1868, *passim*. (8) See Cardinal Archbishop Federigo Borromeo's letter of recommendation of 30 May, 1596, printed by Crivelli, *op. cit.*, pp. 3–4. (9) See Brueghel's letter to Borromeo of 10 October, 1596, printed by Crivelli, *op. cit.*, p. 7. (10) See Ph. Rombouts and Th. van Lerius, *De Liggeren* etc., [1864–1876], I, p. 397. (11) See Rombouts and van Lerius, *op. cit.*, I, p. 397, under note 3. (12) *Ibid.* (13) *Ibid.*, I, pp. 415–416. (14) See van Lerius, *op. cit.*, pp. 309–312; for a résumé of documents describing the privileges Brueghel thus, in time, received; see also de Maeyer, *op. cit.*, pp. 144 ff., for a full discussion of Brueghel's relationship with the court at Brussels, and the work he executed for the Governors. (15) See Winner, *op. cit.*, pp. 211–214 and pp. 220–221. (16) See van Lerius, *op. cit.*, pp. 308–9; a genealogical table of the Brueghel family is printed by J. Denucé, *Letters and Documents concerning Jan Bruegel I and II*, 1934. (17) See van Lerius, *op. cit.*, p. 314; three of his children also died of the epidemic, see de Momper's letter of 21 March, 1625, in Crivelli, *op. cit.*, pp. 337–8. For some documents concerning the estate, see Denucé, *op. cit.*, pp. 51–2, 55–7 & 140–142. (18) See A. von Wurzbach, *Niederländisches Künstler-Lexikon*, 1906, I, pp. 204–5; and Winner, *op. cit.*, *passim*. (19) See for instance, lot 5 of the *Vente publique à la maison mortuaire de Jean Bruegel de Velours*, printed by Vaes, *op. cit.*, p. 207. (20) See under no. 659, and for instance lot 3 of the Jan Brueghel the Elder (†) sale, in Vaes, *loc. cit.* (21) For a recent discussion, see J. Müller Hofstede, *Jahrbuch der Berliner Museen*, 1968, pp. 200 ff. (22) See M. Rooses and Ch. Ruelens (†), *Correspondance de Rubens*, etc., 1898, II. Rubens executed a portrait of his friend as part of his funerary monument in the S. Joriskerk, Antwerp, see van Lerius, *op. cit.*, p. 314. He had also earlier painted the *Family of Jan Brueghel*, coll. Count Antoine Seilern, see Count Seilern, *Flemish Paintings and Drawings* etc., 1955, no. 18; and H. Vlieghe, *Musées Royaux des Beaux-Arts de Belgique, Bulletin*, 1966, pp. 177 ff. (23) See Fr. Wibiral, *L'Iconographie d'Antoine van Dyck*, 1877, p. 55, under no. 1. (24) See Denucé, *op. cit.*, *passim*. (25) See, for instance, Wurzbach, *loc. cit.*

3547 THE ADORATION OF THE KINGS

Body colour on vellum, $12\frac{15}{16} \times 18\frac{7}{8}$ (0·329 × 0·48). The support has been mounted. A narrow border has been bent over the left and right edges of the mount. The top edge of the support is ragged, but what remains of the border has also been bent over; a narrow strip of the painted surface has been bent over at the bottom.

Signed and dated, : (.) *RUEGHEL in 1598*

In fairly good condition. The support is damaged through wrinkling in the top left. The signature has been bent over the mount; the first letter is lost and the next three letters are very faint. There are some water stains in the sky, and a number of small scattered losses. Not all of these are retouched; a few retouchings have darkened.

For the subject, see Matthew, II, 1 ff.[1]; the shepherds are also present.

There is no reason to doubt the authenticity of the signature and date on no. 3547.

No. 3547 is one of the earliest of a series of similar compositions by Jan Brueghel I (see below under *Versions*). The composition was probably inspired in a general way by Pieter Bruegel I's *Adoration of the Kings* at Brussels.[2] However, the tumbledown cottage, the figures standing at its door, and the King kneeling directly in front of Christ derive, presumably indirectly, from Hieronymus Bosch's *Adoration of the Kings* (Prado).[3] The poses of Balthazar (the Moorish King), S. Joseph, and the man whispering to him, and the soldier looking down in the centre, are more or less exactly copied from another *Adoration of the Kings* by Pieter Bruegel I—no. 3556 of this collection.[4] The shepherd leaning on a stick by the hound in the right foreground is copied from a drawing by Pieter Bruegel I at Dresden.[5]

The connections, noted above, with Bosch's *Adoration of the Kings*, are not exact; it is thus uncertain to what extent the relevant iconographic interpretations by Brand Philip[6] of the Prado picture should apply to no. 3547. Probably the only interpretation that might apply is the identification of the tumbledown cottage as being not only the stable at Bethlehem, but also 'the fallen hut of David'.[7] S. Joseph's carpentry tools are in the right foreground.[8]

The view of Bethlehem has not been identified as of any particular town; it is possible that it is imaginary, with the more notable features being reminiscences of identifiable buildings.[9]

VERSIONS: Vienna, Kunsthistorisches Museum, copper, $13 \times 18\frac{7}{8}$ (0.33×0.48), signed and dated 1598[10]; with differences in the figures and background view, Antwerp, Museum van den Bergh, copper, $10\frac{3}{4} \times 14\frac{3}{16}$ (0.274×0.36)[11]; Antwerp, Koninklijk Museum voor schone Kunsten, copper, $9\frac{13}{16} \times 13\frac{3}{4}$ (0.25×0.35), signed and dated, 1600[12]; Leningrad, Hermitage, *ca.* $10\frac{7}{16} \times 13\frac{7}{8}$ (0.265×0.352), signed.[13]

COPIES: Dresden, Gemälde-Galerie, no. 900, panel, $17\frac{11}{16} \times 25\frac{3}{8}$ (0.45×0.645)[14]; Antwerp, Museum van den Bergh, no. 783, panel, $29\frac{11}{16} \times 42\frac{3}{8}$ (0.755×1.076).[15]

DERIVATION: Monsignor O'Connor sale, Christie's, 28 July, 1950 (25), gouache, $9\frac{1}{2} \times 12$ (0.242×0.305).

PROVENANCE: Presented by A. A. de Pass, 1920.

REPRODUCTION: *National Gallery Illustrations, Continental Schools (excluding Italian)*, 1950, p. 36, bottom.

REFERENCES: *In text*: (1) For the *Magi*, see Martin Davies, *National Gallery*

Catalogues, Early Netherlandish School, 1968 (3rd ed.), p. 190. **(2)** Canvas, *ca.*
61¼ × 64⅛ (1·555 × 1·63), see *Musées Royaux des Beaux-Arts de Belgique,
Catalogue de la Peinture Ancienne*, 1957 (ed.), p. 26, no. 778; and F. Grossmann,
Breughel, The Paintings, (n.d.), no. 4. The connection is noted so far as the
Antwerp versions are concerned in the relevant catalogues, see below under
Versions. **(3)** See *Museo del Prado, Catálogo de las Pinturas*, 1963, no. 2048;
the picture was in Brussels for some time until 1567. **(4)** See Davies, *op. cit.*,
(1st ed. 1945), under no. 3556. **(5)** See L. Münz, *Bruegel the Drawings*, 1961,
p. 219, no. 90, and pl. 87. **(6)** See Brand Philip, *The Art Bulletin*, 1953,
pp. 267 ff. **(7)** See Brand Philip, *op. cit.*, p. 269. **(8)** For S. Joseph as carpenter,
see, for instance, Mrs. Jameson, *Legends of the Madonna*, 1879 (6th ed.), pp.
267 ff. **(9)** The tall building before the bridge, may, for instance be a reminiscence of the Roodepoorte (Porte Rouge), Antwerp, built in 1317, the last
remains of which were destroyed in 1865, see P. Génard, *Anvers à travers les
Ages*, II, 1888, p. 33. **(10)** See *Kunsthistorisches Museum, Wien, Katalog der
Gemäldegalerie*, II, 1958, p. 21, no. 60. There are some very minor differences
between this and no. 3547; the most notable is that the fingers of the Virgin's
right hand are not visible in the Vienna picture, where the houses in the right
background also slightly differ. It is difficult to decide which was painted first;
the compiler inclines to believe that it was no. 3547. **(11)** See Joz. de Coo,
Museum Mayer van den Bergh, Catalogus I, 1966, p. 42, no. 497; rep. in colour
by J. Combe, *Breughel de Velours*, 1942, pl. 1. **(12)** See *Musée Royal des Beaux-
Arts, Anvers, Catalogue Descriptif, Maîtres Anciens*, 1958, p. 37, no. 922. **(13)**
See *Musée de L'Ermitage, Département de l'Art Occidental, Catalogue des Peintures*, II, 1958, p. 40, no. 3090, and fig. **(14)** See *Katalog der Staatlichen Gemäldegalerie zu Dresden*, 1930, p. 30; the copy shows the fingers of the Virgin's right
hand. **(15)** See de Coo, *op. cit.*, pp. 45–6.

See also H. VAN STEENWYCK II, nos. 1443 and 2204; for followers
of JAN BRUEGHEL I, see H. VAN BALEN I, no. 659, and H. VAN
STEENWYCK II, no. 1132.

PAUL JEAN CLAYS
1819–1900

Marine painter. Born at Bruges. Taught in Paris by Horace Vernet and
Théodore Gudin. Lived in Antwerp until 1856, and then in Brussels,
where he died.

REFERENCE: *General*: H. Hymans, in Thieme-Becker, *Künstler-Lexikon*, 1912,
VII, pp. 73–4.

814 SHIPS LYING OFF FLUSHING

Oil on panel, 23 9/16 × 33 15/16 (0·599 × 0·868).
Signed and dated, *P. J. Clays, 1869*
In good condition. There is some paint loss round the edges and along
a crack in the support *ca.* 6 (0·152) long on the right. The craquelure
is marked and there may be some retouching in the sky. Slight surface
dirt.
There is no reason to doubt the authenticity of the signature and date[1]
on no. 814.
The view has been identified as on the Dort;[2] but a label on the
reverse, signed by Clays, and dated Brussels 1868, identifies it as 'Un
Calme plat. plusieurs Navires en Rade de Flefsingue [*sic*] par une belle
journée d'été'.

As the label is dated 1868, Clays must have signed no. 814 some time after he had painted it.

PROVENANCE: J. M. Parsons Bequest, 1870; lent to the Royal Museum, Salford, 1895, to the Stockport Museum, 1896–1901, to the Newport Museum, from 1901; transferred to the jurisdiction of the Tate Gallery, 1929, and returned 1956; lent, through the Arts Council to the National Library of Wales, Aberystwyth, 1958–61.

REPRODUCTION: National Gallery photographs available.

REFERENCES: In text: (1) The date has been misread as 1863, see R. N. Wornum, Descriptive and Historical Catalogue of the Pictures in the National Gallery ... British School, 1871, p. 21. (2) See under no. 815.

815 SHIPS LYING NEAR DORDRECHT

Oil on canvas, $29\frac{9}{16} \times 43\frac{3}{8}$ (0·75 × 1·102).
Signed and dated, P. J. Clays, 1870
In good condition. Slight surface dirt.
There is no reason to doubt the authenticity of the signature and date on no. 815.
The view has hitherto been thought to be off Flushing[1]; but a label, signed by Clays and dated Brussels 1870, on the reverse of no. 815, describes it as 'un Calme avant l'Orage aux environs de Dordrecht. (Hollande)'.[2]
The label also states that no. 815 was painted for 'Joh [sic] Parsons (à Londres)'.

PROVENANCE: Painted for John Parsons of London, 1870; J. M. Parsons Bequest, 1870; exh. at the Tate Gallery, 1900–10; transferred to the Tate Gallery, 1929, and returned, 1956.

REPRODUCTION: National Gallery photographs available.

REFERENCES: In text: (1) See for instance R. N. Wornum, Descriptive and Historical Catalogue of the Pictures in the National Gallery ... British School, 1871, p. 22, and the Summary Catalogue, 1958. (2) It seems clear that the labels on the reverse of nos. 814 and 815 were early confused.

DAVID DE CONINCK
1643 (?) or 1645 (?)–1699 or later

Animal and still life painter. Born in Antwerp[1]; spent most of his career in Rome, and died in Brussels. Evidence concerning his date of birth is conflicting: in 1675 he was stated to be 30 years old, in 1693 he was stated to be 50 years old.[2] The earliest, published record of him is as a pupil of Peeter Boel in the list of the guild of S. Luke, Antwerp, for 1659/60.[3] He became a master in the guild in 1663/4.[4] He then probably joined the workshop of Nicasius Bernaets in Paris.[5] In 1669 he decided to go to Rome, and travelled there via Bavaria, Vienna and Venice.[6] He is recorded in Rome from 1672–94.[7] His terms for returning to his native city, set out in a letter of 1687 to the Magistrates,[8] were presumably turned down[9]; he is recorded in 1699 in Brussels, where shortly afterwards he died.[10]

REFERENCE: *General:* G.-J. Hoogewerff, *Annuaire des Musées Royaux des Beaux-Arts de Belgique,* 1943–44, pp. 91–96.
In text: (1) See F. Baldinucci, *Notizie dei Professori del Disegno* etc., ed. F. Ranalli, 1847, V, p. 554. (2) See G.-J. Hoogewerff, *Studiën van het Nederlandsch Historisch Instituut te Rome,* III, *Nederlandsche Kunstenaars te Rome* etc., 1943, pp. 53 and 165. (3) See Ph. Rombouts and Th. van Lerius, *De Liggeren* etc., [1864–1876], II, pp. 304 and 305. (4) See Rombouts and van Lerius, *op. cit.,* p. 346. (5) See Hoogewerff, cited under *General Reference,* pp. 91–2, who gives this gloss on Baldinucci's muddled account. (6) See Baldinucci, *op. cit.,* pp. 554–555. (7) See Hoogewerff, cited under *General Reference,* p. 92; and in note 2, *passim.* In 1687, Coninck stated he had been in Rome for 17 years, see note 8. (8) See F. J. van den Branden, *Geschiedenis der Antwerpsche Schilderschool,* 1883, pp. 1105–6. (9) See Hoogewerff, cited under *General Reference,* p. 94. (10) See van den Branden, *op. cit.,* p. 1106.

1903 A STILL LIFE OF DEAD BIRDS AND GAME
WITH GUN DOGS AND A LITTLE OWL

Oil on relined canvas, *ca.* $37\frac{7}{8} \times 52\frac{9}{16}$ (0·962 × 1·335).
A strip *ca.* $\frac{3}{4}$ (0·02) wide down the right hand edge is wholly retouched.

In good condition. There is some wearing and retouching in the sky especially in the purples. Cleaned, 1960/1.

There are some minor *pentimenti* in the foliage against the sky, where some leaves have been suppressed. It seems probable that the ground, foliage and sky were painted in after the rest, with the sky being added last.

The dead birds include song thrushes, jays and a redstart; the dead game includes a hare, duck and partridge; the owl is a Little Owl used here as a decoy.[1] The gun dogs are probably a type of spaniel.

No. 1903 was first catalogued at the Gallery as by Fyt, and since 1911 as by Peeter Boel, which has been accepted by Greindl.[2] Neither of these attributions seems satisfactory. Mlle. Manneback has more recently suggested that no. 1903 is the work of David de Coninck.[3] This attribution seems to be acceptable, as no. 1903 seems similar in handling to the pictures by de Coninck in the Palazzo Corsini, Rome[4]; a comparable still life with gun dogs, signed by de Coninck, was in a Helbing sale (Munich) 20 December, 1917 (596).[5]

De Coninck's stylistic development is undefined, and thus it is uncertain when he executed no. 1903.

The use of an owl as a decoy bird is illustrated in Johannes Stradanus (1523–1604), *Venationes Ferarum* etc., (n.d.), no. 68.

PROVENANCE: Bought from 'an Italian nobleman' by John Benjamin Smith, *ca.* 1850[6]; presented by his son-in-law, Sir Edwin Durning-Lawrence, Bart., 1902; lent, through the Arts Council, to the Museums and Art Gallery, Leicester, 1951–53, and to the Walker Art Gallery, Liverpool, 1953–59.

REPRODUCTION: *National Gallery Illustrations, Continental Schools (excluding Italian)*, 1950, p. 22, top.

REFERENCES: *In text:* (1) Information kindly provided by M. Goodwin of the Natural History Museum, 1967. (2) See E. Greindl, *Les Peintres Flamands de la Nature Morte au XVIIe Siècle*, 1956, p. 152. (3) Letter of 1959 in the N. G. archives. (4) Nos. 903 and 905, on canvas, 38⅜ × 52⅛ (0·975 × 1·325) and 38 × 52⅛ (0·965 × 1·325), the former signed; rep. by G.-J. Hoogewerff, *Annaire des Musées des Beaux-Arts de Belgique*, 1943–44, pl. LXI (fig. 2) and LXII (fig. 3). (5) Photo in the R.K.D. (6) Letter of 1902 from Sir Edwin Durning-Lawrence in the N. G. archives.

GONZALES COQUES
1614 or 1618–1684

Portrait and figure painter. Born and worked in Antwerp, where he died. Evidence concerning his date of birth is conflicting: van Lerius claimed to have discovered his record of baptism dated 8 December, 1614[1]; on the other hand an inscription on an engraved self portrait, published in 1649, gives the year of his birth as 1618, and in 1666 Coques stated that he was 48.[2] He was listed as the pupil of Peeter Brueghel II or III in the records of the guild of S. Luke, Antwerp, for the year 1626/7.[3] The inscription on the engraved self portrait, published in 1649, states that he was the pupil of David Rijckaert[4]; he married the daughter of David Rijckaert II in 1643.[5] He became a master in the guild of S. Luke in 1640/1,[6] and Dean for the first time in 1665/6,[7] when he played an important role in defending the rights of the Olijftak, a chamber of rhetoric closely connected with the guild.[8] He married for the second time in 1675,[9] and died in 1684.[10] He numbered the House of Orange among his patrons[11]; de Bie[12] records that his work was admired by the Archduke Leopold-Wilhelm and Don Juan of Austria, successive Governor Generals of the Netherlands (from 1646–1659); in 1671 he was in the service of the then Governor General, the Count of Monterey and Fuentes.[13]

His engraved self portrait was republished in C. de Bie's *Het Gulden Cabinet* etc., 1661.[14] There his christian name is spelt Gonzalo; his name is given as Consalo in the record of baptism.[15]

REFERENCE: *General:* Th. van Lerius, *Biographies d'Artistes Anversois*, 1880, I, pp. 132 ff.

In text: (1) See van Lerius, cited under *General Reference*, pp. 134–5. (2) See F. J. van den Branden, *Geschiedenis der Antwerpsche Schilderschool*, 1883, p. 965 and note 1. The engraved self portrait was published in J. Meyssens, *Images de Divers Hommes d'esprit Sublime* etc., 1649, no. 78; and was reprinted in C. de Bie, *Het Gulden Cabinet* etc., 1661, p. 317. (3) See Ph. Rombouts and Th. van Lerius, *De Liggeren* etc., [1864–75], I, p. 635. (4) See under note 2. (5) See van Lerius, *op. cit.*, p. 138. (6) See Rombouts and van Lerius, *op. cit.*, II, p. 115. (7) *Ibid.*, p. 361. (8) See van Lerius, cited under *General Reference*, pp. 149–150, also for Coques' membership of the chamber of rhetoric. (9) See van Lerius, *op. cit.*, pp. 157–8. (10) *Ibid.*, p. 158. (11) For a recent discussion, see J. G. van Gelder, *Oud-Holland*, 1949, pp. 41 ff. (12) *Op. cit.*, p. 316. (13) See van Lerius, *op. cit.*, p. 147. (14) *Op. cit.*, p. 317. (15) See under note 1.

821 A FAMILY GROUP OUT OF DOORS

Oil on relined canvas, $25\frac{1}{4}/\frac{1}{2} \times 33\frac{5}{8}$ (0·642/8 × 0·855).

In good condition. The sky and foliage has darkened, and is retouched in places. Cleaned, 1959.

There is no reason to doubt the traditional view[1] that the figures and architecture in no. 821 are the work of Coques; the landscape and trees may be by another hand. The costumes are comparable to those in the so-called *Verbiest Family* (Royal Collection) which is signed and dated 1664,[2] and it is probable that no. 821 was executed about the same time.

The identity of the family is not known.

The youngest child is being pushed in a *loopstoel*; the girl on the right plays a cittern (?).[3] The young woman picks roses, perhaps in allusion to her forthcoming marriage.[4]

PROVENANCE: Coll. Mr. Mettepenning, Antwerp, from whom bought by C. J. Nieuwenhuys, 1826[5]; by whom sold to the Rt. Hon. Robert Peel (later Sir Robert Peel, Bart.) for 350 gns. in June 1826[6]; purchased with the Peel Collection, 1871.

REPRODUCTION: *National Gallery Illustrations, Continental Schools (excluding Italian)*, 1950, p. 66, bottom.

REFERENCE: *General:* J. Smith, *A Catalogue Raisonné etc.*, 1834, 4, Coques, no. 16.

In text: (1) See under *General Reference*. (2) Copper, $22\frac{1}{2} \times 29\frac{1}{2}$ (0·572 × 0·749), see the catalogue of *The Exhibition of the King's Pictures*, Royal Academy, 1946/7 (353); and under no. 877B. (3) Compare with the instrument played by the girl in no. 1293 of this collection by Molenaer, for which see N. Maclaren, *National Gallery Catalogues, The Dutch School*, 1960. (4) Roses are one of the attributes of Venus, see G. de Tervarent, *Attributs et Symboles dans L'Art profane etc.*, 1958, cols. 324–5. (5) See C. J. Nieuwenhuys, *A Review of the lives and works of some of the most Eminent Painters*, 1834, p. 95. Smith, cited under *General Reference*, wrongly gives the date as 1824. (6) See Peel's note in the Goulburn mss., Surrey County Record Office.

1011 PORTRAIT OF A WOMAN AS S. AGNES

Oil on silver,[1] *ca.* $7\frac{3}{16} \times 5\frac{11}{16}$ (0·183 × 0·144). The support has been slightly cut at the top, right and bottom.

In fair condition. The flesh, hair, costume and drapery are in varying degrees worn and retouched; the base of the right-hand column is worn, and the paint does not extend any more to the top of the support on the right. Cleaned, 1960/1.

No. 1011 has previously been catalogued as the work of Coques and there seems no reason to doubt this attribution.

The style of the costume suggests that no. 1011 was executed *ca.* 1680.[2]

The portico in no. 1011 closely resembles that designed by Rubens and built to join the two wings of his house in Antwerp.[3] Earlier renderings[4] of the portico show that the niches were originally bare of statues and that the outer arches were supported by free-standing columns. The architecture to the left of the portico and beyond it in no. 1011 agrees with that as it is now, although in a print of 1684[5] the wall to the left is shown flat and the window panes are different. In this print the niches contain statues, that in the centre being different from that in no. 1011. It cannot as yet be established that the portico in no. 1011 is that on Rubens' property, but the differences are so slight and the coincidence of the rest of the architecture is sufficiently striking to make it seem probable. And if such was the case, no. 1011 was evidently executed before the additions to the portico shown in the print of 1684.

The identity of the sitter in no. 1011 is not known; she is depicted as S. Agnes,[6] a lamb being this saint's traditional attribute, while the sword would refer to her martyrdom. It is possible that these attributes were included either to allude to the sitter's christian name, or to the fact that she was about to be married.[7] The portico might be a reference to the sitter's surname. Rubens' house was bought in 1660 by Jacob van Eycke († 1670)[8]; in 1680, his widow, Cornelia Hillewerve, sold it to her brother, Canon Hendrick Hillewerve.[9] If the identification of the portico as that on Rubens' property is accepted, it is possible that the sitter is a member of the Hillewerve family. None has been traced with the name Agnes,[10] and no information concerning marriages of the members of the family (or re-marriage as in the case of Cornelia) seems to be available.

PROVENANCE: Dr. Thomas Newton (1704–1782), Lord Bishop of Bristol, and others' sale, by private contract, 125, Pall Mall, 8 ff. April, 1788 (446)[11]; perhaps in the Dr. Newton, Lord Bishop of Bristol (†) sale, 22 March, 1794 (19), apparently not sold.[12] Coll. Lord Northwick (1770–1859) by 1858[13]; Lord Northwick sale, Phillips (at Thirlestane House, Cheltenham), 23 August (=17th day) 1859 (1676) bt. Agnew for James Fallows for 84 gns.[14] James Fallows (†) sale, Christie's, 23 May, 1868 (162)[15] bt. Pearce for 51 gns.[16] Wynn Ellis Bequest, 1876.

REPRODUCTION: *National Gallery Illustrations, Continental Schools (excluding Italian)*, 1950, p. 67, right.

REFERENCES: *In text:* (1) According to H. Mireur, *Dictionnaire des Ventes d'Art*, 1911, 2, p. 247, another portrait on silver given to Coques was in the Bonvoisin sale, Le Havre, 5–10 May, 1862. (2) Compare the hairstyle and costume in the *Portrait of a Woman* by Netscher of 1683 (N.G. no. 4790). (3) See F. Clijmans, *The Reconstruction of the House and Studio of Rubens*, 1946, pls. V, VI and IX. M. Rooses, *Rubens*, trans. H. Child, I, 1904, pp. 145 ff., gives a good discussion of the appearance and history of Rubens' house in Antwerp; followed by A. J. J. Delen, *Het Huis van P. P. Rubens*, 1940. Delen, p. 24, suggests that the new buildings on the site were designed by Rubens, and, p. 34, that the bas-relief's on the portico were executed by Hans van Mildert, *ca.* 1618. (4) See van Dyck's *Portrait of Isabella Brant* at Washington (G. Glück, *Van Dyck, Klassiker der Kunst*, [1931], p. 114); and Jordaens' *Gods and Nymphs before a Bath*, in the Prado (*Museo del Prado, Catálogo de las Pinturas*, 1963, pp. 331–2, no. 1548); both pictures are discussed and reproduced by Delen, *op. cit.*, pp. 61–62. (5) By Jacobus Harrewyn; the best reproduction is in Rooses, *op. cit.*, p. 148. (6) As recently pointed out by E. Plietzsch, *Holländische und Flämische Maler des XVII. Jahrhunderts*, 1960, p. 203. (7) S. Agnes was the patroness of those about to be married, see Oliver Millar, *The Tudor, Stuart and Early Georgian Pictures in the Collection of the Queen*, 1963, p. 102, no. 159. (8) See Rooses, *op. cit.*, p. 154; for this spelling of his name and his date of death, see Clijmans, *op. cit.*, p. 32, who states that van Eycke was a 'negociant ter borse van Antwerpen'. (9) Rooses, *op. cit.*, p. 148. Delen, *op. cit.*, p. 67, describes Hillewerve as priest and apostolic protonotary. Clijmans, *op. cit.*, p. 55, states that 'there is a latin poem by Desiderius Sevin in honour of Hillewerve, hinting at the embellishments of the house and at Hillewerve's new garden'. (**10**) Frans Baudouin of the Kunsthistorische Musea, Antwerp, has kindly confirmed this. (**11**) Described as a portrait of 'Agnes Rubens, painted on silver 1 ft. 3 × 1 ft.'; the sizes given included the frame. The same identification of the sitter occurs in an inscription on the reverse of no. 1011. No Agnes Rubens is known to have existed; the name was probably invented by recognition of the lamb as the emblem of S. Agnes and the portico as resembling that on Rubens' property. (**12**) Described as 'A ladies [*sic*] portrait . . . a miniature in oil'. No buyer is given in Christie's catalogue. No. 1011 certainly does not feature in the Dr. Newton (†) sale of 1790 or other subsequent sales of his collection (**13**) See *Hours in Lord Northwick's Picture Galleries* etc., 1858, p. 26, no. 143: 'Miniature of Agnes Rubens (by) Gonzales Coquis [*sic*]' as in the Principal Gallery. No. 1011 does not feature in the *Thirlestane House Guide* of 1846, and was not noted by Waagen in 1854. (**14**) Information kindly provided by N. Rosenthal. (**15**) As from the Northwick collection. (**16**) See Christie's marked copy of the catalogue.

1114 SIGHT (PORTRAIT OF ROBERT VAN DEN HOECKE)

Oil on oak, $9\frac{15}{16} \times 7\frac{5}{8}$ (0·252 × 0·195).

The reverse of the support is stamped with a flower petal motif.

The plan on the table is inscribed, *OSTENDE*

Apparently in fairly good condition. A yellow varnish makes it difficult properly to assess the state. The top of the sitter's right hand and the right hand top corner seem to be retouched. There are some small losses round the edges.

Robert van den Hoecke (1622–1668) was born in Antwerp and listed as a master in the guild there in 1644/5[1]; he was a painter and engraver, who specialized in views staffed with small figures. He entered the service of the Archduke Leopold-Wilhelm,[2] and was in Brussels in 1649[3]; he is not recorded in the records of the Antwerp guild after 1644/5. In 1661 he was described as 'Controleur des fortifications pour la service de sa Maj.^{te} [*sic*] en Flandre.'[4]

The design of no. 1114 was engraved by Caukercken and published in C. de Bie's *Het Gulden Cabinet* etc., 1661.[5] The rubric states that the engraving was after a painting by Coques. Although the engraving is in the same direction as no. 1114, and although the execution of no. 1114 is freer and coarser than is usual with Coques, it is acceptable as his work.[6]

The identification of the sitter rests on the inscription on Caukercken's engraving.[7] The plan of Ostend, baldric and sword, presumably allude to van den Hoecke's position as 'Controleur des fortifications.'[8] It is not known when he obtained this appointment. A *View of Ostend* by van den Hoecke, at Vienna, was owned by Leopold-Wilhelm,[9] who left the Netherlands in 1656.

A painting of 1659 by van den Hoecke, similar to that held by the artist in no. 1114, is at Berlin.[10] Another, whose pendant is dated 1656, is in a private collection in Brussels.[11]

No. 1114 is one of a series of the Five Senses, for which see below under no. 1117; it clearly represents *Sight*.

For the *Provenance* see under no. 1117.

ENGRAVING: By C. Caukercken. (1626–1680).[12]

DERIVATION: London Art Market, 1952.[13]

REPRODUCTION: *National Gallery Illustrations, Continental Schools (excluding Italian)*, 1950, p. 67, left.

REFERENCES: *In text:* (1) See Ph. Rombouts and Th. van Lerius, *De Liggeren* etc., [1864–1876], II, p. 157. (2) As is to be implied by the dedication in van den Hoecke's hand on a print by him in the Hofbibliothek, Vienna, quoted by A. von Wurzbach, *Niederländisches Künstler-Lexikon*, 1906, I, p. 694. (3) His *Winter Sports on the Town Moat of Brussels* at II is dated 1649, see *Kunsthistorisches Museum, Katalog der Gemäldegalerie*, II, 1958, pp. 68–69, no. 203. (4) See C. de Bie, *Het Gulden Cabinet* etc., 1661, p. 341. (5) *Ibid.* (6) See National Gallery catalogues from 1883; and, for instance, von Wurzbach, *op. cit.*, p. 335. (7) And was made apparently first by Edouard Fétis, *Galerie du Vte. Du Bus de Gisignies* etc., 1878, pp. 30–31. (8) See A. Siret, *Biographie Nationale ... de Belgique*, 1886/7, 9, col. 408. (9) See E. v. Engerth, *Kunsthistorisches Sammlungen des allerhöchsten Kaiserhauses, Gemälde, beschreibendes Verzeichniss*, 1884, II, pp. 195–196, no. 908. (10) Exh. Brussels, Musées des Beaux-Arts, 1965, see the catalogue of *Le Siècle de Rubens*, 1965, no. 111. (11) *Ibid.*, nos. 109–110. (12) See above and note 4. (13) $9\frac{1}{2} \times 7\frac{1}{2}$ (0·241 × 0·19), ascribed to Coques, private information.

1115   HEARING

Oil on oak, $9\frac{7}{8} \times 7\frac{5}{8}$ (0·251 × 0·194).

The reverse of the support is stamped with a flower petal motif.

Apparently in fairly good condition. A yellow varnish makes it difficult properly to assess the state. There are some small losses round the edges.

The man plays a lute; a music score is on the table.

The execution of no. 1115 is similar to that of no. 1114, and is thus acceptable as the work of Coques. It is one of the same series of the *Five Senses*, for which see below under no. 1117, and clearly depicts *Hearing*.[1]

The sitter may have been the flower painter Jan Philip van Thielen (1618–1677).[2]

For the *Provenance*, see under no. 1117.

REPRODUCTION: *National Gallery Illustrations, Continental Schools (excluding Italian)*, 1950, p. 68, right.

REFERENCES: *In text:* (1) See Cesare Ripa, *Iconologia*, 1645 (ed.), p. 562: 'Udito/Donna che suoni un liuto ...' (2) Compare Collin's engraving after Erasmus Quellinus' portrait in C. de Bie, *Het Gulden Cabinet* etc., 1661, p. 345. See also, F. C. Legrand, *Les Peintres Flamands de Genre au XVIIe Siècle*, 1963, p. 99. The sitter seems slightly older and certainly less well kempt in no. 1115. The same sitter occurs in the picture by Coques at the Koninklijk Museum voor schone Kunsten, Antwerp, no. 762, see under no. 1117, where he is similarly identified. Van Thielen was born in Malines, became a master in the guild at Antwerp in 1642, and remained there until 1660, when he entered the guild of his native city, see A. von Wurzbach, *Niederländisches Künstler-Lexikon*, 1910, II, p. 707.

1116   TOUCH

Oil on oak, $9\frac{7}{8} \times 7\frac{5}{8}$ (0·251 × 0·194).

The reverse of the support is stamped with a flower petal motif.

Apparently in fairly good condition. A yellow varnish makes it difficult properly to assess the condition.

The young man is letting blood from his arm.

The execution of no. 1116 is similar to that in no. 1114 and is thus acceptably the work of Coques. It is one of the same series of the *Five Senses*, for which see below under no. 1117.

Blood-letting is a variation on a theme associated with *Touch*,[1] which no. 1116 is clearly meant to depict.

The sitter has not been identified.

For the *Provenance*, see under no. 1117.

REPRODUCTION: *National Gallery Illustrations, Continental Schools (excluding Italian)*, 1950, p. 68, left.

REFERENCE: *In text:* (1) The scene may be a variation and simplification of Ripa's description of *Touch*, see Cesare Ripa, *Iconologia*, 1645 (ed.), p. 562: 'Tatto/ Donna col braccio sinistro ignudo, sopra del quale tiene un Falcone, che con gl' attigli lo stringe . . .'

1117   SMELL (PORTRAIT OF LUCAS FAYD'HERBE)

Oil on oak, $9\frac{15}{16} \times 7\frac{9}{16}$ (0·253 × 0·193).

The reverse of the support is stamped with a flower petal motif.

Apparently in fairly good condition. A yellow varnish makes it difficult properly to assess the state. The edge of the support is damaged in the top left-hand corner, and there are some small paint losses round the edges.

Lucas Fayd'herbe (1617–1697), a noted sculptor and architect, was born and mainly active at Malines; he was one of Rubens' last pupils.[1] There are works by him in many churches in the southern Netherlands.[2]

The execution of no. 1117 is similar to that in no. 1114, and is thus acceptable as the work of Coques.

The sitter has been thought to be Coques himself,[3] but more convincing is the present identification, made by comparison with P. de Jode's engraving after another portrait by Coques in C. de Bie's *Het Gulden Cabinet* etc., 1661.[4] The portrait there shows Fayd'herbe aged 44, and was thus made in 1661.

No. 1117 is one of a series of the *Five Senses* by Coques; three others are nos. 1114–1116. The fifth, *Taste*, is no. 1118, which is probably a copy (see below).

Caukercken's engraving after no. 1114 was published in 1661, see above, which provides a *terminus ante quem* for the date of execution of the whole series. Plietzsch considered the series to be early and dateable in the 1640's[5]; the costumes however do not bear this out, and it seems probable that the series was painted in the second half of 1650's.

There is a similar series by Coques at Antwerp, where the same sitters occur for *Hearing*, *Smell* and *Taste*.[6] In the National Gallery series the light falls from the left in all but no. 1114. Assuming that the series was designed to be hung in a line, the poses suggest the following order: *Smell* (no. 1117), *Hearing* (no. 1115), *Touch* (no. 1116), *Taste* (no. 1118) and *Sight* (no. 1114).

PROVENANCE: Nos. 1114–1118 were acquired from Dr. Decordes, Brussels, by the Vicomte Bernard Du Bus de Gisignies in 1857[7]; Du Bus de Gisignies (†) sale, Le Roy (Brussels), 9 May, 1882 (11–15) bought by the National Gallery.

REPRODUCTION: *National Gallery Illustrations, Continental Schools (excluding Italian)*, 1950, p. 69, right.

REFERENCES: *In text:* (1) See Rubens' letters to Fayd'herbe of 17 August, 1638, and 5 April, 1640 (?), and the certificate signed by Rubens of 5 April, 1640, in R. Magurn, *The Letters of Peter Paul Rubens*, 1955, nos. 244 and 247. (2) See the entry by G. Sobotka in Thieme-Becker. (3) See, for instance, F. C. Legrand, *Les Peintres Flamands de Genre au XVIIᵉ Siècle*, 1963, p. 99. (4) Opp. p. 500. This identification is rejected by Legrand, *op. cit.*, p. 288, note 184. Another, rather damaged and retouched portrait of Fayd'herbe, given to Coques, is in the Musées Royaux des Beaux-Arts, Brussels, see the *Catalogue de la Peinture Ancienne*, 1957, p. 32, no. 113. The same sitter, but younger, may also be the subject of no. 1012 *q.v.* (5) See E. Plietzsch, *Holländische und Flämische Maler des XVII. Jarhrhunderts*, 1960, pp. 202–203. (6) See *Musée Royal des Beaux-Arts, Anvers, Catalogue Descriptif, Maîtres Anciens*, 1958, pp. 53–4, nos. 759–763. F. J. van den Branden, *Geschiedenis der Antwerpsche Schilderschool*, 1883, p. 967, wrongly considered these to be sketches for the National Gallery series. (7) See E. Fétis, *Galerie du Vte. Du Bus de Gisignies* etc., 1878, p. 30. No Dr. Decordes sale features in Lugt.

2527 PORTRAIT OF A MAN

Oil on copper, oval, $6\frac{5}{16} \times 4\frac{13}{16}$ (0·161 × 0·122).

In good condition. Some parts of the hair are retouched, particularly on the left; the blue of the cravat ribbon is diseased and is retouched, and there are some small losses round the edges. Yellow varnish.

No. 2527 has previously been catalogued as the work of Coques, and there is no reason to doubt this attribution.

The 1915–1929 catalogues dated the costume 1640–50. This is certainly too early. Ribbons attached to sleeves, cut away at the elbow, were made popular by Louis XIV and worn *ca.* 1670.[1] The exceptionally large cravat string, worn without—apparently—the cravat, seems unusual, but also occurs in a portrait of the Prince de Ligne (1610–1679).[2]

The identity of the sitter is not known. The suggestion that he was Charles Mordaunt, 3rd Earl of Peterborough (1658–1735)[3] was already rightly rejected in the 1915 Gallery catalogue.

PROVENANCE: Probably coll. J. Lumsden Propert († by 1902), when exh. at the B.F.A.C., 1889 (case XXXV, no. 3)[4]; probably exh. The New Gallery, 1891 (1077).[5] Coll. George Salting; exh. *The Collection of Pictures & Drawings of the late George Salting*, Agnew's, 1910 (264)[6]; George Salting Bequest, 1910.

REPRODUCTION: *National Gallery Illustrations, Continental Schools (excluding Italian)*, 1950, p. 70, right.

REFERENCES: *In text:* (1) They are worn, for instance, by Louis XIV and the Dauphin in the sketch by van der Meulen of *Louis XIV at the siege of Lille*, 1667 (Musée de Versailles, exh. *Louis XIV en Flandre*, Lille, 1967–68, no. 167). (2) See the exhibition catalogue of *La Toison d'Or* etc., Bruges, 1962, no. 208 and rep. (3) A label on the reverse of no. 2527 is recorded, which thus identified the sitter; see also the National Gallery catalogue of 1912; and notes 4, 5 and 6.

(4) A miniature, described as by 'Gonzalez' of Charles, 3rd Earl of Peter-borough, 1658–1735. (5) *Ibid.* (6) Described as a portrait of 'Charles Mordaunt, Earl of Monmouth' by 'Juan G. Gonzalez'.

After COQUES

1118   TASTE

Oil on oak, $9\frac{15}{16} \times 7\frac{5}{8}$ (0·253 × 0·194).
Apparently in fairly good condition.

No. 1118 is part of the same series as nos. 1114–1117 and has thus previously been accepted as the work of Coques.[1] However, the support is thicker and bears no stamp, and the handling is weaker and less fluent. It seems probable that no. 1118 is a substituted copy after a lost original, which was part of the series and which represented *Taste*.

The same sitter occurs as *Taste* in a picture at Antwerp, where he is identified as Coques himself.[2] But the sitter in both pictures seems fairly young. The National Gallery series was probably executed in the second half of the 1650's when Coques was in his late 30's or early 40's. Further, the sitter bears little resemblance to that in Pontius' engraving after a *Self Portrait* by Coques.[3]

For further commentary and the *Provenance*, see under no. 1117.

REPRODUCTION: *National Gallery Illustrations, Continental Schools* (*excluding Italian*), 1950, p. 69, left.

REFERENCES: *In text:* (1) See for instance previous National Gallery cata-logues; and A. von Wurzbach, *Niederländisches Künstler-Lexikon*, 1906, I, p. 333. (2) See *Musée Royal des Beaux-Arts, Anvers, Catalogue Descriptif, Maîtres Anciens*, 1958, p. 54, no. 761. (3) Published in J. Meyssens, *Images de Divers Hommes d'esprit Sublime* etc., 1649, no. 78; and in C. de Bie, *Het Gulden Cabinet*, etc., 1661 etc., p. 317.

IMITATOR OF COQUES

6160   PORTRAIT OF A WOMAN

Oil on oak, $7\frac{7}{8} \times 6\frac{9}{16}$ (0·201 × 0·167).
In good condition. There is some wearing in the black of the costume. Cleaned, 1961/62.

There is a *pentimento* in the bodice, which was first a little higher on the sitter's right shoulder.

No. 6160 was bequeathed to the Gallery as the work of Coques, and has since been ascribed to him.[1] The execution is too weak, however, for this ascription to be retained. The hand responsible was clearly attempt-ing to imitate Coque's manner, but was not necessarily active in the seventeenth century.

The costume and hairstyle are reminiscent of that in fashion about the middle of the seventeenth century.[2]

The use of the niche, popularized by Dou in the northern Nether-lands,[3] does not seem to have been common in the southern Netherlands in the seventeenth century.

PROVENANCE: In the collection of Mrs. Charles S. Carstairs († 1949), Paris[4]; Mrs. Carstairs Bequest, 1952.

REPRODUCTION: *National Gallery Acquisitions, 1953–62, Exhibition Catalogue.*

REFERENCES: *In text:* (1) See the *Summary Catalogue*, 1958; and *National Gallery Acquisitions, 1953–1962, Exhibition Catalogue.* (2) The low-cut bodice and hairstyle seem to have remained in fashion into the 1660's, see no. 821. (3) See, for instance, Dou, no. 825 of this collection, and MacLaren's discussion of it in N. MacLaren, *National Gallery Catalogues, The Dutch School*, 1960, pp. 104–106. (4) Two unidentified seals are on the reverse of no. 6160: one, armorial with an Hebrew (?) inscription around it, is effaced; the second has a plant motif with three stalks, with a flower on the central stalk.

ANTHONY VAN DYCK
1599–1641

Portrait, figure painter and etcher; after Rubens, the most important artist of the seventeenth century Flemish school. Active in the Netherlands, Italy and England, where he died. Born in Antwerp, 22 March, 1599, the son of Frans van Dyck and Maria Cuperis (or Cuyperis).[1] Recorded as the pupil of Hendrick van Balen (*q.v.*) in the list for 1609 of the guild of S. Luke, Antwerp.[2] According to testimony, given in 1660, by Guilliam Verhagen, van Dyck was working independently in Antwerp, *ca.* 1615–16.[3] His payment for admission as a free master to the guild of S. Luke was credited in an account dated 11 February, 1618[4]; his father granted him his majority four days later.[5] In a record of the contract of 29 March, 1620 for paintings for the ceiling of the Jesuit Church, Antwerp, van Dyck was specified as one of Rubens' 'discipelen' who were to execute the paintings after sketches by Rubens.[6] On 17 July of the same year, it was reported that van Dyck 'sta tutavia [*sic*] con il s[r] Ribins [*sic*]'.[7] Their association may already have been of some three years standing, although what form it took—whether it was a consistent and regular arrangement—is a matter of opinion.[8] But certainly the young van Dyck learnt much from Rubens.[9]

By 25 November, 1620, van Dyck was in England in the service of James I.[10] On 26 February, 1621, he was paid £100 for 'speciall [*sic*] service . . .pformed [*sic*] for his Ma[tie]'.[11] Two days later he was issued with a pass to travel for eight months.[12]

He probably returned to Antwerp; thence, probably in November 1621, he set out for Italy; there he travelled widely and visited Sicily; the greater amount of his work was done in Genoa.[13] He made a short trip to the south of France in 1625.[14]

He returned to the Netherlands probably in the autumn of 1627[15]; and was certainly in Antwerp by the following year[16]; where he re-established his studio. In December 1628, he was given a gold chain for having executed a portrait of the Archduchess Isabella, and by 27 May, 1630 was described as her court painter.[17] In the winter of 1628 or before May, 1629, he executed, in The Hague, portraits of the Stadholder Frederick Henry, his wife and son; he was there again early in 1632.[18]

He was in London by 1 April, 1632[19]; on 5 July, he was knighted by Charles I, and was described as 'principalle [sic] paynter [sic] in Ordinary to their Majesties at St. James'.[20] His studio was established at Blackfrairs.[21]

Early in 1634, he returned to the southern Netherlands[22]; he worked mostly at Brussels,[23] where he painted the portrait of the newly appointed Governor General, the Cardinal Infant Ferdinand.[24] In the first half of 1635,[25] he returned to England. There he married Maria Ruthven, by whom he had one daughter.[26]

A passport to leave England was forwarded to him on 13 September, 1640,[27] and in October, 1640 he was in Antwerp.[28] By the 10 November he had left, according to the Cardinal Infant, for England,[29] but possibly directly for Paris, where he is recorded to have been in January, 1641.[30] He had returned to England by May, 1641.[31] He was ill for most of the summer,[32] but on the 13 August, 1641 it was reported that he planned to leave England shortly for the northern Netherlands.[33] From there he made his way to Paris, where, on the 16 November, stating that his illness was daily getting worse, he asked for a passport to return to England.[34] On the 4 December he made his will in London,[35] and died five days later.[36]

Various spellings of van Dyck's christian name occur in contemporary documents. The usual spelling on the Continent seems to have been Antonio/Anthonio,[37] and in England, Anthony (the spelling used here). Various mis-spellings of his surname also occur; he occasionally spelt it 'Dijck'.

REFERENCES: In text: (1) See P. Génard, Vlaamsche School, 1856, p. 118; and later authors. (2) See Ph. Rombouts and Th. van Lerius, De Liggeren etc., [1864–1876], I, p. 457. (3) See L. Galesloot, Annales de l'Académie d'Archéologie de Belgique, 1868, p. 570; the testimony was given in a lawsuit concerning the authenticity of a group of paintings, claimed to be by van Dyck, which had been in Verhagen's possession and had been sold to Canon Hillewerve (for whom, see under no. 1011). Verghagen's testimony and that of his wife, who stated in 1660 that the series was executed 46 years before, are not necessarily reliable. There is in fact no certain evidence concerning van Dyck's activity at this time, although several pictures, reasonably or certainly by him, have been dated or are dateable within the period 1613–17, see G. Glück, Van Dyck, K. der K., [1931], pp. 3 ff. (4) See Rombouts and van Lerius, op. cit., p. 545. (5) See F. J. van den Branden, Geschiedenis der Antwerpsche Schilderschool, 1883, p. 700. (6) For the record of the contract, see M. Rooses, L'Œuvre de P. P. Rubens, 1886, I, pp. 43 ff. (7) See the letter from Francesco Vercellini (?) to the Earl of Arundel, printed by M. Hervey, The Life . . . of Thomas Howard, Earl of Arundel, 1921, p. 175; also printed with different spelling by W. H. Carpenter, Pictorial Notices: consisting of a Memoir of Sir Anthony Van Dyck, 1844, p. 7, note 3; and by M. Rooses and Ch. Ruelens (†), Correspondance de P. P. Rubens etc., 1898, II, p. 250; according to J. S. Held, Rubens Selected Drawings, I, 1959, p. 31, note 2, Hervey's transcript is the most reliable. The information, sent to Arundel, is best seen in the light of the pressure of work to complete the Jesuit Church commission, and of the Earl's desire of getting van Dyck to come to England. (8) See under nos. 50, 680 and 853. (9) See Michael Jaffé, Van Dyck's Antwerp Sketchbook, 2 vols., 1966. As there is no sign of van Balen's influence on van Dyck, it seems fruitful to re-consider whether van Dyck could not have come into contact with Rubens *ca.* 1613, that is earlier than is now generally assumed; their relationship then would have been that of pupil and master. It is difficult to accept that this could have been the nature of their relationship after 1618, when van Dyck became a master in his own right; their relationship after 1618 was possibly increasingly in the nature of collaboration—only intermittent and subject to pressure of work on Rubens. It is noteworthy that G. P. Bellori, *Le Vite* etc., 1672, p. 254, who gives a probably unreliable account of van Dyck's activity in Rubens' studio, states that van Dyck's first work after leaving Rubens' studio was the *Christ on the way to Calvary* (Glück, *op. cit.*, p. 11), which is normally dated 1617. (**10**) See the postscript of T. Matthew's letter of 25 November, 1620, printed by Rooses and Ruelens (†), *op. cit.*, p. 262. (**11**) See Carpenter, *op. cit.*, p. 9. (**12**) *Ibid.*, p. 11. (**13**) See M. Vaes, *Bulletin de l'Institut Historique belge de Rome*, 1924, (4), pp. 163 ff., for a full, detailed discussion of van Dyck's stay in Italy; see also G. Adriani, *Anton van Dyck Italienisches Skizzenbuch*, 1965, *passim.* (**14**) See Vaes, *op. cit.*, pp. 218–19; and *Bulletin de l'Institut Historique belge de Rome*, 1925, (5), p. 152, where he suggests that his departure from Genoa was probably provoked by the war between the Genoese Republic and the Duke of Savoy. (**15**) See Vaes, *Bulletin de l'Institut Historique belge de Rome*, 1924, (4), p. 221; van Dyck's *Portrait of Pieter Stevens* (rep. by G. Glück, *op. cit.*, p. 285) is dated 1627. (**16**) He made his will in Antwerp on 6 March, 1628, see van den Branden, *op. cit.*, pp. 711–12. (**17**) See M. de Maeyer, *Albrecht en Isabella en de Schilderkunst*, 1955, pp. 193–4. (**18**) See J. G. van Gelder, *Musées Royaux des Beaux-Arts, Bulletin*, 1959, p.p 45–53. (**19**) See Carpenter, *op. cit.* p. 27, and Appendix V, p. 70. (**20**) *Ibid.*, p. 29 and note. (**21**) See Carpenter, *op. cit.*, p. 28, and p. 32, note. He presumably moved to Blackfriars round the 21 May, 1632, see Carpenter, *op. cit.*, p. 76. (**22**) On 29 March, 1634, van Dyck acquired the rights on an annual feudal rent of the fief of Steen at Elewijt, see A. Wauters, *Histoire des Environs de Bruxelles*, 1855, II, p. 685. He may have returned with his brother, Theodore Waltman, on 9 March, see F. W., *Vlaamsche School* etc., 1872, p. 133. (**23**) He was there by 14 April, when he gave his sister a proxy to administer his affairs in the southern Netherlands, see van den Branden, *op. cit.*, pp. 730–31. (**24**) Rep. by Glück, *op. cit.*, p. 423. (**25**) The precise date of his return to England is not known; a *terminus ante quem* is provided by the visit of Charles I to van Dyck's studio in June, referred to in a payment of 1635 for the construction of a causeway to van Dyck's studio, printed by L. Cust, *Anthony van Dyck*, 1900, p. 98. (**26**) See Carpenter, *op. cit.*, p. 34; his daughter was baptized on the day of his death, see p. 44. Before his marriage, Margaret Lemmon is said to have been his mistress in London, see O. Millar, *The Tudor, Stuart and early Georgian Pictures in the Collection . . . of The Queen*, 1963, p. 101, no. 157; he also had an illegitimate daughter in Antwerp at the time of his death, who was named in his will, for which see note 35. (**27**) See Carpenter, *op. cit.*, p. 42, note. (**28**) See the letter of the Cardinal Infant Ferdinand of 23 September, 1640, printed by Rooses and Ruelens (†), *op. cit.*, 1909, VI, pp. 310–11. (**29**) *Ibid.*, p. 312. (**30**) Mariette, *Abecedario de P. J. Mariette*, ed. by Ph. de Chennevières and A. de Montaiglon, 1853–4, 2, pp. 174–5, notes having seen a letter from Vignon to Langlois of this date, in which Vignon asked to be taken to visit van Dyck. Van Dyck was in Paris in order to try to gain the commission to decorate the Long Gallery of the Louvre, see Bellori, *op. cit.*, p. 263. Poussin, who was to receive the commission, arrived in Paris on 17 December, 1640; in March, 1641 he received from the King a brief which gave him 'control over the decoration of all the Royal Palaces', see A. Blunt, *The Burlington Magazine*, 1951, pp. 369 ff. (**31**) He was in England for the marriage of Prince William of Orange to Mary Stuart, which took place in London on 12 May, see R. van Luttervelt, *Oud Holland*, 1953, pp. 159 ff. (**32**) See the letter from the Countess of Roxburgh to Johan Wolfert, Count of Brederode, of this date, printed by H. Hymans, *Gazette des Beaux-Arts*, 1887, (II), p. 439; see also van Luttervelt, *op. cit.*, p. 167.

(33) See note 32 and van Gelder, *op. cit.*, p. 70. (34) See J. Guiffrey, *Antoine van Dyck* etc., 1882, pp. 214–5; and later authors. (35) For his will, see Carpenter, *op. cit.*, pp. 75–7. (36) See Carpenter, *op. cit.*, p. 44 and note; the collection of pictures, etc., which he left in England, was brought over to Antwerp in 1645, see J. Denucé, *Na P. P. Rubens*, 1949, p. 34. (37) Van Dyck's baptismal record seems not to have been published; his christian name was spelt 'Antoni' in the records of the guild of S. Luke for 1609, see note 2. He was named after his grandfather, whose christian name was spelt 'Antony' on his tombstone, see P. Génard, *Vlaamsche School*, 1856, p. 118. He spelt his christian name 'Antonius' in his signature on the *Crucifixion with SS. Catherine and Dominic* (Antwerp, Koninklijk Museum voor schone Kunsten, no. 401, rep. by G. Glück, *op. cit.*, p. 236); it was similarly spelt in the records of the church to which he gave this picture in 1629, see Rombouts and van Lerius, *op. cit.*, p. 458.

50 THE EMPEROR THEODOSIUS IS FORBIDDEN BY S. AMBROSIUS TO ENTER MILAN CATHEDRAL

The Emperor Theodosius, accompanied by three of his retinue, is stopped on the steps of Milan cathedral by S. Ambrosius, his deacon and followers.

Oil on relined canvas, $58\frac{5}{8} \times 44\frac{5}{8}$ ($1 \cdot 49 \times 1 \cdot 132$). The canvas edge is masked by binding paper.

Generally in good condition. There is some wearing in the spear, halberd and the sky—an area of blue ends inexplicably just above the heads of Theodosius' retinue—in Theodosius' right arm, and in the drapery behind and beneath it. Some small areas of impasto and dark paint in the figures are also worn. There is a small tear in the canvas in the area of the sky, and there are some losses along the top and bottom edges. The feet, left hand and tunic of the deacon have not been fully worked up. The outer part of the column in the centre and Ambrosius' lappet have become more translucent with time. Cleaned, 1959.

There are several *pentimenti*—some of which are visible to the naked eye and the others in infra-red or X-ray photography. The features of Theodosius, the acolyte with the candle and the spectator to his right have been altered; the head of the soldier on the left was first placed more to the right (and may have been different); the drapery on his shoulder and on Theodosius' shoulder has been altered; a baton held by the soldier on the left has been suppressed; the outer edge of Ambrosius' cope originally fell in a straight line away from him; the position of his hands and Theodosius' right hand have also been slightly altered, and the inner column of the central doorway was first narrower, while the entrance on the right had a more pronounced arch.

S. Ambrosius (*ca.* 340–398), Archbishop of Milan from 374, is said to have refused Theodosius (*ca.* 346–395, Emperor from 379) permission to enter Milan cathedral, because of Theodosius' punishment of the inhabitants of Thessalonica, who had murdered his general, Butheric.[1] In Jacobus de Voragine's account, Ruffinus, the master of the Emperor's knights offered to intercede and obtained from Ambrosius the rebuke 'Thou hast no more shame than an hound for to do such occision' (Caxton's translation).[2] This episode does not feature in the first

edition of Surius' edition *De Vitis Sanctorum* by Lippomani; it occurs
for the first time in the edition of 1617, of which the relevant volume
was published in 1618.[3] The inclusion of the dog in no. 50 may be
partly in allusion to Ambrosius' words, which would also thus allow
the identification of the soldier on the left as Ruffinus.

No. 50 has been generally accepted as the work of van Dyck.[4] There
is no reason to doubt that the figures are by him and much of the
architecture as well; the sky and inner columns of the architecture are
somewhat less assured in handling.

No. 50 is closely related to a larger picture in the Kunsthistorisches
Museum at Vienna, previously thought to be by Rubens, but which is
now ascribed, probably correctly, to van Dyck.[5]

No. 50 differs from the Vienna picture in several respects: the
architecture is different and includes two doorways; a dog (as an after-
thought), a spear and halberd have been added on the left; the head of
the soldier on the left has been moved closer to the edge, and his baton
has been suppressed; the features of two of the soldiers, Theodosius, the
acolyte and the two spectators, nearest the right-hand edge, are different;
the crozier has been reversed and is held higher; the fall of Ambrosius'
cope has more movement, the lappet is placed outside his cope,
and the gestures of his, and Theodosius' hands have been changed.
Infra-red and X-ray photographs of no. 50 show that in its first state,
no. 50 tended to follow the Vienna picture, although not in every
respect, and that the majority of the differences between the two pictures
are the result of *pentimenti* in no. 50. This and the size of no. 50 suggest
that it derives from the Vienna picture, which has been the traditional
view, rather than precedes it, as Glück has more recently suggested.[6]

Scholars have been unanimous in dating no. 50 to van Dyck's first
Antwerp period, that is to the period *ca.* 1615–1620.[7] The Vienna
picture is normally dated towards the end of the second decade.
Rooses[8] has noted, *inter alia*, that types similar to the soldiers occur in
the cartoons of the *History of Decius Mus*,[9] and that the two figures
behind and to the right of the Archbishop recur in the *Last Communion
of S. Francis* of 1619.[10] Van Dyck has been claimed to have had a hand
in the execution of the cartoons which had taken place at least by
early 1618.[11] The Vienna picture was probably executed at about the
same time. There is an evident difference in handling and style between
the Vienna picture and no. 50; thus a date *ca.* 1619–20 is the most
acceptable for no. 50, although granted the fact that the evolution of van
Dyck's style during his first Antwerp period has not been satisfactorily
elucidated.[12] There is nothing in the paint surface of no. 50 to suggest
that there was a significant lapse of time between the execution of the
first stage and the alterations.

The Vienna picture is very Rubensian; and Glück has suggested that
the design may have been Rubens', by associating with it the lost sketch
by Rubens of 'eenen Keyser ende Sinte Ambrosius', listed in the
inventory of Jeremias Wildens (†1653).[13] The connection between this
sketch and the Vienna picture must remain hypothetical,[14] especially

as the precise character of the relationship between the young van Dyck and Rubens is a matter largely for conjecture only—particularly so far as concerns the degree and regularity of collaboration and assistance afforded by van Dyck.[15] Nevertheless Rubens' influence is unquestionable.[16] Glück's thesis may be correct; if it is, no. 50 thus becomes van Dyck's gloss on a design by Rubens.

Rooses identified the model for one of the faces in no. 50—that second from the right—as Nicolaes Rockox (1560–1640).[17] A comparison with engravings in the *Iconography* suggests identifications for three other models, substituted by van Dyck in no. 50; a fourth, unchanged in no. 50, may be identifiable by the same means; and a fifth, altered by van Dyck in no. 50, may be identifiable by comparison with a near contemporary picture. The identities of the first three—the soldiers on the left (Ruffinus?), third from left and the spectator to Rockox's right—may have been (reading from the left): Paul de Vos (*ca.* 1596–1678),[18] Lucas Vorsterman I (1595–1675)[19] and Peeter Brueghel II (*ca.* 1564–1638).[20] The fourth model—the soldier second from the left—may have been Jan Brueghel I (1568–1625).[21] The fifth model—that of the acolyte—may be a reminiscence of van Dyck himself.[22] The model of the deacon looks also to be identifiable.[23] Van Dyck's use of models at about this time is attested by Jan Brueghel II's evidence given in a lawsuit of 1660/1, when he recalled that Peeter de Jode I had posed as an Apostle for van Dyck.[24] But these identifications are only advanced as tentative suggestions; and whether any significance can be attached to the grouping—whether the models were intended to be identifiable as portraits—is obscure.

The face of Theodosius, altered by van Dyck in no. 50, may have been inspired by an antique bust of the Emperor Galba, of which a copy drawn by Rubens was known to van Dyck.[25]

Glück has pointed out that the dog in no. 50, added by van Dyck perhaps to allude to Ruffinus (see above) and to conceal the confused sequence of legs, also occurs in his *Martyrdom of S. Sebastian* (Louvre).[26]

ENGRAVINGS: By R. W. Sievier, 1823;[27] J. H. Robinson; S. Freeman.[28]

COPY: By Sir George Hayter, panel, $17\frac{1}{2} \times 13$ (0·44 × 0·33).[29]

PROVENANCE: Perhaps P. P. Rubens (†) sale, Antwerp, 1640 (233).[30] Probably in the Roger Harenc (†) sale, Langford, 1 March, 1764 (50).[31] Apparently coll. Lord Scarborough (1725–1782) and bought from his heir by Hastings Elwyn[32]; apparently first recorded in Elwyn's possession 29 December, 1785[33]; Elwin (*sic*) sale (by private contract), [January ff.], 1787 (17) not sold[34]; still in Elwyn's possession 13 April, 1799[35]; sold to J. J. Angerstein by 1807, when lent by him to the B. I. for copying[36]; purchased with the Angerstein collection, 1824; exh. *Five Centuries of European Painting*, Whitechapel Art Gallery, 1948 (12).

REPRODUCTION: *National Gallery Illustrations, Continental Schools* (*excluding Italian*), 1950, p. 101, left.

REFERENCES: *General:* J. Smith, *A Catalogue Raisonné* etc., 1831, III, van Dyck, no. 252; M. Rooses, *L'Œuvre de P. P. Rubens*, 1888, II, under no. 387; G. Glück, *Van Dyck, K. der K.*, [1931], p. 18.

In text: (1) See Les Petits Bollandistes, *Vie des Saints* etc., 14, 1882, p. 110.

(2) For Voragine's account, see, for instance, *The Golden Legend . . . as Englished by William Caxton*, III, 1934 ed., pp. 119–121, where the Emperor's name is given as Valentinian. (3) See *De Probatis Sanctorum Vitis . . . R. P. Fr. Laurentius Surius*, 1618, II, p. 58. (4) See the authors cited under *General References*; and, for instance, L. Cust, *Anthony van Dyck* etc., 1900, p. 233, no. 10. L. van Puyvelde's attribution of no. 50 to Rubens, see *Van Dyck*, 1950, pp. 80–1, is quite unacceptable. (5) See Rooses, *op. cit.*, 1888, II, no. 387; rep. R. Oldenbourg, *Rubens, K. der K.*, [1921], p. 191. The attribution to van Dyck is due primarily to Bode, who considered that only the top part was retouched by Rubens, see W. Bode, *Great Masters of Dutch & Flemish Painting*, translated by M. L. Clarke, 1911 (ed.), p. 324–5, under note 2, and to Glück, whose essay of 1926 is reprinted in G. Glück, *Rubens, van Dyck und ihr Kreis*, 1933, pp. 275 ff., of which see p. 281; see also *Kunsthistorisches Museum, Wien, Katalog der Gemäldegalerie*, II, 1958, no. 136. The drawings in the Rubens Cantoor, Print Room of the Royal Museum of Fine Arts, Copenhagen, to which Oldenbourg, *op. cit.*, note to p. 191, refers, support Bode & Glück's contention. They consist of three copies of details of the Vienna picture (not all by the same hand); two are copies of the armour of the soldier on the left and of Theodosius (Tu. Mag. XXIII, 71 & 72), and a copy of the right arm and leg of the soldier on the left and of Theodosius (Tu. Mag. XIX, 5). This copy is inscribed 't'Theodosius naer van Dijck'. A fourth sheet (Tu. Mag. XIX, 6) contains copies of three studies of the model on the far right; the copy on the right of the sheet may derive from the Vienna picture although the eyes differ, those on the left of the sheet, probably derive from a lost drawing or oil sketch by Rubens, of which another record is on a sheet at Chatsworth, reproduced by M. Jaffé, *Van Dyck's Antwerp Sketchbook*, I, 1966, pl. V bottom, and in an oil sketch, probably wrongly attributed to van Dyck, owned by the Trustees of The Warwick Castle Resettlement, see also under note 10. Information concerning the Copenhagen drawings was kindly provided by Jan Würtz Frandsen. (6) See Glück, *loc. cit.* A notable expression of the traditional (English) view concerning no. 50 is that of Sir Thomas Lawrence writing to J. J. Angerstein from Vienna on 3 January, 1819, see D. E. Williams, *The Life and Correspondence of . . . Lawrence* etc., II, 1831, p. 131. (7) See Glück, *op. cit.*, p. 18; Rooses, *op. cit.*, 1888, II, under no. 387; and Cust, *loc. cit.* (8) *Op. cit.*, no. 387. (9) Oldenbourg, *op. cit.*, pp. 142–147. (10) See Oldenbourg, *op. cit.*, p. 190. The coincidences, noted by Rooses, cannot provide a sure indication of the date of execution of the Vienna picture, as one model, that by the door, fourth from the right, is the same as that for the earlier *S. Paul*, Prado, (Oldenbourg, *op. cit.*, p. 7 right); the model for the spectator first on the right also occurs as S. Ignatius in the picture at Genoa (Oldenbourg, *op. cit.*, p. 202) and Vienna (Oldenbourg, *op. cit.*, p. 204), and appears on the sheet of studies of heads engraved by Pontius after Rubens, rep. in Rooses, *op. cit.*, 1892, V, pl. 353. (11) See Rooses, *op. cit.*, under no. 714. Rubens wrote to Sir Dudley Carleton on 12 May and on 26 May, 1618, when he stated that the cartoons for the *History of Decius Mus* were already with the tapestry weavers at Brussels, see M. Rooses & Ch. Ruelens (†), *Correspondance de Rubens*, 1898, II, pp. 150 & 171. Van Dyck's role in their execution is first mentioned only in the 1660's—in Rubens' letter to Carleton of 12 May, 1618, quoted by Rooses, he states that he executed the cartoons. (12) The best discussion of the evolution of van Dyck's early style is that by Glück in G. Glück, *Rubens, van Dyck und ihr Kreis*, 1933, pp. 275 ff. (13) See G. Glück, *Van Dyck, K. der K.*, [1931], note to p. 18. For the sketch in the Wildens inventory, see J. Denucé, *Inventories of the Art-Collections in Antwerp* etc., 1932, p. 165. A picture, panel, 18 × 15½ (0·457 × 0·394) by Rubens of 'Theodosius' submission to St. Ambrose' was in the Edmund Antrobus sale, Christie's, 12 March, 1788 (32). (14) A copy of what may have been the sketch for the Vienna picture was in an Anon. sale, Christie's, 3 May, 1946 (147), grisaille, panel, 21 × 19¼ (0·533 × 0·488). The architecture is hardly suggested and there is no crozier. (15) Bode, *op. cit.*, pp. 298 ff. and Puyvelde, *op. cit.*, pp. 45 ff., are the two authors to claim the maximum and minimum degree of collaboration between Rubens and van Dyck.

For a further discussion of their relationship, see the biography above, and under nos. 680 and 853. (16) As is clearly shown by Jaffé, *op. cit., passim*. (17) *Op. cit.*, under no. 387. Rockox held high office in the government of the city of Antwerp, was an important patron of Rubens, and was a noted numismatist, see M. Rooses in the *Biographie Nationale . . . de Belgique*, 1907, 19, cols. 566–569; compare Paul Pontius' engraving after van Dyck in the *Iconography*. (18) Paul de Vos was an Antwerp painter of animals and hunt scenes; he was listed as a master in the Antwerp guild of S. Luke in 1620, see the entry by M. Manneback in Thieme-Becker, *Künstler-Lexikon*. Glück, *op. cit.*, p. 123, identified van Dyck's portraits in the Louvre and the Kunsthistorisches Museum, Vienna as being of de Vos on the basis of a comparison with the engraved portrait after van Dyck in the *Iconography*. These portraits were painted at the end of van Dyck's first Antwerp period, and the face there has a strong likeness with that in no. 50. Glück's identification has been questioned by L. Baldass, *Gazette des Beaux-Arts*, 1957, 50, p. 265, and in the 1958 catalogue of the pictures in the Kunsthistorisches Museum (no. 138). (19) A noted engraver, whose earlier career was spent working for Rubens, nine of his prints after the master were published in 1620; for a discussion of his career, see H. Hymans, *Histoire de la Gravure dans l'École de Rubens*, 1879, pp. 153 ff. Compare van Dyck's etched portrait of Vorsterman in the *Iconography* dates probably from the early 1630's, and the portrait given to van Dyck now at Lisbon, rep. by Glück, *Van Dyck* etc., p. 302, right. (20) Son of Pieter Brueghel I, listed as a master in the guild of S. Luke, Antwerp, in 1585, specialized in rural scenes; compare van Dyck's etched portrait in the *Iconography*. (21) The second son of Pieter Brueghel I, a flower, figure and landscape painter. See above. Compare van Dyck's etched portrait in the *Iconography*. The model (altered very slightly by van Dyck in no. 50) is not dissimilar to that in a sheet of studies of heads, engraved by Pontius, see under note 10, where the model has more curly hair. (22) Compare for instance with the earlier *Self Portrait* in the Akademie der Bildenden Künste, Vienna, rep. by Glück, *op. cit.*, p. 3, or the, *pace* Jaffé, slightly later *Self Portrait* at Fort Worth, of *ca.* 1614, see M. Jaffé, *Van Dyck's Antwerp Sketchbook*, I, 1966, fig. I, and p. 48. The colour of the hair compares well with that in the Munich *Self Portrait*, reproduced by Glück, *op. cit.*, p. 121. (23) The same model occurs in, *inter alia*, Rubens' *Descent from the Cross* (Oldenbourg, *op. cit.*, p. 52), in the portrait, coll. Prince of Liechtenstein (Oldenbourg, *op. cit.*, p. 134, right), and at Los Angeles, see J.-A. Goris and J. S. Held, *Rubens in America* [1947], no. 25, pl. 8. Jaffé, *op. cit.*, figs. IV and V, has published an oil sketch of the same model, which he gives to van Dyck, and a sheet of studies also given to van Dyck, in which the model in the same position is repeated. (24) See F. J. van den Branden, *Geschiedenis der Antwerpsche Schilderschool*, 1883, pp. 697–8. (25) See Jaffé, *op. cit.*, vol. I, pl. LI and vol. II, 67 *verso*, and note. (26) See *Rubens, van Dyck und ihr Kreis*, 1933, p. 281 and pl. 156. (27) In J. Young, *A Catalogue of the . . . Collection of the late John Julius Angerstein Esq.*, 1823, no. 2. (28) In *The National Gallery of Pictures by the Great Masters* etc. II, [1838], no. 101. (29) See *Old Masters Exhibition*, Agnew's, March–April, 1968 (34); other copies are known to have been made, see under *Provenance* and note 36. (30) See Denucé, *op. cit.*, p. 66 described as: 'Un *S. Ambroise* du mesme [= van Dyck]'. This provenance is normally claimed for the Vienna picture; the claim is to some extent justified by the fact that it, rather than no. 50, seems to have been the one available for copying in Rubens' studio, see under note 5. If its relevance is admitted, it seems more likely that the *S. Ambrosio* offered by Rubens to Vivot in Paris, see Pieresc's letter to Rubens, 14–15 April, 1621, in M. Rooses and Ch. Ruelens (†), *op. cit.*, p. 380, should have been the Vienna picture rather than no. 50 (this *pace* Rooses & Ruelens (†), *op. cit.*, p. 386). The picture in the inventory of Sebastiaan Leerse († 12 November, 1691) of Antwerp, see Denucé, *op. cit.*, p. 366, 'Een groot stuck schilderye, representerende Ambrosius ende Theodosius, van dHeer [*sic*] Antonio van Dyck in vergulde leyste' is also thought, probably rightly, to be the Vienna picture. (31) As by van Dyck: 'St. *Ambrose* refusing

Theodore's Entrance into the Church'. **(32)** See John Young, *op. cit.*, pp. 3–4, no. 2. Young in his ms. notes (National Gallery library) states that it hung in the Nursery 'and was sold at the family seat'; and the *General Evening Post*, 29 December, 1785, see The Whitley Papers, *Notes on Artists*, British Museum, Print Room, p. 1576, reported that 'It [no. 50] was some years since purchased from the Antwerp Collection [?] by the late Earl of Scarborough'. *The World* newspaper, 7 May, 1787, see The Whitley Papers, *loc. cit.*, stated 'the reputed Vandyke [=no. 50], was bought for £100 at Lord Scarborough's sale. The picture was not at Lumley Castle but at Lord Scarborough's house in Yorkshire'. No. 50 was not in the Lord Scarborough sale at Lumley 12 August, 1785; Lord Scarborough has kindly informed the writer that there are no eighteenth century inventories of the pictures at Sandbeck in his possession, and there is no catalogue of a sale at Sandbeck at this time. Edith Milner, *Records of the Lumleys of Lumley Castle*, 1904, pp. 251 and 265, refers to sales at Glentworth and Sandbeck after the deaths of the Earl of Scarborough (1782) and Sir George Savile (1784), which were made to pay off the debts of the Earl contracted in 1780–2. **(33)** See the *General Evening Post*, 29 December, 1785 (Whitley Papers, *loc. cit.*). **(34)** The sale was held in the 'Great Rooms, late the Royal Academy'. *The World*, 4 May, 1787 (Whitley Papers, *loc. cit.*) reported that '... the other day at an auction [it] sold for £100 [i.e. it was bought in at that price]. Lord Exeter is already talked of as a purchaser ...'; *The Morning Herald*, 8 May, 1787, (Whitley Papers, *loc. cit.*) reported that '£2,500 was offered Mr. Elwyn for the above Picture [=no. 50], on Wednesday, the 2nd of May'. **(35)** See Farington's entry (Farington Diary, typescript copy, British Museum, Print Room) for 13 April, 1799; 'I saw Elwin's [*sic*] picture of Theodosias [*sic*] by Vandyke [*sic*]'. Farington also records, 20 October, 1798, that Desenfans offered Elwyn 1,000 gns. for it. **(36)** See T. Smith, *Recollections of the British Institution* etc., 1860, p. 40. Young, *loc. cit.*, recorded that Angerstein had been in love with the picture for 40 years before acquiring it, which anecdote would place the date of the purchase at *ca.* 1805.

52 PORTRAIT OF CORNELIS VAN DER GEEST

Oil on oak, *ca.* $14\frac{3}{4} \times 12\frac{3}{4}$ (0·375 × 0·325).

The support is inset into another oak support, $32\frac{1}{2} \times 26\frac{3}{8}$ (0·825 × 0·67). This is made up out of four members, joined vertically. On the reverse is the brand of the coat of arms of the city of Antwerp (partly effaced), and the incised initials, *M V* (in monogram).[1]

The face and collar are in good condition. There are one or two small losses in the face, and perhaps some later, but minor amplification of the folds of the collar. The rest of the paint is much restored, and towards the edges is wholly new. Remains of a simulated, oval, porphyry surround towards the top left-hand corner have been suppressed by retouching; the high back of the collar has been reduced. Cleaned, 1948.

There are minor *pentimenti* in the outline of the ear and in some of the folds of the collar.

Cornelis van der Geest (1577–1638) was a successful Antwerp spice merchant, and an important patron of the arts and collector.[2]

The cleaning in 1948 confirmed Wornum's[3] observation that the head and collar had been inset into a larger support. But it also showed that only the head and collar was the work of van Dyck, whose authorship of the whole (bust length) had not previously been generally doubted.[4]

The Reverend James Dallaway[5] identified the sitter—previously thought to be 'Gevartius'[6]—as Cornelis van der Geest, by comparison with the portrait by van Dyck engraved for the *Iconography*,[7] where the sitter appears older than in no. 52. Dallaway's identification has rightly not been questioned.

The handling of the face and collar makes it clear that no. 52 was executed by van Dyck during his first Antwerp period, that is between *ca.* 1615–20. It may well have been executed towards the end of this period, as has been generally supposed.[8]

The cleaning in 1948 also showed that some additions on the second, larger support had themselves been painted out. These consisted in another simulated, oval, porphyry surround and an extension to bust length with the inclusion of the left hand of the sitter. Part of the Antwerp city brand on the second support has been erased by chamfering the edge. This suggests that the second support may have been cut down; perhaps the suppression of the surround and hand followed as a result. It is not known when this occurred.

The second support also bears the incised monogram of its maker, Michiel Vriendt, whose date of death—1636/7[9]—provides an approximate *terminus ante quem* for the date of execution of the second stage (not by van Dyck) in the evolution of no. 52.

It is not certain why the second stage was undertaken or whether it it followed van Dyck's original intention. Not enough remains of the surround on the inset panel to ascribe it with certainty to van Dyck. Assuming it to be his work, it can be said that the original picture would not have been a bust length, as an estimated compass of the surround would not have been sufficiently large to allow for it. This being the case, it can be said that the additions on the second support do not follow van Dyck's intentions.

However, it is also possible that this surround was added after mutilation or damage to the original, and before it was decided fully to restore it. It may thus represent a preliminary effort of a restorer, as an estimated compass of the surround also shows that the original support has been cut down. But this proposal is improbable because the poorly rendered hand, cuff and pose of the arm is the same as that used by Willem van Haecht for his rendering of van der Geest in his picture of 1628 recording the visit of the Archduke Albert and the Archduchess Isabella to van der Geest's house in 1615.[10] Several of the portraits (but not all the relevant poses) in van Haecht's picture correspond with portraits by other hands, which are known to have been executed before 1628. But it is reasonable to suppose that the particular pose of van der Geest was evolved by van Haecht specially for his picture and that it was his invention (although no. 52 may of course have inspired his rendering of the face).

It thus seems likely that the addition to no. 52 was executed after 1628 and before *ca.* 1636/7, by an artist who had van Haecht's picture in mind. If such was the case, it follows that the additions do not follow van Dyck's original intention, and that no. 52 originally showed only the head and shoulders of van der Geest in a simulated, oval, porphyry surround.[11]

It is possible that the high back of the collar in no. 52 was reduced at the same time as the additions were made (and when the first, inner oval surround was suppressed). X-radiographs show that it was as high at the back as that worn by Jan Brueghel I in Rubens' *Group Portrait of the Family of Jan Brueghel* of ca. 1612–14,[12] whereas its present appearance corresponds with that in van Haecht's picture.

ENGRAVINGS: Anon;[13] R. W. Sievier;[14] T. Woolnoth; G. T. Doo; J. Rogers;[15] W. H. Worthington; P. A. Rajon (etching).

COPIES: By [Benjamin] West, 1806;[16] perhaps Canon Wauters sale, Brussels, 1 April, 1794 (64);[17] The European Museum, St. James's Square, 26–27 February, 1796;[18] Bryan sale, Peter Coxe, 18 May (= 2nd day) 1798 (52);[19] Sir Simon Clarke and John Hibbert sale, Christie's, 14 May, 1802 (34); Caleb Whitefoord sale, Christie's, 5 May (= 2nd day) 1810 (5); William Seguier (†) sale, Christie's, 4 May, 1844 (78); Anon. sale, Christie's, 27 February, 1847 (104); a number of other copies, apparently mostly of the nineteenth century, are recorded in the National Gallery archives.[20]

PROVENANCE: Liss (of Antwerp) sale, Christie's, 27 February (= 2nd day) 1796 (99) bt. Pratbernon for 230 gns.;[21] still in his possession 26 March, 1797.[22] Bryan sale, Peter Coxe, 18 May (= 2nd day) 1798 (51) bt. Angerstein for 340 gns.;[23] exh. at the B.I., 1806, for copying;[24] exh. at the B. I., 1815 (9);[25] purchased with the Angerstein collection, 1824.

REPRODUCTION: *National Gallery Illustrations, Continental Schools (excluding Italian)* 1950, p. 102, right.

REFERENCES: *General:* J. Smith, *A Catalogue Raisonné* etc., 1831, III, van Dyck, no. 251; L. Cust, *Anthony van Dyck* etc., 1900, p. 234, no. 24; G. Glück, *Van Dyck, Klassiker der Kunst* [1931], p. 125.

In text: (1) See G. Gepts, *Jaarboek Koninklijk Museum voor Schone Kunsten,* Antwerp, 1954–1960, pp. 83 ff., for the identification of the initials M V as those of the Antwerp panel maker Michiel Vriendt. (2) For the most recent of many biographies of van der Geest, see J. S. Held, *Gazette des Beaux-Arts,* 1957, 50, pp. 53 ff.; H. Vey, *Die Zeichnungen Anton van Dycks,* 1962, under no. 262, gives van der Geest's date of birth. (3) See R. N. Wornum, *Descriptive and Historical Catalogue of the Pictures in the National Gallery* etc., 1847, p. 187, note; he did not identify the nature of the original support. (4) The addition is now concealed by the frame. No. 52 was exhibited at the British Institution in 1815 as by Rubens (see under *Provenance*); and J. D. Passavant, *Tour of a German Artist in England,* I, 1836, p. 43, stated that 'By some connoisseurs the head [in no. 52] is ascribed to Rubens, and the drapery only to van Dyck, in which opinion I am inclined to join'. Such a view did not, however, gain a wide currency. (5) See *Anecdotes of Painting in England* etc., ed. J. Dallaway, II, 1826, p. 186, note. His identification was finally adopted, without reservation, in the National Gallery catalogue of 1864. (6) See under *Provenance.* (7) See for instance, Vey, *loc. cit.* (8) See, for instance, Cust and Glück cited under *General References*; H. Rosenbaum, *Der Junge Van Dyck,* 1928, p. 25; L. van Puyvelde, *Van Dyck,* 1950, p. 127; and also L. Baldass, *Gazette des Beaux-Arts,* 1957, 50, pp. 264–5 who wrongly considered that no. 52 was overcleaned in 1948. (9) See Gepts, *op. cit.,* p. 87. (10) See Held, *op. cit.,* pp. 61 ff. and figs. 4 and 5. (11) To be compared with the *Portrait of a Man* bearing the date 1619, (Brussels, Musées Royaux des Beaux-Arts, no. 659), although as far as can be judged through a discoloured varnish, the surround (and thus the date) may be false; see also Rosenbaum, *loc. cit.* (12) Coll. Count Antoine Seilern, see his *Flemish Paintings and Drawings* etc., 1955, no. 18, and plates XL–XLIV; and more recently H. Vlieghe, *Bulletin, Musées Royaux des*

Beaux-Arts de Belgique, 1966, pp. 177 ff. (13) In John Young, *Catalogue of the Celebrated Collection of Pictures of the late John Julius Angerstein, Esq.*, 1823, no. 17. (14) See Smith, cited under *General References* for this and the two following prints. (15) In *The National Gallery of Pictures by the Great Masters* etc., I, [1838], no. 27. (16) See Joseph Farington's entry in his diary (typescript copy, British Museum, Print Room) for 18 November, 1806, 'West was copying *Rembrants* [*sic*] *Mill*.—He also showed me his copy of Govartius [*sic*] by Vandyke [*sic*]'. On 20 November, 1806, he recorded, *ibid.*, p. 3510: '[Westall] spoke of the copy by West of the picture by Gavartius [*sic*] by Vandyke [*sic*] and said it was far superior to any other copy made at the British Institution'. For the loan of no. 52 to the British Institution for copying in 1806, see under *Provenance*. (17) It measured 2 pieds 4 pouces × 1 pied 10 pouces (= 29¾ × 23⅜), see *Catalogue de Tableaux, Vendus à Bruxelles depuis l'année 1773*, p. 93. (18) See Wilson's advertisement in the *True Briton*, 26 February, 1796 (the day before no. 52 was sold at Christie's, see under *Provenance*), Whitley Papers, *Notes on Artists*, British Museum, Print Room: 'This day & tomorrow the celebrated portrait called Grovartius [*sic*] is to be placed in the public Gallery at the European Museum by permission of the nobleman who has purchased it.' (19) This lot followed no. 52 in the sale, see under *Provenance*, and was described as the copy; it could be identical with the previous copy referred to above. (20) J. Young, in his ms. notes (in the National Gallery library) to his catalogue of the Angerstein collection, see note 13, stated that no. 52 was already a much copied picture. (21) Described as 'Vandyck [*sic*]. Portrait of Govartius . . .'. Buyer and price in Christie's marked catalogue. According to the frontispiece of the sale catalogue, Liss brought his collection to England after the French invasion of the southern Netherlands, i.e. after the winter of 1792. (22) See Farington's entry for this date (Farington's *Diary*, typescript copy, British Museum, Print Room), 'Pratburn [*sic*] has the head of Grovartius [*sic*]'. (23) As by van Dyck and described as 'The celebrated Portrait of Govartius'; for the buyer see W. Buchanan, *Memoirs of Painting*, I, 1824, p. 286. (24) See W. T. Whitley, *Art in England 1800–1820*, 1928, p. 111. (25) Described as a portrait of 'Govartius' by Rubens.

877B   CARLO AND UBALDO SEE RINALDO CONQUERED BY LOVE FOR ARMIDA

Carlo and Ubaldo watch Rinaldo and Armida from behind a bush, while *putti* frolic round the two lovers.

Oil on oak, 22½ × 16⅜ (0·57 × 0·415).

The reverse of the support bears the brand of the coat of arms of the city of Antwerp and the incised initials, *MV* (in monogram).

Grisaille, apparently in fairly good condition. A certain amount of wearing may be concealed by retouching especially in the face of the *putto* in the tree, the left side of the *putto* holding the mirror, the face of the *putto* holding the spaniel and the legs of the *putto* on the extreme left. Some of the dark shadows, and foliage and sky may also be retouched. There is a *pentimento* in the right hand of the *putto* about to catch the apples. Traces of a border created by an incised line *ca.* $\frac{1}{16}$ (0·002) from the left and right edges are evident; no traces of the border remain at the bottom edge and very slight ones only at the top. It is thus likely that the support has been very slightly cut down, but not so as to affect the design.

For the subject, see Stanzas XVII–XXIII of Canto 16 of Tasso's *Gerusalemme Liberata*, 1574.[1] Carlo and Ubaldo have been sent to recall

the crusader Rinaldo from the sorceress, Armida, who had taken him to
the Fortunate Isles. No. 877B follows particularly Stanzas XVII, XX
and part of XXI: 'Ella [Armida] dinanzi al petto ha il vel diviso | E'l
crin sparge incomposto al vento estivo . . . sovra lui [Rinaldo] | pende;
ed ei nel grembo molle | Le posa il capo, e'l volto al volto attolle. . . . Dal
fianco dell' amante, estranio arnese | Un cristallo pendea lucido, e
netto. | Sorse, e quel fra le mani a lui sospese, | A i misteri d'amor
ministro eletto. | Con luci ella ridente, ei con accese, | Mirano in vari
oggetti un solo oggetto: | Ella del vetro a se fa specchio; ed egli | Gli
occhi di lei sereni a se fa spegli. | L'uno di servitù, l'altra d'impero | Si
gloria: ella in se stessa, ed egli in lei . . .'.

As Lee[2] has pointed out, the design shows several characteristics
normally associated with the *Toilet of Venus*, but his view that no.
877B fails 'to follow Tasso's poetry' seems not wholly justifiable.

No. 877B has generally been accepted[3] as the work of van Dyck,
although it has been rejected by Vey.[4] Its quality may in some degree
be obscured by retouching, but there is no good reason to doubt its
authenticity.

Glück's[5] view that no. 877B is van Dyck's *modello* for the engraving
by Peeter de Jode II,[6] rather than for a picture in the Louvre as was
previously thought[7] and recently reiterated by van Gelder,[8] is borne out
by the use of the grisaille technique and the close similarity in size
between no. 877B and the engraving. The squaring up of the design
in no. 877B was done before the heightening in oil paint and perhaps
after the brushing in of the oil wash. It is probable that the squaring up
was done for the benefit of the engraver.

The dating of no. 877B is somewhat problematic. The view, expressed
in National Gallery catalogues from 1915 which accepted no. 877B as
preparatory to the picture in the Louvre, was to date it before *ca.* 1630
(*sic* = 1629), for the Louvre picture was thought to have been that
painted by van Dyck in 1629 and acquired by Charles I through
Endymion Porter by March, 1630.[9] This provenance has been claimed,
with slightly more justification for the picture now at Baltimore.[10] The
Louvre picture itself should not necessarily be brought into the discussion as it is not above dispute as an autograph work.[11]

No. 877B seems clearly to be a work of the 1630's. The design accords
with a description of a picture by van Dyck, recorded in the possession
of the Stadholder Frederick Henry in 1632 when called *Mars and
Venus*.[12] It is not certain, but possible, that no. 877B derives directly
from this picture. But whether this is so or not, it would not have been
necessary for van Dyck to have had the picture before him, when he
executed no. 877B. De Jode's print is dated 1644; he is recorded in the
lists of the Antwerp guild of S. Luke and of the *Violere*, regularly from
1634/5 to 1641/2; a record of payment, made to the guild in 1642/3,
was noted on 19 September, 1644.[13] The print was probably made and
published in Antwerp (see below), and its quality suggests that van Dyck
corrected the plate as well as providing the *modello*. The presence of the
Antwerp coat of arms on the reverse of no. 877B suggests, at the least,

that van Dyck bought the support in Antwerp; the initials, also on the reverse, are probably those of the Antwerp panel maker, Michiel Vriendt, whose date of death—1636/7 [14]—provides a reasonable *terminus ante quem* for van Dyck's acquisition of the support. Bearing in mind van Dyck's own movements in the 1630's, it seems probable that this took place during his stay in the southern Netherlands in 1634/5. This is also the most likely date for execution of no. 877B; the delay in publication of the print may well be partly explained by van Dyck's absence from Antwerp; and it is possible that he corrected the plate during his visit to Antwerp in the autumn of 1640. The reason for the ensuing delay of four years before the publication of the print is not known.

Lee has compared the composition of no. 877B with that by Annibale Carracci at Naples, and drawn attention to the influence of Titian; he also adumbrates other influences, some classical, for certain details, which are not totally convincing.[15] The motif of a *putto* riding on a sword appears earlier in Caraglio's print of *Mars and Venus* after Rosso.[16]

ENGRAVING: By Peeter de Jode II, in reverse, dated 1644.[17]

COPY: Mme. Pauwels-Allard sale, Brussels, 21 November, 1927 (50).[18]

PROVENANCE: Coll. Jan-Baptista Anthoine (†1687), Antwerp[19]; probably inherited by one of his two sons, Louis or Jan-Baptista.[20] Perhaps Mme. Lenglier (†) sale, Paris, 10 ff. March, 1788 (102) sold for 62 livres.[21] Coll. Sir Thomas Lawrence (1769–1830); exh. *The Lawrence Gallery. 2nd Exhibition . . .* 209, Regent St. [= S. & A. Woodburn], 1835 (21)[22]; sold by Woodburn to Sir Robert Peel, Bt., 13 December, 1837[23]; purchased with the Peel collection, 1871.

REPRODUCTION: *National Gallery Illustrations, Continental Schools (excluding Italian)*, 1950, p. 103, right.

REFERENCES: (1) For a discussion of the treatment of Tasso's poem by painters (including van Dyck) in the seventeenth century, see R. W. Lee, *The Art Bulletin*, 1940, pp. 242 ff.; see also the same author in *Latin American Art and the Baroque Period in Europe*, III, 1963, pp. 12 ff., for a fuller discussion of van Dyck's treatment of the subject. (2) See *Latin, American Art, and the Baroque Period in Europe*, III, 1963, p. 25. (3) See for instance, L. Cust *Anthony van Dyck*, 1900, p. 251, under no. 95; G. Glück, *Van Dyck, K. der K.*, [1931], p. 558, note to p. 363; L. van Puyvelde, *Van Dyck*, 1950, p. 186; J. G. van Gelder *Bulletin, Musées Royaux des Beaux-Arts*, 1959, p. 59. The first two authors followed National Gallery catalogues from 1892–1929 in stating that no. 877B was on paper. (4) See H. Vey, *Bulletin Musées Royaux des Beaux-Arts*, 1956, p. 205, under note 32. E. Schaeffer in his edition of the *Van Dyck, K. der K.*, 1909, made no mention of no. 877B. (5) *Loc. cit.*; see also Puyvelde, *loc. cit.* (6) See below under *Engraving*. (7) See for instance Cust, *loc. cit.*; and previous National Gallery catalogues from 1915. (8) *Loc. cit.* (9) See van Dyck's letter to Porter of 29 December, 1629 and the note of payment made by the Exchequer to Porter of 23 March, 1629/30, printed by W. H. Carpenter, *Pictorial Notices: . . . of . . . Van Dyck*, 1844, pp. 23–26. (10) See Cust, *loc. cit.*; and Lee, *op. cit.*, p. 21. (11) Michael Jaffé has kindly informed the writer that what he believes to be a fragment of van Dyck's original (on panel) is in the collection of Dr. Bob Jones, Bob Jones University, South Carolina, see also note 13. (12) The inventory was published by S. W. A. Drossaers, with notes by C. Hofstede de Groot and C. H. de Jonge, *Oud Holland*, 1930, pp. 193 ff. The entry supposedly relevant to no. 887B is no. 57 (p. 204): 'Een stuck schilderie, daerinne Mars leyt en rust met sijn hooft in de schoot van Venus, daerbij sit een Cupido met roode fluweele muyl aen de voet ende een coussebant aen sijn been, dienende om voor een schoorsteen te stellen, door van Dijck gedaen'. This picture last featured in the inventory of 1708 of the collection left by Henriette Catharine van Anhalt-Dessau, when it was called *Rinaldo and Armida*. As van Gelder, *op. cit.*, p. 62, has pointed out this could not have been the picture in the Het Loo sale, Amsterdam, 26 July, 1713 (6) (see G. Hoet, *Catalogus* etc., 1752, I, p. 150) as the picture passed to Henriette Amalia who died in 1726; he accepted the suggestion that the picture in the Het Loo sale was that now at Los Angeles, and, p. 59, the generally held view that the *Mars and Venus* (*sic?*) of the 1632 inventory was the picture now in the Louvre. (13) See Ph. Rombouts and Th. van Lerius, *De Liggeren* etc., [1864–1876], II, *passim*. (14) See G. Gepts, *Jaarboek Koninklijk Museum voor schone Kunsten*, Antwerp, 1954–60, pp. 83 ff., for the identification of these initials as those of the panel maker, Michiel Vriendt, and for his date of death. (15) *Op. cit.*, pp. 23–26. (16) See A. Bartsch, *Le Peintre Graveur*, 1813, XV, pp. 87–88, no. 51; the same motif recurs in J. Matham's engraving of *Mars and Venus*, see Bartsch, *op. cit.*, 1803, III, p. 138, no. 15. (17) The plate measures $21\frac{13}{16} \times 16\frac{3}{16}$ (0.554×0.411); the size of the sheet is $23\frac{13}{16} \times 16\frac{1}{2}$ (0.605×0.419). The print bears the rubric 'Antonis van Dÿck Eques pinxit' and some verses by L. Lancellottus; it was published by Joan Caspeel (= Jan Casspeel or Cassepeel), dealer, who was made a master in the Antwerp guild of S. Luke in 1634/5, and whose payment for the authorization to hold a sale in the 'Geschildert Huys' was noted on 19 September, 1644, see Rombouts and van Lerius, *op. cit.*, pp. 60, 67 and 139. It is reproduced by A. Rosenberg, *Die Rubensstecher*, 1893, p. 144; an impression appears beneath the clock in Jan Steen's *Visit of the Doctor* (Wellington Museum, Apsley House) (MacLaren, ms. notes). (18) Grisaille, canvas, $25\frac{9}{16} \times 16\frac{9}{16}$ (0.65×0.42). (19) On the reverse of no. 877B is a seal bearing the Anthoine coat of arms: 'd'arg. au chev. d'azur, ch. de trois étoiles d'or et acc. de trois taux ou béquilles de St. Antoine du même', see J. B. Rietstap, *Armorial Général*, 1950, I, p. 55. The same coat of arms, as was noted by MacLaren, ms. notes, occurs in the so-called *Group Portrait of the Verbiest Family* by Coques in the Royal Collection. No. 877B is listed in the inventory of Jan-Baptista Anthoine, see J. Denucé, *The Antwerp Art Galleries, Inventories of the Art-Collections in Antwerp* etc., 1932, pp. 353 ff.; no. 59 (on p. 356) 'Een schetse van Hermide ende Renalde, van Dyck' valued at 300 florins. The 'Een Armida, wit en swert, van van Dyck', listed in the inventory dated 1689 of Alexander Voet, see Denucé *op. cit.*, p. 311, was thus probably the sketch, oil on panel, $22\frac{1}{4} \times 16\frac{3}{8}$ (0.565×0.415) coll. the Musées Royaux des Beaux-Arts de Belgique, Brussels (no. 711) for Baillu's print after the picture at Baltimore (reproduced by Glück, *op. cit.*, p. 265). N. Tessin noted the price of this sketch in 1687 to be 600 guilders, see *Oud Holland*, 1900, XVIII, p. 203. (20) Anthoine had four children; one daughter († 1723) married Count Fraula, see F. V. Goethals, *Dictionnaire Généalogique ... des Familles Nobles ... de Belgique*, 1849, II, pp. 193–5. No. 877B does not feature in the Count Fraula (†) sale of 1738, for which see G. Hoet, *Catalogus* etc., 1750, I, pp. 518 ff; another daughter became a nun, and no. 877B does not feature in the inventory of her pictures, for which see Denucé, *op. cit.*, p. 375. This inventory mentions Anthoine's two sons. (21) See C. Blanc, *Trésor de la Curiosité*, 1858, II, p. 120. The entry reads: Renaud et Armide, esquisse en grisaille riche composition ce sujet est connu par l'estampe qui en [*sic*] a faite d'après. Hauteur 21 pouces 6 lig., largeur 16 pouces [= $22\frac{7}{8} \times 17$] T'. The entry could of course refer to the grisaille at Brussels; if it was correctly stated to be on canvas, then the entry would refer to another sketch. It did not feature in the Lenglier sales of 1786, 1789 or 1812; information concerning the Lenglier sales kindly supplied by Mlle. Damiron of the Bibliothèque d'Art etc. (Fondation Doucet), University of Paris. The 1810 catalogue has not been checked. (22) Where stated to be ex coll. M. van Loo, Amsterdam; this collection has not been traced; the reference may probably only be a mistaken one to the Het Loo sale of 1713, for which see above, under note 12. (23) See Peel's note in the Goulburn mss., Surrey County Record Office. This and 8 drawings from the Lawrence collection cost Peel £1,300.

1172 EQUESTRIAN PORTRAIT OF CHARLES I

King Charles I in Greenwich-made armour,[1] wearing the lesser George[2] and supporting a baton, rides a dun charger; to the right, an equerry carries his helmet.

Inscribed on the tablet hanging on the tree, *CAROLVS· | REX MAGNAE* (AE in monogram) | *BRITAÑIAE* (AE in monogram).

Oil on relined canvas, *ca.* 144½ × 115 (*ca.* 3·67 × 2·921). The canvas edge is slightly ragged.

Charles I's collection mark is stamped or painted on the reverse of the original canvas.[3]

Generally in fairly good condition for a picture of this size. The foliage in the bottom left and right-hand corners is worn, and the area behind and between the horse's rear legs is difficult to read. The horse, the two figures and much of the foliage above are quite well preserved, although Charles' hair, the horse's mane and harness are slightly worn; the horse's tail is very worn; the saddle may also be worn. Not much remains of the top layer of blue in the sky, where there is some re-touching. The paint of the sky round Charles' head and behind him has discoloured; this area, which includes the leaves directly above Charles and the sky and foliage immediately behind him, is unsatisfactory and/or difficult to read. Cleaned, 1952.

Pentimenti, visible to the naked eye, in the horse's rear left leg, which was first placed farther in, and in the outline of the horse's rump; in the outline of Charles' right shoulder, in the position of the rock in the right foreground; and on the breastplate of Charles' armour where the gold chain may have replaced the garter ribbon or sash. The culet is an after-thought. A number 'I·', probably a later addition, inserted after *CAROLUS* in the inscription, has been suppressed.[4]

Charles I (1600–1649) became king of Great Britain and Ireland in 1625; his implementation of the concept of the Divine Right of Kings and consequent personal rule alienated important elements in the country, and resulted in civil war that ended in Charles' execution. He made an important collection of paintings; and appointed van Dyck as court painter in 1632.

No. 1172 is clearly an autograph work by van Dyck, and has been accepted as such by all authorities (see for instance under *General References*); it is thus one of the two certain equestrian portraits of Charles I, painted by van Dyck for the king. Not all the foliage immediately above and behind Charles may be autograph. This area is confused and unreliable; and the culet, poorly executed in comparison to the rest of the armour, is probably not by van Dyck.

There is a study by van Dyck for the horse, with an anonymous rider posing for the king more sketchily suggested, in the British Museum (see under *Drawing*). The position of the horse's rear left leg tends to correspond to the *pentimento* in no. 1172. Van der Doort catalogued what he considered to be van Dyck's 'first moddell' for no. 1172 in the Chair Room at Whitehall.[5] This is generally assumed to be the picture now at Windsor.[6] The Windsor picture shows less sky and foliage, and shows the horse, as in no. 1172, set in deeper perspective than in the drawing; the position of the horse's rear legs is closer in spirit to that in the drawing than that finally adopted in no. 1172. But in spite of the likelihood that this is the picture catalogued by van der Doort, and in spite of the *pentimenti* in Charles' right arm and on the breastplate (which corresponds to that in no. 1172), its execution seems to be too weak for an attribution to van Dyck to be accepted with certainty.[7] In particular the pose of the equerry (the vizor of the helmet which he carries is open) is quite misunderstood. Both pictures show an addition of a culet to the armour. This 'defense' is not known to have been worn with the armour made in the Royal Workshops at Greenwich that Charles wears.[8] It was however a 'defense' worn on most cuirassier armours of the period, and appears for instance in the equestrian portrait of the Count of Arenberg by van Dyck.[9] The culet in no. 1172 is weakly executed, but may have been added in van Dyck's studio; the alternative that it was added to no. 1172 and the Windsor picture while both were in the possession of the king seems also possible but perhaps less likely, because its inclusion is not correct. Taking these factors into account, the status of the Windsor picture may be that of a reduction made simultaneously with van Dyck's execution of no. 1172.

No. 1172 is evidently a work of the 1630's, executed after van Dyck had been appointed painter to Charles I in 1632; but there is no means of dating it precisely. It is not specifically mentioned in any of the Privy Seal warrants of payment to van Dyck,[10] or in van Dyck's account for a period up to March 1638 that he tendered to the king.[11] No. 1172 is first recorded in van der Doort's catalogue (see under *Provenance*), but the date of the compilation of the catalogue—1637/40[12]—does not provide a meaningful *terminus ante quem* for the date of execution of the picture. No. 1172 has usually been dated 1635/6;[13] the evidence of costume suggests that this may be too early. During the 1630's the trend of fashion in the English court tended towards shorter collars: Charles' collar in no. 1172 is shorter than in his other equestrian portrait by van Dyck, which is dated 1633;[14] it is also shorter than that in Le Sueur's bronze equestrian portrait of the same year,[15] and than that worn by the Duke of Northumberland in his portrait as High Admiral, which he became in 1638, by van Dyck.[16] On grounds of costume, therefore, no. 1172 could be dated after the group of pictures painted for the King and Queen up to March 1638, that were specified by van Dyck in his account. A Privy Seal warrant was issued for the payment of this account in December 1638;[17] no. 1172 could therefore be one of the unspecified works mentioned in the next and last Privy Seal warrant of payment of February 1639.[18]

Glück has associated van Dyck's grisaille sketch at Wilton with a commission for an equestrian portrait from Charles I.[19] The sitter in the sketch, however, bears some resemblance to Prince Thomas of Savoy;[20] van Dyck was paid for his portrait of this prince (now at Turin) early in 1635,[21] and it may be that the sketch was a rejected *modello* for this commission, executed during van Dyck's stay in the southern Netherlands in 1634–5. The poses of the sitter and horse in the sketch are in reverse to those in no. 1172; but while there are obvious differences in conception, it is noteworthy that the position of the rear legs of the horse in the sketch corresponds with that finally adopted in no. 1172. It thus seems likely that the British Museum drawing for the horse in no. 1172, was taken from the life, and that van Dyck reverted to an earlier idea, expressed in the Wilton grisaille, during the execution of no. 1172.

Bellori,[22] evidently referring to no. 1172, stated that van Dyck painted Charles I 'à cavallo ad imitatione di Carlo Quinto espresso da Titiano. . .' On this basis, Millar[23] has described no. 1172 as a re-interpretation of Titian's *Equestrian Portrait of Charles V*;[24] but as the compositional connections are slight, Bellori's words should probably be taken to mean no more than what he says. Millar also considered that van Dyck may have been influenced by contemporary English engravings like Thomas Cockson's print of the 2nd Earl of Essex.[25] Rubens is, however, more likely as van Dyck's chief source: the poses of Charles I and the helmet bearer being probably developments of those in a lost equestrian portrait by Rubens, which is known by a copy at Vienna.[26]

Van der Doort described no. 1172 as 'ye king in greate on horsback'.[27] The 'in greate' may refer no more than to the size of no. 1172; but it may also be a confused indication that the king is riding a 'great horse'. Sir Walter Gilbey considered that the horse in no. 1172 was a 'great horse' of the type which had appeared on royal seals since 1200.[28] There is a vague similarity between the horse in no. 1172 and Le Sueur's horse which was based on studies of the king's 'great horses'.[29] Lady Apsley's view that both these horses were of Spanish breed[30] cannot be proved or disproved with certainty, nor can Cust's that the horse in no. 1172 was of Flemish breed.[31] It is noteworthy that the physiognomy of the horse does not exactly agree with that in the preliminary drawing.

No. 1172 is peculiar for the limited claim of the king's sovereignty expressed on the tablet. The phrase 'Magnae Britanniae', in an abbreviated form, was first used on medals struck in the reign of James I;[32] and appears for the first time on a royal seal in Charles I's second seal of 1626–7.[33] The third seal of 1627–1640 did not include it.[34] Even when used on the second seal, the words *Hiberniae* and *Franciae* were also included. The omission of France and Ireland on the tablet in no. 1172 may however be no more than an unfortunate accident.

There is a tradition, which cannot be verified, that the equerry is 'Sir Thomas Morton'.[35]

DRAWING: Study for the horse with the pose of the king sketched in, British

Museum, pen and sepia, sepia wash heightened with white, $11\frac{1}{8} \times 9\frac{3}{8}$ (0·283 × 0·239).[36]

SKETCHES(?): Anon. sale, 29 May (= 3rd day), 1789 (68) bt. Ibetson for £5 10sh.; Hart Davies sale, Coxe, 1 June, 1814 (11) sold for £95.

COPIES: Prado Museum, Madrid, canvas, $144 \times 110\frac{1}{2}$ (3·66 × 2·81);[37] by Bernard Lens III, Anon. sale, Sotheby's, 9 June, 1955 (26) vellum, $19 \times 16\frac{1}{4}$ (0·482 × 0·412), signed and dated 1720;[38] by Charles Jarvis, Charles Jarvis sale, 12 March (= 2nd day) 1739/40 (47), 88 × 52 (2·235 × 1·321); ascribed to Samuel Drummond, Sir Allan Adair sale, Christie's, 8 December, 1950 (166), 49 × 39 (1·245 × 0·991);[39] coll. Sir Ralph Delme-Radcliffe, Hitchen Priory.[40]

REDUCED VARIANT: Coll. H.M. the Queen, Windsor Castle, 38 × 34 (0·965 × 0·864).[41] Many copies are known which follow the Windsor picture rather than no. 1172 (i.e. the vizor of the helmet is open etc.) and are therefore not listed here.[42]

DERIVATIONS: *Equestrian Portrait of the Cardinal Infant Ferdinand*, ascribed to T. van Thulden, $118\frac{7}{8} \times 95\frac{5}{8}$ (3·02 × 2·43), Louvre, no. 1954;[43] *Equestrian Portrait of John 1st Duke of Marlborough*, ownership and dimensions unknown.[44]

PROVENANCE: Painted for Charles I;[45] recorded by van der Doort, as 'at present' in the Prince's Gallery, Hampton Court, *ca.* 1637–40;[46] valued at £200 by the Trustees for Sale of Charles I's collection and sold to Sir Balthazar Gerbier († 1667), 21 June, 1650.[47] Owned by Gisbert van Ceulen, by whom sold, at Antwerp, to Duke Maximilian II Emanuel, Elector of Bavaria and Governor of the Southern Netherlands (from 1696), 17 September, 1698;[48] looted by Emperor Joseph I (Emperor from 1705) from Munich;[49] given by him to John 1st Duke of Marlborough by 8 November, 1706;[50] seen by Vertue at Blenheim Palace, 1737;[51] exh. B.I., 1815 (1); purchased from the 8th Duke of Marlborough, 1885.

REPRODUCTION: *National Gallery Illustrations, Continental Schools (excluding Italian)*, 1950, p. 105.

REFERENCES: *General:* J. Smith, *A Catalogue Raisonné* etc., 1831, III, van Dyck, no. 255; L. Cust, *Anthony van Dyck*, 1900, p. 263, no. 6; G. Glück, *Van Dyck, K. der K.*, [1931], p. 381.

In text: (1) The author thanks H. R. Robinson, Assistant to Master of the Armouries, H.M. Tower of London, for clarifying the problems connected with the armour. He explained (letters in Gallery archives) that: 'The armour that the King is wearing [in no. 1172] is one of a series of armours for tilt and foot-combat made in the Royal Workshops at Greenwich Palace between 1610 and 1620 . . . [and] may well be one which we still have in the Armouries. There are certain peculiarities in the construction of the arms which no other surviving armours have . . . Charles's sword is a contemporary horseman's rapier made without a knuckle-guard for use with a steel gauntlet.' (2) E. Ashmole, *The Institution, Laws & Ceremonies of the most noble order of the Garter*, 1672, pp. 226–8, recounts the particulars relating to the wearing of the badge of the Order. Henry VIII had decreed that Knights of the Order should wear the George on a gold chain or ribbon, which James I had decreed should be blue; and Ashmole stated that 'The ordinary manner of wearing this *Ribband* in time of peace, was (till of late) about the neck, down to the middle of the Breast, where the *Lesser George* hung; but now for the more conveniency of riding or action, the same is spread over the left shoulder, and brought under the right arm. . . . But where the Pictures of the *Soveraign* or any of the *Knights-Companions* are drawn in Armour, then even to this day, the George is represented, as fixed at a *Gold Chain* instead of the *Blue Ribband* and worn about the neck. . . .' (3) There is some illegible writing on the reverse near the right-hand edge of the canvas. (4) The number 'I' never appears, understandably, on royal seals of Charles I; it must presumably have been added to the inscription some time (perhaps soon) after the death of Charles I or the accession of Charles II, and certainly before 1720 as Lens's copy includes it; it also features in the copy in the Prado (see under *Copies*). (5) See O. Millar, *The Walpole Society*, XXXVII, 1958–60, p. 62. (6) See O. Millar, *Pictures in the Royal Collection, Tudor, Stuart and Early Georgian Pictures*, I, 1963, pp. 94–5, no. 144, and rep. in vol. II, pl. 64; earlier authorities with similar views are cited by Millar. Two pictures also claimed to be sketches for no. 1172 are recorded as having been on the London Art Market (see under *Sketches?*). (7) Millar, *loc. cit.*, records the demotion of the Windsor picture between the reigns of Anne and George III and by Walpole, see also the National Gallery catalogues, 1889–1913; MacLaren, ms. notes, referred to the Windsor picture as a small version. (8) See note 1. Robinson, *loc. cit.*, also stated that the culet was 'not a defence . . . ever put on a Greenwich armour. One would expect the King to be wearing a rich cloth skirt or at most one of mail. . . . We have a portrait of Charles as Prince of Wales wearing this same armour without the thigh defences.' (9) Coll. The Earl of Leicester, Holkham Hall, Norfolk. (10) See W. H. Carpenter, *Pictorial Notices: consisting of a Memoir of Sir Anthony Van Dyck* etc., 1844, pp. 72–74. (11) *Ibid.*, pp. 67–8. The period probably ended in March 1638 as the Privy Seal warrant (pp. 73–4) makes the pension payable up to the Feast of the Annunciation, 1638. (12) See O. Millar, *The Walpole Society*, XXXVII, 1958–60, pp. XIX–XX. (13) See L. Cust, *Anthony van Dyck*, 1900, p. 103; *National Gallery Descriptive Catalogue* etc., 1913; G. Glück, *The Burlington Magazine*, 1937, p. 217; O. Millar, *Pictures in the Royal Collection* etc., *loc. cit.* (14) Millar, *op. cit.*, p. 93, no. 143 and rep. vol. II, pl. 65. (15) See J. G. Mann, *Country Life*, 16 May, 1947, p. 908, fig. 1. (16) Coll. The Duke of Northumberland; exh. *Flemish Art*, R.A., 1953/4 (436). (17) Carpenter, *op. cit.*, pp. 73–4. (18) *Ibid.*, p. 74. (19) *Loc. cit.*; see also G. Glück, *Van Dyck, K. der K.*, [1931] p. 380 and note p. 560. (20) Compare the face in the Turin portrait, rep. by Glück, *Van Dyck, K. der K.*, [1931], p. 421. (21) *Ibid.*, p. 556, note to p. 421. (22) See G. P. Bellori, *Le Vite* etc., 1672, p. 260. Bellori's source of information on van Dyck's activity in England was an acquaintance of van Dyck's at the time—Sir Kenelm Digby, see Bellori, *op. cit.*, p. 261. (23) *Op. cit.*, p. 95, also including Rubens' equestrian portraits of Philip IV (known from a copy) and of the Cardinal Infant Ferdinand, for which see R. Oldenbourg, *Rubens, K. der K.*, [1921], pp. 446 and 377. (24) See O. Fischel, *Tizian, K. der K.*, n.d., p. 151. (25) The print is reproduced by Millar, *op. cit.*, I, fig. 4. (26) See G. Glück, *Rubens, van Dyck und ihr Kreis*, 1933, p. 42 and fig. 30. The pose of the king approximates even more closely with that of Buckingham in Rubens' *Equestrian Portrait*, destroyed in 1949, rep. Oldenbourg, *op. cit.*, p. 267. The helmet bearer was earlier sketched by van Dyck in the grisaille at Wilton. (27) See O. Millar, *The Walpole Society*, XXXVII, 1958–60, p. 62. (28) See Sir Walter Gilbey, *The Great Horse*, 1899, p. 42. (29) See Mann, *loc. cit.* (30) See Lady Apsley, *Bridleways through History*, 1948, p. 295. (31) Cust, *op. cit.*, p. 104. (32) See *Medallic Illustrations of the History of Great Britain* etc., compiled by E. Hawkins, and edited by A. W. Franks and H. A. Grueber, I, 1885, p. 194, nos. 16 ff. (33) See W. de G. Birch, *Catalogue of Seals in the Department of Manuscripts in the British Museum*, I, 1887, no. 567. (34) *Ibid.*, no. 571. (35) See H. Walpole, *Anecdotes of Painting in England* etc., ed. J. Dallaway, II, 1826, p. 214; and Smith, cited under *General References*; followed by J. D. Passervant, *Kunstreise durch England und Belgien* [1831] 1833, p. 177. The identification was accepted by the relevant National Gallery catalogues until 1958. (36) See A. M. Hind, *Catalogue of Drawings by Dutch and Flemish Artists . . . in the British Museum*, 1923, II, pp. 65–6, no. 49. The sitter in the study seems not to be Charles I as has been suggested, nor did van Dyck follow this drawing closely either for pose or for the physiognomy of the horse when he executed no. 1172. It is possible that this drawing resulted from van Dyck having received instructions similar to those given to Le Sueur by Lord Weston, for his statue of Charles I; namely to take the advice of the 'King's riders of great horses for the shape and action of the horse and of His Majesty's figures on the same', see M. Whinney and O. Millar, *English Art, 1625–1714*, 1957, p. 118. (37) See *Museo del Prado, Catálogo de las Pintura*, 1963, p. 192, no. 1501; see also under note 48. (38) This shows slightly more of the equerry on the right, which suggests that no. 1172 may have been cut down a little; it also shows the base of the tree trunk behind the horse's rear right leg. (39) Acquired in a sale of 1 May, 1852 (82) [=Lugt no. 20800?] according to a note in the Gallery archives. (40) Information kindly supplied by Mr. Oliver Millar. (41) O. Millar, *Pictures in the Royal Collection* etc., pp. 94–5, no. 144, considers this to be the picture recorded by van der Doort in the Chair Room, Whitehall and that it is, therefore, the *modello* for no. 1172. Reasons for the rejection of this view are given above. Certainly, because of the differences, it could not have been the working *modello*. For the history of the Queen's picture, see Millar, *loc. cit.* (42) M. Whinney and O. Millar, *op. cit.*, p. 70, state that no. 1172 inspired Gainsborough's *General Honeywood* (Ringling Museum, Sarasota); but the source seems rather to have been the Royal Collection variant. (43) See Louis Demonts, *Musée National du Louvre, Catalogue des Peintures* etc., 1922, III, p. 30. The attribution to van Thulden seems improbable. The quality of execution is not high and seems to be worthy only of a copyist. Nevertheless, the status of the Louvre painting is puzzling. It is possible that it is a copy after a lost portrait executed by van Dyck in the southern Netherlands late in 1634 or early in 1635. If this is the case, no. 1172 (if correctly dated here) would be little more than an autograph repetition of a composition, adapted for another sitter. However, the collar seems not the type then in fashion (compare Oldenbourg, *op. cit.*, p. 377 or G. Glück, *Van Dyck, K. der K.*, [1931], p. 423). Thus it is probable that the Louvre picture is either an (enlarged?) copy after a portrait by van Dyck executed in Antwerp in the autumn of 1640, or a copy after a portrait (perhaps posthumous) by an artist who knew the composition of no. 1172. (44) See the reproduction in the *Tatler and Bystander*, 23 May, 1956, p. 417. Thieme-Becker, under Bernard Lens III, notes an equestrian portrait of the Duke of Marlborough, in the collection of the Earl of Brownlow, Ashridge. (45) See above. (46) See O. Millar, *Walpole Society*, 1958–1960, XXXVII, p. 62, under no. 2. (47) See O. Millar, *Pictures in the Royal Collection* etc., I, 1963, p. 95 under no. 144, thus correcting his view expressed in a letter to *The Times*, 1 August, 1952, which identified no. 1172 with the *Equestrian Portrait* bought by Mr. Pope for £150 on 22 December, 1652. (48) See *Vertue Note Books, The Walpole Society*, XX, 1931–32, p. 147: 'Afterwards in Oliver's Days, the then Spanish Ambassador here Don Alonso de Cardenes bought . . . y° King on the Dun Horse by Van-Dyck . . . which some say remain in the Escuriall to this Day, tho; others, affirm the Picture of King Charles on the Dun Horse is now in the Possession of the Duke of Bavaria, who bought it off one myn-Heer Van Cullen.' The copy at the Middle Temple, noted by Vertue, seems to be after the Royal Collection picture of 1633; information kindly supplied by R. H. Williams of the Honourable Society of the Middle Temple. For the sale by van Ceulen to Maximilian II Emanuel, see the *Katalog der Gemälde-Sammlung . . . München*, 1896 ed., pp. IX–X; and M. Goldsmith, *The Wandering Portrait*, 1954, whose subject is the provenance of no. 1172, p. 86. Gisbert van Ceulen is probably identical with the Gisberto van Ceulen mentioned in the accounts of the Antwerp tapestry firm of Wauters, Cockx and de Wael in 1682, see J. Denucé, *Antwerp Art-Tapestry and Trade*, 1936, pp. 95 and 101; he is also probably the Gisbert van Colen (1636–1703), the third child of Jean van Colen († 1643), Lord of Broechem, Beckerzeel etc.; he married Marie Fourment († 1697), the daughter of Daniel Fourment in 1668, see F. V. Goethals, *Dictionnaire Généalogique . . . de Belgique*, 1849, I, p. 700, and probably the grand-daughter of Daniel Fourment, a prominent tapestry merchant of Antwerp, and the father of Rubens' second wife. (49) See the Munich catalogue etc., p. X; & Goldsmith, *op. cit.*, pp. 76–79. Bavaria was reduced by Marlborough and the allies after the battle of Blenheim, 1704. (50) See Marlborough's letter to his wife of this date, printed, for instance, by Goldsmith, *op. cit.*, pp. 76–77. Exactly how and when no. 1172 reached England is not known. Marlborough, in his letter of 8 November, stated that he hoped the picture was 'by this time in Holland'. Goldsmith, *op. cit.*, p. 72, prints a letter from

Maximilian to his wife—not giving the date, but perhaps of 1706—in which he wrote 'Trevisons [one of his aides] saw in Brussels with his own eyes how the painting was transported through the streets on its way to England.' L. Gachard, *Bulletin-Rubens*, 1883, II, pp. 281–2, identified no. 1172 with the picture 'nombré 57, qui est le portrait de Sa Majesté Britannique Charles Stuart de Van Dyck', which featured in a receipt for a group of paintings, signed by Cadogan in Brussels on 28 May, 1708 on behalf of Marlborough. The receipt is also printed by M. de Maeyer, *Albrecht en Isabella en de Schilderkunst*, 1955, pp. 461–2, document 277. The paintings had come from Tervueren; no. 57 had been moved from the court at Brussels to Tervueren in 1701, see Ch. Terlinden, *Annales de l'Académie Royale d'Archéologie de Belgique*, 1921, 6th series, 9, p. 362, and along with 35 others had been returned (as no. 57B) from Tervueren between 11–15 May, 1708, see Terlinden, *op. cit.*, pp. 365–366. Such being the case, Gachard's thesis collapses. Nos. 53 and 57, referred to in the receipt (no. 53 being described as a 'portrait d'une reine d'Angeleterre de Van Dyck') are rather to be identified with the half length portraits of Charles I and Henrietta Maria, also owned by the Duke of Marlborough (Smith, *op. cit.*, Van Dyck, nos. 256 and 257). **(51)** see *Vertue Note Books, The Walpole Society*, XXIV, 1935–6, p. 138.

3011 PORTRAIT OF A WOMAN AND CHILD

The child wears a yellow leading rein.

Oil on relined canvas, $51\frac{3}{4} \times 41\frac{13}{16}$ ($1 \cdot 315 \times 1 \cdot 062$).

In fairly good condition. There is a good deal of wearing, now retouched, notably in the black drapery, and in the woman's stomacher (but in neither instance in the highlights), ruff, hair and ear, and in the child's face, hair and the rim of its bonnet. A damage, *ca.* $1\frac{1}{2} \times \frac{1}{2}$ ($0 \cdot 038 \times 0 \cdot 018$) in the stomacher is now also retouched. The top layer of paint has worn thin over some areas of impasto in the costume of the child. Traces of *pentimenti* (see below) have been suppressed by retouching. Cleaned, 1968.

Several *pentimenti* showed up light after cleaning: the woman's ruff may have been slightly higher at the back on the left; the red curtain extended further to the right and came down at least as low as it does just to the left of the woman's face.

No. 3011 has been generally accepted as the work of van Dyck,[1] and there is no reason to doubt the attribution. The yellow scumble on the child's face, recently retouched, is probably not original; but it proved resistant to solvents and thus has not been removed. No. 3011 has been generally dated towards the end of van Dyck's first Antwerp period.[2] It is probable that it was executed in Antwerp either in 1620 or 1621.

The sitters have not been satisfactorily identified;[3] it is probable that they are a mother and child, and possible that no. 3011 was originally executed as one of a pair, the other showing the husband.

ENGRAVING: By E. Smith.

COPIES: Coll. Lord Kinnaird;[4] of the child by M. W. Peters († 1814), Manchester City Art Gallery.[5]

PROVENANCE: Apparently recorded for the first time in the Palazzo S. Giacomo Balbi (= coll. Francesco-Maria Balbi b.1734), Genoa, in 1758,[6] also recorded in coll. Francesco-Maria Balbi, 1780.[7] Coll. Sir Abraham Hume (1749–1838) by 1815,[8] when lent to the B.I. (2); exh. B.I. 1836 (7); inherited by his grandson, Lord Alford (1812–1851); exh. B.I. 1838 (22), 1843 (80); inherited by his son, Earl Brownlow (1842–1867), and then by the latter's brother, Earl Brownlow (1844–1921); exh. R.A. 1871 (125), 1893 (127) and 1900 (11), Grosvenor Gallery, 1887 (118), Musée des Beaux-Arts, Antwerp, 1899 (98); purchased from Earl Brownlow, 1914.

REPRODUCTION: *National Gallery Illustrations, Continental Schools (excluding Italian)*, 1950, p. 104, left.

REFERENCES: *General:* J. Smith, *A Catalogue Raisonné* etc., 1831, III, van Dyck, no. 533; G. Glück, *Van Dyck, K. der K.*, [1931], p. 109.

In text: (1) See the authors cited in *General References*; and, for instance, G. F. Waagen, *Works of Art and Artists in England*, II, 1838, p. 204; L. Cust, *Anthony van Dyck*, 1900, p. 237, no. 67; and E. Schaeffer, *Van Dyck, K. der K.*, 1909, p. 153. (2) See Glück, cited under *General References*; and Cust, *loc. cit.* (3) It was known in Genoa in the eighteenth century (see below under *Provenance*) as the portrait of van Dyck's wife and child, which silly title was already rejected by C. G. Ratti, *Instruzione di quanto puo' vedersi . . . in Genova* etc., 1780, p. 192. (4) Exh. *Glasgow International Exhibition*, 1901, see the *Fine Art Catalogue*, 1901, p. 106 and reproduction in *Old Masters at the Glasgow International Exhibition*, 1902; perhaps noted by Waagen as coll. Lord Kinnaird, at Rossie Priory, see G. F. Waagen, *Galleries and Cabinets of Art in Great Britain*, 1857, (Supplement), p. 445. Still in the collection in 1951. (5) Photo. in Gallery archives. (6) See C. N. Cochin, *Voyage d'Italie* etc., III, 1758, pp. 278 and 282: 'Palais del S. Giacomo Balbi, in Strada Balbi. . . . Le Portrait de la femme & de l'enfant de *Vandick* [*sic*], peint par lui-même.' Cochin, here, printed the catalogue supplied by the Marquess Balbi for tourists, see his note 1 on pp. 278–279. (7) See Ratti, *loc. cit.* (8) No. 3011 is no. 100 of *A Descriptive Catalogue of a Collection of Pictures . . . belonging to* [*Sir Abraham Hume*], 1824, as ex the François Balbi Palace at Genoa. It is not stated there, or known when, Hume bought it; but no doubt it was after the fall of the Genoese Republic in 1797.

4889 THE ABBOT SCAGLIA ADORING THE VIRGIN AND CHILD

Oil on relined canvas, oval, *ca.* 42 × 47¼ (1·067 × 1·200).

Generally in good condition. The edges of the canvas are a little ragged, and the canvas may have been a little cut down. Parts of the Abbot's face, notably his left eye and mouth, appear to have been rather coarsely retouched; there is wearing in his hair and costume, which may be repainted in certain areas (see below). The top of the curtain is damaged and retouched. The grey underpaint shows up where the sky does not extend to the left edge of the curtain. There are some areas of engrained yellow varnish in the declivities of the impasto.

There are several *pentimenti*, visible in X-ray or infra-red photography: the Virgin's right sleeve may have been widened; the drapery she holds may have extended a little more to the left, and there are some small alterations in its folds; the drapery over her right knee has been extended to the left; Christ's foot was first lower and the Abbot's collar, narrower. X-ray photography also shows that Christ's right foot was first painted in, and that it was essayed in two positions, both lower than the final position of the leg would now suggest.

Cesare Alessandro Scaglia, the second son of Count Filibert of Verrua, served the house of Savoy as Ambassador at Rome (1614–1623) and at

Paris (1625–1627).[1] He then played a very active part, on behalf of the house of Savoy, in promoting peace between England and Spain. This brought him into contact with Rubens (see under no. 46) and took him to Spain, England and more briefly to the Netherlands.[2] However, following the success of the French armies in Piedmont and the settlement of Cherasco made by Victor Amadeus I with the French in 1631, Scaglia became isolated because of his strong anti-French views. Having been appointed Ambassador to the English court in 1631, he left the following spring, discredited and at odds with the Duke of Savoy, and settled in Brussels.[3] By this time he was a rich man;[4] although he failed to re-establish his position with his old master,[5] he remained in contact with Philip IV, and sometime after September 1637,[6] he entered the monastery of the Récollets, Antwerp, where he died in 1641.[7] He was appointed Abbot of Staffarda (in Piedmont) at least by 1615;[8] in 1631, Philip IV created him Abbot of Mandanici (in Sicily).[9]

No. 4889 has been generally accepted as the work of van Dyck.[10] The Abbot, his hands apart, is less satisfactory in execution than the rest. The retouchings on the face, which may be old, may explain the difference in its appearance from that of other areas of flesh. The cuff is also weakly executed. Other parts of his costume, notably over his left shoulder and his left arm, are coarsely painted and probably not autograph. Despite these unsatisfactory features, there is no overriding reason to doubt the attribution of no. 4889 to van Dyck.

The sitter is identified as the Abbot Scaglia in Waumans' engraving (see below under *Engraving*), and is established beyond any doubt by comparison with the engraved portrait after van Dyck in the *Iconography*.[11]

No. 4889 is normally dated in the 1630's[12] and there seems no reason to doubt this. Scaglia briefly visited the southern Netherlands in the summer of 1627[13] and the autumn of 1628,[14] when he could have sat to van Dyck; and van Dyck may have arrived in England very shortly before the Abbot's departure in the spring of 1632.[15] But in 1628 Scaglia was much involved in affairs of state and the possibility of any meeting in 1632 is remote. Scaglia could also have sat to van Dyck in 1634–5 when van Dyck spent some time in the southern Netherlands, or in the autumn of 1640 when he was in Antwerp. Of these dates, on grounds of style, 1634–5, seems most acceptable.

Scaglia was then living in Brussels; and was much in contact with Prince Thomas of Savoy,[16] who arrived in Brussels in April of that year, as captain general of the Spanish troops in the Netherlands, and himself sat to van Dyck (see under no. 1172).

The model for the Virgin in no. 4889 is traditionally supposed to have been the Duchess (*sic*) of Arenberg,[17] but there seems no proper justification for this.[18] It is possible that the Virgin and Child are an allusion to, or reminiscence of, the Duchess of Savoy, Christina of France (1606–1663), and her eldest son, Francis Hyacinth, who was born in 1632.[19]

The composition derives from a lost picture by Titian, copied by van

Dyck in his *Italian Sketchbook*.[20] Here Christ's right foot is placed in front of the sitter's wrist, and this was probably van Dyck's first intention in no. 4889 (see above under *pentimenti*).

ENGRAVING: By Coenrad Waumans (1619–after 1675).[21]

COPIES: Lille Museum;[22] Currie sale, Christie's, 16 April, 1937 (126);[23] private collection, Ghent, 1963;[24] of the Abbot alone: private collection (?), Solingen, 1956;[25] drawing of the head and right arm of Christ, ascribed to Charles Beale, British Museum.[26] Perhaps in the Gérard van der Pot sale, Rotterdam, 6 ff. June, 1808 (33).[27]

Variants with S. Catherine in the place of the Abbot Scaglia: Coll. V. Thorne, New York, 1938;[28] London Art Market, 1940;[29] coll. Mme. Georges Janssens de Bisthoven, Bruges, 1946;[30] Coll. Sir Somerled Macdonald of the Isles, Bt., Rudston, 1952;[31] with the Virgin and Child alone, and a cradle with a landscape view on the left: Anon. sale, Robinson and Fisher, 20 January, 1938 (91).[32]

PROVENANCE: Madame la Douairière Peytier de Merchten (†)[33] sale, Antwerp, 3 August 1791 (2) sold for 3000 glds.[34] John Knight (of Portland Place) sale, Phillips, 24 March, 1819 (80)[35] bt. in;[36] John Knight sale, Phillips, 17 March, 1821 (35)[37] bt. in; John Knight sale, Phillips, 24 May, 1839 (16).[38] Coll. Edmund Higginson, Saltmarsh Castle, Herefordshire, by 1841;[39] Edmund Higginson sale, Christie's, 6 June (=3rd day), 1846 (215) bt. by Rothschild (=Anthony de Rothschild (1810–1876, Baronet from 1847)) for 410 gns.;[40] exh., R.A. 1870 (30); exh. R.A. 1900 (24) lent by his widow, Lady de Rothschild († 1910); inherited by his daughter Constance, Lady Battersea († 1931); sold to Agnew's;[41] from whom bought by Anthony de Rothschild, and presented in memory of Louisa, Lady de Rothschild, and Constance, Lady Battersea, 1937.

REFERENCES: *General:* J. Smith, *A Catalogue Raisonné* etc., 1831, III, van Dyck, no. 362 (with an incorrect reference to a preparatory drawing (*sic*) in the Julienne sale of 1767); L. Cust, *Anthony van Dyck* etc., 1900, p. 249, no. 46; G. Glück, *Van Dyck, K. der K.*, [1931], p. 366.

In text: (1) See D. Carrutti, *Storia della Diplomazia della Corte di Savoia*, II, 1876, p. 264, note. L. Cust, *Anthony van Dyck* etc., 1900, p. 93, and others wrongly state that Scaglia came from Genoa. For an unfriendly account of his career while in France, see Contarini's notes for a *Relazione*, in *Calendar of State Papers, Venetian* etc., ed. A. B. Hinds, 1914, 20, p. 624: 'Abbot Scaglia was driven from France owing to his bad relations with the favourite, Richelieu, the ill opinions of that realm which he disseminated and his relations with the king's enemies because he did not find Richelieu so ready to help him get that red hat, for which he was most anxious . . . .' (2) For the movements of Scaglia at this period, see below; his activity is pretty fully described in the *Calendar of State Papers, Venetian* etc., ed. A. B. Hinds, 1914–19, 20–22, for the years 1627–1631. For his relations with Rubens, see R. Magurn, *The Letters of Peter Paul Rubens*, 1955, pp. 181 ff. (3) See the report of Giovanni Soranzo, the Venetian Ambassador in England, for 31 October, 1631, in *Calendar of State Papers, Venetian* etc., ed. A. B. Hinds, 1919, 22, p. 558: 'He [Scaglia] is suffering from bodily indisposition in addition to his mental troubles, and is very little seen. The talk about his departure is uncertain, but the soundest conjecture is that he himself does not know whither to turn, as he is on bad terms with France and his master, and to all present appearance does not enjoy the confidence of Spain, where he hoped to make his fortune. He is not on very good terms with the duke himself . . .' For his settling in Brussels, see the report of Vicenzo Gussoni, Venetian Ambassador in England, *ibid.*, p. 613, of 23 April, 1632. (4) See Gussoni's report, for May, 1633, in *Calendar of State Papers, Venetian* etc., ed. A. B. Hinds, 1921, 23, p. 109: 'He [Scaglia] lives privately and in great comfort. He is in disgrace with his master but does not mind as he is well off. . . .'; see also note 9. (5) See Gussoni's report for 9 December, 1633, *ibid.*, p. 171: 'Scaglia's correspondents here say that more than anything else he is contemplating in what way he can make his peace with the duke, his master.' **(6)** See the catalogue *Rubens Diplomate*, château Rubens, Elewijt, 1962, p. 66. In 1639–40, he acted on behalf of Charles I in negotiations with Rubens and Jordaens for the ceiling paintings of the Queen's house at Greenwich, see M. Rooses and Ch. Ruelens (†), *Correspondance de Rubens* etc., 1909, VI, pp. 240 ff. **(7)** See the *Catalogue du Musée d'Anvers*, 1874, pp. 462–463, under no. 405. **(8)** He was already referred to as 'Abbot' in that year, see *Calendar of State Papers, Venetian* etc., ed. A. B. Hinds, 1907, 13, p. 508. The in-scriptions on the portrait at Antwerp, see note 7, and on Waumans' engraving of no. 4889, see below under *Engraving*, describe him as abbot of 'Staphardae' and 'Mandanices'. **(9)** See Carleton's letter from The Hague 8/18 July, 1631, printed by W. Noël Sainsbury, *Original Unpublished Papers illustrative of the life of . . . Rubens* etc., 1859, p. 161, note 220: 'The Abbot de la Skalia [*sic*] is appointed by the King of Spaine for that service [the Truce] . . . his entertainement is mentioned to be 6000 crownes per mensem: besides a rich Abbey given him in Sicilia of 6000 ducats revenue, and a pension for life of as much more'. **(10)** See the authors cited under *General References*; and, for instance, E. Schaeffer, *Van Dyck, K. der K.*, 1909, p. 123. **(11)** See Fr. Wibiral, *L'Iconographie d'Antoine van Dyck*, 1877, no. 64, pp. 94–95. Van Dyck also painted a full length portrait of the Abbot (coll. Lord Camrose), rep. in G. Glück, *Van Dyck, K. der K.*, [1933], p. 426. **(12)** See note 10. **(13)** On 5 May, he had left Paris for Flanders, see *Calendar of State Papers, Venetian* etc., ed. A. B. Hinds, 1914, 20, p. 211; and he was at The Hague by 7 June, see *ibid.*, p. 307. **(14)** He left England 22 August, see *Calendar of State Papers, Venetian* etc., ed. A. B. Hinds, 1915, 21, pp. 241 and 252; and reached Turin, travelling via The Hague and Brussels, by 2 October, see *ibid.*, p. 327. **(15)** He had left England by 26 March, see *Calendar of State Papers, Venetian* etc., ed. A. B. Hinds, 1919, 22, p. 603. For the date of van Dyck's arrival in England, see, W. H. Carpenter, *Pictorial Notices: consisting of a Memoir of Sir Anthony Van Dyck* etc., 1844, p. 27 and Appendix V. **(16)** See the report of the Venetian Secretary in England, Francesco Zonca, for 12 May, 1634, in the *Calendar of State Papers, Venetian* etc., ed. A. B. Hinds, 1921, 23, p. 220: 'The intimates of the Abbot Scaglia here announce that Prince Tomaso makes much of him. He conducts all the prince's affairs at Brussels, and his Highness's plans and actions are all guided by the abbot's views and advice. . . . It causes great astonishment here, where it is known that the Abbot is not in favour with the Duke, the Prince's brother. . . .' **(17)** See under *Provenance*; and, more recently, G. Laloire, *Recueil Iconographique de la maison d'Arenberg*, 1940, pl. 27. **(18)** The model for the Virgin in no. 4889 does not at all resemble Mary, Countess of Arenberg and Princess of Barbanson in Pontius' engraving after van Dyck in the *Iconography*, see Wibiral, *op. cit.*, no. 146, p. 131, rep. by Laloire, *op. cit.*, pl 25. Neither resembles the por-trait also thought to be of the Duchess (i.e. Countess) of Arenberg at Chantilly, rep. in Glück, *op. cit.*, p. 319. **(19)** Compare the features of Christina in the portrait of her by Garzoni, in *Mostra del Barocco Piedmontese*, Turin, II, 1963, no. 10 and pl. 6 right, in the anonymous portrait at the Residenz Museum, Munich, and in Giovenale Boetto's print of 1635, for which see N. Brancaccio and M. A. Prolo, *Dal Nido Savoiardo al Trono d'Italia*, 1930, pp. 131 top and 130 bottom. If the identification is accepted, no. 4889 should be seen in the context of Scaglia's attempts to re-establish better relations with the Duke of Savoy, which he was known to be planning in December, 1633, see *The Calendar of State Papers, Venetian* etc., ed. A. B. Hinds, 1921, 23, p. 171. But there are difficulties in the way of this suggestion: van Dyck would have had to rely on his memory of the Duchess, whom he might well have seen during his stay in Turin in 1623, or on a portrait or print made in the intervening years, although none is known to the compiler; and Scaglia's espousal of Prince Thomas in 1634 could well have meant opposition to the Duchess, the leader of the French element in Savoy, which Prince Thomas strongly opposed. **(20)** Rep. in G. Adriani, *Anton van Dyck, Italienisches Skizzenbuch*, 1965 ed., pl. 46. **(21)** Published by C. Galle as after van Dyck; inscribed 'Vera Effigies de Cæsar Alexander Scaglia Abbas Staphardæ et Mandanices' with some latin verses. The print is rectangular, showing more at the top, and a column behind the curtain. Slightly more of the Abbot is also depicted, and his costume is rendered with more detail. The *pentimento* in his collar is also evident. (22) Canvas, circular, diameter $45\frac{1}{4}$ ($1\cdot15$), see *Catalogue des Tableaux du Musée de Lille*, 1893, no. 292, pp. 102–3. (23) $43 \times 40\frac{1}{2}$ ($1\cdot093 \times 1\cdot029$); as the Duchess d'Aremberg [*sic*] with her son and confessor. (24) Canvas, $40\frac{1}{8} \times 44\frac{1}{16}$ ($1\cdot02 \times 1\cdot12$), photo. in Gallery archives. (25) $25\frac{5}{8} \times 22\frac{1}{16}$ ($0\cdot65 \times 0\cdot56$); photograph kindly sent by Dr. Uhlemann, of the Deutsches Klingenmuseum, Solingen. (26) See E. Croft-Murray and P. Hulton, *British Museum, Catalogue of British Drawings*, 1960, p. 178, no. 114. See also note 32. (27) Panel, $12\frac{3}{4} \times 17\frac{3}{4}$ pouces: Une dame representant la Sainte Vierge, tient l'Enfant Jésus sur ces genoux, on voit devant lui une figure (le portrait de l'Abbé César Alexandre Scaglia) qui, les mains jointes, est dans une attitude d'adoration'. The status of this picture is not clear: despite the facts of its size and support, it seems more likely that it is a copy after, rather than a *modello* for no. 4889, if it is to be connected with it at all. For the van der Pot collection, see E. Wiersum, *Oud Holland*, 1931 pp. 201 ff. (28) See Inquiry no. 1006 and the reproduction in *The Connoisseur*, September, 1938. (29) Photo., in Gallery archives. (30) Photo. in Gallery archives; the picture bears the monogram V A D and date 1627. (31) Note by MacLaren. (32) As by Lely, no size given. The features and position of the Virgin's head differ. The drawing, noted above, ascribed to Charles Beale, should probably be related to the execution of this picture. (33) Smith, cited under *General Reference*, wrongly gives the seller's name as M. Pieters, Sig. Merchten; Madame la Douairière Peytier de Merchten may have been Marie-Thérèse, the wife of André Peytier († 1767) échevin of Antwerp, see F. V. Goethals, *Dictionnaire généalogique et héraldique des Familles Nobles ... de Belgique*, 1850, III, p. 680. (34) Described as: 'La Sainte Vierge assise ... tenant L'Enfant Jesus sur son giron, devant elle est l'Abbé Scaglia en prières ayant les mains jointes ... L'Estampe en est gravée par C. Waumans. En Oval. H $41\frac{1}{2}$ p. L46 T [=toile]'; information from the sale catalogue at the RKD, that also gives the price, kindly supplied by J. Nieuwstraten. (35) Described as by van Dyck 'Portraits of the Duchesse d'Aremberg and Child, as Virgin and Child with Saint in Adoration.' (36) See marked catalogue in the RKD; and Smith, under *General References*. (37) Same description as in note 35. (38) Described as by van Dyck 'The Virgin and Child, with Saint in Adoration.' (39) See Henry Artaria, *A Descriptive Catalogue of the Gallery of Edmund Higginson* etc., 1841, p. 144, as ex coll. J. Knight of Portland Place. (40) Buyer and price in Christie's copy of the catalogue. (41) Agnew's label was noted on the reverse of no. 4889 by MacLaren.

5633 PORTRAIT OF WILLIAM FEILDING, 1ST EARL OF DENBIGH

The Earl wears a silk Hindu or Indian jacket, with a lace collar and cuffs attached, and pyjamas, and is shown hunting with an oriental servant, who points to a parrot in a palm tree.

Oil on relined canvas, $97\frac{1}{2} \times 58\frac{1}{2}$ ($2\cdot475 \times 1\cdot485$). Ca. $\frac{5}{8}$ ($0\cdot015$) of the painted surface is turned over the edges of the stretcher.

In good condition. There are several retouched damages in the sky, beneath the palm tree, and some wearing in the costume of the Earl near his left hand, and in the hand and tunic[1] of the servant. The brown underpaint shows up in parts of the foliage in the top left. The ground on the left, a small area behind the Earl's left leg, and the lower part of the trunk of the palm tree are not as fully worked up as the rest. Cleaned, 1950/1.

There are several *pentimenti* evident to the naked eye or in infra-red photography: the top part of the Earl's left leg was first placed more to the left; he was first intended to carry a wide brimmed castor in his left hand, the black paint of which shows up through the pink at the top outer edge of his left leg and in the bottom left-hand corner of his jacket; there is also a minor *pentimento* in the outline of his left arm.

William Feilding (*ca.* 1582–1643) obtained royal favour by virtue of his being brother-in-law of James I's last favourite, George Villiers, created Duke of Buckingham in 1623 (see under no. 187). Feilding was created Master of the Great Wardrobe and Earl of Denbigh in 1622; he was one of the attendants of the Prince of Wales in Madrid in 1623 during the negotiations for the Spanish match, and subsequently held several naval commands. After Buckingham's assassination in 1628 he commanded the abortive expedition to relieve La Rochelle. From 1631–33 he visited Persia and India, with letters of introduction from Charles I, travelling on the East India Company's ships.[2] He supported Charles I in the civil war, and died, 8 April, 1643, from wounds received during the attack on Birmingham.

No. 5633 was thought to be the work of van Dyck as early as the 1640's and for long afterwards (see under *Provenance*); and although not included in either Klassiker der Kunst editions of van Dyck's œuvre, there is no reason to doubt this traditional attribution.[3]

The identification of the sitter as the 1st Earl of Denbigh is also traditional (see under *Provenance*); the face in no. 5633 is similar to that in an engraved portrait of Denbigh published in 1631[4] and to a portrait, inscribed with Denbigh's name, bearing an attribution to B. Gerbier.[5]

Cust's[6] view that no. 5633 was executed by van Dyck in England after 1632 is acceptable on stylistic grounds. Yule[7] seems first to have associated no. 5633 with the Earl's trip to India and Persia. There seems to be no reason to doubt that no. 5633 was commissioned to commemorate the trip; the costume,[8] oriental servant, and setting can be nothing other than allusions to it. The Earl returned to England on 26 August, 1633;[9] and it seems probable that no. 5633 was executed soon afterwards, probably before van Dyck's departure for the southern Netherlands in 1634.

The pose of the Earl is comparable, though in reverse, to that of Monsieur de St. Antoine in van Dyck's *Equestrian Portrait of Charles I* of 1633 (Royal Collection).[10]

Lady Denbigh thought that no. 5633 showed a moment, recounted by family tradition, when the Earl lost his way and was led to safety by a native boy;[11] but it is more probable that no. 5633 was intended to depict the Earl out hunting and exploring.

ENGRAVINGS: By T. A. Dean, three-quarter length, 1826; H. T. Ryall, three-quarter length, 1833;[12] J. Beugo, 1843; Anon.[13]

COPIES: Galleria Sabauda, Turin;[14] Sir David Ogilvy, Bart., Winton Castle, Pencaitland, three quarter length, $18\frac{1}{2} \times 23\frac{3}{4}$ (0·47 × 0·64); The Earl of Denbigh,

Newnham Paddox, three-quarter length;[15] The Earl of Haddington, Tyning-hame, bust length, 26 × 23½ (0·66 × 0·547);[16] The Duke of Hamilton, Lennoxlove, bust length, miniature.

PROVENANCE: Probably first recorded coll. the Marquess (later Duke) of Hamilton (1606–1649),[17] before 12 April, 1643;[18] recorded with certainty coll. the Duke of Hamilton, 1641/9;[19] noted at Hamilton, 1698(?)/1712;[20] exh. R.A., 1873 (135); *Old Masters and Scottish National Portraits*, Royal Scottish Academy, Edinburgh, 1883 (394); Grosvenor Gallery, 1887 (100); Trustees of His Grace the late Duke of Hamilton sale, Christie's, 6 November, 1919 (72) bt. Amor for 6300 gns. The Rt. Hon. Viscount Feilding sale, Christie's, 1 July, 1938 (127) bt. Colnaghi for 1900 gns. Coll. Count Antoine Seilern; by whom presented, 1945.

REPRODUCTION: National Gallery photographs available.

REFERENCES: *General:* J. Smith, *A Catalogue Raisonné* etc., 1831 III, van Dyck, no. 551; L. Cust, *Anthony van Dyck* etc., 1900, p. 273, no. 64.

In text: (**1**) The two buttonholes at the top of his tunic are clearly shown in the copies at Turin and Pencaitland, see below under *Copies.* (**2**) Documents connected with his journey are printed in *The Diary of William Hedges, Esq.* (II), ed. Col. H. Yule, *The Hakluyt Society*, 1878, 75, pp. cccxliv ff.; and in *Calendar of State Papers, Colonial Series, East Indies & Persia, 1630–1634*, ed. W. Noël Sainsbury, 1892, 8, *passim.* See also Cecilia, Countess of Denbigh, *Royalist Father and Roundhead Son*, 1915, pp. 74–81; V. Sloman, *Bizarre Designs in Silk*, 1953, p. 97; and E. P. Quigly, *The Guardian*, 27 October, 1959. Lady Denbigh, *op. cit.*, pp. 75–6, prints a letter of introduction from Charles I 'to the excellent . . . Mogul, director of the wise and faithful counsels of the Eastern Empire'; the addresses of others are printed by Yule, *loc. cit.* A print, published by Will. Webb in 1631, of Denbigh (rep. by Yule, *op. cit.*, opp. p. ccxlv) describes him as 'Ambassador to the high & mighty King of Persiæ'; but Denbigh's visit was privately undertaken—in his own words 'to better my understanding and not impeach my estate' (see the letter to his son, printed by Lady Denbigh, *op. cit.*, p. 76). (**3**) An attribution to Dobson, current in 1945 and for some years afterwards, was rejected by implication in the 1958 *Summary Catalogue.* (**4**) See under note 2. (**5**) Canvas, 61 × 50 (2·057 × 1·270), Viscount Feilding sale, Christie's, 1 July, 1938 (49). (**6**) See under *General References.* (**7**) See Yule, *op. cit.*, pp. cccxliv ff. (**8**) *Loc. cit.* He states that the Earl is dressed in an Indian or Hindu jacket and pyjamas and that such costume, for sleeping or as déshabillé, was worn by Europeans in India and was apparently known in England by the first quarter of the seventeenth century. It might also be pointed out that among the goods brought back by Denbigh were '17 pieces of Mesopotamia cloth . . . (and) an old pagan coat', see *Calendar of State Papers, Domestic Series, of the Reign of Charles I, 1634–5*, ed. J. Bruce, 1864, 7, p. 2. Denbigh's gun 'is a flint-lock fowling piece of *ca.* 1620–30 and probably of French or Flemish origin', letter in Gallery archives, kindly written by H. R. Robinson of the Armouries, H.M. Tower of London. (**9**) See the *Calendar of State Papers, Colonial Series, East Indies and Persia, 1630–34* etc., p. 674. On 28 August, 1633, James Howell wrote from Westminster to Secretary Windebank: ' . . . Lord Denbigh is returned from the Great Mogor [Mogul], full of jewels', see *Calendar of State Papers, Domestic Series, of the Reign of Charles I, 1633–4*, ed. J. Bruce, 1863, 6, pp. 194–5. (**10**) See O. Millar, *The Tudor, Stuart and Early Georgian Pictures in the Collection of H.M. the Queen*, 1963, no. 143, and pl. 65. (**11**) *Op. cit.*, p. 77. (**12**) Rep. in Edmund Lodge, *Portraits of Illustrious Personages of Great Britain*, VI, 1835, no. 102; see also Smith, cited under *General References.* (**13**) Rep. by Lord Nugent, *Memorials of John Hampden*, 1889 (ed.), opp. p. 57. (**14**) With additions to left, right and top; information and photograph kindly given by Peter Ward-Jackson, 1962. (**15**) A print after which is reproduced by Lady Denbigh, opp. p. 78; Cust, see under *General References*, refers to a copy at Newnham Paddox of the head only. (16) Inscribed 'Earl of Denbigh | killed at the Battle of Edgehill [*sic*]'. (17) He was Denbigh's son in law, having married his eldest daughter, Margaret († 1638), in 1620. (18) See the ms. inventory (in the possession of the Duke of Hamilton, Lennoxlove) headed: 'A Catalogue of my Loj [*sic*]: Marqueff.ˢ | Pictureˢ . . .' in the 21st case: 'My lo: picture of Vandike [*sic*] | My lo. Denbeig [*sic*]'. The inventory must have been drawn up before 12 April, 1643, when the Marquess of Hamilton was made a Duke. As no. 5633 seems to have been the only portrait of the Earl of Denbigh owned by the Hamiltons in the seventeenth century, it is reasonable to assume that this entry refers to it. (19) See the ms. inventory (in the possession of the Duke of Hamilton, Lennoxlove), dateable, 1641/9: no. 291 'One peice [*sic*] of my lords [*sic*] denbighs [*sic*] at lengthe [*sic*], with a fowlinge [*sic*] peece [*sic*] in his hande [*sic*], and a Blackamore [*sic*] by him of Sᵗ Anthony Vandyke [*sic*]'. At about the beginning of the Civil War, Hamilton's collection was placed, by order of Parliament, under the care of his brother-in-law, Denbigh's son, a Puritan; in 1648—the year before the Duke's execution—a petition from the Scottish Parliament to the English Parliament requested that the Duke's collection be restored to him, see Lady Denbigh, *op. cit.*, p. 273. The collection was probably inherited by his second, but only surviving daughter, Anne, Duchess of Hamilton (1631 or 2–1716), who married Lord William Douglas († 1694), created Duke of Hamilton in 1660. At his death, his widow resigned her title to her son († 1712); it then passed to the latter's son, James (1703–1771), by his second marriage. (20) See the ms. inventory (in the possession of the Duke of Hamilton, Lennoxlove) headed: *Inventory of the Pictures at Hamilton*, and dateable 1698(?)/1712: 'In the Gallery . . . 6 The Earle [*sic*] of Denbigh's Picture at full length with a Gunn [*sic*] in his hand in an Indian habitt [*sic*] a tawny (?) Moor pointing up to a Maccaw [*sic*] upon a tree. done by Sᵗ Anthony Vandike [*sic*]'. No. 5633 is also listed in subsequent Hamilton inventories; and was noted at Hamilton by, for instance: T. Pennant, *A Tour of Scotland MDCCLXIX*, 1776 [4th ed.], I, p. 255, sitter then described by the guide as Governor of Jamaica; *ibid.*, *A Tour of Scotland and Voyage to the Hebrides, MDCCLXXII*, I, 1772 [2nd ed.], p. 141 (where ascribed to Rubens); S. H. Spiker, *Travels through England. . . . in the year 1816*, I, 1820, pp. 246–7; and G. F. Waagen, *Treasures of Art in Great Britain*, III, 1854, p. 297.

Ascribed to VAN DYCK

2127   PORTRAIT OF A MAN

Oil on relined canvas, $28\frac{15}{16} \times 23\frac{7}{8}$ (0·735 × 0·605).

There are additions to the support of *ca.* $\frac{3}{4}$ (0·02) at the right and top, and of *ca.* $\frac{9}{16}$ (0·015) at the left; the original canvas thus measured *ca.* $28\frac{1}{8} \times 22\frac{1}{2}$ (0·715 × 0·57).[1]

In fairly poor condition. The darks are worn, retouched, and unreliable. The areas of flesh, which are less worn, are also somewhat retouched and have been flattened by ironing. The collar and cuffs may be overpainted and the lace work a later addition. Discoloured varnish.

No. 2127 has been accepted as the work of van Dyck by recent authorities.[2] It is clearly an old picture, and executed in a style which accords with that of van Dyck in the 1620's. But the poor state is such that it is no longer possible clearly to recognize van Dyck's hand in no. 2127; for this reason, it is here catalogued as only ascribed to him.

The sitter has been identified as the Marchese Giovanni Battista

Cattaneo,[3] on the basis of an inscription on the letter. It is probable that the letter did once bear an inscription, relevant to the identity of the sitter; Mündler and Eastlake[4] noted that the name Cattaneo appeared on it, and MacLaren read traces of the inscription as: 'Al . . . | Gio Batt . . . Cattan . . . | Genova[?]'.[5] However, bearing in mind the poor state of no. 2127, the inscription should be treated with caution: it seems to be thoroughly unreliable. The provenance, see below, would support an identification of the sitter as a member of the Cattaneo family of Genoa,[6] but there are no other grounds to substantiate this.

No. 2127 is thought to have been a pendant to no. 2144, see below, which came from the same collection; but because no. 2127 lacks the curtain in the background of no. 2144, and, as Burchard pointed out,[7] because both sitters face in the same direction, this is highly improbable.

COPIES: Exh. Graves Galleries, 1907;[8] Anon. sale, Christie's, 25 April, 1952 (146);[9] Anon. sale, Sotheby's, 18 October, 1967 (89).[10]

PROVENANCE: See below, under no. 2144.

REPRODUCTION: *National Gallery Illustrations, Continental Schools (excluding Italian)*, p. 103, left.

REFERENCES: (1) Both Mündler and Eastlake, see their diary entries for 2.V.1857 and 30.VIII.1857 (both in the N.G. library) considered that no. 2127, along with the other van Dyck's in the same collection, had been enlarged; Eastlake considered that it was a kitcat made into half length. According to Conte Giuseppe Dal Verme in an interview in the *Corriere della Sera*, 28 Jan., 1907, two of the pictures in the Cattaneo collection, thus perhaps including no. 2127, depicting a man and a woman, 'subirono più che un ritocco, un vero rappezzamento: in entrambi si riscontra che un quadrato di tela comprendente la testa, ebbe ad essere rimesso e ricucito nel quadro, dopo essere state evidentemente asportato. . . .' (2) See L. Cust, *The Burlington Magazine*, 1907, II, pp. 325–326; E. Schaeffer, *Van Dyck, K. der K.*, 1909, p. 186; G. Glück, *Van Dyck, K. der K.*, [1931], p. 198; L. van Puyelde, *Van Dyck*, 1950, p. 113; and the relevant National Gallery catalogues. (3) See note 2. (4) See note 1. (5) Ms. notes. (6) L. Burchard in G. Glück, *Rubens, van Dyck und ihr Kreis*, 1933, p. 413, suggested that the sitter was a scholar, perhaps the philosopher Giovanni Battista Cattaneo. (7) *Ibid.* (8) Inscribed: *Edmund Spenser 1592.* (9) Canvas, 32 × 25 (0·813 × 0·635), in a painted oval. (10) Canvas, 29⅞ × 24⅞ (0·758 × 0·631).

2144   PORTRAIT OF A WOMAN

Oil on relined canvas, 29⅛ × 23¾ (0·74 × 0·604).

There is an addition to the support of *ca.* ¾ (0·02) at the bottom.[1]

In fairly poor condition. A tear *ca.* 6 (0·152) below the left ear has been repaired. The areas of flesh are worn, flattened by ironing and probably retouched, as is the hair. The ruff and cuff are worn; the state of the rest of the costume and the background is obscured by dirt and discoloured varnish.

No. 2144 has been accepted as the work of van Dyck by recent authorities.[2] The head and hand give a better impression than does no. 2127 *q.v.*, and have characteristics that are obviously to be associated with van Dyck's style during his stay in Italy. But the state of no. 2144 is such that it is not possible to detect van Dyck's hand on it with any certainty, thus it is here catalogued as only ascribed to him.

The sitter in no. 2144 has been identified as the Marchesa Cattaneo on the assumption that it is a pendant to no. 2127. However, the identity of the sitter in no. 2127 is not certain, and the two pictures are almost certainly not pendants, being different in style and composition, and facing in the same direction.[3] Menotti[4] followed by Burchard,[5] identified the sitter, on the basis of an old label on the back of a copy of no. 2144 (see below under *Copies*), as Antonia Demarini (b. 1603), who married Francesco Lercari, Doge of Genoa in 1638. However, there is no other evidence to corroborate this identification.

COPIES: David T. Watson sale, New York, 16–17 April 1917 (149);[6] Sarah Mellon Scaife (†) sale, Sotheby's, 29 June, 1966 (136).[7]

PROVENANCE: With no. 2127, coll. the Cattaneo family of Genoa; perhaps noted by Wilson in the palace of Nicola Cataneo (*sic*), Genoa, 1828;[8] noted by Mündler in the Casa Casaretto, 1857;[9] sold by the heirs of Marchese Giuseppe della Volta to Antonio Monti and Conte Trotti, 1907;[10] purchased by Messrs. Colnaghi, 1907; from whom bought with the aid of a contribution from Messrs. Colnaghi, 1907.

REPRODUCTION: *National Gallery Illustrations, Continental Schools (excluding Italian)*, 1958, p. 104, right.

REFERENCES: (1) See note 1 under no. 2127. (2) See E. Schaeffer, *Van Dyck, K. der K.*, 1909, p. 187; G. Glück, *Van Dyck, K. der K.*, [1931], p. 199; L. van Puyvelde, *Van Dyck*, 1950, p. 113; and the relevant National Gallery catalogues. (3) See L. Burchard in G. Glück, *Rubens, van Dyck und ihr Kreis*, 1933, p. 413. (4) See M. Menotti, *Archivo Storico dell'Arte*, 1897, pp. 296–8. (5) See note 3. (6) Canvas, 30 × 24½ (0·762 × 0·621); ex colls. Marchese Coccapani Imperiale Lercari, Modena, see Menotti, *loc. cit.*, & fig.; and Schaeffer, *op. cit.*, p. 185, right; Laurie & Co., 1904. (7) Canvas, 29¼ × 24¼ (0·743 × 0·615) bt. Weitzner, now coll. Dr. Bob Jones, of the Bob Jones University, South Carolina, information kindly supplied by Michael Jaffé. Perhaps identical with the previous picture. (8) See the copy of Wilson's letter made by Wilkie and sent to the Rt. Hon. Robert Peel, in Allan Cunningham, *The Life of Sir David Wilkie* etc., II, 1843, pp. 494–5: 'I was taken to the palace of Nicola Cataneo . . . in one room there are nine Vandykes . . . The remaining six pictures head-size, but all with hands introduced . . .'. (9) See his diary entry (N.G. library) for 2 May, 1857: 'Returned to Casa Casaretto to examine the *Cattaneo van Dycks*. Nine portraits, eight of them being unquestionably original . . . 8: Head of a Lady, a red knot in the hair (ribbons)'. (10) See *Bollettino d'Arte*, IV, no. 1, 1907, p. 26, and newspaper cuttings, 1907–08, concerning the export of the pictures, acquisition by the Gallery and trial of the two Italian dealers.

After VAN DYCK

3537 PORTRAIT OF ROBERT RICH, 2ND EARL OF WARWICK

Oil on relined canvas, 24¹³⁄₁₆ × 13¹¹⁄₁₆ (0·63 × 0·348).

Grisaille, in fair condition. Some areas are worn, and there are several scattered losses, some retouched.

Robert Rich, 2nd Earl of Warwick (1587–1658) gained a reputation as a privateer (commissioned by Charles I) in 1627; he early developed strong interests in the New England and West Indian colonies. A supporter of the Puritans in the 1630's, he soon became estranged from Charles I, and fought for the Parliamentarians in the Civil War, chiefly as Lord High Admiral.

Although thought to be by van Dyck in the 1925 and 1929 National Gallery catalogues, no. 3537 is of poor quality and only derives from him, as was recognized in the 1958 *Summary Catalogue*. It need not even date from the seventeenth century. No. 3537 derives from, but does not follow exactly, a design considered to be by van Dyck, of which several versions are known, none of whose claims to be autograph, rather than contemporary, are particularly good.[1]

The identity of the sitter is established by contemporary engraved portraits as, for instance, that ascribed to R. van der Voerst.[2]

In no. 3537, and the versions from which it derives, the Earl is shown in armour and with a commander's baton and sash. He was not created Lord High Admiral until 1642, and held no important military post in the 1630's. He was, however, joint Lord Lieutenant of Essex, and in 1637 he went with the Prince Elector and the Prince Rupert to The Hague to see the siege of Breda.[3] Maybe it was in allusion to one of these facts or to his exploits as a privateer, that the design showed him thus.

PROVENANCE: Presented by A. A. de Pass, 1920.

REPRODUCTION: National Gallery photographs available.

REFERENCES: (1) See, for instance, L. Cust, *Anthony van Dyck*, 1900, p. 285, no. 219; and G. Glück, *Van Dyck, K. der K.*, [1931], p. 394, and note. (2) See Freeman O'Donoghue, *Catalogue of Engraved British Portraits in the British Museum*, 1914, IV, p. 410. The face in this engraving relates to that in the versions referred to in note 1; Warwick is described in the print as Lord Lieutenant of Essex and Norfolk, which he was made in March 1642. (3) See *The Complete Peerage*, ed. by G. H. White, XII, part II, 1959, p. 409.

After (?) van Dyck

49 PORTRAITS OF THREE MEN

The principal sitter leans against an antique-type altar, decorated with a carved ram's head and a S. Andrew's cross motif, on which is placed an antique (?) statue of a woman (?), held by the man on the right.

Oil on relined canvas, ca. $45\frac{1}{4} \times 44\frac{11}{16}$ ($1 \cdot 15 \times 1 \cdot 135$).

The support is made up of 4 pieces of canvas: strips have been added to the right and bottom, with a separate, small rectangular piece making up the right-hand bottom corner. The right-hand piece is ca. $8\frac{1}{2}$ ($0 \cdot 215$) wide at the top and ca. $7\frac{1}{8}$ ($0 \cdot 18$) wide at the bottom; the piece at the bottom right-hand corner is ca. $3\frac{1}{8}$ ($0 \cdot 08$) high, and the strip along the rest of the bottom is ca. $2\frac{13}{16}$ ($0 \cdot 072$) high.

In fair condition. The top edge is very ragged and has been made up with additions, now retouched, which are as much as $1\frac{1}{8}$($0 \cdot 03$) high here and there. The bottom edge and the area round the principal sitter's right hand are much retouched; there is also retouching over areas of wearing in the sky, columns and black drapery. The negro's head and the right-hand half of the head on the right are thinly painted and somewhat retouched. The flesh of the main sitter has been flattened by ironing; the top half of the statue and the part of the altar near the right-hand edge are very worn. There are a number of small losses overall and a tear in the altar which are all retouched. Cleaned, 1968.

X-ray photography shows that the profile of the man on the right was originally different.

No. 49 has been accepted as the work of van Dyck since 1795 at least,[1] although both Smith and Waagen[2] had reservations. Cleaning has made it clear that obvious inadequacies in the execution of no. 49 cannot be wholly explained by its only fair condition. The handling of the principal sitter, especially his flesh, seems to differ from that of the other two men. But all the flesh, although flattened in the case of the main sitter, and worn in the case of the negro and man on the right, is coarse and clumsy in different ways; the highlights in the drapery are quite well preserved, but meaningless—especially so far as the area of black drapery is concerned—while the sky, landscape and architecture is sketchy without being convincing. Thus it is not possible to accept the traditional view that no. 49 is by van Dyck. No. 49 is, however, clearly painted in the manner of van Dyck and in a style reminiscent of his work in the early 1620's.[3]

The head and shoulders of the main figure correspond with a print by Jan de Visscher (ca. 1636– after 1692)[4] which is probably after a drawing by van Dyck.[5] It thus seems possible that no. 49 is a copy after a portrait by van Dyck, of which Visscher's print records perhaps a preparatory drawing.

It is uncertain to what extent no. 49 accords with van Dyck's original intentions. It may not do so in every respect. For although the ground on the main piece of canvas does not differ radically from that on the right-hand piece, the make up of the support is peculiar with the small added strips of canvas to the right and bottom. The *pentimento* in the profile of the man on the right extends as far as the join in the canvas; and no undermodelling is evident in X-ray photography of the part of the head on the right-hand piece of canvas. This together with differences in handling, noted above, might suggest that the paint on the right-hand piece of canvas was added (and fancifully extended onto the main piece of canvas) to make good extensive damage.

Various identifications of the main sitter and the man on the right have been advanced. Van Dyck's drawing, etched by Visscher, was identified on the plate as a portrait of Rubens, on which basis probably rests the traditional identification of the main sitter, recently revived by Evers.[6] But the sitter bears little resemblance to Rubens as Smith[7] and Rooses,[8] *inter alia*, have pointed out. Other proposals including Cornelis Saftleven[9] as the main sitter, and van Dyck and Bernini (as the man on the right)[10] are also unsatisfactory and have been rejected. Burchard[11] suggested that the main figure was Daniel Nys, who was, he thought, the subject of a portrait by Rubens, of which two versions are known.[12] While there are no grounds to support Burchard's identification,[13] it is possible that the sitter in no. 49 and the Rubens are the same. Recently Millar has read the carved decoration on the altar as the top half of the coat of arms of the Gage family, and suggested that the principal sitter is George Gage (*ca.* 1582–1638).[14] This proposal is stimulating, but it is possible that the main motif is pseudo-antique decoration and not heraldic, and it is difficult to accept his reading of the random brush strokes to the right as the heraldic sun in splendour.

The lack of quality in no. 49 is such that the figures lack psychological coherence and that the situation is ambiguous. It is not clear what the interest of the main figure is in the statue (itself unidentified)[15] and in the man holding it.

ENGRAVINGS: By W. Holl;[16] J. H. Robinson;[17] and Anon.[18]

PROVENANCE: Sir Joshua Reynolds (†) sale, 17 March (=4th day), 1795,[19] Christie's, (73) bt. Angerstein for £147;[20] purchased with the Angerstein collection, 1824.

REPRODUCTION: *National Gallery Illustrations, Continental Schools (excluding Italian)*, 1950, p. 101, right.

REFERENCES: (1) See under *Provenance*; and, for instance, L. Cust, *Anthony Van Dyck* etc., 1900, p. 245; E. Schaeffer, *Van Dyck, K. der K.*, 1909, p. 220; and G. Glück, *Van Dyck, K. der K.*, [1931] p. 129. (2) See J. Smith, *A Catalogue Raisonné*, 1831, III, van Dyck, no. 318; and G. F. Waagen, *Treasures of Art in Great Britain*, I, 1854, p. 352, no. 2; see also *The National Gallery of Pictures* etc., [1838], note to no. 43. (3) This is the period normally assigned to no. 49 by the authorities who have accepted it, see for instance Cust, *loc. cit.*; and Glück, *loc. cit.*; Burchard and Puyvelde, see below, considered that no. 49 was executed soon after van Dyck's arrival in Italy. The 1795 sale catalogue (see below) stated that no. 49 was executed by van Dyck when he was 18, i.e. in 1617. H. G. Evers, *Rubens und sein Werk*, 1944, p. 343, proposed a date of *ca.* 1618. (4) Rep. by Evers, *op. cit.*, fig. 368. (5) See the rubric to the plate included by Evers. (6) *Op. cit.*, pp. 341–344. (7) *Loc. cit.* (8) See *L'Œuvre de P. P. Rubens*, 1890, IV, p. 258. (9) Suggested by F. M. Halberditzl, see Glück, *op. cit.*, note to p. 129. (10) Suggested by L. van Puyvelde, *The Connoisseur*, September, 1944, pp. 3 ff.; (and *Van Dyck*, 1950, pp. 141–2). (11) See G. Glück, *op. cit.*, p. 533 note to p. 129, and *Rubens, van Dyck und ihr Kreis*, 1933, p. 412. (12) See J.-A. Goris and J. S. Held, *Rubens in America*, [1947], p. 29, no. 20, pl. 12. (13) As Puyvelde, *op. cit.*, pp. 3–4, pointed out; a further point against the identification, is the fact that Nys was born in 1572, see I. H. van Eeghen, *Amstelodanum*, 1968, p. 100; the sitter seems to be younger than 51—Nys' age in 1623, when van Dyck met him in Venice, see M. Vaes, *Bulletin de l'Institut historique Belge de Rome*, 1924, 4, p. 205. (14) See Oliver Millar, *The Burlington Magazine*, July, 1969; the compiler wishes to thank him for kindly making available a typescript of this article before publication. (15) Puyvelde, *op. cit.*, p. 8 proposed that the statue was Bernini's *bozzetto* for his *S. Bibiana*, but it hardly agrees. (16) See C. G. V. Schneevoogt, *Catalogue de Etampes gravées . . . après P. P. Rubens*, 1873, p. 163, no. 78. National Gallery catalogues from 1847–1906 state that this engraving is that in *The National Gallery of Pictures* etc. (see note 2), although the print is unsigned. (17) See Schneevoogt, *op. cit.*, p. 162, no. 72. (18) An unsigned print also features in John Young, *A Catalogue of the celebrated collection of Pictures of the late John Julius Angerstein* etc., 1823, no. 24. (19) For the correct date of the sale, not that given on the catalogue, see A. Graves and W. V. Cronin, *A History of the Works of Sir Joshua Reynolds, P.R.A.*, 1901, IV, p. 1627. Puyvelde, *Van Dyck*, 1950, pp. 141–142, stated that no. 49 came from the Algarotti collection, but there is no evidence to support this. (20) See Graves and Cronin, *op. cit.*, p. 1630. The catalogue entry given there, reads: 'Vandyck [*sic*] . . . Rubens's portrait, half length, with two other artists. It is well authenticated Van Dyck painted this picture at the age of 18 years . . .'

Style of VAN DYCK

156 THE HORSES OF ACHILLES

Oil on canvas, stuck on oak, $41\frac{1}{2} \times ca.\ 35\frac{5}{8}$ ($1\cdot055 \times 0\cdot915$).

The canvas support is made up of three irregularly shaped pieces of canvas of two different weaves. The oak support is made up of four members, joined vertically.

Inscribed on the cartellino, bottom left, *EQUI | AQUILLIS | ex Zephyro | . . .*

In fairly poor condition (but see below). The right-hand edge of the canvas support is ragged. The landscape and sky seem to be very worn, as is the smaller horse. The principal horse is apparently better preserved, though its legs are worn, and its flank and tail are somewhat retouched. Strains in the joins of the oak support have communicated themselves to the canvas causing some parting in it. The bottom line of the inscription, apparently made up of Greek letters, is so worn as to be illegible. Cleaned, 1966.

A horse similar to that on the left has been suppressed in the sky. The canvas is cut round it.

Xanthus and Balius, the horses of Achilles, were the offspring of Zephyrus, see Homer, *Iliad*, XVI, 146. The wind god may be intended as a personification of Zephyrus.

Although traditionally thought to be the work of van Dyck,[1] no. 156 does not feature in either of the Klassiker der Kunst editions of his *œuvre*, and was only ascribed to van Dyck in the 1958 *Summary Catalogue*. Glück[2] considered it to be a copy after Rubens; the landscape to which he referred and in which two similar horses occur, has not been seen, but it seems improbable that it is the work of Rubens. No. 156 is obviously painted in the style of van Dyck in the 1620's; but neither of the poses derive directly from him.[3] The recent cleaning has shown that the quality of execution is poor, and certainly not up to the standard of van Dyck. It also showed that it was apparently executed in order not to look well preserved and to give the appearance of its being unfinished.

The make up of the canvas support, revealed by X-radiographs, is complicated: the smaller horse is on one piece; the head, forequarters and tail of the principal horse are on the central piece, and Zephyrus (?), the hindquarters and flank of the main horse are on the third piece. The join under the flank of the main horse is so irregular that the only likely explanation is that the outer pieces of canvas were inserted and added to make good damage and loss to the central piece. The new canvas support was made sound by pasting it to the oak support. At an early stage, the repairer may have considered replacing the loss at the bottom left by cutting out a piece of the main canvas in the top left-hand corner, having already sketched in the horse on it. But he later abandoned this idea, joined up the cut and painted out the sketch.

The handling seems fairly homogeneous; differences are perhaps discernible in the handling on the outer pieces of canvas from that on the inner. But as the general standard is anyway low, it would be rash to advance any hypothesis as to whether two hands are responsible for no. 156, or whether the repair work faithfully and reliably replaced and made good damaged areas of the original.[4] By the same token, it would be rash to attempt to determine whether the inscription is original, or whether Zephyrus(?) and the inscription were added in order to give the sketch a classical subject.[5] Indeed all that can safely be said of no. 156 is that the hand (or hands) responsible for it, was working in imitation of van Dyck, perhaps in the second half of the seventeenth century or early in the eighteenth century.

COPY (?) of the principal horse: Anon. sale, Christie's, 4 December, 1953 (149).[6]

PROVENANCE: Apparently recorded for the first time by Vertue when coll. Delmé, Grosvenor Square, London, 1743;[7] Peter Delme (*sic*) (†) sale, Christie's, 13 February, 1790 (45) bt. Grosier;[8] Sir Joshua Reynolds (†) sale, Christie's, 8 (= 17) March (= 4th day), 1795 (69) bt. Ossory (= ? Lord Upper Ossory (1745–1818)) for £99. 15sh.[9] Coll. the Rt. Hon. Charles Long (later Lord Farnborough) by 1815 when exh. at the B.I. (22); Lord Farnborough Bequest, 1838.

REPRODUCTION: *National Gallery Illustrations, Continental Schools (excluding Italian)*, 1950, p. 102, left.

REFERENCES: *General:* J. Smith, *A Catalogue Raisonné* etc., 1831, III, van Dyck, no. 316 (as by van Dyck); L. Cust, *Anthony van Dyck*, 1900, p. 254, no. 158 (as by van Dyck).

In text: (1) See below under *Provenance*; and the authors cited under *General References*. (2) See G. Glück, *Die Landschaften von Peter Paul Rubens*, 1940/5, under no. 27. (3) The pose of the forepart of the main horse is comparable to that in the *Crucifixion of Christ*, at Ghent, rep. by G. Glück, *Van Dyck, K. der K.*, [1931], p. 247. (4) Thus the significance, if any, to be attached to the fact that Vertue, see under *Provenance*, described what was probably no. 156 as 'a white horse, a sketch by van Dyck', is obscure. (5) The inscription and title is first referred to in the Reynolds' sale catalogue of 1795, see under *Provenance*. (6) 31 × 23 (noted by MacLaren, ms. notes). (7) See *Vertue Note Books III, The Walpole Society*, 1933–34, 23, p. 117. (8) Described as 'A Study of Horses'; buyer and price in Christie's marked catalogue. The same buyer bought Rembrandt, no. 43 of this collection, at the Dalton sale of 1791, apparently for Reynolds, see N. Mac-Laren, *National Gallery Catalogues, The Dutch School*, 1960, p. 307, and note 22 on p. 308. (9) Described as 'The Horses of Achilles. A quotation from Homer is at the corner of the picture. From the collection of Mr. Delme [*sic*]'. For the date of the sale, buyer and price, see A. Graves and W. Cronin, *A History of the Works of Sir Joshua Reynolds* etc., 1901, IV, pp. 1627 & 1630.

3132 PORTRAIT OF A WOMAN

Oil on copper, oval, $23\frac{1}{2} \times 18\frac{9}{16}$ (0·597 × 0·472).

Probably in fairly good condition. There are two losses at the edge of the support. The craquelure is marked in the lower left. One area of discoloured varnish was removed in 1947.

No. 3132 was attributed to van Dyck in the latter part of the nine-teenth century;[1] it was first catalogued at the Gallery as after van Dyck,[2] and then attributed to the Flemish School *ca.* 1630–40 in the catalogue of *An Exhibition of Cleaned Pictures* of 1947.[3] The connection with van Dyck is evident, but the quality of execution is poor. No. 3132 may well be a copy after a portrait executed by van Dyck in the first half of the 1630's; but as no original has been traced, it seems best to attribute no. 3132 to the style of van Dyck.

No. 3132 seems to be old, but it is probably not contemporary with van Dyck.

A label on the reverse of no. 3132 wrongly identifies it as the portrait of Marie Anne Schotten (= Schotti), recorded as part of the epitaph of the Schotti family in S. Gudule, Brussels.[4] This identification and provenance is now claimed for the full length portrait at Boston[5] (which bears no relation with no. 3132). The identification of the sitter in no. 3132 thus remains unknown.

PROVENANCE: Prince de Beauvau sale, Paris, 21 April, 1865 (4) bt. Sir Austen Henry Layard († 1894),[7] by whom bequeathed with a life interest to his widow († 1912), 1916; *An Exhibition of Cleaned Pictures*, The National Gallery, 1947/8 (88).

REPRODUCTION: National Gallery photographs available.

REFERENCES: *in text:* (1) See under *Provenance.* (2) See National Gallery catalogues, 1920–29. (3) See under *Provenance.* (4) See G. P. Mensaert, *Le Peintre Amateur et Curieux,* I, 1763, p. 79, who refers to the sitter's hands in the portrait; and J. B. Descamps, *Voyage Pittoresque . . . du Brabant,* 1769, p. 56. (5) See G. Glück, *Van Dyck, K. der K.,* [1931], p. 351 and note. (6) Described as the portrait of Marie Anne Schotten by van Dyck which 'was fixed on [the] monument erected to the lady in S. Gudule, Brussels'. (7) Layard ms. in National Gallery library.

3605 PORTRAITS OF TWO YOUNG ENGLISHMEN

Oil on relined canvas, *ca.* $76\frac{1}{4} \times 49\frac{5}{8}$ ($1 \cdot 937 \times 1 \cdot 26$). The edges of the support are masked by a binding canvas.

Additions to the top of the support of *ca.* $5\frac{1}{8}$ ($0 \cdot 13$) and to the bottom of *ca.* 8 ($0 \cdot 203$).[1]

Inscribed at the bottom, on the addition, *Lord Iohn and Lord Bernard Stuart.* | *Sons of the Duke of Lenox* [sic].

In fairly poor condition. A darkened, yellow varnish makes a proper assessment concerning condition difficult. But there is much wearing in, and repaint and/or retouching on both figures. The paint of the scab-bard is later than the rest.

X-ray photography shows that the sitter on the left was originally depicted with a short collar, a more pointed chin and a slightly concave nose, and that the other sitter may first have worn a glove on his left hand. Further, the cloak has been extended a little over the right hand of the sitter on the left.

No. 3605 was traditionally[2] thought to be by van Dyck. Among recent authorities, only Puyvelde[3] has doubted this attribution. But in view of the poor state of no. 3605, it is foolhardy to accept the traditional view. Indeed van Dyck's hand seems to be nowhere indisputably present. In attempting to define the status of no. 3605, the following remarks should be borne in mind. It was in existence by 1682, when acquired by the Earl of Kent (see below under *Provenance*). The composition and poses are closely related to those in van Dyck's repertoire.[4] The alterations, noted above, probably result not from *pentimenti* by the artist, but from early retouching, as the short collar originally worn by the sitter on the left and the glove on the left hand of the sitter on the right occur, in the first case not precisely, in what appears to be an early copy of no. 3605.[5]

This being the case, the least that can be said for no. 3605 is that it is in the style of van Dyck. Thus it is possible that it is the remnants of: 1) a design invented by van Dyck and executed in his studio; 2) an old copy after a lost original; or 3) the work of an artist working in the style of van Dyck in the 1640's.[6] It is difficult to decide which of these is the most likely, and thus an attribution to the style of van Dyck seems the best in the circumstances.

No. 3605 is generally thought to have been executed in the last years of van Dyck's life, in England;[7] certainly it is painted in a manner reminiscent of that of van Dyck in the late 1630's.

No. 3605 was traditionally thought to depict Lords John and Bernard Stuart. Lord John Stuart (1621(?)–1644) and Lord Bernard Stuart (1622–1645), designated the Earl of Lichfield shortly before his death, were the third and fourth sons of Esmé Stuart, 3rd Duke of Lennox; both died fighting for Charles I in the Civil War. No. 3605 was engraved as such not later than 1693[8], the identification was accepted by the Duke of Hamilton in 1698[9] and features in the Earl of Kent's inventory of 1702.[10] However, van Dyck's double portrait, owned by the late Countess Mountbatten,[11] also has claims to depict these sitters, as it may be the picture in the inventory of 1672 in the possession of their nephew, the Duke of Richmond and Lennox († 1672), at Cobham.[12] And despite the fact that the faces of the two sitters in no. 3605 have been distorted by damage and retouching, it is highly improbable that they could ever have been intended to look the same as those in the Mountbatten picture. And if it is considered that there is no proof that the Mountbatten picture is identical with that at Cobham in 1672, it must be stated that the claims of no. 3605 are weakened by its poor state and uncertain status. Thus of the two pictures, the Mountbatten picture has the better claim to represent Lords John and Bernard Stuart.[13] Other proposals for the identification of the sitters in no. 3605, some made in recognition of this, are also unsatisfactory.[14] The most that can be stated about them is that they appear to be in their 'teens and are probably English.[15]

The costumes in no. 3605 are peculiar; Miss Stella Mary Pearce thought the costumes were 'fancy or masquerade dress'.[16] So far as can be made out, one of the canopy bearers in van Dyck's sketch of the *Procession of the Knights of the Garter* (coll. the Duke of Rutland), which was probably executed in 1637–38, seems to wear somewhat similar clothes.[17] However, costumes, not dissimilar from that worn by the sitter on the left occur in portraits by Jan Mytens of the late 'forties and 'fifties.[18]

ENGRAVINGS: Mezzotint published by Richard Tomson, in reverse;[19] mezzotint by James MacArdell;[20] of the head and shoulders of the sitter on the right, by G. Vertue.[21]

COPIES: By J. Closterman(1660–1711), coll. the Duke of Hamilton, Lennoxlove;[22] Blakeslee Gallery sale, Plaza Hotel, New York, 21 April, 1915 (160);[23] Anon. sale, Sotheby's, 2 April, 1952 (71);[24] asc. to H. P. Bone, A. E. Guinness sale, Christie's, 10 July, 1953 (52);[25] private coll., London, 1962;[26] coll. Shastran Petit, 1963;[27] of the head of the sitter on the right: Audley End, Ministry of Public Buildings and Works.[28]

DERIVATION: Coll. J. F. Montagu, Leicestershire, as by Dobson, noted ca. 1935 (?).[29]

PROVENANCE: Bought from Jan Baptist Gaspers (1620?–1690?)[30] by Anthony de Grey, 11th Earl of Kent († 1702) for £30 in June, 1682;[31] inherited by his son, Henry († 1740), Duke of Kent from 1710, Marquess Grey (1740), in whose collection at St. James's Sq., London, seen by Vertue, 1730;[32] inherited by his grand-daughter, Jemima († 1797), created Marchioness de Grey, 1740, with the barony of Lucas,[33] in the collection of whose husband, Philip Yorke, styled Viscount Royston (from 1754–1764), later Earl of Hardwicke, at St. James' Sq., seen by Walpole in 1761;[34] inherited by her daughter, Amabel († 1833), created Countess de Grey of Wrest, 1816, with the barony of Lucas, in whose collection recorded by Smith, 1831;[35] inherited by her nephew, Thomas Philip, Earl de Grey († 1889) with the barony of Lucas, in whose collection seen by Waagen, 1851;[36] exh. Manchester Art Treasures, 1857 (117); inherited by his daughter, Anne Florence, Dowager Countess Cowper († 1880) with the barony of Lucas; exh. R.A., 1873 (117); inherited by her son Earl Cowper († 1905) with the barony of Lucas, and recorded at Panshanger in 1885;[37] exh. Grosvenor Gallery, 1887 (47); inherited by his nephew, Auberon Thomas Herbert, 8th Baron Lucas († 1916); bought from his sister, Lady Lucas, with the aid of the Temple West Fund, 1922.

REPRODUCTION: *National Gallery Illustrations, Continental Schools (excluding Italian)*, 1950, p. 106.

REFERENCES: (1) The additions were probably made after the execution of the copy by Closterman (see below under *Copies*). (2) See under *Engravings* and *Provenance*. (3) See L. van Puyvelde, *Van Dyck*, 1950, pp. 88 & 163. Otherwise no. 3605 has been generally accepted: for instance by L. Cust, *Anthony van Dyck*, 1906, p. 283, no. 190; G. Glück, *Van Dyck*, K. der K., [1931], p. 458; and the relevant National Gallery catalogues. (4) The composition is a variation of that by van Dyck, which probably depicts Lords John and Bernard Stuart (see below), coll. the late Countess Mountbatten (rep. by Glück, *op. cit.*, p. 459), see the catalogue of *Flemish Art*, The Royal Academy, 1953/4 (139). The pose of the sitter on the left in no. 3605 is a variation of that of the Abbé Scaglia, coll. Lord Camrose (see Glück, *op. cit.*, p. 426), and of the young Prince Rupert at Vienna (see Glück, *op. cit.*, p. 334). The pose of the sitter on the right connects with that in the late Countess Mountbatten's picture. The top part of the pose recurs in the portrait of Constantijn Huygens II in the group portrait of 1640 in the Mauritshuis (no. 241), where ascribed to Hanneman, who is thought to have left van Dyck's studio ca. 1637, see the entry in Thieme-Becker. (5) See below under *Copies*. (6) Puyvelde, *loc. cit.*, considered Peter Lely as a possible attribution for no. 3605. This seems not wholly unreasonable, as Lely was active in England in the 1640's; although the evidence used by R. van Luttervelt, *Oud Holland*, 1953, p. 168 and figs. 1 and 4, to show that he was in England by 1641, should be treated with caution, as Oliver

Millar has kindly pointed out to the compiler. Gaspers, who owned no. 3605
(see under *Provenance*), was an assistant of Lely's (see note 30); no. 3605 did not
feature in the sale of Lely's collection of 1682. (7) See for instance Cust, *loc.
cit.*; and Glück, *op. cit.*, p. 458. (8) See below under *Engravings*. (9) See note 22.
(10) See below under *Provenance*. (11) See Glück, *op. cit.*, p. 459. If correctly
identified, the picture must have been executed before 30 January, 1639, when
the two brothers received permission to go abroad, see the entry for
Lord Bernard in the D.N.B. (12) For the inventory, see Canon Scott
Robertson, *Archæologia Cantiana*, XVII, 1887, pp. 393 ff.; p. 405: 'In
the Wardrobe of Pictures . . . no. 82 My Lord John and Lord Bernard
(Stuart)'. The Duke's possessions at Cobham passed to his sister (†
1703) and finally to the 1st Earl of Darnley by his marriage to her
grand-daughter Theodosia, see also the catalogue of *Flemish Art*, The
Royal Academy 1953/4, no. 139. It is to be noted that the Cobham inventory
does not specify that the picture was by van Dyck. (13) The identification is
generally accepted, see for instance, Cust, *op. cit.*, p. 118; and Glück, *loc. cit.*
(14) Vertue, see *Vertue Note Books*, III, *The Walpole Society*, 1933–34, XXII, p. 47,
accepted the identification of the right hand figure as Lord Bernard (see below
under *Engravings*) and called the other the Duke of Richmond (= Lord John's
elder brother, James (1612–55)), but he bears no resemblance to van Dyck's
portraits of him (see Glück, *op. cit.*, pp. 409, 410, 411 etc.). Walpole followed
Vertue for the right hand figure, and called the other Lord Esmé Stuart,
see *Horace Walpole's Journals etc.*, ed. Paget Toynbee, *The Walpole Society*,
XV, 1927–28, p. 40; but Lord Esmé was born in 1649 and died at
the age of 10. More recently, Cust, *loc. cit.*, tentatively suggested two
sons of the Marquis of Newcastle (= the Earl, later Marquis and then
Duke of Newcastle (1593–1677)), one of whom was born *ca.* 1626, but there
seem to be no certain portraits with which to make a comparison. Charles
Holmes, *The Burlington Magazine*, 1922, I, pp. 54–56, proposed George
(1628–1687) and Francis Villiers (1629–1648), the sons of the Duke of Buckingham, of whom there is a double portrait by van Dyck in the Royal Collection
(see Glück, *op. cit.*, p. 439). This was accepted in the National Gallery catalogue
of 1929, but rejected by C. R. Cammel, *The Connoisseur*, 1937, pp. 202 ff. Cammel,
who accepted the attribution no. 3605 to van Dyck, argued that the sitters
there looked older than 13 and 12—the ages of the two Villiers boys at van
Dyck's death. In fact, if no. 3605 is not associated directly with van Dyck—
and there is no overriding reason why it should be—and if it could be shown to
derive rather from an artist working in imitation of van Dyck towards the end
of the 1640's, then Holmes' identification becomes less improbable. X-ray
photographs of the two heads in no. 3605 show them to be not wholly dissimilar
from the two heads in the Windsor *Group Portrait*; the face of the sitter
on the left in no. 3605 is more bony with a sharper chin in the X-ray photograph,
and does bear some resemblance to the portrait of George Villiers, reproduced
by Cammell (his fig. III) which shows him as an older man. George, 2nd Duke
of Buckingham and his brother, Lord Francis, both supported Charles I in the
Civil War, during which for a short time they were placed in the care of the Duke
of Northumberland and spent some time abroad. Lord Francis was killed
fighting for the king, but his elder brother escaped. All these recent proposals
have been rejected by Glück, *op. cit.*, p. 571, note to page 458, and (by implication) in the *Summary Catalogue* of 1958. (15) See the *Summary Catalogue*, 1958;
and the catalogue of an *Exhibition of Flemish Art*, The Royal Academy, 1953/4,
under no. 139 (16) Note in Gallery archives. (17) As hinted by Holmes, *op. cit.*,
p. 55. For the Rutland sketch, see, for instance, O. Millar, *The Burlington
Magazine*, 1954, pp. 39 ff. (18) Compare for instance, the costume of the
father in the *Group Portrait* of 1648, ex coll. W. D. Clarke, of Willem van
der Does in the *Group Portrait* in the Museum Mayer van den Bergh, Antwerp (no. 13) of 1650, and of Clement Cotterell, in the *Group Portrait of the
Cotterell Family* of 1658, coll. R. Leon, exh. The Royal Academy, 1956/7 (65).
(19) The field shows as much as the addition to the top, but only half the

addition to the bottom in no. 3605. The print was probably designed by J. B. Gaspers, whose name is inscribed on a squared up drawing for the print, which is in the British Museum, see E. Croft-Murray and Paul Hulton, *Catalogue of British Drawings, British Museum*, 1960, I, p. 326, no. 1, and plate 129 (vol. II). The print is inscribed: 'Ant: Van Dyck Eques pinxit. Collection Earle [*sic*] of Kent. R. Tompson [*sic*] exct.| The Lord John & ye Lord Bernard Stuart ye youngest sons of Esme [*sic*] Duke of Lenox [*sic*]'. Gaspers died in 1690(?) and the publisher, Tomson, in 1693. (20) This shows less at the bottom than the previous print, but still more than the original field of no. 3605; the top corresponds to the field after the addition to no. 3605. The print is inscribed: 'Vandyke [*sic*] pinxit. J. McArdell fecit | Lord John & Lord Bernard Stuart Sons of Esme [*sic*] Duke of Lenox [*sic*]'. (21) One of a set of *Loyalists*, inscribed: 'Ld Litchfield', with a brief record of service. (22) Oil on canvas, 25 × 18 (0·635 × 0·457). The field is the same as in no. 3605 without the addition at the bottom, but shows less at the top. The sword of the sitter on the right has no scabbard. First recorded in an ms. note (coll. the Duke of Hamilton) by the then Duke, 2 April, 1698: 'Thes [*sic*] hung in my room . . . My Lord John & My Lord Bernard Stewart | pictures [*sic*] done after Vandick [*sic*] by Mr | Closterman the Earle [*sic*] of Kent has the | originall [*sic*].' (23) Oil on canvas, 85 × 48 (2·16 × 1·22) as by Dobson. Judging from a reproduction, not correctly attributed. It shows half the addition at the bottom, but more at the top. The sitter on the left is shown with a short frilled, lace collar, similar but not identical, because of the frills, to that evident in X-radiographs of no. 3605. The right-hand sitter's left hand is gloved, as it seems to be in X-rays of no. 3605; in the copy, the hand holds another glove, which is not present in X-rays of no. 3605. The fall of the cloak of the sitter on the left differs from that in no. 3605. (24) 39½ × 29½ (1·003 × 0·75). (25) Enamel, 13½ × 9½ (0·343 × 0·242); ex colls. the 1st Earl of Iveagh and the Earl de Grey. Cammel, *op. cit.*, note 1 on p. 205, records a version, cited by Cust, in Earl de Grey's collection. Cust, *op. cit.*, p. 283, under no. 190, is not correct to state that there is a copy of no. 3605 at Welbeck. (26) *Ca*. 36 × 18 (0·915 × 0·457). (27) Letter in Gallery archives. (28) Note of 1941 in Gallery archives. (29) 66 × 54 (1·677 × 1·372) perhaps by John Hayls. The costume of the sitter on the left, with a short collar (see above) is very similar. (30) Gaspers or Caspers, a Fleming, came to England during the Civil War, bought pictures at the sale of Charles I's collection and after the Restoration joined Lely's studio. After Lely's death in 1680, he was involved in completing pictures left unfinished by the master, see Croft-Murray and Hulton, *op. cit.*, p. 325; see also under *Engravings*. (31) In an ms. inventory of the pictures belonging to Anthony, 11th Earl of Kent, of 1702, p. 5, where stated to have been bought from Mr. Janbatis [*sic*] Caspers, June, 1682, for £30 and called Lords John and Bernard Stuart (information kindly provided by the present Lady Lucas, quoting from a catalogue of the Wrest Park pictures compiled by her mother). (32) See Vertue, *loc. cit.*; an earlier visit and note of no. 3605 by Vertue is recorded in *Vertue Note Books*, II, *Walpole Society*, 1931–32, XX, p. 106. (33) Jemima's great-grand-mother, the wife of the 11th Earl of Kent, was the first Baroness Lucas, which title could be passed down the male or female line. (34) See Paget Toynbee, *loc. cit.* (35) See J. Smith, *A Catalogue Raisonné* etc., 1831, III, pp. 151–152, van Dyck, no. 537. (36) See G. F. Waagen, *Treasures of Art in Great Britain* etc., II, 1854, pp. 84–85. (39) See M. L. Boyle, *Biographical Catalogue of the Portraits at Panshanger* etc., 1885, pp. 389–390.

Josephus Laurentius DYCKMANS

1811–1888

Painter of genre subjects. Born at Lierre, 9 August, 1811, where he was taught drawing; in 1833 he studied under G. Wappers at Antwerp.

He exhibited at Antwerp, London (1846–69), Paris (1855), Vienna, etc. He died at Antwerp, 8 January, 1888.

REFERENCE: *General:* Thieme-Becker, *Künstler-Lexikon*, 1914, X, p. 273.

600 THE BLIND BEGGAR

A blind beggar sits in the porch of a church, with a young girl beside him.

Oil on mahogany, $19\frac{13}{16} \times 18\frac{5}{16}$ (0·503 × 0·465).

Signed, *J. Dyckmans. 1853.*

On the tablet over the entrance to the church is inscribed: *HOND(?)EN D(?)YT/GODTS TEMPEL*

In good condition. There are some losses round the edges. The varnish is discoloured and engrained in the background.

There is no reason to doubt the authenticity of the signature and date on no. 600.

No. 600 is apparently the second in a series of pictures of the same subject by Dyckmans.[1] The first, executed in the previous year, and now in the Koninklijk Museum voor schone Kunsten, Antwerp,[2] differs from no. 600 in several details.

ENGRAVING: By W. H. Simmons.[3]

COPY: Private collection, Huddersfield, 1954, dated 1928.[4]

PROVENANCE: Leopold Redpath sale, Christie's, 23 May (= 3rd day), 1857 (353) bt. (Miss Jane) Clarke for £955 10sh.[5]; Miss J. Clarke Bequest, 1859; hung at South Kensington, 1865; transferred to the Tate Gallery, 1900–10, and from 1912–1956.

REPRODUCTION: National Gallery photographs available.

REFERENCES: *In text:* (1) For further pictures, bearing the same title as no. 600, see A. Graves, *Art Sales* etc., 1918, I, p. 249. (2) Panel, $14\frac{9}{16} \times 11\frac{3}{8}$ (0·37 × 0·29), see E. Buschmann-van Rijswick, *Musée Royal des Beaux-Arts, Anvers, Catalogue II, Maîtres Modernes*, 1950, p. 44, no. 1520. (3) See R. N. Wornum, *Descriptive and Historical Catalogue of the Pictures in the National Gallery* etc., 1862, p. 96. (4) See letters of 1954 from James L. Brooke, Huddersfield (who was cleaning and restoring the picture) in the Gallery archives. (5) See Graves, *loc. cit.*

FLEMISH SCHOOL, *ca.* 1620

1287 COGNOSCENTI IN A ROOM HUNG WITH PICTURES

Oil on oak, *ca.* $37\frac{3}{4} \times 48\frac{5}{8}$ (0·959 × 1·235).

The support, which is cradled, may be made up of four members. There are additions to the right and left edges of *ca.* $\frac{3}{8}$ (0·01). It is possible that there is an addition to the bottom of *ca.* 1 (0·025), but this is not certain.

Apparently in fairly good condition. There are some cracks in the support, and some small amount of paint loss and retouching along them. Some of the pictures are worn; there are many scattered areas of retouching especially in the floor and ceiling.

The objects on the table on the left include: spectacles, a pair of dividers, a rule, an astrolabe, an angle measuring instrument with sights—possibly a clinometer—a celestial globe, sundial with compass and a magnifying glass.[1] There is also a circular miniature portrait of a man, nine antique cameos or coins, a statuette, two drawings, a loose print and an open folio of prints. The costume of the sitter in the miniature, suggests a date early in the first half of the fifteenth century. One of the drawings is of a male nude, possibly Mercury, the other is indecipherable; the loose print is a state, without the inscription of *Ceres mocked by Peasants*, engraved by Count H. Goudt after Elsheimer.[2] On the open folio of prints are impressions of Dürer's *The Coat of Arms with a Skull*,[3] an adaptation of his *Virgin and Child with a Crown of Stars*,[4] his *S. George on horseback*,[5] and *The Little Horse*,[6] and of Lucas van Leyden's *Musicians*[7] and *Young man with a Skull*.[8]

On the far table are 6 pieces of sculpture, reading from the left: *A Man with a raised Arm*; *The Rape of Dejanira* (?); *A crouching Woman*[9]; *An Hermaphrodite*[10]; *The Wrestlers*[11]; *Diana* (?). There are also some shells, a container, and a framed cameo or *bas-relief* of a head of a man in profile, wearing a crown.

On the cupboard, on the right, is a pot, jug and cup, with some metal cups visible in an opened compartment.

Standing on the wooden, recessed porch opposite, are two marble statues of *Minerva* and *Mercury*.

The five paintings in the right foreground are reading from the left, beginning with the top row: *The Four Elements* in a style reminiscent of Hendrick van Balen I and Jan Brueghel I; a mythological (?) scene; *The Virgin and Child in a Garland of Flowers*, in a style reminiscent of Hendrick van Balen I and Jan Brueghel I; *Alexander & Diogenes* after David Teniers I[12]; and a *Still Life with dead Game* in a style reminiscent of Frans Snijders.

The man standing in the left foreground holds a painting of insects, (with the protective cover drawn back) in a style perhaps reminiscent of Georges Hoefnagel; the man beside him holds a picture of *Cupid* (?); the boy holds a miniature portrait of a woman in a style reminiscent of a Netherlandish artist active about the middle of the sixteenth century.

The paintings on the wall of the wooden, recessed porch, reading from the top are: *An Interior of a Church with Men receiving Holy Communion* in the style of Hendrick van Steenwyck II; *A Landscape with classical Ruins* in a style reminiscent of Paul Bril or Willem van Nieulandt; *A Landscape with a Windmill* in the style of Jan Brueghel I[13]; beside it, a *Landscape with Diana hunting*, in a style reminiscent of Hendrick de Clerck and Denis van Alsloot; beneath it, a circular *Landscape* in a style perhaps reminiscent of Christiaen de Coninck; beside it, a *Still Life with Flowers* in a style reminiscent of Jan Brueghel I[14]; beneath it, a figure composition.

Above the porch, *The Betrayal of Christ*, in the style of a Netherlandish artist working under the influence of Caravaggio and Dürer.[15]

On the far wall, reading from the left, top row: *A Fishmonger's Stall* in a style reminiscent of Joachim Beuckelaer; *A mountainous Landscape* in a style reminiscent of Joos de Momper II; *A Portrait of a Man and Woman* in a style reminiscent of a Netherlandish artist active about the middle of the first half of the sixteenth century; second row: *Venus at the Forge of Vulcan* in a style perhaps reminiscent of Johann Rotten-hammer; *Ships running before the Wind in a heavy Swell*, in a style reminiscent of Andries van Ertveldt; *A Herd of Cows in a Landscape*, in a style perhaps reminiscent of Jan Wildens; *The Adoration of the Kings* in a style perhaps reminiscent of Frans Francken II; third row: *Croesus and Solon* (?), in a style perhaps reminiscent of Hendrick van Steenwyck II and a collaborator[16]; *Christ on the Way to Emmaus*, perhaps reminiscent of a south Netherlandish artist active about the middle of the sixteenth century; *A View of a burning Town*, perhaps in a style reminiscent of a follower of Bosch; *The Infant S. John the Baptist*, in a style perhaps reminiscent of a follower of Elsheimer; *The Contest of Apollo and Marsyas before Midas*, in a style perhaps reminiscent of a Flemish artist active in the early seventeenth century; fourth row: *A mountainous Landscape* in a style perhaps reminiscent of Paul Bril; *A woody Landscape with Horsemen* in a style perhaps reminiscent of Jan Brueghel I; *Bathsheba receiving David's Letter* in a style perhaps reminiscent of a follower of Elsheimer; *A Landscape with the Death of Procris* in a style perhaps reminiscent of Christiaen de Coninck; *A Portrait of a Man* (roundel), in a style reminiscent of a Netherlandish artist active about the middle of the sixteenth century; below, *Pan and Syrinx* in a style perhaps reminiscent of Hendrick van Balen I and a collaborator[17]; fifth row: *King Cepheus of the Ethiopians remonstrates with his wife Cassiope before their daughter, Andromeda chained to a Rock*, in a style perhaps reminiscent of Frans Francken II; *The Triumph of Bacchus* in a style reminiscent of a Netherlandish artist active in the early seventeenth century; *A Landscape with a Bridge* in a style perhaps reminiscent of Gillis van Coninxloo; *A Still Life with Flowers* in a style perhaps reminiscent of Jan Brueghel I; below, *A Cavalry Skirmish in a Landscape* in a style reminiscent of Sebastian Vrancx; *The Flight into Egypt*, in a style reminiscent of Elsheimer; *The Deliverance of S. Peter*, in a style perhaps reminiscent of Hendrick van Steenwyck II; *S. Jerome in his Study*, in a style reminiscent of Marinus van Reymerswaele[18]; below, a picture with its face to the wall.

The five paintings on the wall on the right are, reading from the left, top row: *Salome with the head of S. John the Baptist* in a style reminiscent of Rubens; *The Virgin and Child* after Rubens[19]; second row: *A woody Landscape*; below, *A panoramic View of a River* in a style deriving from that of Pieter Bruegel I; *The Union of Earth and Water* in a style reminiscent of Rubens.[20]

The attribution of no. 1287 has been disputed and is not known. It was first catalogued at the National Gallery as the work of an anonymous Dutch artist.[21] W. Martin[22] then attributed it to 'Hans Jordaens the Younger', on the basis of the similarity of the room depicted with that

in a picture at Vienna, which has a reliably old attribution to Hans
Jordaens III (?).[23] This was accepted in National Gallery catalogues from
1919–29. Frimmel[24] had, however, previously drawn attention to the
similarity between no. 1287 and a picture at Brussels,[25] which he
attributed to Hendrick Staben. This picture includes some initials on
two of the window panels, and the date *1621*. Speth-Holterhoff,[26]
perhaps correctly, took these initials to be those of the painter(s) responsible for the picture, and read them as '*F/AW*' (in monogram) and
'*IF*' (in monogram). These were taken to stand for 'Antwerpen' and
'Jérôme Francken'; and on this basis, she attributed the picture to Frans
Francken II and Jérôme Francken II—the latter being responsible for
the figures.[27] She thought an attribution of no. 1287 to the same artists
'plausible'.[28] But this reading of the initials is not above dispute, a
more satisfactory reading is: '*F/MW*' or '*WM*' (in monogram) followed by '*TF*' (in monogram).[29] Further, as the figures in the Brussels
picture bear no relationship to those in the only signed work by Hier-
onymous Francken II,[30] her thesis becomes unacceptable.

Speth-Holterhoff's suggestion that two hands, working in collaboration, were responsible for the Brussels picture and no. 1287 may well be
correct, especially if the two sets of initials on the former are accepted
as representing signatures. Another factor in support of this is the
similarity between the interior of no. 1287 with that in the picture at
Vienna, noted by Martin, and with that signed by C. de Baillieur,
published by Kelly.[31] An explanation of the recurrence of these
interiors is that they are the work of the same artist,[32] who collaborated
with different figure painters.

W. Martin's attribution of the whole (or part) of no. 1287 is unacceptable, as there is no connection between the execution of the figures in the
Vienna picture and those in no. 1287. Frimmel's suggestion of Staben
seems more attractive, but for the elusiveness of this artist's style. And
neither the figures nor the architecture in no. 1287 are strictly comparable
with those in an interior owned by the Prince de Ligne, thought to be by
Staben.[33] Furthermore, neither pair of initials on the Brussels picture
can be his.

The two (?) artists responsible for no. 1287 may have had the initials
which appear on the Brussels picture: '*F/MW*' or '*WM*' and '*TF*'[34];
the one responsible for the architecture may have continued to be active
into the 1630's, the other may have died soon after the execution of the
Brussels picture in 1621. They were both probably active in the southern
Netherlands, particularly because of the number of pictures depicted
of south Netherlandish origin. No likely candidates, active in one of the
main centres—for instance Antwerp[35]—have been traced, whose
personalities are known. For this reason, no. 1287 is here attributed
to the Flemish School, thus following the entry in the catalogue of the
Exhibition of Cleaned Pictures of 1947 (see below).

No. 1287 seems to have been executed about the same time as the
Brussels picture. A *terminus post quem* of *ca.* 1616 for its date of
execution is provided by the presence of the copy after the Sanssouci

Virgin and Child by Rubens, which should be dated about this time.[36]

The people depicted are probably not imaginary; the young man in the centre is not unlike the self portrait by Jacques Jordaens in a group portrait in the Hermitage[37]; the older man beside him is not unlike Hendrick van Balen I,[38] but may seem to be older than in his forties—van Balen's age when no. 1287 is thought to have been executed. A boy similar to that holding the miniature in no. 1287 occurs in the centre of the Brussels picture.

The collection of pictures, instruments and *objets d'art* depicted in no. 1287 is probably imaginary.

PROVENANCE: Count de Morny (of Paris) sale, Phillips, 20 June, 1848 (16)[39] probably bt. Smith; by whom sold to John Staniforth Beckett for £125 on 21 August, 1848[40]; by whom bequeathed, 1889; exh. *An Exhibition of Cleaned Pictures*, The National Gallery, 1947/8 (3).

REPRODUCTION: *National Gallery Illustrations, Continental Schools (excluding Italian)*, 1950, p. 180, bottom.

REFERENCES: *In text:* (1) Information kindly provided by H. Holstein, Research Assistant, Science Museum, who also states that the Science Museum possesses a sundial in a similar style, estimated to have been made *ca.* 1600, and a similar globe made by Blaeu in Amsterdam, whose earliest celestial globes date from 1603. (2) See H. Weizsäcker, *Adam Elsheimer der Maler von Frankfurt*, III, 1936, pl. 105. (3) See F. W. H. Hollstein, *German Engravings, Etchings and Woodcuts* etc., VII, ed. by K. G. Boon and R. W. Scheller, p. 89. (4) See Hollstein, *op. cit.*, p. 28; the compiler wishes to thank Mr. John Rowlands of the Department of Prints and Drawings, British Museum, for his help in trying to identify this print. (5) See Hollstein, *op. cit.*, p. 46. (6) See Hollstein, *op. cit.*, p. 85 (left). (7) See F. W. H. Hollstein, *Dutch and Flemish Etchings, Engravings and Woodcuts* etc., X, p. 174. (8) See Hollstein, *op. cit.*, p. 195. (9) Probably deriving from a classical *Crouching Aphrodite*. (10) Probably deriving from the *Apollino* in the Uffizi. (11) Deriving from the sculpture in the Uffizi. (12) As kindly pointed out to the compiler by Dr. Hans Vlieghe in 1965; see also J. G. van Gelder & I. Jost, *Simiolus*, 1966-7, p. 151; and no. 49 of the exhibition catalogue, Rondom Rembrandt, Museum de Lakenhal, Leiden, 1968. (13) A similar picture, but with more people on the bank, given to Jan Brueghel I, was in the collection of Mrs. L. H. Haas, Detroit, 1938, see E. P. Richardson, *The Art Quarterly*, 1938, p. 190 and fig. 6 (on p. 188); another, also with more people on the bank, catalogued as by Peeter Gysels, is at Aschaffenburg, see *Galerie Aschaffenburg Katalog*, 1964, p. 86, no. 6409. (14) A similar still life, on panel, has been noted in a private collection, England, 1969. (15) Compare Dürer's renderings of the theme, see F. W. H. Hollstein, *German Engravings, Etchings & Woodcuts* etc., VII, by K. G. Boon & R. W. Scheller, pp. 9 (left) and 120 (left). The picture in no. 1287 should also be connected with van Dyck, see G. Glück, *Van Dyck, K. der K.*, [1931], pp. 69-71; and Jordaens, see Michael Jaffé, *Jacob Jordaens ... Exhibition Catalogue*, Ottawa, 1968, no. 28. (16) Compare no. 1132 *q.v.* (17) Compare no. 659 *q.v.* (18) For Marinus van Reymerswaele's rendering of S. Jerome, see M. Friedländer, *Pantheon*, 1934, pp. 33 ff.; and, for instance, the catalogue of *Le Siècle de Bruegel*, Musées Royaux des Beaux-Arts de Belgique, Brussels, 1963, no. 212. (19) See R. Oldenbourg, *Rubens, K. der K.*, [1921], p. 70 right, by whom dated (probably a little too early) *ca.* 1614. (20) See Oldenbourg, *op. cit.*, p. 109, right; and M. Jaffé, *The Burlington Magazine*, 1960, pp. 448 ff. (21) See National Gallery catalogues, 1892-1906. (22) See W. Martin, *The Burlington Magazine*, 1908-9, XIV, pp. 236-9. (23) See W. Martin, *loc. cit.*; and F. M. Kelly, *The*

Burlington Magazine, 1920, XXXVI, p. 294. To judge from reproductions, the figures are certainly in the style of Hans Jordaens; but whether this artist, whose personality is so clear, is Hans Jordaens II († 1653) or the III († 1643) is not certain. **(24)** See Th. von Frimmel, *Gemalte Galerien*, 1928, p. 5, reference from S. Speth-Holterhoff, *Les Peintres Flamands de Cabinets d'Amateurs* etc., 1957, note 144. **(25)** Panel 37 × 49$\frac{1}{10}$ (0·94 × 1·247), see *Musées Royaux des Beaux-Arts de Belgique, Catalogue de la Peinture Ancienne*, 1957, p. 44, no. 656. **(26)** See S. Speth-Holterhoff in *Miscellanea Leo van Puyvelde*, 1949, pp. 183–186; and *Les Peintres Flamands de Cabinets d'Amateurs* etc., 1957, pp. 63 ff. **(27)** This picture was ascribed to Jérôme Francken in the catalogue of *Le Siècle du Rubens*, cited under note 18, no. 90. **(28)** See S. Speth-Holterhoff, *op. cit.*, p. 116. **(29)** A slightly different reading is given in the catalogue cited in note 18. **(30)** That is the *Horatius Cocles defending the Bridge on the Tiber* of 1620, in the Koninklijk Museum voor shone Kunsten, Antwerp, no. 163, see *Museé Royal des Beaux-Arts, Anvers, Catalogue descriptif, Maîtres Anciens*, 1958, p. 92. **(31)** *Loc. cit.* **(32)** P. Bautier, *The Burlington Magazine*, 1920, XXXVII, p. 165 and fig. B, drew attention to a picture at Dijon, which he ascribed to C. de Baillieur; the architecture may also be by the same hand as that responsible for the Brussels picture and no. 1287. **(33)** Rep. by Speth-Holterhoff, *op. cit.*, fig. 42; a comparable picture, said to be signed, is at Brussels, Musées Royaux des Beaux-Arts de Belgique, 1957 catalogue, no. 951. **(34)** In both cases the 'F' might stand for 'fecit'. **(35)** See Th. van Lerius & Ph. Rombouts, *De Liggeren* etc., [1864–76], I. **(36)** See under note 19. **(37)** See J. Held, *The Art Bulletin*, 1940, pp. 70 ff.; and M. Jaffé, *Jacob Jordaens . . . Exhibition Catalogue*, Ottawa, 1968, no. 3. **(38)** Compare van Dyck's etched portrait for the *Iconography*. **(39)** As by Mireveldt (*sic*). **(40)** See Smith and Successors, *Day Book*, IV, 1848–67, no. 3142 (Victoria and Albert Museum Library).

FLEMISH SCHOOL, *ca.* 1650

1700 PORTRAIT OF A MAN

Oil on relined canvas, 39$\frac{3}{8}$ × 31$\frac{3}{4}$ (1·00 × 0·807).

In fair condition. There is a scratch *ca.* 4 (0·10) long in the top left-hand corner, and a retouched damage *ca.* $\frac{3}{4}$ × 2$\frac{3}{4}$ (0·02 × 0·07) to the left of the sitter's left shoulder. The paint surface is a good deal obscured by a discoloured varnish. The background, curtain, costume, hair, beard and moustache are in varying degrees worn and retouched. The hands are also worn and retouched; the index finger of the right hand seems unreliable. There may be a *pentimento* in the fingers of the left hand, but this may be due to clumsy retouching.

Since no. 1700 entered the collection in 1900, it has until recently been associated in one form or another with the Dutch School of the seventeenth century.[1] Mayer seems first to have considered it to be Flemish,[2] and the 1958 *Summary Catalogue* rightly attributed it to the Flemish School of the Seventeenth Century.

Mayer[3] thought that no. 1700 should possibly be connected with the work of Lucas Franchoijs II[4]; a more fruitful direction may rather be towards Peeter Thijs I. But even granted the amount of wearing and retouching, the quality of execution of no. 1700 does not seem to be high.

The costume seems to be of the late 1640's or of the 1650's.[5]

The sitter has not been identified.

PROVENANCE: Bequeathed by Miss Pilbrow, 1900; lent to the Usher Art Gallery, Lincoln, 1929, to the Art Gallery and Museum, Doncaster, 1929, to the Public Library and Art Gallery, Harrogate, 1930, City of Bradford Art Gallery and Museum, 1931, and, through the Arts Council, 1958–63.

REPRODUCTION: *National Gallery Illustrations, Continental Schools (excluding Italian)*, 1950, p. 99, left.

REFERENCES: *In text:* (1) From 1901 attributed to the Dutch School, Seventeenth Century; from 1915 catalogued as by Govert Flink; from 1929 tentatively ascribed to Jan Victors, though attributed to the Dutch School, Seventeenth Century. (2) Note of a letter of 1940 in the Gallery archives. (3) *Ibid.* (4) The style is not however like that of the only two portraits that can be certainly associated with Franchoijs, for which, see F. de Saligny, *Musées Royaux des Beaux-Arts de Belgique, Bulletin*, 1967, pp. 218–219, nos. 10 and 11 bis, and figs. 8 and 9. (5) Compare the costume in the *Portrait of Jacques Lemercier* by Philippe de Champagne of 1644 at Versailles, for which see the catalogue of *Le Siècle de Rubens*, Brussels, 1965, no. 39 and fig., and in the *Portrait of a Man* by Meert of 1661 (Brussels, Musées Royaux des Beaux-Arts, *Catalogue de la Peinture Ancienne*, 1957, no. 1009), rep. *Trésor de l'Art Belge au XVIIe Siècle, Mémorial de l'Exposition d'Art Ancien à Bruxelles en 1910*, 1912, pl. 79 (left).

FLEMISH SCHOOL, *ca.* 1660

1810 PORTRAIT OF A BOY HOLDING A ROSE

Oil on relined canvas, $36\frac{3}{4} \times 25\frac{1}{2}$ (0.934×0.648).

In fairly good condition. The blacks in the costume are badly worn and are retouched; there seems to be a certain amount of wearing and retouching in the background, to the left.

The attribution of no. 1810 is uncertain; the influence of Velazquez and his followers is evident in the handling of the flesh, but no. 1810 seems acceptably to be the work of a painter active in the southern Netherlands.[1] The costume seems to be of *ca.* 1660.

No. 1810 was bequeathed as by François Duchastel (1625?–1694?); and was catalogued as by him from 1901–1913; from 1915–24, it was ascribed to him. Duchastel's personality remains somewhat blurred, through want of signed and dated works. No. 1810 has no connection in handling with his *Inauguration of Charles II of Spain as Count of Flanders* of 1668 at Ghent.[2] However, the attribution to Duchastel is accepted in the entry in Thieme-Becker; and Dr. Hans Vlieghe,[3] judging from a photograph, thinks there is a connection in handling between no. 1810 and a group portrait said to be signed and dated by Duchastel of 1672.[4] To the compiler the handling of no. 1810 seems not unlike that of David Teniers III (1638–1685), who was in Spain in the early 1660's.[5] But it seems best, at this stage, to attribute no. 1810 to the Flemish school, *ca.* 1660.

The identity of the sitter in no. 1810 is not known; as he holds a rose, no. 1810 may be a betrothal portrait.

PROVENANCE: Henry Vaughan Bequest, 1900; lent to the Ministry of Works (now Public Building and Works), 1938–41; and, through the Arts Council, to the City Art Gallery, Manchester, 1958–63.

REPRODUCTION: *National Gallery Illustrations, Continental Schools (excluding Italian)*, 1950, p. 95, right.

REFERENCES: *In text:* (1) Louis Demonts (letter of 1927 in the Gallery archives) suggested that no. 1810 is the work of the Dutch artist, Joannes van Noordt (*ca.* 1644–1676); but this seems improbable. (2) See pp. 47–8 of the 1937 catalogue of the *Musée des Beaux-Arts.* (3) Letter to the compiler, 1968. (4) The *Group Portrait of the Janssens Family,* coll. the Master of Heydonck, rep. by F. C. Legrand, *Les Peintres Flamand de Genre* etc., 1963, fig. 44. (5) For a recent discussion, see H. Vlieghe, *Musées Royaux des Beaux-Arts, Bulletin,* 1962, pp. 123–6; compare the *Portrait of Charles II of Spain,* by David Teniers III, see his fig. 1; see also P. Lambotte, *Onze Kunst,* 1910, pp. 33 ff. Some of Lambotte's attributions are unacceptable; but compare David Teniers III's *Portrait of his Wife* and *Self Portrait with his Family,* of the 1670's, rep. by Lambotte, opp. p. 40 and on p. 43.

FLEMISH SCHOOL, seventeenth century

1895 PORTRAIT OF A MAN

Oil on relined canvas, $45\frac{3}{4} \times 33\frac{3}{4}$ ($1 \cdot 162 \times 0 \cdot 858$).

Above right, a coat of arms; gules, an eagle displayed ermine, armed with a crest: a demi eagle displayed ermine, beaked or.[1]

Beneath the coat of arms, an inscription: *AETATIS·* [A E linked] *SVE | 63 1626*

In fairly poor condition. The state is obscured by a patchy, discoloured varnish, but there is a good deal of wearing and repaint; best preserved are the hands and cuffs. There are wrinkles in the paint of the face, and a number of small, scattered losses. The coat of arms and inscription are later additions.

No. 1895 was apparently traditionally thought to be by Rubens[2]; in 1902 it was attributed to J. Jordaens[3]—an attribution which was accepted by Rooses[4] with qualification, and by Puyvelde.[5] It was catalogued as such at the Gallery until 1958[6] when it was attributed to the seventeenth-century Flemish School.

The attribution of no. 1895 to Jordaens is clearly wrong; the composition derives from Pontius' print of 1624[7] after a portrait by Rubens of Prince Vladislav Sigismond (1598–1648), later King of Poland.[8] The hands and cuffs in no. 1895 are evidently painted in imitation of Rubens' manner. The handling of the face is different; the wrinkled paint suggests that the present face may have been substituted for another, but this is not confirmed by X-ray photography that shows no *pentimento.*

The status of no. 1895 is thus peculiar; two hands may have been responsible for it (not counting that responsible for the coat of arms and inscription). However in both cases the handling is feeble.

The costume of the sitter is acceptably of the 1620's—and compatible with the date on the (later) inscription of 1626. No. 1895 is an old picture; it is just conceivable that it was executed in the 1620's (after 1624) and probable that it is a work of the seventeenth century. The attribution of the 1958 *Summary Catalogue* is thus retained.

The coat of arms is that of the Waha family of the southern Netherlands.[9] Both it and the inscription are later additions; their relevance to
no. 1895 is at the moment obscure (no member of the family, born in
1563, has been traced).

PROVENANCE: Said to have been 'for generations' in the possession of a
Maastricht family.[10] Coll. T. Humphry Ward by 1902 when exh. at the R.A.
(99); from whom purchased by the National Gallery (out of the Clarke Fund) in
1902; lent to H.R.H. The Prince of Wales, 1930–36.

REPRODUCTION: *National Gallery Illustrations, Continental Schools (excluding
Italian)*, 1950, p. 181, left.

REFERENCES: *In text:* (1) See MacLaren, ms. notes. (2) According to T.
Humphry Ward in a letter of 1902 in the National Gallery archives. (3) In the
R.A. catalogue of 1902, see under *Provenance*. (4) See M. Rooses, *Jordaens, Sa
Vie et Ses Oeuvres*, 1906, p. 55. (5) See L. van Puyvelde, *Jordaens*, 1953, pp.
121 and 208. (6) See *The National Gallery Summary Catalogue*, 1958, p. 80.
(7) See F. van den Wijngaert, *Inventaris van der Rubeniaansche Prentkunst*,
1940, no. 541; rep. by M. Rooses, *L'Oeuvre de P. P. Rubens*, 1890, IV, pl. 319.
(8) See Rooses, *op. cit.*, no. 1078; and J.-A. Goris and J. S. Held, *Rubens in
America*, (1947), no. 18, and pl. 23; neither picture there discussed is likely to
have been Rubens' prototype for Pontius' print. (9) See the 1902 catalogue
(reference under *Provenance*). F. Goethals, *Dictionnaire Généalogique et Heraldique des Familles Nobles . . . de Belgique*, 1850, III, p. 568, gives the coat of arms
of the Waha family as 'de gueules à l'aigle d'hermines membrée et becquée
d'or'. According to J. B. Rietstap, *Armorial Général*, 1950 (ed.), IV, p. 1036, only
the Waha de Grummelscheyde and Waha de Lintere branches included the
beak and feet of the eagle as gold. The 1902 R.A. catalogue and previous
National Gallery catalogues assumed that the coat of arms was of the latter
branch; neither branch features in Goethals, *op. cit.*, pp. 568 ff. (10) See a
letter from T. Humphry Ward of 1902 in the Gallery archives.

Ascribed to the FLEMISH SCHOOL,
first half of the Seventeenth Century

6384   THE RAISING OF LAZARUS

Oil on relined canvas, 43 × 63 (1·092 × 1·60).
In fairly good condition. The shadows are very thinly modelled.
Cleaned, 1967.
For the subject, see John, XI, 1–46.
The artist responsible for no. 6384 is not known. He shows a know-
ledge of the styles of both Rubens [1] and van Dyck in the second decade
of the century; and it seems likely that no. 6384 is the work of a
minor Flemish master active at this time or in the following decade.

PROVENANCE: Mrs. Marion C. Smith Bequest, 1967; on loan to the Scunthorpe
Art Gallery, from 1968.

REPRODUCTION: *The National Gallery Report, Jan. 1967–Dec. 1968*, fig. 4.

REFERENCE: *In text:* (1) The technique of rendering the blue robe of S. Mary
Magdalen, kneeling behind Christ, is similar to that used by Rubens in the
Descent from the Cross of 1611–14 (for which see R. Oldenbourg, *Rubens, K. der
K.*, [1921], p. 52), see the note by Miss Joyce Plesters in the National Gallery
archives.

Ascribed to the FLEMISH SCHOOL, 1636

5631 PORTRAIT OF A MAN

Oil on relined canvas, $53\frac{5}{8} \times 40\frac{3}{16}$ ($1\cdot362 \times 1\cdot022$).
Dated, *1636*
Inscribed, *AETAT'. 26·½ | AB:J:*
In fairly good condition. The black of the costume may be a little worn. There are numerous small retouchings, and there is a loss in the left-hand cuff. The sky is discoloured.

The authorship of no. 5631 is not known. The date is authentic, but the rest of the inscription seems to be false. It was thought to be by Rubens when exhibited at the Royal Academy in 1880 (see below); this is clearly wrong. It was attributed to the seventeenth century Flemish School in the 1958 *Summary Catalogue*. But no. 5631 seems not to be executed in a style typically reminiscent of a Flemish artist active *ca.* 1636, thus this attribution is only accepted here with reservation.

PROVENANCE: Probably 5th Viscount Midleton (1806–1848) sale Christie's, 31 July, 1851 (67)[1] bt. in for £27 6sh;[2] certainly coll. the 8th Viscount Midleton (1830–1907) when exh. at the R. A., 1880 (61);[3] the 2nd Earl of Midleton sale, Christie's, 26 October, 1945 (18) bt. Roland for 480 gns. for the National Gallery; lent, through the Arts Council, to Temple Newsam House, Leeds, 1951–1955.

REPRODUCTION: National Gallery photographs available.

REFERENCES *in text:* (1) As by A. Jansens [*sic*], described as 'A Portrait of Gentleman, in a Black Dress, and Hat, with lace Collar, holding his Gloves, his Arm resting on a Pedestal'. The collection had been removed from Peper Harow Park. No. 5631 is not among the pictures, noted by Vertue in 1722, in the possession of Thomas Brodrick M. P., who left no. 221 of this collection and other pictures to his brother, Alan, 1st Viscount Midleton, see N. MacLaren, *National Gallery Catalogues, The Dutch School*, 1960, p. 318. (2) See Christie's marked copy of the sale catalogue. (3) As by Rubens.

Ascribed to the FLEMISH SCHOOL,
later part of the seventeenth century

3963 PORTRAIT OF AN ELDERLY WOMAN

Oil on relined canvas, $27\frac{7}{8} \times 23\frac{13}{16}$ ($0\cdot709 \times 0\cdot606$).
In fair condition. The costume and curtain are worn, and the darks may have been strengthened. There are some scattered, repaired damages, notably in the left arm and right shoulder.

No. 3963 was ascribed with qualification to Hanneman in the 1929 catalogue[1] and to the Flemish School (?) XVII century in the 1958 *Summary Catalogue*.

No. 3963 may be the work of a Flemish artist; but there seem to be some stylistic connections with the work of the Middleburg artist, Pieter Borsseler (active 1665–87). For this reason the attribution of the

1958 *Summary Catalogue* is retained. The quality of execution is not high.

The costume is of the 1670's, or later.

The sitter has not been identified.

PROVENANCE: Sir Claude Phillips Bequest, 1924.

REPRODUCTION: *National Gallery Illustrations, Continental Schools (excluding Italian)*, 1950, p. 152, right.

REFERENCE: *In text:* (1) The entry records a previous attribution to J. Jordaens.

PEETER FRANCHOIJS
1606–1654

Portrait and figure painter. Active in France and at Malines, where he was born, the son of Lucas Franchoijs, on 20 October, 1606.[1] According to de Bie, he was the pupil of his father and then of Gerard Seghers in Antwerp,[2] although there is no record of him in the lists of the Antwerp guild of S. Luke. He worked in Paris[3] and is recorded at Fontainebleau in 1631.[4] He had returned to Malines by 1635[5]; and is noted there in 1646[6]; but he was not received as a master in the guild of S. Luke at Malines until 1649.[7] De Bie states that he worked for the Archduke Leopold-Willhelm, Governor of the southern Netherlands from 1646. He died on 11 August, 1654.[9]

His portrait by his brother Lucas Franchoijs was engraved by C. Waumans.[10]

De Bie referred to him as 'Peeter Franchois'[11]; on at least two occasions he signed himself 'Peeter Franchoijs'.[12]

REFERENCES: *In text:* (1) See C. de Bie, *Het Gulden Cabinet* etc., 1661, p. 152; see also E. Neeffs, *Messager des Sciences Historiques*, 1874, pp. 165 ff. (2) *Ibid.* (3) See de Bie, *op. cit.*, pp. 152–4. (4) See Z. V. M.'s entry for Peeter Franchoijs in Thieme-Becker. (5) See Neeffs, *loc. cit.* (6) See, for instance, *ibid.* According to Neeffs and later authors, the portrait (Lille Museum) signed by Franchoijs, of the provost of the Leliendael Priory, Malines, is dated 1645. (7) See Neeffs, *loc. cit.* (8) See de Bie, *op. cit.*, p. 152. None of his paintings is recorded in the inventory of the Archduke Leopold-Wilhelm's collection. (9) See de Bie, *op. cit.*, p. 152. (10) In de Bie, *op. cit.*, p. 153. (11) *Op. cit.*, p. 152. (12) In the pictures at Brussels and Cologne, see note 4, under no. 1012, below.

Ascribed to PEETER FRANCHOIJS

1012 PORTRAIT OF LUCAS FAYD'HERBE (?)

Oil on relined canvas, 39 × 31⅜ (0·991 × 0·797).

Apparently in fairly good condition. The areas of flesh and white paint seem to be well preserved; there may be some retouchings in the black of the costume. The background seems to be worn. Yellow varnish overall.

Lucas Fayd'herbe (1617–1697), one of Rubens' last pupils, and a

noted sculptor and architect; he had returned to his native Malines, after
working in Rubens' studio, by 1640.[1]

The attribution of no. 1012 has not been clarified since it entered the
collection. It was catalogued as by Mattheus Merian the Younger
in the National Gallery catalogues from 1889–1915; from 1920–1929
it was attributed to the school of van Dyck[2]; and the *Summary Catalogue*
of 1958 ascribed it with reservation to the 17th century Flemish
School. More recently Plietzsch[3] has suggested that it is the work
of Peeter Franchoijs. Plietzsch's proposal is attractive; the handling
of the face seems to be comparable with that in a signed portrait
of 1650 at Cologne[4]; but because some areas of no. 1012 seem to be
rather weak in execution, and because of the uncertainty surrounding
the character of Peeter Franchoijs' œuvre, it seems best at this stage to
catalogue no. 1012 as ascribed to him.

The costume in no. 1012 has been dated *ca.* 1640–50[5]; both the pose
and the costume recall to some extent that of Thomas Killigrew in van
Dyck's double portrait of 1638 in the Royal Collection.[6]

The identification of the sitter, suggested here, is based on a comparison with P. de Jode's engraving after a portrait by Coques (showing
the sitter aged 44), which was published in 1661.[7] Fayd'herbe was a
cousin of Peeter Franchoijs[8]; and like Franchoijs, was based in Malines
in the 1640's.

PROVENANCE: Possibly coll. Wynn Ellis by 1861, when exh. B.I. (32)[9]; Wynn
Ellis Bequest, 1876; on loan to the Ministry of Works, now the Ministry of
Public Building and Works, from 1929.

REPRODUCTION: *National Gallery Illustrations, Continental Schools (excluding
Italian)*, 1950, p. 107, top.

REFERENCES: *In text:* (1) See the entry for Fayd'herbe by G. Sobotka in Thieme-
Becker; and under no. 1117. (2) No. 1012 was also attributed to van Dyck when
in the collection of Wynn Ellis, see R. N. Wornum, *Descriptive . . . Catalogue
of the Pictures in the National Gallery* etc., 1877, p. 329, under no. 1012; see also
under *Provenance.* (3) See E. Plietzsch, *Holländische und Flämische Maler des
XVII. Jahrhunderts*, 1960, p. 194. (4) See *Wallraf-Richartz-Museum . . .
Verzeichnis der Gemälde*, 1965, p. 58, no. 1030. Compare also the signed portrait
at Frankfort, rep. by Plietzsch, *op. cit.*, fig. 357; and the signed and dated portrait of 1639 at Brussels, for which see the catalogue of *Le Siècle de Rubens*,
Musées Royaux des Beaux-Arts de Belgique, Brussels, 1965, no. 84 and fig.
(5) See National Gallery catalogues, 1920–29. (6) For which see O. Millar, *The
Tudor, Stuart and early Georgian Pictures in the Collection of H.M. the Queen*,
1963, p. 101, no. 156. (7) See C. de Bie, *Het Gulden Cabinet* etc., 1661, opp. p.
500; and see also no. 1117 for a later portrait of Fayd'herbe. It is difficult to
accept the identification of the sitter in a portrait, sometimes given to P.
Franchoijs in the Hof van Busleyden Museum, Malines, as Fayd'herbe, see, for
instance, A. von Wurzbach, *Niederländisches Künstler-Lexikon*, 1906, I, p. 549;
or A. van der Meersch, *Biographie Nationale . . . de Belgique* 7, 1880–3, col. 238.
The picture is rep. by M. Kocken, *Stad Mechelen Catalogus van de . . . Schild-
erijn in der Hof van Busleyden*, n.d., fig. XIII, by whom ascribed to Lucas
Franchoijs II. (8) See the genealogical table published by E. Neeffs, *Messager
des Sciences Historiques*, 1874, opp. p. 161. (9) Described as 'A Gentleman' by
van Dyck; see also note 2. No. 1012 was not noted in the possession of Wynn
Ellis by G. F. Waagen, *Art Treasures in Great Britain*, II, 1854, pp. 195 ff.

JOANNES FYT

1611-1661

Still life, animal and flower painter, and engraver. Active for most of his career in Antwerp, where he was baptized, on 15 March, 1611.[1] Listed in the records of the Antwerp guild of S. Luke for 1620/1 as the pupil of Hans van den Berch.[2] He then entered the studio of Frans Snijders, who, as his master, made a payment to his mother for the year October 1629–October 1630,[3] in which year Fyt is also listed as a master in the records of the guild.[4] He remained in Snijders' studio for another year.[5] In 1633 and 1634 he was in Paris[6]; from France he made his way to Italy, where he worked in Venice[7] and may have visited Rome.[8] He was back in Antwerp by 1641[9]; in April, 1642 he may have briefly visited the northern Netherlands.[10] He married in Antwerp in 1654,[11] and died there on 11 September, 1661.[12]

There is a record of a signed and dated picture of 1638[13]; a number of paintings are dated in the early 1640's.[14] A painting in the Prado is dated 1661.[15] He collaborated on occasions with figure painters[16]; and may well have executed the landscape backgrounds which sometimes feature round still lifes by him.[17]

Various spellings of his surname occur[18]; he occasionally spelt it Fijt.

REFERENCE: *General:* F. J. van den Branden, *Geschiedenis der Antwerpsche Schilderschool*, 1883, pp. 1085–1092.

In text: (1) See van den Branden, cited under *General Reference*, p. 1085; earlier authors give his date of baptism as 19 August, 1609, see for instance, Th. van Lerius, *Catalogue de Musée d'Anvers*, 1874 (3rd ed.), p. 174. (2) See Ph. Rombouts and Th. van Lerius, *De Liggeren* etc., [1864–74], I, p. 573. (3) See van den Branden, *op. cit.*, p. 1086. (4) See Rombouts and van Lerius, *op. cit.*, II, p. 2. (5) See note 3. (6) See van den Branden, *op. cit.*, pp. 1086–7. (7) See L. Lanzi, *Geschichte der Malerei in Italien*, translated and annotated by J. G. von Quandt, 1831, II, p. 214. (8) Because he was made a member of the guild of Romanists, Antwerp, in 1650, see Rombouts and van Lerius, *op. cit.*, I, p. 573, note. E. J. Smeyers (1694–1771) stated that Fyt's *Bent* name in Rome was Gautvinck, see T. Levin, *Zeitschrift für bildende Kunst*, 1888, p. 171; and C. Hofstede de Groot, *Arnold Houkraken und sein 'Groote Schouburgh'*, 1893, p. 414. But G.-J. Hoogewerff, *Nederlandsche Kunstenaars te Rome*, 1942, p. 338, states that this was the name given to Ignatius Croon; Fyt does not appear to have been listed as having lived in Rome. E. Greindl, *Les Peintres Flamands de Nature Morte au XVIIe Siècle*, 1956, p. 83 and note 161, states that Fyt also visited Florence and Naples, but her source does not state this. (9) See van den Branden, *op. cit.*, p. 1087. (10) *Ibid.* (11) See van Lerius, *op. cit.*, p. 175; and van den Branden, *op. cit.*, p. 1088. (12) See van den Branden, *op. cit.*, p. 1092. (13) See Greindl, *op. cit.*, p. 161; and Maurice Kann sale, Georges Petit (Paris), 9 June, 1911 (24) and rep. One print by Fyt is dated 1640, this is in a series of 'Les Chiens' of which the first bears the inscription: 'All. Ill. mo . . . Don Carlo Guasco Marchese di Solario . . . Alzatia. In segno del suo ossequio dedica Gio. Fyt . . . 1642', see A. Bartsch, *Le Peintre Graveur*, 1805, V, pp. 211–212. (14) See Greindl, *op. cit.*, pp. 159 ff. (15) See *Museo del Prado, Catálogo de las Pinturas*, 1963, pp. 229–30, no. 1534. (16) See G. Glück, *Rubens, van Dyck und ihr Kreis*, 1933, pp. 342–348, for collaboration with Erasmus Quellinus; for collaboration with Thomas Willeboirts Bosschaert, see for instance, E. R. V.

Engerth, *Kunsthistorische Sammlungen des allerhöchsten Kaiserhauses, Gemälde*
... *Verzeichniss*, 1884, II, pp. 152–3, no. 846. (17) See under no. 1003 below.
(18) See Rombouts and van Lerius, *op. cit.*, II, *passim.*

1003   DEAD BIRDS IN A LANDSCAPE

Oil on relined canvas, $16\frac{3}{8} \times 22\frac{3}{8}$ (0·416 × 0·568).

Signed, *Joannes Fyt·*

In good condition. There are some spotty remains of varnish in the
sky and a few small, retouched losses. The 'J' of the signature may have
been tampered with.

The dead birds are: partridges (2), a greenfinch, chaffinch, brambling,
robin and quail.[1] Greindl[2] calls the object behind the tree trunk a bird
trap, but it is probably a portable bird cage, with the covers down.

The signature on no. 1003 seems to be reliable, and there is no
reason to doubt that the still life in no. 1003 is by Fyt. The landscape
is differently handled, but it may be his work as well.[3]

No. 1003 is probably to be dated in the 1640's.

There are a number of other somewhat similar works by Fyt, most of
which, however, include the head of a sportman's dog.[4]

If the object is a bird trap, it is not at all clear how it worked; if, as
seems probable, it is a bird cage, it would probably have been used to
carry a decoy bird or a bird of prey.[5]

PROVENANCE: Wynn Ellis Bequest, 1876; lent to the Corporation Art Gallery,
Bradford, 1935, and, through the Arts Council, to the National Museum of
Wales, Cardiff, 1951–63.

REPRODUCTION: *National Gallery Illustrations, Continental Schools* (*excluding
Italian*), 1950, p. 133, bottom.

REFERENCES: *In text:* (1) Information kindly provided by M. Goodwin of the
Natural History Museum. (2) See E. Greindl, *Les Peintures Flamands de
Nature Morte au XVIIe Siècle*, 1956, p. 160; it was wrongly identified as a
carriage in National Gallery catalogues, 1877–1929. (3) The landscape is
handled in a similar way to that in the Vienna picture of 1647, see E. R. V.
Engerth, *Kunsthistorisches Sammlungen des allerhöchsten Kaiserhauses, Gemälde.
... Verzeichniss*, 1884, p. 151, no. 843, where the date is read as 1641. As Dr.
Heinz, of the Kunsthistorisches Museum, told the compiler, this picture
is not described as a work of collaboration in the Leopold-Wilhelm inventory of
1659. (4) Greindl, *loc. cit.*, lists 8 pictures by Fyt as 'variants': of these the
pictures at Dahlem (Staatliche Museum, Preussischer Kulturbesitz, no. 883 F)
and at Vienna can be ruled out; the variant she lists at Cambridge is thought to
be a 'late copy after a lost original', see H. Gerson and J. W. Goodison, *Fitz-
William Museum, Cambridge, Catalogue of Paintings*, 1960, p. 51, no. 305. The
rest are: Bayer. Staatsgemäldesammlungen, Munich (noted by Griendl as at
Augsburg) no. 4801, copper (not wood), $16\frac{1}{8} \times 23\frac{5}{8}$ (0·41 × 0·60), signed and
dated 1652 (not 1657); Städelsches Kunstinstitut, Frankfurt-am-Main, no. 985,
canvas, $18\frac{1}{2} \times 24\frac{3}{8}$ (0·47 × 0·62), signed and dated 1647, see the catalogue of 1966;
Musée de Picardie, Amiens, nos. 91 and 92 of the 1911 catalogue, one of which
is signed and dated 1661, not 1656 (information kindly given by the curator,
1968). To these can be added: Prado, no. 1528, canvas, $28\frac{3}{8} \times 47\frac{5}{8}$ (0·72 × 1·21),
signed and dated 1649, see *Museo del Prado, Catálogo de las Pinturas*, 1963,
p. 228; Mauritshuis, no. 687, $19\frac{1}{16} \times 28\frac{1}{8}$ (0·484 × 0·715), see the 1935 catalogue;
Copenhagen, Royal Museum of Fine Arts, canvas, $31\frac{11}{16} \times 40\frac{15}{16}$ (0·805 × 1·04),

signed, see no. 220 of the 1951 catalogue; canvas, $20\frac{5}{8} \times 30\frac{1}{8}$ (0·525 × 0·765), see no. 221 of the 1951 catalogue; coll. Sir Edmund Bacon, canvas, $23\frac{3}{4} \times 30\frac{1}{2}$ (0·604 × 0·775); the picture, coll. the Duke of Wellington, canvas, $14\frac{1}{4} \times 23\frac{1}{4}$ (0·362 × 0·591), signed and dated 1647, see the exhibition catalogue *Pictures from Hampshire Houses*, Winchester and Southampton, 1955, no. 141. All these, except the unsigned picture at Amiens, include the head of a sportsman's dog, or a different or more elaborate still life; the variants listed by Greindl at Spire and Dresden (not known to the compiler) also include a dog. While these pictures are in a general way comparable to no. 1003, none can be described as a variant. (5) For a decoy bird, see under no. 1903. What seems to be the head of a bird of prey appears through the bars of the cage (part of whose covers are up) in the picture at Munich, see under note 4, and in the picture catalogued as by Fyt in an Anon. sale, Sotheby's, 29 November, 1961 (92), ex Lord Bagot sale, Christie's, 17 November, 1945 (79).

Ascribed to FYT

6335 A STILL LIFE WITH FRUIT, DEAD GAME AND A PARROT

Oil on relined canvas, $33\frac{5}{16} \times 44\frac{5}{8}$ (0·847 × 1·134).
Bears initials, *J·f·*

In fairly good condition. The background is a good deal retouched, as are perhaps the darker areas of the greens. The bottom half of the 'J' in the inscription is missing.

The parrot is a Grey Parrot (Africa); the dead game consists of a hare and a brace of partridges, beside which is a jay.[1]

No. 6335 has been accepted as the work of Fyt[2]; however, the initials seem not reliable, and the handling seems rather coarse. It is best, therefore, to catalogue no. 6335 as ascribed to Fyt.[3]

The style of no. 6335 is reminiscent of works by Fyt executed in the late 1640's.[4]

PROVENANCE: Coll. C. D. Rotch, by 1953/4, when exh. at the R.A. (283); exh. Musée Communal, Bruges, and at Groeningen, 1956 (102); Claude Dickason Rotch Bequest, 1962.

REPRODUCTION: *National Gallery Acquisitions, 1953–62, Exhibition Catalogue.*

REFERENCES: *In text:* (1) Information about the birds kindly given by J. C. MacDonald of the Natural History Museum. (2) See the catalogues of *Flemish Art*, The Royal Academy, 1953/4 (283), of *Flemish Art from British Collections*, Bruges and Groeningen, 1956 (102), and of *National Gallery Acquisitions, 1953–62.* (3) See also E. Greindl, *Les Peintres Flamands de Natures Mortes au XVIIᵉ Siècle*, 1956, p. 165. (4) Compare for instance Prado, no. 1529, of 1649, rep. by Greindl, *op. cit.*, fig. 59; Metropolitan Museum of Art, no. 32.100.141, of the same year; and Hermitage, nos. 613 and 616 of 1645 and 1647 respectively, see *Musée de l'Ermitage Département de l'Art Occidental, Catalogue des Peintures*, 1958, II, p. 110 and fig. 102; and *The State Hermitage, West-Euroyean Painting, Album*, 1957, p. 181.

GUILLIAM VAN HERP I

1614 (?)–1677

Figure painter. Active in Antwerp, where he was probably born; no baptismal record has been traced; but in 1676, he recorded that he was 62 years old.[1] Recorded as the pupil of Damiaen Wortlemans in the list of the Antwerp guild of S. Luke for the year 1625/26[2]; in the list for 1628/9, he is recorded as the pupil of Hans Biermans.[3] He became a master in the guild in the year 1637/8.[4] From 1651 at least he was associated with the Antwerp dealer, Musson, for whom he also retouched copies after Rubens.[5] He married Maria Wolffort, the daughter of Artus Wolffort, in 1654, by whom he had previously had one child; this child and his youngest son, Guilliam (born 1657), also became painters.[6] Van Herp was buried in Antwerp, 23 June, 1677.[7]

His christian name was also spelt Gilliam[8]; he normally spelt his surname Herp.

REFERENCES: *In text:* (1) See F. J. van den Branden, *Geschiedenis der Antwerpsche Schilderschool*, 1883, p. 916. (2) See Ph. Rombouts and Th. van Lerius, *De Liggeren* etc., [1864–1876], I, p. 623. (3) *Ibid.*, p. 662. (4) *Ibid.*, II, p. 91. (5) See J. Denucé, *Na P. P. Rubens*, 1949, pp. 101 ff.; summarized by L. van Puyvelde, *Zeitschrift für Kunstgeschichte*, 1959, pp. 46–48. (6) See van den Branden, *op. cit.*, pp. 917–918. (7) See Rombouts and van Lerius, *op. cit.*, I, p. 662, note 2. (8) See for instance, *ibid.*, pp. 623 and 632.

203 S. ANTHONY OF PADUA (?) DISTRIBUTING BREAD

Oil on copper, $31\frac{1}{2} \times 45$ (0·80 × 1·143).
Signed, *G·V·HERP*
In good condition. There are losses round the edges; the legs on the right are a little worn, as is the signature. Yellow varnish.

Pentimenti in the outline of the negress's face and in that of the child to her left.

The friars are Franciscan; the one in the centre has a Glory, and may be intended to depict S. Anthony of Padua (1195–1231), see below. Among the poor receiving bread are two pilgrims on the right.

No. 203 is signed; and there is no reason to doubt its attribution to Guilliam van Herp I.

Few dated works are known by van Herp; it is thus difficult to propose a date of execution for no. 203. The handling is not so very different from that in *Soldiers in a Cottage* (Harrach Collection) of 1664.[1] Indeed, no. 203 may be identical with the picture of 'Sᵗ Antonius de Paduwa broot wtdeelt aen de aermen' valued at 95 guilders 10 stuyvers, noted in an account of 4 May, 1662, of the Antwerp dealer, Musson.[2] It is on this basis that the identification of the Saint in no. 203 as S. Anthony of Padua is advanced, although no other rendering of him distributing bread has been traced.[3]

COPY: Anon. sale, Sotheby's, 14 February, 1968 (112).[4]

PROVENANCE: Perhaps commissioned and exported to Spain by the Antwerp dealers M. Musson and C. de Bailleur by 4 May, 1662.[5] Perhaps His Excellency Count Reventlow (Danish Ambassador) sale, Christie's, 11 December [=4th day] 1778 (72)[6] sold for £58 16sh.[7] Anon. [=Hart Davis] sale, Coxe, 1 June, 1814 (33)[8] bt. Smart for Webb for 152 gns.[9]; John Webb, sale Phillips, 31 May = 2nd day] 1821 (180)[10] bt. Simmons for £135 gns.[11]; Richard Simmons

Bequest, 1846; lent to the Department of Science and Art, South Kensington Museum (now the Victoria and Albert Museum) 1862–1889, to the Grosvenor Museum, Chester, 1898–1929, to the Corporation Art Gallery, Bradford, 1935.

REPRODUCTION: *National Gallery Illustrations, Continental Schools (excluding Italian)*, 1950, p. 156, left.

REFERENCES: *In text:* (1) See G. Heinz, *Katalog der Graf Harrach'schen Gemäldegalerie*, 1960, p. 39, no. 28. (2) See J. Denucé, *Na P. P. Rubens*, 1949, p. 268. The introductory heading to the bill shows that the picture was on copper. (3) For S. Anthony of Padua, see Les Petits Bollandistes, *Vie des Saints*, 16, 1882, pp. 612 ff. (4) Metal, $27\frac{1}{4} \times 38$ ($0 \cdot 699 \times 0 \cdot 965$); probably identical with the *S. Francis distributing Alms*, ascribed to the School of Rubens, in the Viscount Weymouth sale, Sotheby's, 4 October, 1944 (115). (5) See Denucé, *loc. cit.* The breakdown of the total cost of the previous picture, depicting a *Miracle of S. Anthony of Padua* by van Herp, also valued at 95 guilders 10 stuyvers, was 21 guilders for the copper plate; the gilt frame 22 guilders, 10 stuyvers; and 52 guilders for van Herp for executing the picture. For the connection between Musson and de Bailleur, see Denucé, *op. cit.*, pp. xxxvii–xxxix. (6) Copper, described as 'One of the Acts of Charity, distributing bread' by Herp; the following lot was a pendant, not described. The identity of the buyer is not clear in Christie's marked catalogue. G. Redford, *Art Sales* etc., II, 1888, p. 299, records a picture by van Herp of '*St. Francis giving bread to the Poor. On copper. large*' in an Anon. sale of 1778 bt. by Campbell for £105. But the lot cannot be traced in any Anon. sale for 1778; nor was such a picture in the Alexander Campbell sale of 1782, or in the Sir Archibald Campbell (†) sale of 1792. (7) See Christie's marked catalogue, no buyer's name is given. (8) Described as 'Van Harp [*sic*] . . . Saint Charles Borromeo distributing Bread to the Poor . . .' (9) Ms. note by MacLaren. (10) As ex coll. Hart Davis. (11) Ms. note by MacLaren.

JAN-BAPTIST HUYSMANS
1654–1716

Landscape painter. Active in Antwerp, where he was baptized on 7 October, 1654.[1] He is recorded as a pupil in the lists of the Antwerp guild of S. Luke for the year 1674/5[2]; and as a master in the guild in the list for 1676/77.[3] He died in Antwerp on 14 July, 1716.[4] He is said to have been the pupil of his elder brother, Cornelis[5]; certainly his style seems close to those pictures thought to be by Cornelis.[6]

REFERENCES: *In text:* (1) See F. J. van den Branden, *Geschiedenis der Antwerpsche Schilderschool*, 1883, p. 1078. (2) See Ph. Rombouts and Th. van Lerius, *De Liggeren* etc., [1864–1876], II, p. 439. (3) *Ibid.*, p. 450. (4) See van den Branden, *loc. cit.*; and Rombouts and van Lerius, *op. cit.*, p. 701. (5) See, for instance, van den Branden, *loc. cit.*; and A. von Wurzbach, *Niederländisches Künstler-Lexikon*, 1906, I, p. 740. (6) See, for instance, Wurzbach, *op. cit.*, p. 739.

954 A COWHERD IN A WOODY LANDSCAPE

Oil on relined canvas, $26\frac{1}{8} \times 33\frac{5}{8}$ ($0 \cdot 665 \times 0 \cdot 855$).

Apparently in fairly good condition. A discoloured varnish obscures the paint surface. The support is damaged in the bottom right-hand corner. There are a few scattered losses in the paint especially near the bottom edge, and probably some wearing and retouching in the landscape and foliage, notably in the top left-hand corner.

No. 954 has previously been attributed to Cornelis Huysmans. This could be correct, but his style is difficult to define through the want of signed works.[1] Further, no. 954 is not necessarily by the same hand as the landscape at Brussels, there catalogued as by Cornelis Huysmans[2] and thus accepted, for instance, by Bernt.[3] No. 954 is in fact more comparable to the landscape by Jan-Baptist Huysmans also at Brussels.[4] For these reasons no. 954 is here ascribed to the latter.

PROVENANCE: Wynn Ellis Bequest, 1876; lent, through the Arts Council, to the City of Bradford Art Gallery and Museums, 1958–63.

REPRODUCTION: *National Gallery Illustrations, Continental Schools (excluding Italian)*, 1950, p. 173, bottom.

REFERENCES: *In text:* (1) See the entry in Thieme-Becker. A. Laes, *Revue Belge d'Archéologie et d'Histoire de l'Art*, 1958, pp. 13 ff., does not greatly clarify the position. (2) No. 228 of the *Musées Royaux des Beaux-Arts de Belgique*. (3) See W. Bernt, *Die Niederländischen Maler des 17. Jahrhunderts*, 1948/1960, II, no. 411. (4) No. 229 of the *Musées Royaux des Beaux-Arts de Belgique*, signed and dated 1697, see *Catalogue de la Peinture Ancienne*, 1957, p. 55.

HIERONYMUS JANSSENS
1624–1693

Painter of conversation pieces. Active in Antwerp, where he was baptized on 1 October, 1624. He is listed as the pupil of C. J. van der Lamen in the records of the Antwerp guild of S. Luke for the year 1636/7.[1] He became a master in the guild in the year 1643/44.[2] He married Catharina van Dooren in 1650, and died at Antwerp in the summer of 1693.

Various spellings of his names occur.

GENERAL REFERENCE: F. J. van den Branden, *Geschiedenis der Antwerpsche Schilderschool*, 1883, pp. 1024–1026.

In text: (1) See Ch. Rombouts & Th. van Lerius, *De Liggeren* etc., [1864–1876], II, p. 86. (2) *Ibid.*, p. 143.

Follower of JANSSENS

4976 LADIES & GENTLEMEN PLAYING "LA MAIN CHAUDE"

Oil on oak, $10\frac{9}{16} \times 16\frac{3}{8}$ (0·268 × 0·39).

In fair condition. There seems to be some repaint on the floor, and the hat there is certainly unreliable. There is probably some repaint in the architecture, and some wearing, retouched, in the figures. Many small, scattered losses are also retouched.

The point of the game—'La main chaude'—is for the player, whose head is on the lap of the seated woman, to guess who has hit his hand.[1]

No. 4976 was presented as the work of Hieronymus Janssens[2]; and the 1958 *Summary Catalogue* ascribed it to him. There is some connection between the figures in no. 4976 and those in a picture at Montargis, now said to be signed by Janssens.[3]

The costume is of the late 1650's or the 1660's; and no. 4976 could be a work dating from this time.

No. 4976 seems to be by a mediocre hand, influenced by, or imitating Janssens; thus no. 4976 is here catalogued as by a follower of Janssens.

The same game is the subject of pictures acceptably by Hieronymus Janssens.[4] It is the subject of a print in Johan de Brune's *Emblemata*, 1624,[5] and also of paintings by C. J. van der Lamen (*ca.* 1615–1651),[6] and J. M. Molenaer (1615–1668).[7]

PROVENANCE: Purchased (possibly in Paris) by Albert Kingsley[8]; presented by his son, George Kingsley, 1939; lent, through the Arts Council, to the Museum and Art Gallery, Nottingham, 1958–63.

REPRODUCTION: National Gallery photographs available.

REFERENCES: *In text:* (1) See, for instance, P. Larousse, *Grand Dictionnaire Universel du XIX Siècle*, 10, 1873, pp. 951–2. (2) MacLaren noted a label on the reverse of no. 4976 that stated: 'No. 941/Janssens . . . Dr. Bredius (June, 1899) declares this to be a very pure example of this rare master'. (3) Musée Girodet, no. 157 of the 1937 catalogue, where ascribed to Dietrich; information kindly supplied by Madame P. M. Auzas. (4) For example, Brussels, Musées Royaux des Beaux-Arts, no. 678, signed and dated 1656, see *Musées Royaux des Beaux-Arts de Belgique, Catalogue de la Peinture Ancienne*, 1957 (ed.), p. 56; and the picture in the Lord Ducie sale, Christie's, 17 June, 1949 (113), signed and dated 1655. (5) On p. 231, with the rubric: 'Een hoeren schoot is duyvels boot'; rep. by H. G. Evers, *Peter Paul Rubens*, trans. into Dutch by K. Ruyssinck, 1946, fig. 186. (6) For example the picture in an Anon. sale, Christie's, 21 January, 1927 (65). (7) See the picture in the Budapest Museum, no. 264 of the 1954 catalogue, as kindly pointed out by Dr. Gudlaugsson. (8) Letter from George Kingsley in the National Gallery archives.

JACQUES JORDAENS
1593–1678

Portrait and figure painter, and etcher. After Rubens and van Dyck, the leading figure painter of the seventeenth century Flemish School. Active in Antwerp, where he was born on 19 May, 1593.[1] He is recorded as the pupil of Adam van Noort in the list of the Antwerp guild of S. Luke for the year 1607.[2] In 1615 he was admitted as a master in the guild of S. Luke, when noted to be a 'waterscilder [*sic*]'.[3] With Rubens and van Dyck he received a commission to execute an altarpiece for the Augustijnerkerk, Antwerp, which he delivered in 1628.[4] In 1635 he received payment for work on the decorations for the Triumphal Entry of the Cardinal Infant Ferdinand into Antwerp.[5] In 1636/7 he was one of the artists to execute the paintings for the Torre de la Parada after designs by Rubens.[6] In 1639, discussions were broached with Jordaens to execute paintings for Charles I intended for the Queen's House at Greenwich, the first of which Jordaens had completed by May, 1640.[7] After Rubens' death, Jordaens became the 'prime painter' in Antwerp—

in Gerbier's view.[8] A series of important commissions followed from the
Queen of Sweden,[9] the Prince of Orange[10] and the Burgomasters of
Amsterdam (both the latter shared with other Flemish artists).[11] In
1661 he went to Amsterdam with his picture for the Town Hall, which
the Burgomasters had commissioned.[12] He died at Antwerp on 18
October, 1678.[13]

Jordaens married Catharina († 1659), the daughter of his former
master, in 1616.[14] His only son also became a painter.[15] Jordaens was
baptized a catholic; but he and his family developed protestant sym-
pathies, perhaps already in the 1630's, which he was able to declare
after the Peace of Münster in 1648.[16] His wife, followed by himself and
one daughter, were buried at Putte, across the border in the northern
Netherlands.[17]

Jordaens' portrait by van Dyck was engraved by P. de Jode for the
Iconography; a subsequent state of the print is inscribed: 'Pictor
Antverpiæ. Humanarum Figurarum, in Maioribus'[18]; his *Self Portrait*
was also engraved by P. de Jode.[19]

Jordaens' christian name is normally given as Jacob; but Jacques was
the form used, for instance, in the lists of the Antwerp guild,[20] by
de Bie[21] and on his tombstone[22]; and for these reasons is adopted here.

REFERENCES: *In text:* (1) See, for instance, Th. van Lerius, *Catalogue du
Musée d'Anvers*, 1874 (3rd ed.), p. 217. A complete summary of the known
events in Jordaens' life is given in R. A. d'Hulst, *Tekeningen van Jacob Jordaens*,
Antwerp/Rotterdam, 1966/7, pp. 13–21. C. de Bie, *Het Gulden Cabinet* etc.,
1661, p. 238, wrongly gives the year of his birth as 1594. (2) See Ph. Rombouts
and Th. van Lerius, *De Liggeren* etc., [1864–1876], I, p. 443. (3) *Ibid.*, p. 514.
(4) See M. Rooses, *L'Œuvre de P. P. Rubens*, 1886, I, p. 287. (5) See, for
instance, M. Rooses, *op. cit.*, 1890, III, pp. 299–316. (6) See H. Vlieghe, *The
Burlington Magazine*, 1968, pp. 262 ff.; see also under no. 2598. (7) See M.
Rooses and Ch. Ruelens (†), *Correspondance de Rubens*, 1909, VI, pp. 240 ff.;
and under no. 4889. (8) See Rooses and Ruelens (†), *op. cit.*, p. 303. (9) See M.
Rooses, *Jordaens, Sa Vie et Ses Œuvres*, 1906, pp. 141–143. (10) See Rooses, *op.
cit.*, pp. 160–174; and J. G. van Gelder, *Nederlandsch Kunsthistorisch Jaarboek*,
1948–9, pp. 119 ff. (11) See Rooses, *op. cit.*, pp. 208–9. (12) See Rooses, *op. cit.*,
p. 208; he had previously obtained a passport to travel in the northern Netherlands in 1632, see F. J. van den Branden, *Geschiedenis der Antwerpsche Schilderschool*, 1883, p. 835. (13) See, for instance, van den Branden, *op. cit.*, pp. 841–2.
(14) See, for instance, P. Génard, *Messager des Sciences Historiques de Belgique*,
1852, p. 212; J. S. Held, *The Art Bulletin*, 1940, pp. 70–82, gives a full discussion
of Jordaens' family. (15) See, for instance, A. von Wurzbach, *Niederländsches
Künstler-Lexikon*, 1906, I, p. 772. (16) See Génard, *op. cit.*; and, for
instance, van den Branden, *op. cit.*, pp. 835–842; and M. C. Donnelly, *The Art
Quarterly*, 1959, pp. 356–366. (17) The inscription on his tombstone is printed
by, for instance, van den Branden, *op. cit.*, p. 842. (18) See Fr. Wibiral, *L'Iconographie d'Antoine van Dyck*, 1877, pp. 79–80, no. 33. (19) Published by J.
Meyssens, *Images de Divers Hommes d'esprit Sublime* etc., 1649; and reprinted
by de Bie, *op. cit.*, p. 239. (20) See Rombouts and van Lerius, *op. cit.*, I,
pp. 443 ff., and II, *passim*. (21) *Loc. cit.* (22) See note 17.

164 THE HOLY FAMILY AND S. JOHN THE BAPTIST

Christ, supported by the Virgin, holds a rosary; beside Him is the
Infant S. John the Baptist, holding a cross; S. Joseph stands behind.

Oil on oak, $48\frac{7}{16} \times 36\frac{15}{16}$ ($1 \cdot 23 \times 0 \cdot 939$).

The support is made up of 4 (?) members, joined vertically. It is painted up to an irregular border, ca. $\frac{1}{4}$ ($0 \cdot 007$) wide at the left and bottom, and ca. $\frac{1}{8}$ ($0 \cdot 003$) wide (at the most) at the top.

Generally in good condition. Small losses to the support have been made good along the right and bottom edges. There are losses in the paint along the bottom edge and along the right-hand edge, the latter perhaps due to scraping, which has also probably removed evidence of a border. There are also small paint losses along the joins and cracks in the support, and larger ones in the Virgin's robe and in S. Joseph's hair, where very little original paint remains. The craquelure in the Virgin's robe is rather marked. The pendant of the rosary, which hangs free from Christ's hand, is very worn. Cleaned, 1969.

There are *pentimenti* in the background best seen in X-ray photographs: a scalloped niche behind S. Joseph's head, and a vertical relief and a horizontal moulding to the left and right of the Virgin have been suppressed.

Although a somewhat neglected picture,[1] no. 164 has been accepted[2] as the work of Jordaens, and there is no reason to doubt this attribution; the pendant of the rosary may be an old addition.

Attempts to date no. 164 by the identification of the model for either Christ or S. John the Baptist as Jordaens' son, born in 1625, are unsatisfactory, because based on conjecture and conflicting.[3] Puyvelde[4] thought that no. 164 was an early work, but it does not fit easily into the early group constructed by Burchard[5] and elaborated by d'Hulst.[6] Although there is no precisely comparable dated picture by Jordaens, it seems likely that no. 164 is later than both the Stockholm *Adoration of the Shepherds* of 1618[7] and the Prado *Self Portrait with his Wife and Child* of ca. 1620–1,[8] and that it was probably executed in the first half of the 1620's, perhaps under the influence of Caravaggio's *Madonna of the Rosary* (Vienna), acquired for the Dominican church at Antwerp probably in the early 1620's.[9]

The poses of the Virgin and Child recur with slight variation in the Stockholm *Holy Family by Candlelight*,[10] and probably derive from Rubens' composition known both by the Leningrad[11] and Munich[12] pictures, probably of ca. 1616.[13] The central part of this design was engraved by Panneels; the print bears an inscription from Psalm 131: 'De fructu ventris tui ponam super sedem tuam.'[14] This may give some indication of the devotional meaning to be attached to no. 164.

COPY: Canvas, coll. Van Diemen & Co., 1926.[15]

PROVENANCE: Presented by the 5th Duke of Northumberland (1785–1847) 1838; lent to the National Gallery of Ireland, 1862–1929.

REPRODUCTION: *National Gallery Illustrations, Continental Schools (excluding Italian)*, 1950, p. 181, right.

REFERENCES: *In text:* (1) No. 164 was catalogued at the Gallery as by Jordaens from 1840–1861; it was not catalogued from 1863–1913; and from 1915–1925 it was attributed to Hans Jordaens III. It is not mentioned by, for instance, M. Rooses, *Jordaens, Sa Vie et Ses Œuvres*, 1906. (2) See the Gallery catalogues from 1929; and L. Van Puyvelde, *Jordaens*, 1953, p. 92 and p. 188. (3) J. S. Held,

The Art Bulletin, 1940, pp. 81–82, identified the model for Christ in the picture at Southampton (his fig. 18) as Jordaens' son; the same model may well have been used for the S. John in no. 164. R. A. d'Hulst, *De Tekeningen van Jakob Jordaens*, 1956, pp. 89–90, identified the model for Christ in the Stockholm *Holy Family by Candlelight* (Stockholm, Nationalmuseum, no. 1768 of the 1958 catalogue) as this son; the same model occurs also as Christ in no. 164. In the variant of the Stockholm picture, published by Puyvelde, *op. cit.*, p. 130, and fig. 67, the model for the woman in the background appears to be similar to that for the Virgin in no. 164. (4) *Op. cit.* p. 92. (5) See L. Burchard, *Jahrbuch der preuszischen Kunstsammlungen*, 1928, pp. 207 ff. (6) *Op. cit.*, pp. 27 ff.; see also, *Gentse Bijdragen*, 1953, pp. 89 ff. (7) See *Stockholm, Nationalmuseum, Peintures et Sculptures des Écoles Étrangères antérieures à l'Époque Moderne*, 1958, p. 102, no. 488 and colour plate opp. p. 95. (8) See *Museo del Prado, Catálogo de las Pinturas*, 1963, no. 1549, pp. 332–333; and for instance Held, *op. cit.*, pp. 78–9; and d'Hulst, *op. cit.*, pp. 77–8. (9) See *Kunsthistorisches Museum, Wien, Katalog der Gemäldegalerie*, I, 1960, pp. 29–30, no. 483; and W. Friedlaender, *Cara-vaggio Studies*, 1955, pp. 198–202 (no. 29). (10) See under note 3. (11) See *Musée de l'Ermitage, Département de l'Art Occidental, Catalogue des Peintures*, II, 1958, p. 80, no. 497, reproduced in *The State Hermitage, West-European Painting, Album* etc., 1957, I, p. 146, no. 300. (12) See *Alte Pinakothek München, Kurzes Verzeichnis der Bilder*, 1958 ed., p. 86, no. 331 and fig. 132; and M. Rooses, *L'Œuvre de P. P. Rubens*, 1886, I, no. 198. This connection is also noted by M. Jaffé, *Jacob Jordaens ... Exhibition Catalogue*, Ottawa, 1968, p. 44. (13) Normally dated *ca.* 1615–1620, see Rooses, *loc. cit.* The model for Christ may well have been Rubens' son, Albert, born in 1614, see under no. 853. (14) See F. W. H. Hollstein, *Dutch and Flemish Etchings, Engravings and Woodcuts* etc., XV, by K. G. Boon and J. Verbeek, p. 112, bottom. (15) Photo in Gallery archives.

**3215 THE VIRGIN AND CHILD WITH
       SS. ZACHARIAS, ELIZABETH AND
       JOHN THE BAPTIST**

Christ points at the goldfinch released from the cage held by S. John the Baptist.

Oil on canvas, *ca.* $44\frac{7}{8} \times 59\frac{3}{4}/60\frac{1}{4}$ ($1\cdot14 \times 1\cdot518/\cdot53$). The edges of the support have been irregularly trimmed.

In fairly good condition. There is a little wearing, much of which is retouched, in the background, the chair and the darker parts of the Saints' costumes. The hair on top of Christ's swaddling cap is also worn but, like the ear, may be a later addition. The left-hand edge is retouched. Cleaned, 1959.

The lamb is the emblem of S. John the Baptist; and the goldfinch is a symbol of the Passion.[1]

No. 3215 has been generally accepted as the work of Jordaens,[2] and is clearly executed in a manner very reminiscent of him. A number of other pictures—all of which are at the least to be associated with Jordaens[3]—are related to no. 3215 in composition. Of these, the most closely connected is the signed picture at the North Carolina Museum of Art, which differs only in some details. No. 3215 is less articulated and less distinguished in handling; and it is probably at the most an auto-graph variant, as Jaffé has also suggested.[4] The fact that the design is basically merely repeated in no. 3215 explains the rather cursory handling, evident in several areas, particularly in the drapery.

Jaffé has dated the Raleigh picture *ca.* 1615–16.[5] Held, believing that the model for the Virgin (in no. 3215) was Jordaens' wife, Catharina van Noort, dated no. 3215 *ca.* 1625.[6] Although there is some similarity between the face of the Virgin in no. 3215 and that of Catharina van Noort, it is not sufficiently close to accept Held's thesis, which has also been rejected by Jaffé.[7] The model may well have been the same as that for the daughter of Cecrops holding Erichthonius in the picture at Antwerp of 1617,[8] where the model for the old woman is the same as that for S. Elizabeth. These models occur in other works by Jordaens generally thought to have been executed before 1620; and it is likely that no. 3215 was executed *ca.* 1620.

The visit of the Virgin and Child to S. John and his parents is outlined in the *Meditations* of the Pseudo-Bonaventura. Another rendering of the subject by Jordaens at the Metropolitan Museum of Art is inscribed: *Radix Santa [sic] et Rami/Rom. II [=XI]. 16'* [9] ('For if the first fruit be holy, the lump is also holy; and if the root be holy, so are the branches'). No bird features in the Metropolitan picture; nor is there any direct reference to the bird in the inscription on a print by Matham after M. de Bois, in which the bird is handed by S. John to Christ, with S. Elizabeth and the Virgin present. The inscription may however be relevant in a general way to no. 3215: 'Felices amba ante alias salvete parentes, | Cum puero imprimis Virgo pudica tuo. | Ex te nata salus hominum: laetare triumpha: | Fac nos laetitia participesque tuo.'[10] Jansen has suggested that the depiction of a bird in a cage 'suggests a simile familiar from late medieval sermons of the Soul longing for God as a bird in a cage longs for freedom.'[11] Friedman commenting on a picture, related to no. 3215 in composition,[12] stated 'Inasmuch as a bird in cage was an old symbol of the soul imprisoned in the body, it is possible that there is intended here some such meaning as that the coming of Christ presaged the salvation of souls from their physically mortal habiliments'.[13] Further, as the bird is a goldfinch, Christ's gesture in no. 3215 may be interpreted more precisely as his longing for the Passion, which had been foretold by S. John, who holds the bird cage.

PROVENANCE: Perhaps purchased by Mr. Greenwood and sold by him at Christie's, 22 February, 1773 (78).[14] Lord [Henry] Francis Pelham-Clinton-Hope (portion of The Hope Heirlooms removed from Deepdene, Dorking)[15] sale, Christie's, 20 July, 1917 (101) bt. for the National Gallery (out of the Clarke Fund); lent to the Corporation Art Gallery and Museum, Bradford, 1935.

REPRODUCTION: *National Gallery Illustrations, Continental Schools (excluding Italian)*, 1950, p. 182, top.

REFERENCES: *In text:* (1) See, for instance, George Ferguson, *Signs and Symbols in Christian Art*, 1954, p. 17. (2) See, for instance, J. S. Held, *The Art Bulletin*, 1940, p. 80; L. van Puyvelde, *Jordaens*, 1953, pp. 92 and 188; and M. Jaffé, *Jacob Jordaens ... Exhibition Catalogue*, Ottawa, 1968, under no. 9. (3) These are, Vanderkel-Mertens Museum, Louvain, canvas, $35\frac{7}{16} \times 41\frac{5}{16}$ (0·90 × 1·05) in which S. Zacharias hands Christ an apple, a copy (?) of which, was in an Anon. sale, Palais de Beaux-Arts (Brussels), 29 October, 1958, canvas, $34\frac{1}{4} \times 44\frac{7}{8}$ (0·87 × 1·14); North Carolina Museum of Art, Raleigh, 45 × 56 (1·145 ×

1·425), see Jaffé, *loc. cit.*; a copy of which was once on the Belfast Art Market, canvas, 41 × 60 (1·04 × 1·524); M. C. B. sale, Brussels, 10 December, 1928 (32), canvas, $54\frac{5}{16} \times 71\frac{1}{4}$ (1·38 × 1·81); Admiral A. Walker-Heneage-Vivian (†) and V. G. Lloyd sale, Sotheby's, 3 December, 1952 (75), $44\frac{1}{2} \times 66$ (1·33 × 1·677); a similar picture was in the possession of Gaston Dulière, Brussels, 1968; coll. Herbert von Pastor, Aachen, 1960, canvas, $44\frac{1}{4} \times 58\frac{1}{4}$ (1·125 × 1·48), exh. Münster, Landesmuseum der Provinz Westfalen etc., 1939 (29), and Aachen, Suermondt Museum, 1955 (45). (4) *Loc. cit.* For portraits of Catharina van Noort, see Jordaens' group portraits at Cassel and Madrid, rep. by Jaffé, *op. cit.*, pl. 4, and Held, *op. cit.*, fig. 8, respectively. (5) *Op. cit.*, under no. 9. (6) *Loc. cit.* He has recently stated that he considers Jaffé's dating to be too early, see *The Burlington Magazine*, 1969, p. 271. (7) *Loc. cit.* (8) Rep. by Jaffé, *op. cit.*, pl. 14. (9) Rep. by Held, *The Art Bulletin*, 1940, fig. 11. (10) See F. W. H. Hollstein, *Dutch & Flemish, Etchings & Engravings* etc., XI, p. 222, no. 112. (11) See H. W. Janson, *Apes & Ape Lore*, 1952, p. 181. (12) That is the picture coll. H. von Pastor, see under note 3; see H. Friedman, *The Symbolic Goldfinch*, 1946, p. 139. (13) *Ibid.*, pp. 55–6. (14) By Jordaens, described as 'A Holy Family' etc., 41 × 60 (1·042 × 1·523). (15) No. 3215 is not noted in the *Catalogue of the Principal Sculptures . . . and Pictures at Deepdene*, 1859; or in earlier descriptions of the Hope collection. For a brief history of the Hope collection, see A. Wertheimer, *Introduction to the Hope Collection of Pictures of the Dutch & Flemish Schools*, 1898.

6293 PORTRAIT OF GOVAERT VAN SURPELE (?) AND HIS WIFE

The man wears a red sash with gold trimmings, holds a staff and carries a dagger and a sword slung from a baldrick.

Oil on relined canvas, $84 \times 74\frac{3}{8}$ (2·133 × 1·89).

The support is made up of six pieces of canvas; two strips at the top, which are *ca.* $4\frac{5}{16}$ (0·11) wide, are probably later additions.

A coat of arms on the pier above the term: *de vair à la fasce de gueules ornée de trois martels d'or* (see below).

In fairly good condition. There is much retouched wearing in the blacks of the costumes, and to a lesser degree in the architecture. Some of the paint in the architecture and sky has become more translucent with time, such that several *pentimenti* (see below) show up light. The state of preservation of the floor is obscure; a scumble seems to have become more translucent to the left of and behind the legs of the chair. The edges of the support are ragged and retouched, as is the bottom join. The *pièces de vair* may have been retouched; some faint traces of what may have been light grey or blue are evident in them here and there. Cleaned, 1958.

Several *pentimenti* are visible, the majority to the naked eye and others in infra-red photography. These mainly concern the background; the curtain, then a darker red, originally extended more to the left—as far as the middle of the central pier; narrow mouldings at the base of the term applied to this pier have been suppressed; the architecture on the left seems originally to have consisted in a pedestal supporting a column, whose base (now showing up light) was about level with the woman's shoulders. A building and some trees have been suppressed in the landscape, as have some leaves against the sky; part of the parrot's tail has also been painted out. So far as concerns the figures, the woman was first shown wearing a different ear-ring, and there is a small *pentimento* in the outline of the top of her collar.

Govaert van Surpele (1593–1674) held important posts in the government of his native city, Diest. He was *échevin* in 1629–1632; burgomaster in 1634/5, 1649/50 and 1651/2; and *président de la loi* in 1636/7.[1] He married twice: first in 1614 to Catharina Cools († 1629), and second in 1636 to Catharina Coninckx († 1639).[2]

The traditional[3] attribution of no. 6293 to Jordaens, has been generally accepted,[4] and there is no reason to doubt it in the main. However, the parrot and foliage may be the work of a collaborator. Further, it seems unlikely that the coat of arms is by Jordaens; but it is certainly old, and probably contemporary with the rest. The handling of paint on the two pieces of canvas at the top is not worthy of Jordaens; they are probably old additions.[5]

It seems probable that no. 6293 was evolved in at least two stages. Concave strains in the weave towards the bottom of the two inner pieces of canvas suggest that they were once fixed to a stretcher and thus that at an early stage the sitters were depicted three-quarter length. This is confirmed by a drawing[6] which shows the sitters three-quarter length and which, because of the inclusion of other features later suppressed in no. 6293, seems to be a free copy made during the execution of no. 6293 (other differences between the drawing and no. 6293 not being explained by *pentimenti* in the painting).[7] But in so far as the drawing seems to be a free record of a stage in the execution of no. 6293, it can be said that the architecture on the left and the curtain were altered before the support was extended at the bottom, and that alterations to the central pier (including the addition of the coat of arms) and to the area above and behind the woman were made after this extension.

The style of the costumes in no. 6293 is very similar to that in C. de Vos' *Portrait of a Husband and Wife* (Berlin), which is signed and dated 1629.[8] Puyvelde has suggested that no. 6293 was executed *ca.* 1630 which seems acceptable; although the handling is sufficiently loose to suggest a date *ca.* 1635.[9]

The coat of arms was identified as that of the van Surpele family of Diest in south Brabant by Hymans.[10] Despite small inaccuracies,[11] there seems no reason to doubt this identification. Further, while it seems improbable that the coat of arms was added by Jordaens himself, it is unlikely that it should not reliably refer to the identity of the male sitter. Several members of the van Surpele family have been proposed.[12] However, bearing in mind the probable date of execution of no. 6293, the most likely candidate is Govaert van Surpele. The problem concerning which of his two wives is depicted is not so clear cut. On the basis of the similarity of the costume with that in de Vos' picture at Dahlem of 1629, it is possible that the woman is van Surpele's first wife, Catharina Cools (†1629), and that no. 6293 was executed shortly before her death. However, it is just as possible that no. 6293 was executed shortly after his second marriage to Catharina Coninckx in 1636. And of the alternatives, the second seems more acceptable.

It is evident that no. 6293 was not commissioned as a straightforward marriage portrait, but rather to commemorate van Surpele's appointment to a position, whose emblem is the staff he holds.[13] The office may have been that of *président de la loi*, which van Surpele held in the year 1636/7. At all events because he wears a sword and sash, it seems likely that the office was military rather than civilian.[14] There were three militia companies (or schutsgilden) in Diest: the S. Jorisgilde (crossbow men), S. Barbaragilde (harquebusiers), and the S. Sebastiangilde (longbow men).[15] It is not as yet known to which of these companies van Surpele belonged.

ENGRAVING: Mezzotint by J. van Rymsdyck, published by J. Boydell, 1767.[16]

COPY: Drawing, black and red chalk, $11\frac{1}{2} \times 15\frac{1}{4}$ (0·292 × 0·388), coll. Bernard Houthakker, Amsterdam, 1959.[17]

PROVENANCE: Perhaps coll. the van Surpele family of Diest.[18] Thomas Scawen[19] sale, Cocks, 26 January (=2nd day), 1742/3 (49) sold for £117.[20] Coll. the 4th Duke of Devonshire (1698–1755) by 1743 when noted by Vertue at Devonshire House, London[21]; exh. at the B.I., 1837 (143)[22]; R.A., 1895 (122)[23]; *Jordaens Exhibition*, Antwerp, 1905 (75)[24]; *Exhibition of Works of Flemish and Modern Belgian Painters*, Guildhall, 1906 (88)[25]; R.A., 1910 (121)[26]; R.A., 1927 (159)[27]; R.A., 1938 (38)[28]; *Devonshire Collection Exhibition*, Agnews', 1948 (27)[29]; on loan to Manchester City Art Gallery, 1949; ceded by the 11th Duke of Devonshire in lieu of death duties, 1958, under the terms of the Finance Act of 1956; exh. *Jacob Jordaens Exhibition*, The National Gallery of Canada, Ottawa, 1968/9, (44).

REPRODUCTION: *National Gallery Acquisitions, 1953–1962, Exhibition Catalogue*.

REFERENCE: *General: National Gallery Acquisitions, 1953–1962, Exhibition Catalogue*, pp. 45–47.
In text: (1) Information kindly provided by G. van der Linden, Stadsarchivaris of Diest, in a letter in the Gallery archives. Several other spellings of the family name occur in contemporary documents and the more recent literature. The spelling given here is that engraved on a copper plate, made in commemoration of Govaert van Surpele and placed on the balustrade round the main altarpiece in S. Sulpice, Diest. (2) For the dates of death of his two wives, see the description, in the Diest Archives by Monsieur Le Chevalier van Zurpele de Reynrode, of the inscription on Govaert's tombstone, now worn away, in S. Sulpice, Diest. For the dates of his marriages, see information kindly provided by Monsieur le Très Révérend Doyen H. Fierens, Diest, in a memorandum, derived from the Archives Communales, Diest. (3) See below under *Provenance*. (4) See for instance M. Rooses, *Jordaens, Sa Vie et ses Œuvres*, 1906, pp. 55–6; and L. van Puyvelde, *Jordaens*, 1953, pp. 126–7. (5) They feature in Rymsdyck's mezzotint of 1767, see below under *Engraving*. (6) See below under *Copy*. (7) *Ibid.* (8) See, for instance, the 1931 catalogue of Staatl. Museen, Berlin, p. 516, no. 831; not in the post war Dahlem catalogues. (9) See van Puyvelde, *loc. cit.*; Michael Jaffé, *Jacob Jordaens . . . Exhibition Catalogue*, Ottawa, 1968, no. 44, proposed a date of 1629 (or before); while J. S. Held, *The Burlington Magazine*, 1969, p. 271, proposed a date not earlier than 1635. (10) See under H. Hyman's entry for Jordaens, in the *Biographie Nationale . . . de Belgique*, 1888–9, 10, col. 530. For the description of the van Surpele coat of arms, see Philippe d'Arschot and Gilbert van der Linden, *Diest Inventaire des Peintures*, II, 1958, under no. 9. Dr. J. Verbeemen, letter in the Gallery archives, has also kindly provided a slightly different description. (11) Verbeemen, *loc. cit.*, has pointed out that the *martels d'or* should face left; this is confirmed by the coat of arms on the tombstone in S. Sulpice, Diest, of C. J. van

Surpele († 1700), and that the *pièces de vair* should be azur; they are now black but, what could be traces of azur are perhaps evident here and there, see above. (**12**) See *National Gallery Acquisitions . . . Exhibition Catalogue*, cited under *General Reference*. (**13**) Described as a Commandostab, by M. Rooses, *Geschichte der Malerschule Antwerpens*, 1889, p. 336. (**14**) The costume seems to be comparable to that of a 'koning' or 'hoofdman' of a militia company. (**15**) See E. van Even, *Geschiedenis der stadt Diest*, 1848, pp. 232–7. (**16**) As 'Frederick Henry and Emilia van Solms, Prince and Princess of Orange in the Collection of His Grace the Duke of Devonshire'. The sitters in no. 6293 were thought to be members of the House of Orange for much of the eighteenth and nineteenth centuries, see under *General Reference*, This may have been because the van Surpele family lived at Diest, which had been a fief of the House of Orange. (**17**) Exh. Houthakker's, Amsterdam, 1959 (27), rep. in the catalogue. It shows the sitters three-quarter length and the architecture without the additions at the top; some differences correspond to *pentimenti* in no. 6293: the central pier, the foliage, parrot's tail and the landscape view, although there are more buildings in the drawing; others do not correspond: the sitters are placed further apart, and the top of a pier is depicted in the top right-hand corner above the curtain. See also above. (**18**) Govaert van Surpele's will has not been traced; but it seems likely that no. 6239 was commissioned by him; his possessions and those of his first wife were divided in the months following his death, see J. Th. de Raadt, *Sceaux Armoriées des Pays Bas et des Pays Avoisinats* etc., 1901, 3, pp. 502 ff.; no. 6293 may have passed to his son († 1676) and thence to his grandson, Govaert-Jan († 1707), who was 'conseiller et reçeveur des domaines du roi d'Angleterre, Guillaume III, [who was also Lord of Diest] et membre de la Chambre d'appel des fiefs de ce prince, en Brabant,' see de Raadt, *loc. cit.* (**19**) Thomas Scawen († 1774) was the son of Sir Thomas Scawen († 1730), citizen and alderman of London, and the heir of his uncle Sir William Scawen († 1722), who was 'vastly rich'; Sir William helped to finance William III, and legend records a visit by him to the king during the siege of Namur in 1692, see O. Manning and W. Bray, *The History of Antiquities of . . . Surrey*, II, 1809, p. 510. (**20**) Described as 'The first Prince & Princess of Orange' by 'Jordans [*sic*] of Antwerp', for the price see the marked catalogue in the V. & A. Library. (**21**) See *The Walpole Society*, 1938, XXVI, p. 23: 'at the Duke of Devonshires [*sic*] new built house a great & noble collection of pictures . . . the great picture of the Prince of Orange & princes [*sic*]', reference due to T. Wragg, Keeper of the Devonshire Collections. No. 6293 is not mentioned at Devonshire House by J. Dodsley, *London & its Environs Described*, 1761, pp. 225 ff. (as T. Wragg has kindly pointed out) or in subsequent guides, until by J. D. Passavant, *Kunstreise durch England und Belgien* etc., 1833, p. 71. Wragg thinks that no. 6293 may have been moved to Chatsworth in the intervening period, but it seems not to have been mentioned in relevant guides to Chatsworth (or to Chiswick, for that matter). (**22**) As 'Prince & Princess of Orange'. (**23**) As 'Portrait Group'. (**24**) As 'Portraits of van Zurpelan [*sic*] and his wife'. (**25**) *Ibid.* (**26**) As 'Portrait Group'. (**27**) As 'The Burgomaster of Diest & his Wife'. (**28**) As 'Portraits called Frederick Henry of Orange & his Wife Amalia of Solms'. (**29**) As 'Portrait of a Man & his Wife'.

ADAM-FRANÇOIS VAN DER MEULEN
1632–1690

Painter of views, travel scenes and battles, and print maker. Born in Brussels where he was baptized on 11 January, 1632.[1] Listed as the pupil of Peeter Snayers in the Brussels guild of painters on 18 May 1646;[2] he became a master in the guild in 1651.[3] He entered the service of Louis XIV of France on 1 April, 1664,[4] and specialized in topographical views and battle scenes, depicting many of the battles waged by the French in the Netherlands (having travelled in the company of the king); he also made designs for tapestries woven at the Gobelins' factory.[5] He was made a member of the *Académie Royale* on 13 May, 1673.[6] He married three times; his third wife, whom he married on 12 January, 1681, was a cousin of Lebrun.[7] He died at the *Hôtel des Gobelins* on 15 October, 1690.[8]

His portrait by Largillierre was engraved by P. van Schuppen.[9]

REFERENCE: *General:* A. Wauters, *Biographie Nationale de . . . Belgique*, 1897, 14, cols., 668–682.

In text: (1) See A Wauters, *Bulletin des Commissions Royales d'Art et d'Archéologie*, 1877, p. 313; and under *General, Reference*, col. 669. (2) See A. Pinchart, *Messager des Sciences Historiques*, 1878 p. 317; see also C. de Bie, *Het Gulden Cabinet* etc., 1661, p. 399. (3) See Pinchart, *op. cit.*, p. 320. (4) See Bautier, *op. cit.*, col. 671. (5) For his œuvre while in France, see M. J. Guiffrey, *Nouvelles Archives de l'Art Français*, 1879, pp. 119 ff., who prints van der Meulen's *Mémoire* of works executed for the King, and the inventory of pictures and drawings in the artist's possession at his death. (6) A. de Montaiglon, *Procès-Verbaux de l'Académie Royale* etc., 1878, 2, p. 6: 'Le sieur Frantçois [*sic*] Vander Meulen, Peintre, natif de Brusel, c'est présenté . . . l'Académie, cognoissant la capasité [*sic*] extraordinaire dud. sieur Vander Meulen et les emplois [*sic*] continuelz [*sic*] qu'il a pour les ouvrages du Roy, sens [*sic*] s'arrester aux formalitéz d'usage accouttumées [*sic*], l'a resçeu en calité [*sic*] d'Académicien . . .'. (7) See Wauters, *op. cit.*, col. 679. (8) *Ibid.*, col. 680. (9) *Ibid.*, col. 678.

1447 PHILIPPE-FRANÇOIS D'ARENBERG SALUTED BY THE LEADER OF A TROOP OF HORSEMEN

The outrider performs a *levade* as the leader of the troop salutes the Duke of Arenberg, who sits before the door of his coach. A dog-handler bows on the right.

Oil on relined canvas, $23\frac{1}{16} \times 31\frac{7}{8}$ (0·585 × 0·81).

Signed and dated, *A. F. V. MEVLEN.FEC: 1662. BRVXEL.*

Generally in good condition. There is some wearing in the clouds and losses in the studs of the harness.

Pentimenti in the right hind leg of the offside horse of the first pair, in the nearside rein joining the first and second pair, and in the ground before the coach, where some foliage has been suppressed.

Philippe-François, 1st Duke of Arenberg and Duke of Arschot and Croy (1625–1674), was an important figure at the court of Brussels. He was made a knight of the Golden Fleece in 1646; served in the army of the southern Netherlands and distinguished himself at the siege of Arras in 1654. He was made captain general of the Flemish fleet in 1660, and *grand bailli*, governor and captain general of Hainault in 1663.[1] The outrider wears his colours of yellow and red.

There is no reason to doubt the authenticity of the signature and date on no. 1447. The landscape was probably worked up after the figures.

The identification of the main sitter in the coach as the 1st Duke of Arenberg is due to Count Th. de Limburg Stirum;[2] the face is closely comparable to that in an engraved portrait of 1666.[3] Byss writing in 1713[4] considered that the occupant of the coach was the 'old' Duke of Lorraine; the man seated in the back of the coach, who also doffs his hat, bears a slight resemblance to Charles, 4th Duke of Lorraine (1604–1675), as depicted in an anonymous engraving of 1654.[5] Yet in spite of his connections with Brussels, it seems unlikely that he should have been thus dressed and placed in the coach.

No. 1447 is comparable to van der Meulen's picture at Cassel of *The Journey of a Princess* of 1659.[6]

COPY: J. de Winter sale, Giroux (Brussels), 12 March, 1928 (35), canvas, $24\frac{3}{4} \times 30\frac{5}{16} (0.63 \times 0.77)$.[7]

PROVENANCE: Coll. Prince Lothar Franz of Schönborn (1655–1729) at Pommersfelden by 1719[8]; Comte de Schönborn (Galerie de Pommersfelden) sale, Drouot (Paris), 17 ff. May, 1867 (194) bt. Reiset for 8100 francs.[9] Mrs. Lyne Stephens sale, Christie's 11 May (= 3rd day), 1895 (336) bt. Agnew for £147 for the National Gallery.

REPRODUCTION: *National Gallery Illustrations, Continental Schools (excluding Italian)*, 1950, p. 230, bottom.

REFERENCES: *In text:* (1) See Gachard's entry in the *Biographie Nationale . . . de Belgique*, 1866, I, cols. 405–10. (2) Letter of 14 February, 1966 in National Gallery archives; the compiler would like to thank Count Th. de Limburg Stirum for all his help in this matter. The suggestion that the main occupant of the coach is Louis XIV, see A. von. Wurzbach, *Niederländisches Künstler-Lexikon*, II, 1910, p. 153, is clearly wrong. (3) Engraved by R. Collin and L. Vorsterman II and J. van Werden, as one of the medallions in the print after F. Duchastel of the *Proclamation of King Charles II of Spain as Count of Flanders at Ghent, 2nd May, 1666*; rep. E. Laloire, *Recueil Iconographique de la Maison d'Arenberg*, 1940, pl. 33. (4) See note 8. (5) Reproduced by G. Winter, *Geschichte des Dreisigjähren Krieges*, 1893, p. 507. (6) No. 153 signed and dated 1659, canvas, $25\frac{3}{16} \times 36\frac{5}{8}$ (0.64 × 0.93). The outrider, in this picture, wears the same colours as his equivalent in no. 1447 (information concerning his colours kindly provided by Dr. Pilz of the Staatliche Kunstsammlungen, Cassel); H. Vogel, *Katalog der Staatlichen Gemäldegalerie zu Kassel*, 1958, p. 93, wrongly states that the pendant of this picture, no. 154, is a variant of no. 1447. (7) Rep. in catalogue; exh. *Paysage Flamand*, Musée Royal des Beaux-Arts de Belgique, 1926 (396); ex Anon. sale, Fiévez (Brussels), 10–11 December, 1919 (49); information kindly provided by W. L. van de Watering of the R.K.D. (8) See J. R. Byss, *Fürtrefflicher Gemähld-und Bild-Schatz, so in denen Gallerie und Zimmern des Churfürststl. Pommersfeldischen . . . Privat Schloss zu finden ist*, 1719, p. 10: 'Eine Landschafft | worinen eine Kutsch mit 6. Pferden | nebst noch anderen reitenden | in der Kutsch des Alten Hertzogs von Lotharingen Contrefait, mit Jägern und Hunden zur Jagt. Von der Moeulen. Schuh | Zoll: Hoch 1/11, breit 2/7'. Information kindly provided by Dr. Dressler, of the Staatliche Bibliothek, Bamberg. The 1867 sale catalogue first refers to the 1719 catalogue. No. 1447 is also recorded at Pommersfelden in the *Verzeichniss der Schildereyen in der Gallerie des hochgräflichen Schönbornischen Schlosses zu Pommersfelden*, 1774, p. 26, no. 205 (information from Dr. Dressler); and by J. Heller, *Die gräflich Schönborn'sche . . . Gemälde-Sammlung . . . in Pommers-felden*, 1845, p. 43; both identify the sitter as a Duke of Lorraine. (9) Marked sale catalogue in the National Gallery library.

JOOS DE MOMPER II
1564–1634/5

Landscape painter. Active in Antwerp, where he was born, according to his own testimony, in 1564.[1] He is not listed as a pupil in the records of the Antwerp guild of S. Luke, from which it may be inferred that he was taught by his father, Bartholomeus.[2] He became a master (listed as one of the 'meestersoonen') in the guild in 1581—during his father's tenure of office as Dean.[3] It is possible that he then went to Italy and studied under L. Toeput at Treviso.[4] He had returned to Antwerp by 1590, in which year he married there Elizabeth Gobijn († 1622)[5]; two sons also became painters.[6] In 1594 he took part in executing the decorations for the triumphal entry of the Governor of the Netherlands, the Archduke Ernest, into Antwerp.[7] In 1610 he was Dean of the guild of S. Luke.[8] He worked for both the Archduke Ernest and his successors, the Archduke Albert and Archduchess Isabella; in 1626 he laid claim to, and obtained from the Archduchess the same privileges and tax exemptions that Jan Brueghel I had enjoyed as a result of his employment by the court at Brussels.[9] He made his will on 2 November, 1634,[10] and had died by 9 March, 1635.[11]

The staffage in his landscapes was frequently the work of other artists, in particular, Jan Brueghel I.[12]

His portrait was etched by van Dyck for the *Iconography*; a later state was inscribed: 'Judocus de Momper, Pictor Montium Antverpiæ'.[13]

Various spellings of de Momper's christian name are given in contemporary documents; that used here was quite common.[14]

REFERENCES: *In text:* (1) See F. J. van den Branden, *Geschiedenis der Antwerpsche Schilderschool*, 1883, p. 310. (2) *Ibid.*, pp. 310–311. (3) See Ph. Rombouts and Th. van Lerius, *De Liggeren* etc., [1864–1876], I, p. 279. (4) See J. A. Graf Raczyński, *Die Flämische Landschaft vor Rubens*, 1937, p. 66 and pp. 92–3, note 118. His source is the entry in Herman de Neyt's inventory of 1642: 'Een lantschap van Mompers Meester Lodewyck van Treni' (for Treni read Trevi), see J. Denucé, *The Antwerp Art Galleries, Inventories of the Art-Collections in Antwerp* etc., 1932, p. 97. For Toeput, see for instance, A. von Wurzbach, *Die Niederländsches Künstler-Lexikon*, 1910, II, p. 715. (5) See van den Branden, *op. cit.*, pp. 311 and 314. (6) See the entries for Gaspard and Philips I de Momper in Thieme-Becker. (7) See van den Branden, *op. cit.*, pp. 252–3. (8) See Rombouts and van Lerius, *op. cit.*, p. 459. (9) See M. de Maeyer, *Albrecht en Isabella en de Schilderkunst*, 1955, pp. 160–1, and documents, 203–7. (10) See van den Branden, *op. cit.*, p. 315. (11) *Ibid.*, p. 316. (12) See, for instance, van den Branden, *op. cit.*, pp. 312–3; J. Denucé, *Letters and Documents concerning Jan Breugel I and II*, 1934, pp. 141–3; and the entry for Joos de Momper II by H. G. Törnell in Thieme-Becker. (13) See Fr. Wibiral, *L'Iconographie d'Antoine van Dyck*, 1877, p. 59, no. 7. (14) See, for instance, Rombouts and van Lerius, *op. cit.*, I, *passim*, and II, pp. 20 and 67. See also *Le Livre des Peintres de Carel van Mander* etc., trans. and ed. by H. Hymans, 1885, II, p. 290; and C. de Bie, *Het Gulden Cabinet* etc., 1661, p. 90.

Follower of Joos DE MOMPER II

1017 A MUSIC PARTY BEFORE A VILLAGE

Oil on relined canvas, $56\frac{3}{16} \times 71\frac{3}{4}$ ($1 \cdot 427 \times 1 \cdot 823$).
Bears initials and date, *D:D:V:* | *1633*
Apparently in fairly good condition. A yellow varnish obscures the paint; certain areas seem to be worn, notably the church on the right, the clouds, and the darks in the middle ground. The tree trunks in the centre appear to have been retouched.

The status of no. 1017 has not been clarified since it entered the collection[1] and remains somewhat obscure; the quality of execution does not seem to be distinguished. The initials and date[2] are coarsely written, and are not reliable.

The 1880 Gallery catalogue first associated Joos de Momper with no. 1017; and it is evident that no. 1017 is by a hand working in de Momper's manner.[3]

The rather feebly executed figures in no. 1017 seem to be by a different hand; they recall those in the *Landscape with a Stream and Castle* in the Akademie at Vienna, which has recently, but not wholly convincingly, been attributed to Jan Wildens.[4]

The costumes recall those in fashion in the 1640's and 50's; and no. 1017 may well have been executed about this time.

The two figures on the left and those just right of centre in the foreground may have been inspired by Rubens' *Garden of Love*, which was also engraved by Jegher.[5] A work in the same vein as no. 1017 is P. Meulener's picture of 1645 in the Rijkmuseum (no. 1563).

The view in no. 1017 has not been identified.

PROVENANCE: Wynn Ellis Bequest, 1876; lent to the Ministry of Works (now Public Building and Works), 1938–1952.

REPRODUCTION: *National Gallery Illustrations, Continental Schools (excluding Italian)*, 1950, p. 366, bottom.

REFERENCES: *In text:* (1) First catalogued, 1877–1878, as Unknown; from 1880–1887 as Unknown Flemish; from 1889–1906 as Flemish, Seventeenth Century; from 1911–1915 as by de Momper and Rubens; from 1920–1929 as by 'D. D. V.', with an ascription to David Vinckeboons from 1925; in the 1958 *Summary Catalogue* as Flemish School, Seventeenth Century. (2) First (and subsequently) published in the 1877 catalogue as 'D. D. V. 1622'. (3) Compare, for instance, Joos de Momper II's *Summer*, at Brunswick, oak, $21\frac{7}{8} \times 38\frac{3}{10}$ (0·555 × 0·97), see *Kurzes Verzeichnis der Gemäldesammlung im Herzog Anton Ulrich Museum zu Braunschweig*, 1932, p. 32, no. 65; and the picture, given to J. de Momper II, exh. *Paysage Flamand*, Musée Royal des Beaux-Arts de Belgique, 1926 (198), rep. in the catalogue. The hand responsible for the landscape of no. 1017 may also have executed that in the picture sold at Christie's, 2 August, 1928 (113). No. 1017 might also be compared with the picture signed by Frans de Momper at Brussels, for which see A. Laes, *Musées Royaux des Beaux-Arts, Bulletin*, 1952, p. 62 and fig. 3 on p. 64. (4) See M. Poch-Kalous, *Akademie der Bildenden Künste, Katalog der Gemälde Galerie*, 1961, no. 139, pp. 91–2. A. J. Wauters, *Catalogue . . . des Tableaux anciens du Musée de Bruxelles*, 1906, p. 207, under no. 518, thought that the same hand was responsible for the staffage in no. 1017 as in the *View of Antwerp* by Wildens (Brussels, Muséees Royaux des Beaux-Arts, no. 518). The figures in this picture, however, are not like those in no. 1017. (5) See F. van den Wijngaert, *Inventaris der Rubeniaansche Prentkunst*, 1940, no. 319.

PEETER NEEFFS I
active 1605–died between 1656 and 1661

Painter of church interiors. Active in Antwerp, where his parents lived and where he was probably born.[1] His elder brothers were born there in

1576 and 1577[2]; on these grounds it has been suggested that he was born in the following year,[3] but no record of his date of birth has been traced. It is not known who his master was; because of the connection between his work and that of Hendrick van Steenwyck II (*q.v.*), it has been suggested that Neeffs was taught in Antwerp by the latter's father.[4] The earliest record of Neeffs is his signed and dated picture of 1605 at Dresden[5]; four years later he was listed as a master in the Antwerp guild of S. Luke.[6] He married in Antwerp in 1612,[7] and had five children, born between 1614–1623.[8] Neeffs' wife died in 1655/6[9]; he was still alive in February, 1656[10]; but died probably not long after, and certainly before 1661.[11]

Two of his sons were also painters, working in his style: only a few signed paintings by Lodewijck (born 1617) are known[12]; the younger son, Peeter (1620–died after 1675) was probably more prolific. He was never enrolled as an independent master in the Antwerp guild of S. Luke; and it may be assumed that he worked with his father until the latter's death. Various attempts have been made to distinguish the son's paintings from the father's,[13] who on one occasion signed himself 'DEN AUDEN NEEFS'[14]; none is wholly satisfactory.

Other artists normally executed the figures in the paintings produced in Neeffs' studio.[15]

Other spellings of the father's surname in his lifetime included: Nefs, Neefs,[16] Neeff, and Neuff.[17]

REFERENCES: *In text:* (1) See F. J. van den Branden, *Geschiedenis der Antwerpsche Schilderschool*, 1883, pp. 608–9. (2) *Ibid.*, p. 609. (3) *Ibid.* (4) See H. Jantzen, *Das Niederländische Architeckturbild*, 1910, pp. 40–43. (5) See Jantzen, *op. cit.*, pp. 40–41, and p. 165, no. 242. (6) See Ph. Rombouts and Th. van Lerius, *De Liggeren* etc., [1864–1876], I, p. 454. (7) See van den Branden, *op. cit.*, p. 611. (8) *Ibid.*, pp. 611–612. (9) See Rombouts and Lerius, *op. cit.*, II, p. 272. (10) See van den Branden, *op. cit.*, p. 613–614. (11) C. de Bie, *Het Gulden Cabinet* etc., 1661, p. 155, describes Neeffs' art, and while not giving a date of death, refers to him in the past tense. (12) See, for instance, Jantzen, *op. cit.*, pp. 46–47, p. 164, nos. 238–241; and under no. 2206. On one occasion, he signed himself 'Frater Lodevicus . . .', on others 'F. L. . . .'; on this ambiguous basis, it has been assumed that he was a monk. (13) See A. von Wurzbach, *Niederländisches Künstler-Lexikon*, 1910, II, pp. 219–220; and Jantzen, *op. cit.*, pp. 45–46 (but see also N. MacLaren, *National Gallery Catalogues, The Dutch School*, 1960, no. 924), and pp. 167–168, some of those listed there being dated before 1656. (14) See von Wurzbach, *op. cit.*, p. 220. (15) See von Wurzbach, *op. cit.*, p. 219, who gives a list of artists who collaborated with Peeter Neeffs I and II, although the division he there assumes cannot be so hard and fast, see for instance under no. 2206. (16) By Neeffs himself, see Wurzbach, *op. cit.*, p. 220. (17) In the records of the Antwerp guild of S. Luke, see Rombouts and van Lerius, *op. cit.*, pp. 454 and 487.

Peeter NEEFFS I

2207 VIEW OF A CHAPEL AT EVENING

Oil on oak, $11\frac{1}{4} \times 8\frac{1}{2}$ (0·286 × 0·216).

In good condition. There are some small losses in the figures and probably some retouched losses along a vertical crack.

The cleric in white was first depicted wearing a hat.

The painting on the high altar is of a *Holy Family*.

Although considered to be by Steenwyck at least in the nineteenth century,[1] the quality of execution of the architecture in no. 2207 is comparable to that in no. 2206 *q.v.*; and it has been accepted as the work of Peeter Neeffs I by Jantzen.[2] But as with no. 2206, it is best to admit the possibility that it could have been the work of Neeffs' studio. The figures are by a different hand, perhaps working in a style connected with that of Peeter Snayers (1582–1667).[3]

The architecture in no. 2207 was probably executed some years before that in no. 2206, as the style of the costumes indicate that the figures were added in the early 1640's.

The view in no. 2207 is a variant of that in the left half of no. 2206. More is shown on the left in no. 2207; there are minor differences in the altarpiece, panelling, and in the number of pieces of church furniture.

The youth is lighting the candles on the altar, which indicates that a service is about to begin. It is likely that it is evening, in which case the service would have been Benediction as in no. 2206.

VERSIONS: Avignon, Musée Calvet, panel, $14\frac{3}{16} \times 10\frac{5}{8}$ (0·36 × 0·27)[4]; Budapest Museum, panel, $11\frac{3}{16} \times 8\frac{3}{4}$ (0·285 × 0·222)[5]; coll. A. M. Bouwens, The Hague, (n.d.), $11 \times 8\frac{1}{2}$ (0·28 × 0·216).[6]

PROVENANCE: Perhaps noted in the collection of the 4th Duke of Marlborough (1739–1817) at Blenheim Palace (in the Duke's Dressing Room) after 1777[7] and in 1789[8]; recorded in the Octangular Sitting Room of the Prince of Wales's Rooms, Blenheim Palace, 1862[9]; 8th Duke of Marlborough (Blenheim Palace) sale, Christie's, 24 July, 1886 (49) bt. Brunning £33 12sh.[10]; Henry Calcott Brunning Bequest, 1907; lent to the Public Library, Museum and Art Gallery, Burton-on-Trent, 1939, and, through the Arts Council, to the Municipal Art Gallery and Museum, Wolverhampton, 1952–1954.

REPRODUCTION: *National Gallery Illustrations, Continental Schools (excluding Italian)*, 1950, p. 243, bottom.

REFERENCES: *In text:* (1) See below under *Provenance*. (2) H. Jantzen, *Das Niederländische Architekturbild*, 1910, p. 166, no. 311. (3) One possibility is the Antwerp painter, Peeter Meulener (1602–1654), compare the figures in: Prado Museum, no. 1566, of 1644; in an Anon. sale, Christie's, 4 December, 1936 (135) said to be signed and dated 1651; and in an Anon. sale, Dorotheum (Vienna), 21 July, 1960 (61); said to be signed and dated 165(.); an alternative might be the youthful Adam-François van der Meulen (*q.v.*); especially, on the grounds of his youth, if the young man in the centre, whose gesture of pointing at himself, while looking at the spectator, might be taken as an indication of a self portrait. (4) See J. Girard, *Musée Calvet de la ville d'Avignon, Catalogue Illustré*, 1924, no. 541. The west entrance to the chapel and the altarpiece are different, as are the figures. (5) See p. 384 of the 1954 catalogue. (6) Photo in Witt Library, where under Steenwyck. (7) See *The New Oxford Guide* (6th ed. after 1777), p. 100: 'The Inside of a Church by Steenwyck'. There was also an *Interior of a Church* by Neeffs at Blenheim, noted, for instance, by J. P. Neale, *Views of the Seats of Noblemen* etc., *Blenheim House*, 1822, V, p. 6, as in the Bow Window Room; and by G. F. Waagen, *Treasures of Art in Great Britain*, III, 1854, p. 122, as in the Duke's Study, but this was not no. 2207—as is evident from its description by G. Scharf, *Catalogue ... of the Pictures at Blenheim Palace* etc., 1862, p. 63. (8) See W. Mavor, *New Description of Blenheim* etc., 1789 (ed.), p. 55: 'The

Inside view of a Church by Steenwyck'. (9) See Scharf, *op. cit.*, p. 175: 'Steen-wyck. A small upright picture. Interior of a church, looking into a side chapel . . .'
(10) Buyer and price from Christie's marked copy of the sale catalogue.

Peeter NEEFFS I
and
Bonaventura PEETERS I

2206 AN EVENING SERVICE IN A CHURCH

The service takes place in a side chapel, lit by candles.
Oil on oak, $10\frac{9}{16} \times 15\frac{1}{16}$ (0·268 × 0·382).
Signed and dated, *PEETER.NEEFFS. | 1649*
In good condition. There are a few scattered losses, notably round the edges and in the bottom left-hand corner, all retouched. There is a retouched scratch *ca.* $3\frac{1}{8}$ (0·08) long in the top right-hand corner.

There are two candles, a missal (?) and a carved Crucifix on the altar of the side chapel; the top of the stone altarpiece is decorated by three statues of: *S. Mary Magdalen* (?) and two angels. The central area at the altarpiece is veiled by a white cloth with a red cross on it. Attached to the second column on the right, above the candle, is a statue of the *Virgin and Child.*

No. 2206 is one of a series of views (all variations on the same form-ula) by Peeter Neeffs I or his studio, in which figures, variously disposed, are by other hands.[1] The formula was probably inspired by Hendrick van Steenwyck II.[2] By the standards of Peeter Neeffs I, the quality of the execution of the architecture in no. 2206 is fairly high, if rather mechanical, and it is accepted as his work by Jantzen.[3] There is no reason to doubt the authenticity of the signature on no. 2206, but bearing in mind the lack of definition of Neeffs' œuvre (and even more so that of his sons),[4] it is best to admit the possibility that no. 2206 would have been produced in the studio of the elder Neeffs. The figures seem clearly to be by Bonaventura Peeters I[5]; the statues are also by him.

Two pictures in the series are dated 1637[6]; the date—1649—on no. 2206 is evident in infra-red photography. The figures were probably added very soon after the execution of the architecture.

On the reasonable assumption that no. 2206 depicts an evening scene, it seems likely that the service is that of Benediction.[7]

The church has not been satisfactorily identified.

COPY: Aschaffenburg, Staatsgemäldegalerie, no. 6412, panel, $10\frac{7}{16} \times 15$ (0·267 × 0·381).[8]

VARIANTS: Cassel, Staatliche Gemäldegalerie, copper, $10\frac{3}{4} \times 15\frac{7}{16}$ (0·274 × 0·392) signed[9]; and copper, $3\frac{13}{16} \times 5\frac{11}{16}$ (0·097 × 0·145)[10]; Dunkirk Museum[11]; Leipzig, Museum der bildenden Künste, copper, $16\frac{1}{16} \times 22\frac{13}{16}$ (0·408 × 0·58)[12]; Leningrad, Hermitage, panel, $15\frac{3}{16} \times 21\frac{1}{16}$ (0·386 × 0·535), signed with initials[13]; and panel, $16\frac{1}{8} \times 21\frac{1}{16}$ (0·41 × 0·535)[14]; Lille Museum, panel, $9\frac{7}{16} \times 13\frac{3}{8}$ (0·24 × 0·34), signed and dated 1637[15]; Mainz, Gemäldegalerie, $14\frac{15}{16} \times 25\frac{3}{16}$ (0·38 × 0·64), signed[16]; Valenciennes Museum, panel, $9\frac{7}{16} \times 13\frac{3}{8}$ (0·24 × 0·34)[17];

Vienna, Kunsthistorisches Museum, panel, $13\frac{3}{4} \times 21\frac{5}{8}$ (0.35×0.55)[18]; coll. the Duke of Buccleuch, Boughton House, $9\frac{1}{4} \times 13\frac{1}{4}$ (0.235×0.337)[19]; National Trust, Brodrick Castle, $4 \times 5\frac{3}{4}$ (0.012×0.146)[20]; coll. the Earl of Wemyss, Gosford, $15\frac{1}{2} \times 20\frac{1}{2}$ (0.394×0.521)[21]; Galerie Musée Napoléon, 1810[22]; Slatner sale, Prague, 7–9 June, 1926, panel, *ca.* $15\frac{3}{8} \times 22\frac{13}{16}$ (0.39×0.58)[23]; Anon. sale, Lepke (Berlin), 30 April, 1929 (55), canvas, $13\frac{3}{4} \times 18\frac{7}{8}$ (0.35×0.48)[24]; Sneyd sale, Christie's, 27 June, 1924, panel, $9\frac{1}{2} \times 13$ (0.242×0.33), apparently signed and dated 1637; Dr. Douglas Heath sale, Christie's, 15 July, 1937 (142) panel, $10\frac{1}{2} \times 14\frac{1}{2}$ (0.267×0.368), apparently signed and dated, F. L. Neeffs 1645[25]; of the side chapel only, see under no. 2207.

PROVENANCE: Sir William W(ellesley) Knighton, Bart., (†)[26] sale, Christie's, 23 May (= 3rd day), 1885 (479) bt. Brunning for £27 6sh.[27]; Henry Calcott Brunning Bequest, 1907.

REPRODUCTION: *National Gallery Illustrations, Continental Schools (excluding Italian)*, 1950, p. 243, top.

REFERENCES: *In text:* (1) See below, under *Variants*. (2) See the pictures at Vienna (E. R. V. Engerth, *Kunsthistorische Sammlungen des allerhöchsten Kaiserhauses, Gemälde . . . Verzeichniss*, 1884, II, no. 1270, where attributed to Hendrick van Steenwyck I); and coll. Sir Edmund Bacon, which bears a signature and a date, not properly legible on a photograph. Both seem to be connected with Hendrick van Steenwyck's style *ca.* 1609 (see no. 4040); but may be later repetitions by him. (3) See H. Jantzen, *Das Niederländische Architecturbild*, 1910, p. 166, no. 281. (4) See Jantzen, *op. cit.*, pp. 45–47; and A. von Wurzbach, *Niederländisches Künstler-Lexikon*, II, 1910, p. 220. (5) The attribution is based on a comparison with the figures by Bonaventura Peeters in the *Interior of Antwerp Cathedral* by Peeter Neeffs II (?) in the Kunsthistorisches Museum, Vienna, see E. R. V. Engerth, *op. cit.*, no. 1044, p. 301. (6) See below under *Variants*. (7) R. T. Blackwood (letters in Gallery archives) thought that one of the figures in a surplice to the left of the west entrance of the chapel was a deacon; the coincidence of the deacon's position, the veiled altarpiece, and the priest in a cope, led him to suggest that the service was vespers on Maundy Thursday. In his view the moment in the service is that when the deacon sings the 'Ite missa est' to the congregation. Although this theory is attractive, it is by no means certain that one of the two figures is a deacon; and the fact that the statues and Crucifix are not veiled makes it unlikely that the season is Lent. (8) See *Bayerische Staatsgemäldesammlungen, Galerie Aschaffenburg, Katalog*, 1964, p. 117; and Jantzen, *op. cit.*, p. 171, no. 489. (9) No. 67 of the 1958 catalogue, where the figures are attributed to Frans Francken II. (10) No. 74 of the 1958 catalogue, where stated to be signed with initials by Hendrick van Steenwyck II; but to judge from a photograph, this attribution seems unlikely. (11) Photo. in Witt Library. (12) No. 1615; ex coll. Speck von Sternburg, as by H. van Steenwyck, see Jantzen, *op. cit.*, p. 171, no. 507; photo. in R.K.D. (13) Inv. no. 644; information kindly supplied by Dr. Miller of the State Hermitage Museum. (14) Inv. no. 645; acquired from Malmaison, 1814; information kindly supplied by Dr. Miller of the State Hermitage Museum. (15) No. 553 of the 1893 catalogue; for the signature and date, see F. Benoit, *La Peinture au Musée de Lille*, I, 1909, no. 20 and fig. 37. The figures there attributed to Frans Francken. Benoit gives a list of variants, but he is mistaken so far as nos. 323 and 717 of the Musées Royaux des Beaux-Arts, Brussels, are concerned, as W. Laureyssens has kindly informed the compiler. Benoit states that the composition features in a picture by F. Francken II at Schönborn (no. 116). (16) See *Verzeichnis der Gemälde-Sammlung der Stadt Mainz*, 1911, p. 19, no. 188; photo. in R. K. D. (17) See *Valenciennes, Palais des Beaux-Arts, Tableaux*, etc., 1931, p. 53, no. 80. (18) See Engerth, *op. cit.*, pp. 300–1, no. 1043; the figures may be by Bonaventura Peeters I. (19) Photo. in Witt Library. (20) *Ibid.* (21) *Ibid.* (22) When engraved by J. de la Porte; perhaps identical with the Hermitage picture, see note 14. (23) Photo. in Witt Library. (24) Rep. in sale catalogue. (25) F. L. Neeffs is probably Lodewijck Neeffs, see above under the biography of Peeter Neeffs. (26) The collection was founded by Sir William Knighton (1776–1836), see G. F. Waagen, *Galleries & Cabinets of Art in Great Britain*, 1857, pp. 373–4. For Sir William Knighton see the entry in the D.N.B. No. 2206 may have been in the Edward Coxe sale, Coxe, 25 April (= 3rd day), 1807 (34) described as 'The Interior of the great Church at Antwerp, lighted up for vespers . . .', ex Countess of Holderness (†) sale, Christie's 6 March, 1802 (69). The 1929 catalogue suggested that no. 2206 may have been the Thomas Bladen sale, Christie's, 11 March (= 2nd day), 1775 (56) as by 'H. Neeffs' and 'O. Frank', and described as 'The Inside of a church with a priest at the altar . . .'. (27) Buyer and price from Christie's marked copy of the catalogue.

JACQUES VAN OOST I
1601–1671

Portrait and figure painter. Active in Bruges where he was born in February, 1601. He was enrolled as the pupil of his elder brother, Frans, in the guild of S. Luke, Bruges, on 3 January, 1619. On 18 October, 1621 he was listed as a master in the guild. He then visited Italy; and had returned to Bruges by 12 October, 1628. He was Dean of the guild in 1633; and was twice 'stedehouder'. He died in 1671.

His christian name seems more frequently to have been spelt Jacques than Jacob in the records of the Bruges guild of S. Luke.

REFERENCE: *General:* R. A. d'Hulst, *Gentse Bijdragen* etc., 1951, pp. 169–173.

1137 PORTRAIT OF A BOY AGED ELEVEN

The sitter wears a muff and a fur cap.

Oil on relined canvas, $31\frac{11}{16} \times 24\frac{13}{16}$ (0·805 × 0·63).

Signed, inscribed and dated, *AETAT* (AE in monogram)*: SVAE* (AE in monogram) *ii 1650·IVO.* (VO in monogram).

In fairly good condition. The background is disfigured by a fair number of discoloured retouchings, particularly to the left of the fur cap, which itself may also be retouched. The state of the jacket is somewhat obscured by an ingrained varnish.

Although no. 1137 was acquired and first catalogued as the work of Isack van Ostade, there is no reason to doubt the identification of the monogram as that of Jacques van Oost I, first made in the 1898 catalogue, and recently accepted by d'Hulst.[1]

The identity of the sitter is not known.

PROVENANCE: Purchased from Miss M. A. Thomas (with the aid of the Clarke Fund), 1883; lent, through the Arts Council, to the Graves Art Gallery, Sheffield, 1958–63.

REPRODUCTION: *National Gallery Illustrations, Continental Schools (excluding Italian)*, 1950, p. 254, bottom.

REFERENCE: *In text:* (1) See R. A. d'Hulst, *Gentse Bijdragen* etc., 1951, XIII, pp. 186 and 191.

Ascribed to JACQUES VAN OOST I

3649 TWO BOYS BEFORE AN EASEL

Oil on relined canvas, $22\frac{1}{8}/\frac{1}{4} \times 22\frac{7}{8}/23\frac{1}{8}$ (0·562/5 × 0·582/7).
In good condition. The canvas edges are a little ragged. There are a
few, small damages, all retouched. The damage is most extensive in the
top right-hand corner and down the right-hand edge. Strains in the
canvas weave towards the left and right-hand edges and at the top
suggest that these edges have not, at least recently, been much cut
down; no strains are evident at the bottom edge, which has therefore
been perhaps quite significantly cut down. Cleaned, 1960/61.
On the easel is a grisaille of the Story of Gideon, from *Judges*, VII,
5–6.[1]
No. 3649 has been attributed both to Tintoretto[2] and Dirk Helmbreker[3]; Holmes[4] published the attribution to Jacques van Oost, which
has been accepted by d'Hulst.[5] The handling resembles that in no. 1137,
but the hand and chin of the elder boy are less accomplished. The
scene and handling bring to mind the signed and dated picture of 1666
at Bruges which Pauwels has recently attributed to Jacques van Oost
II (1639–1713).[6] D'Hulst, however, has dated no. 3649 *ca.* 1645, which
may be right on grounds of the costumes. Bearing these points in mind,
it seems best at this stage to catalogue no. 3649 as ascribed to Jacques
van Oost I.

PROVENANCE: Presented by Sir Henry H. Howorth (through the National Art-
Collections Fund) in memory of Lady Howorth, 1922; lent, through the Arts
Council to the Walker Art Gallery, Liverpool, 1951–59.

REPRODUCTION: *National Gallery Illustrations, Continental Schools (excluding
Italian)*, 1950, p. 255, right.

REFERENCE: *General:* C. J. Holmes, *The Burlington Magazine*, 41, 1929,
pp. 82 and 87.

REFERENCES: *In text:* (1) The subject was identified by Holmes, cited under
General Reference. (2) On the back is a nineteenth-century label which reads:
'An artist and his Attendant | Tintoretto.' (3) On the back is an excerpt of a
cutting from a sale (?) catalogue: 'Portrait of Theodore Helmbreker and his
brother by h. . . .lf'. (4) See under *General Reference.* (5) See R. A. d'Hulst,
Gentse Bijdragen etc., XIII, 1951, pp. 182 and 191. (6) See H. Pauwels, *Musée
Groeninge, Catalogue*, 1963, pp. 133–4, no. 126.

BONAVENTURA PEETERS I
1614–1652

Marine, landscape, and small-scale figure painter, and engraver. Active
in Antwerp, where he was baptized 23 (?) July, 1614.[1] It is not known
who his master was; although his style shows the influence of Jan Por-
cellis. He is recorded as a master in the Antwerp guild of S. Luke in the
list for the year 1634/5.[2] He seems to have shared his studio with his
elder brother, Gillis (1612–1653).[3] Perhaps because of attacks on the

Jesuits, made towards the end of his life, he had to leave Antwerp and settle in nearby Hoboken,[4] where he died on 25 July, 1652.[5]

His portrait by J. Meyssens was engraved by W. Hollar.[6]

REFERENCES: *In text:* (1) See F. J. van den Branden, *Geschiedenis der Ant-werpsche Schilderschool*, 1883, p. 1046; Th. van Lerius, *Catalogue du Musée d'Anvers*, 1874 (3rd ed.), p. 267, gives his date of baptism as 25 July, 1614. (2) See Ph. Rombouts and Th. van Lerius, *De Liggeren* etc. [1864–1876], II, p. 59. (3) Their younger brother Jan (1624–died after 7 January, 1677) is recorded as the pupil of Gillis and Bonavontuer (*sic*) Peeters in the list of the Antwerp guild of S. Luke for the year 1641-2, see Rombouts and van Lerius, *op. cit.*, p. 133. (4) See Mols, quoted by C. Kramm, *De Levens en werken der . . . Kunstschilders* etc., 1859, 3, p. 1263. The inscription beneath Meyssen's print of 1649, see under note 6, makes no mention of his move. He was at Hoboken at least by 24 May, 1652, see van den Branden, *op. cit.*, pp. 1047–8. His brothers and sister, also lived with him at Hoboken, see van den Branden, *op. cit.*, pp. 1047, and 1051–2. (5) See van den Branden, *op. cit.*, p. 1048, who reproduces the inscription under the funerary pictures by Jan Peeters and A. Matthijs, and the inscription on his tombstone. (6) In J. Meyssens, *Images de Divers Hommes d'esprit Sublime* etc., 1649; reprinted by C. de Bie, *Het Gulden Cabinet* etc., 1661, p. 171.

See PEETER NEEFFS I, no. 2206

PEETER PAUWEL RUBENS

1577–1640

Scholar, antiquarian, collector and diplomat, as well as painter. One of the outstanding artists of the seventeenth century. Active in several countries of Europe, but chiefly in Antwerp, his parents' native city.

The record of his baptism has not been traced; but he was almost certainly born on 28 June, 1577 at Siegen in west Germany. The following year his family moved to Cologne; and *ca.* 1588, his mother, then a widow, took her family to Antwerp. Rubens is not listed as a pupil in the records of the Antwerp guild of S. Luke, but he probably had three masters in Antwerp: Tobias Verhaecht, Adam van Noort and Otho van Veen. He became a master in the Antwerp guild of S. Luke in 1598.

In 1600 he set out for Italy; and soon after his arrival entered the service of Vincenzo Gonzaga, Duke of Mantua, in which he was to remain for nearly eight years. He studied and worked in several cities in Italy, notably Rome; in 1603 he was sent by the Duke to Spain to take presents for members of the Spanish court. He left Italy at the end of October, 1608, and had reached Antwerp by 11 December, 1608, where he was to establish his studio. In June, 1609 he was made a member of the Antwerp guild of Romanists (of which he was Dean for the year 1613/14); on 23 September he was appointed court painter to the Governors of the Netherlands, the Archduke Albert & Archduchess Isabella (see nos. 3818–9). On 3 October, 1609, in Antwerp, he married Isabella Brant (1591–1626), by whom he had 4 children.

Rubens is frequently recorded in Antwerp in the next twelve years; he probably worked there uninterruptedly, except for brief visits to Brussels, other cities in the southern Netherlands, and perhaps a short trip to the northern Netherlands.

By the end of 1621, he had received a commission from Marie de Médicis to decorate two galleries in the Luxembourg Palace, Paris. Work on the decorations for the first gallery involved three journeys to Paris, the third undertaken in February 1625, to supervise the installation of the last group of canvases. The decoration of the second gallery was never completed.

In Paris, in 1625, Rubens met George Villiers, Duke of Buckingham (see no. 187)—an event of significance in Rubens' concern to gain peace in the Netherlands. He had been engaged in this activity by the Archduchess Isabella since at least September, 1623; and it involved him in a series of discussions held in Paris and the Netherlands between 1626–7. At the end of August, 1628, he set out for Madrid to promote a peace plan. Philip IV appointed him one of the secretaries of the privy council in the Netherlands; and sent him to England to arrange an exchange of ambassadors to negotiate a peace settlement between the two countries (see no. 46). Rubens successfully carried out his brief, and returned to Antwerp towards the end of March, 1630, with the finalized commission from Charles I to execute the ceiling paintings for the Banqueting Hall, Whitehall.

On 6 December, 1630, at Antwerp, he married Helena Fourment (1614–73), by whom he had 5 children, the last born just over eight months after his death. He continued to be active as one of the Archduchess' political agents until early in 1633. He designed and supervised the work for the decorations for the triumphal entry into Antwerp of the Cardinal Infant Ferdinand (the successor to the Archduchess as Governor of the Netherlands), which took place on 17 April, 1635. In May, 1635 he bought the castle and fief of Steen (see no. 66). The following April he was appointed court painter to the Cardinal Infant. In the autumn of 1636 he received Philip IV's commission for a series of paintings to decorate the Torre de la Parada, near Madrid (see no. 2598). He died at Antwerp on 30 May, 1640, and was buried in the S. Jacobskerk.

The inscription on his tombstone described him as 'steini Toparcha' (Lord of Steen); he had been granted a patent of nobility by Philip IV in 1624; he was knighted by Charles I in 1630.

His christian names are spelt in several languages in contemporary documents (they are given here in a Flemish form); he normally signed his letters using the Italianate 'Pietro Pauolo'.

REFERENCES: *General:* M. Rooses, *Rubens*, trans. H. Child, 1904, 2 vols., on which the above is based; H. G. Evers, *Rubens und sein Werk*, 1944, pp. 12–93, gives a useful abstract of his life and contemporary events; the best, recent biography and review of his art with a full bibliography is that by H. Gerson, in *Art and Architecture in Belgium* etc., 1960, pp. 70–108, and notes; and pp. 211–16 for bibliography.

The Studio of RUBENS

Rubens maintained an active studio in Antwerp from soon after his return from Italy. Its existence was not exceptional, but its size and activity are notable. In May, 1611 he wrote regretting that he could not take in a pupil, adding that he had had to turn down over a hundred applicants.[1] In 1618, Rubens specified studio assistance in a list of his paintings available for sale.[2] In the first half of 1621 a visitor to Antwerp, Otto Sperling, described a large room in Rubens' house 'der keine Fenster hatte, sondern sein Licht durch eine grosse Oeffnung mitten in der Decke erhielt. In diesem Saale sassen viele junge Maler, die alle an verschiedenen Stücken malten, welche mit Kreide von Hrn. Rubbens [*sic*] vorgezeichnet worden waren und auf denen er hier und da ein Farbenfleck angebracht hatte. Diese Bilder mussten die jungen Leute ganz in Farben ausführen, bis zuletzt Hr. Rubbens [*sic*] selbst das Ganze durch Striche und Farben zur Vollendung brachte . . .'.[3] The problem as to whether a painting was by Rubens or a studio assistant seems on occasions to have bothered his English admirers.[4] As late as 1640, Norgate mistook a landscape which he had seen in Rubens' studio as a work of the master, for as Rubens explained 'il ne me sembla pas nécessaire alors de le désabuser pour ne luy donner quelque mes-contentement . . . Je confesse que la susdite peinture n'est pas de ma main, mais faitte entierem^t par un Peintre des plus communs . . . de ceste ville après un mien dessein fait sur le lieu mesme . . .'; and later he stated that the painting was ' . . . achevée selon la capacité du Maistre toutesfois avecq mon advis . . .'.[5] Studio assistance is thus an important, and probably after 1609 a constant but, indeterminate, element in his art. It can be expected to varying extents in many of his larger works (see no. 59).

The composition of his studio may have varied from year to year. The number of his pupils is not known; his position as court painter absolved him from the duty of registering his pupils with the Antwerp guild of S. Luke,[6] although one of his pupils is in fact listed in the records of the guild.[7] Several artists are known to have been his pupils.[8] The studio remained active during his absence. While he was abroad in 1628–30, Willem Panneels, an ex pupil, and registered as a master in the guild,[9] was deputed by him to be in charge of it.[10] In 1638, he wrote to his pupil, Fayd'herbe: 'Siet toch wel toe, als ghij vertrecken sult, dat alles wel opgesloten sij ende datter geene originaelen en blijven staen boven op het schilderhuys oft eenige schetsen . . . Compt toch over soo haest als ghij cont, opdat het huys mach gesloten worden; want, soo langhe als ghij daer sijt en cont de andere niet buyten sluyten. . . .'[11]

In the list of paintings available for sale in 1618, Rubens also specified collaboration with established, specialist painters.[12] This was common practice at Antwerp at the time; several examples of collaboration between Rubens and another artist are known.[13] In such cases Rubens and/or a studio assistant drew the figures and the collaborator or collaborators added their speciality (see no. 853). Such a distinction is not always hard and fast; the precise status of van Dyck and the other 'discipelen', who executed the ceiling paintings of the Jesuit Church in 1620–1, is uncertain.[14] Van Dyck by this time was certainly an established figure painter. Finally, many of the canvases for the Torre de la Parada were executed by established figure painters, and not by studio assistants (see under no. 2598).

REFERENCE: *General:* L. van Puyvelde, *Gazette des Beaux-Arts*, 1949, XXXVI, pp. 230 ff.

In text: (1) See Rubens' letter to Jacques de Bie of 11 May, 1611, in M. Rooses and Ch. Ruelens (†), *Correspondance de Rubens* etc., 1898, II, p. 35. (2) See the list of paintings sent by Rubens to Sir Dudley Carleton on 28 April, 1618, printed by Rooses and Ruelens (†), *op. cit.*, pp. 136–7. (3) Printed by W. v. S. in *Repertorium für Kunstwissenschaft*, 1887, p. 111; an English translation is given in M. Rooses, *Rubens*, trans. by H. Child, I, 1904, pp. 315–6. (4) See the correspondence concerning the *Hunt* painted for Lord Danvers, printed by Rooses and Ruelens (†), *op. cit.*, pp. 261 ff.; and Rubens' letter to Trumbull of 13 September, 1621 in which he stated that Carleton 'ne s'est laissé jamais entendre clairem^t touteslesfoix que je luy ay fait instance de vouloir déclarer si ceste pièce devoit estre un vray originel entièremen^t ou seulem^t touchée de ma main . ', see Rooses and Ruelens (†), *op. cit.*, p. 286. (5) See Rubens' letter to Gerbier of 15 March, 1640, and of April, 1640, printed by Rooses and Ruelens (†), *op. cit.*, 1909, VI, pp. 257–8 and 279. (6) See Ph. Rombouts and Th. van Lerius, *De Liggeren* etc., [1864–1876], I, p. 558, under note 1. (7) That is Jacques Moermans, registered in the year 1621/2, see Rombouts and van Lerius, *op. cit.*, p. 574. (8) See, for instance, Rooses, *Rubens* etc., I, pp. 314 ff. (and under the biography of van Dyck *q.v.*), and II, pp. 611–4. (9) See Rombouts and van Lerius, *op. cit.*, p. 649: 'Gilliam Panels, schilder, tot Rubens . . .'; in the same year (1627/8) Justus van Egmont was likewise registered as a master. (10) See Rubens' certificate for Panneels, of 1 June, 1630, printed by Rooses and Ruelens (†), *op. cit.*, 1907, V, pp. 295–6. (11) See Rooses and Ruelens (†), *op. cit.*, 1909, VI, p. 223; for an English translation, see R. S. Magurn, *The Letters of P. P. Rubens*, 1955, p. 411. (12) See note 2. (13) See under the biographies of Jan Brueghel I, Frans Snijders and Jan Wildens; he also collaborated with Jan Brueghel II, see J. Denucé, *Letters & Documents concerning Jan Breugel I & II*, 1934, pp. 147 and 151. (14) For a record of the contract for the ceiling paintings for the Jesuit Church, drawn up between Rubens and Tirinus, in which van Dyck and the other artists are thus mentioned, see M. Rooses, *L'Œuvre de P. P. Rubens*, 1886, I, pp. 43 ff.

Two aspects of Rubens' creative genius should be mentioned here as an introduction to the entries below: his versatile adaptation of poses for use in different contexts, and his many quotations from the work of other masters and from the antique. So far as the first is concerned, it can be said that it is a characteristic of many masters; but particular emphasis has been placed on it in studies on Rubens to demonstrate the complexity of his visual vocabulary. Quotations from other masters are by no means exceptional among figure painters; but in Rubens' case it is particularly marked as can be inferred from the many copies he himself drew or painted. It was already remarked on by S. van Hoogstraten in 1678, as Held has pointed out (see J. S. Held, *Rubens Selected Drawings*, I, 1959, p. 49, note 1).

38 THE RAPE OF THE SABINE WOMEN

Roman soldiers carry off Sabine women; on the throne on the right, Romulus, with two *lictors* beneath; in the background, behind a rail and on a lower level, mounted Sabines attack Romans before a festooned arch leading to a temple.

Oil on oak, $66\frac{7}{8} \times 93$ ($1 \cdot 699 \times 2 \cdot 362$). The ground has been mostly removed, or has worn away on the left and right edges to form a border *ca.* $\frac{7}{16}$ ($0 \cdot 012$).

For the make up of the support, see Appendix I. Rebates on the reverse have been gauged at the left and right edges. The reverse is coated with a ground similar to that on the front, and painted brown, probably for Rubens.[1]

Generally in good condition. There is some wearing and retouching in the black costumes of the elderly Sabine woman on the left and the Sabine woman in the centre, and probably in the dress of the Sabine woman crouching before the dais, the armour of the Roman, who carries off the Sabine in the black cloak, and the tunic of the young Roman in the right foreground. The lap-dog in the left foreground is also worn. There are some long, thin scratches in the paint in the upper part of the picture. Some of the *pentimenti* in the architecture (see below) now show up light. Cleaned, 1939.

There are several *pentimenti*, some visible to the naked eye the others in X-radiographs. The main alterations were made to the architecture, and to the Sabine woman and Roman soldier in the centre foreground. A column to the left of the arch has been suppressed; the column, second from the left, has been moved a little to the right; the inner part of the entablature on the left was first set in deeper perspective, while the building on the left was first set in less deep perspective (the right arm of the Sabine woman on the dais, clutching the ledge, has not been adjusted to correspond with this *pentimento*). The Sabine man on the dais was first shown holding his sword before him. The head of the Sabine woman in the centre was first lower, and the Roman abducting her was probably first placed behind her and in profile; he was first shown wearing a helmet in the final position adopted for him. There are many minor *pentimenti*, notably in the outlines of the horse's right leg, in the leg of the Roman who lifts up the Sabine woman, and in the leg, arm, shoulder and helmet of the Roman immediately to the left. *Pentimenti* are also evident, but illegible, in the red cloak of the Roman who grabs the Sabine woman's dress.

The Sabine tribe originally lived to the north-east of Rome; varying accounts of the rape of the Sabine women during the reign of Romulus are given by classical authors. No. 38 loosely follows the description of the event given by Plutarch,[2] who relates that after the discovery of an altar, Romulus proclaimed games to be held to which the Sabines were invited. At a given sign from him, which is not rendered in no. 38 as Plutarch describes it, the Romans carried off a number of Sabine women. Later the Sabines under Tatius attacked the Romans and were defeated. In no. 38 the Sabine women and Romulus are suitably placed and protected to watch the games, and the arch is appropriately festooned;[3] the ensuing battle is depicted in the background, where the Sabines attack Romans, who carry standards and are urged on by men playing a *cornu* and *tuba*.

No one has ever suggested that no. 38 is not wholly by Rubens, and there are clearly no grounds for doing so. It was probably executed early in the second half of the 1630's.[4]

There is a preparatory, grisaille sketch for no. 38 in a private collection,[5] which, judging from photographs, appears to be stylistically comparable to the Copenhagen grisaille of *Christ on the Way to Calvary*, that has been dated *ca.* 1634.[6]

There are considerable differences between sketch and picture. The majority of poses, which appear in the picture but not in the sketch, derive from ideas that Rubens either considered for, or used in, other compositions. And for this reason it seems unlikely that there was an intervening *modello*. The sketch itself contains ideas, which Rubens had previously used; and thus the project, which culminated in no. 38, presents a very full compendium of Rubens' pictorial ideas.

The main difference between the sketch and picture, is that the sketch shows less at the top—Romulus' head being placed just beneath the edge of the support. The sketch does not include the rail, or the scene beyond; while the architecture on the left is only suggested. It is thus noteworthy that among the most pronounced *pentimenti* in the picture are those in the architecture, which with the sky was probably executed after the figures had been blocked in. The suppression of the column suggests either that Rubens first intended the whole arch to be farther to the left, or that he intended it to be supported by six columns on the left; of these alternatives, the first seems more probable. The musicians may have been inspired by those on the right in Giulio Romano's drawing of *Lictors and Musicians Crossing a Bridge* (Louvre),[7] of which Rubens had made a copy.[8]

The foreground action in the sketch and picture is made up by three distinct groups of Romans grappling with Sabine women. The chief difference, here, is in the central group, where there is a significant *pentimento* in no. 38. In the sketch, a Roman soldier drags at the dress of a Sabine and assists a colleague in abducting another Sabine woman. The pose of the Roman soldier is similar to that of Mars in the Louvre sketch of *Hercules and Minerva fighting Mars*.[9] Rubens abandoned this group in no. 38, and in its place introduced two Sabine women being led away by two Romans. His first idea was probably to show the Romans in the centre pushing the Sabine woman, but finally he adopted a pose, which made this couple a variation of the couple on the left in the Madrid/Waddesdon *Garden of Love*.[10] He retained the Sabine being pulled away by her dress, but moved her farther to the left, and altered her pose and the poses of her two abductors. He also abandoned the two crouching Sabines behind her, and introduced the crouching woman, whose pose recalls that of one of the victims in the

centre foreground of the Royal Collection S. *George and the Dragon* of
1629–30,[10a] altered the pose of the Roman with the drawn sword in
front of her, and abandoned two of the Roman foot soldiers on the right.

In the sketch, there are at least four fewer Sabine women and two
extra men on the dais, which is uncovered. The Sabine man with the
drawn sword was twice altered by Rubens, first so that he was directed
towards the Roman nearest him, and then so that he hid his sword
behind his back. The final pose was based on the preparatory drawing
in Madrid[11] for Tarquin in the Sanssouci *Death of Lucretia*.[12] In front
of the elderly Sabine woman on the dais, Rubens introduced the kneeling
Sabine woman, whose pose derives from an unused study in the
Gemeente Musea, Amsterdam,[13] of the young woman second on
the left in Rubens' preparatory drawing for Jegher's woodcut of the
Garden of Love.[14] Behind the elderly Sabine woman to the left, Rubens
reversed the pose of the Sabine woman clinging to the wall of the
building, and, to the right, introduced the Sabine woman looking down,
whose pose was based on that of S. Apollonia in the *Mystic Marriage of
S. Catherine* of 1628.[15] Finally, the Roman at the far end of the dais
grabs his own Sabine woman in no. 38; her pose is similar to that of the
mother on the steps in the Munich *Massacre of the Innocents*.[16]

The two motifs in the left and right foreground of the preparatory
sketch and the finished picture are suggested in a drawing at Copenhagen, which has been ascribed by Evers to the School of Rubens.[17]
This drawing is probably a copy after an earlier, lost composition by
Rubens,[18] dating from perhaps the second decade of the century. Evers
showed that the poses of the mounted Roman and attendant were taken
from a print by Enea Vico[19] (where in reverse) and which was thus
first used by Rubens in the Munich *Rape of the Daughters of Leucippus*.[20]
The pose of the abducted woman differs in all three instances. A preliminary idea, adopted for this abducted Sabine in the preparatory
sketch and the finished picture, is to be found on a sheet of studies of
Hippodameia abducted by the Centaur[21] where it is in reverse; and it
could well derive from Michelangelo.[22]

The central motif in the Copenhagen drawing is of a Sabine woman,
with her arms above her head, borne off by a Roman. This motif appears,
in reverse, in the centre of another painted sketch of the *Rape of the
Sabines*,[23] which only may be by Rubens and a little earlier than no. 38.
The sketch also shows a group of Sabine women with their menfolk
and abductors placed on a dais, and the Sabine being dragged by
her dress;[24] her Roman abductor is closer in pose and costume to that
in no. 38 than to that in the preparatory sketch.

Romulus is not clearly identifiable in any of Rubens's earlier renderings of the subject; his position in the preparatory sketch and no. 38
is reminiscent of that of James I in *James I destining his son Charles to be
King of England and Scotland* (Banqueting Hall).[25]

No. 38 is peculiar, because, while the men are in 'classical' costume,
the women appear to be in contemporary, Flemish dress.[26] It may
be that Rubens intended no. 38 to be in some way a classical counter-

part to the concept of the *Garden of Love*. Certainly the faces of the
two Sabine women and the three Romans in the foreground are
comparable to those in his renderings of the *Garden of Love*. Rooses[27]
has suggested that the Sabine woman, who looks down on the dais, is a
portrait of Rubens' second wife, Helena Fourment;[28] there seems to be
some justification for the view that she was the model, despite Held's
doubts concerning such an identification in a related drawing.[29] But
there is no sound evidence with which to advance an interpretation of
no. 38 based on an identification of some of the participants.[30] The
model for the elderly Sabine woman on the dais was also used by
Rubens for S. Elizabeth in several renderings of the *Holy Family*.[31]

SKETCHES: Private collection, oil on panel, $11\frac{3}{8} \times 23\frac{3}{4}$ ($0\cdot29 \times 0\cdot60$);[32] perhaps related to no. 38: Baron Willebroek sale, Brussels, 25 June, 1785 (5), 1 p.
10 pouces × 2 p. 9 pouces ($= ca.$ $23\frac{3}{8} \times 35\frac{1}{8}$ ($0\cdot594 \times 0\cdot892$);[33] Sir Joshua Reynolds
(†) sale, Christie's, 7 ($= 16$) March ($= $3rd day), 1795 (5).

ENGRAVINGS: By Pierre-François Martenasie, 1769 (in reverse);[34] Anon;[35]
T. Bolton; J. Stuart; J. Outrim; J. Burnet (acquatint).

COPIES: Hermitage, canvas, $70\frac{3}{4} \times 97\frac{3}{4}$ ($1\cdot795 \times 2\cdot48$);[36] Cook collection, canvas,
$67\frac{1}{2} \times 92$ ($1\cdot715 \times 2\cdot337$);[37] Frau Baronin de Benda, Rome, 1935, panel(?),
22×28 ($0\cdot56 \times 0\cdot711$); Anon. sale, Christie's, 16 October, 1959 (31), canvas,
$31\frac{1}{2} \times 42$ ($0\cdot80 \times 1\cdot068$); Anon. sale, Sotheby's, 23 July, 1958 (177), canvas, 67×89
($1\cdot702 \times 2\cdot26$);[38] of the central foreground group, coll. Mrs. E. Jones, 1938.

DERIVATION: William Etty, City Art Gallery, York.[39]

PROVENANCE: Perhaps painted for the man dressed as a Roman in the centre
foreground.[40] Possibly recorded in the inventory of Guilliam van Hamme, Antwerp, († 24 May, 1668).[41] Probably coll. the Duc. de Richelieu, Paris, 1676.[42]
By 1746[43] coll. Goubouw ($= $Georges-Alexandre Goubau († 1761)), Antwerp; passed to his brother-in-law, M. Bosschaert, Antwerp, by 1763;[44]
by 1776[45] coll. Madame la Douarière Bosschaert († 17 March, 1785); for
sale by her two sons by 15 May, 1785;[46] perhaps sold to the Duc d'Orléans
(† 1792).[47] Coll. F. L. J. Laborde-Méréville (1761–1802), by whom brought to
England *ca.* 1793 and sold in London after 1797/8.[48] Sold by Charles(?) Birch(?)
to J. J. Angerstein by 19 February, 1803, for 1600 gns.;[49] lent to the B. I. for
copying, 1807;[50] purchased with the Angerstein Collection, 1824; exh. *An
Exhibition of Cleaned Pictures*, The National Gallery, 1947/8 (no. 51).

REPRODUCTION: *National Gallery Illustrations, Continental Schools* (*excluding
Italian*), 1950, p. 302.

REFERENCES: *General*: J. Smith, *A Catalogue Raisonné* etc., 1830, II, no. 815;
M. Rooses, *L'Œuvre de P. P. Rubens*, 1890, IV, no. 803; R. Oldenbourg,
Rubens, K. der K., [1921], p. 379.

In text: (1) See the *Catalogue of An Exhibition of Cleaned Pictures*, The
National Gallery, 1947, no. 51. (2) See *Plutarch's Lives*, with an introduction by
A. H. Clough, I, 1921, pp. 39–40. (3) As noted by de Piles, although he was mistaken in believing the architectural style to be Ionic, see B. Teyssèdre, *Gazette
des Beaux-Arts*, 1963, p. 251. (4) According to Philippe Rubens, *The Rape of the
Sabines*, then in the collection of the Duc de Richelieu and which is probably
no. 38 (see under *Provenance*), was painted 'entre les années trente et quarante',
see his *Mémoire* of 1676, addressed to de Piles, printed in the *Rubens Bulletijn*,
1883, II, p. 166. See also Rooses and Oldenbourg, cited under *General
References*, who date it *ca.* 1635. The handling has much in common with that of
the sketches for the decorations of the Torre de la Parada (see under no. 2598),

for this reason a date early in the second half of the 1630's seems most acceptable. (5) See under *Sketches*; perhaps to be identified with the 'Teeckeningen van Rubens, wesende den Rooff vande Sabienen, op panneel', coll. Victor Wolfoet († 23 October, 1652), see J. Denucé, *Inventories of the Art-Collections in Antwerp* etc., 1932, p. 140; probably in the Tower sale, Sotheby's, 7 December, 1927 (75) as by van Dyck bt. Stephens. Burchard Documentation records it in an S. J. Mak van Waay sale, 7 April, 1936 (69); sold by F. Rozendaal to Louis Richter, London, 1939; exh. Höckammer's, Helsinki, 1939 (29); Galerie Fischer sale, Lucerne, 25/29 June, 1957 (2640), rep. in the catalogue; London Art Market 1959(?). Mr. Michael Jaffé has kindly told the compiler that he is to discuss and reproduce this sketch in the July number of *The Burlington Magazine* for 1969. (6) See the catalogue of *Olieverfschetsen van Rubens*, Rotterdam, 1953, no. 93, and rep. fig. 82. (7) See F. Hartt, *Giulio Romano*, 1, 1958, no. 262, and rep., II, fig. 477. (8) See F. Lugt, *Musée du Louvre, Inventaire Général des Dessins des Écoles du Nord*, II, 1949, no. 1081. (9) *Ibid.*, no. 1014; see also J. S. Held, *Rubens Selected Drawings*, I, 1959, no. 66, p. 124, who dates it *ca.* 1635–37. (10) Rep. by Oldenbourg, *op. cit.*, pp. 348 and 349. (10a) *Ibid.*, p. 311. (11) See *Real Academia de Bellas Artes de San Fernando, Catálogo de la Sala de Dibujos*, 1941, no. 284 (and fig.), crayon, $12\frac{9}{16} \times 10\frac{3}{16}$ ($0\cdot32 \times 0\cdot259$). This drawing is also discussed and reproduced by J. Müller Hofstede, *Wallraf-Richartz-Jahrbuch*, 1965, pp. 298–9, fig. 214. (12) See E. Henschel-Simon, *Die Gemälde und Skulpturen in die Bildergalerie von Sanssouci*, 1930, p. 27, no. 89 (and rep.), by whom dated 1608–10. In the painting, Tarquin's head is turned slightly to the left, while in the drawing the young man looks straight down as does the Sabine. None of the three heads agree. The drapery of the Sabine is similar to Tarquin's. (13) Black, red and white crayon, $17\frac{7}{8} \times 18\frac{9}{16}$ ($0\cdot403 \times 0\cdot472$), see L. Burchard and R. A. d'Hulst, *Rubens Drawings*, 1963, p. 287 under no. 184. These authors note that Rubens used the same pose in the *Entombment* engraved by H. Witdoeck (F. van den Wijngaert, *Inventaris van der Rubeniaansche Prentkunst*, 1940, no. 761) which was probably published after Rubens's death. Held *op. cit.*, no. 121, suggests that Rubens first evolved this pose in the *Massacre of the Innocents* (Brussels, Musées Royaux des Beaux-Arts, no. 682), which appears at most to be a copy after Rubens. Burchard/d'Hulst, catalogue of *Tekeningen van P. P. Rubens*, Antwerp, 1956, no. 131, point out that a similar pose occurs in the Cleveland drawing of *Tomyris with the Head of Cyrus*, which is reproduced by J. S. Held, *The Burlington Magazine*, 1956, p. 124, fig. 32. (14) See Burchard/d'Hulst, *Rubens Drawings* etc., no. 180, where they propose a date *ca.* 1632/33. Held, *Selected Rubens Drawings* etc., no. 121, dates the Gemeente Musea drawing, 1632–5. (15) Rep. by Oldenbourg, *op. cit.*, p. 305. Burchard/d'Hulst, catalogue of *Tekeningen van P. P. Rubens* etc., no. 109 (and *Rubens Drawings* etc., no. 148); and J. S. Held, *Selected Rubens Drawings* etc., no. 113, suggest that it was the study for this saint in the altarpiece (Florence, Uffizi, no. 1043E, black and red chalk, $16\frac{1}{4} \times 11\frac{1}{4}$ ($0\cdot414 \times 0\cdot286$)) which was used by Rubens for the Sabine woman in no. 38; but this drawing does not include the left arm which appears in the finished picture and the painted sketches for it. The hair style, but not the costume, in no. 38 follows the drawing. Held discounts the theory, advanced by M. Freeman, *Master Draughtsmen*, 1932, no. 2 that the drawing is a portrait of Helena Fourment. (16) Rep. by Oldenbourg, *op. cit.*, p. 378. A study for this and another mother in the picture, is in the Louvre, black and red chalk, $18\frac{7}{8} \times 11\frac{1}{4}$ ($0\cdot48 \times 0\cdot29$), see Lugt, *op. cit.*, no. 1025; Held, *op. cit.*, no. 124; and Burchard/d'Hulst, *Rubens Drawings* etc., no. 203. Burchard/d'Hulst date the picture *ca.* 1635; Held dates the drawing to the same year. The former authors note that the same pose (for the upper part of the body) appears in the Hermitage sketch of *The Apotheosis of the Archduchess Isabella* (rep. Oldenbourg, *op. cit.*, p. 370) of *ca.* 1634. (17) See H. G. Evers, *Rubens und sein Werk*, 1944, p. 253 and fig. 265. He records that G. Falk ascribed it to W. Panneels, see *Kunstmuseets Aarschrift*, 1918, p. 77. (18) It has some stylistic affinities with the sheet at Princeton of *Cephalus lamenting the Death of Procris*, the *verso* of which has been dated 1614–1617 by Burchard/

d'Hulst, *op. cit.* no. 84, p. 141, who ascribe both sides of the sheet to Rubens. M. Jaffé, *The Burlington Magazine*, 1956, p. 321 ascribed the sheet to van Dyck and dated the *verso* 1617–20. (**19**) Evers, *op. cit.*, pp. 249 ff. and fig. 262. (**20**) Rep. by Oldenbourg, *op. cit.*, p. 131. (**21**) Ex. coll. Dr. L. Burchard, red chalk, $12\frac{3}{16} \times 18\frac{3}{8}$ (0·31 × 0·47), see Burchard/d'Hulst, *op. cit.*, no. 191. The pose occurs in the top left. The *verso* has studies for canvases, executed 1636–7, for the Torre de la Parada. (**22**) The pose is related to that of the centaur being dragged by the neck on the right of Michelangelo's *bas-relief*, Casa Buonarroti, Florence, of which Rubens made two copies, one being coll. F. Lugt, Paris. (**23**) Coll. Garfield Weston, panel, $21\frac{1}{2} \times 34$ (0·55 × 0·85); exh. R.A., 1953/4 (175) as ex colls. Prince Rubempré, 1765, M. Danoot, 1829, Buchanan, Alexander Baring (Lord Northbrook), Alfred, Lionel and Edmund de Rothschild. A derivative, panel, $24 \times 34\frac{1}{4}$ (0·61 × 0·83) was with Buttery, 1938 (ex coll. Gleyn Vivien). (**24**) Both motifs of a woman being dragged by her dress and a woman carried off with her arms above her head were drawn by van Dyck, on a sheet in the sketchbook at Chatsworth, p. 55v, see M. Jaffé, *Van Dyck's Antwerp Sketchbook*, II, 1966, p. 239. (**25**) The oil sketch for which is reproduced by Oldenbourg, *op. cit.*, p. 334. (**26**) For Rubens' treatment of antique armour, see H. D. Rodee, *The Art Bulletin*, 1967, pp. 223 ff. The women in no. 38 do not wear collars, and are naturally rather décolletées, but compare the costumes in Rubens' rendering of *The Garden of Love*. The Sabine women in the Duc de Richelieu's picture—probably no. 38, see below under *Provenance*—were described as 'Brasseuses de biere [*sic*]' and as 'grosses hostellieres de Bruxelles revetues de leurs habits de dimanche . . .' in two anonymous pamphlets published in Paris, of *ca.* 1676 and 12 April, 1676, for which see J. Thuillier, *Archives de l'Art Français*, 1968, pp. 178 & 190. (**27**) See under *General References*. (**28**) Compare Rubens' portrait of her at Munich (rep. by Oldenbourg, *op. cit.*, p. 328). (**29**) See note 15. Rubens would have known the Fourment family well before his marriage to Helena as her father's second wife (whom he married 22 September, 1619) was a sister of Rubens' first wife, Isabella Brant. (**30**) That Rubens intended some contemporary reference in no. 38, which is suggested by the costume, is corroborated by de Piles' statement that the Roman in the centre foreground 'est le portrait de celuy qui a fait faire le Tableau, et qui a desiré que la Sabine qu'il enleve fust aussi le portrait de sa femme', see B. Teyssèdre, *op. cit.*, p. 252. (**31**) See Oldenbourg, *op. cit.*, pp. 285, 338, 340, and 342. (**32**) See note 5. (**33**) See *Catalogue de Tableaux Vendus à Bruxelles depuis l'année 1773*, p. 234. The measurements correspond more with those of the Garfield Weston sketch, see note 23. A sketch ascribed to the 'Rubens School' was in an Anon. sale, Christie's, 7 March, 1840 (40). (**34**) As in the collection of Mme. Bosschaert. The entry for Martenasie in the *Biographie Nationale . . . de Belgique*, 1894/5, 43, col. 873, wrongly gives the date of the print as 1759. A portrait of Martenasie of 1762 by A. C. Lens in the Koninklijk Museum voor schone Kunsten, Antwerp, see the 1958 catalogue, no. 1091, shows Martenasie at work engraving no. 38. (**35**) In J. Young, *Catalogue of the . . . Collection of the late J. J. Angerstein Esq.*, 1823, no. 6; Rooses, cited under *General References*, refers to another anonymous print. (**36**) See *Musée de l'Ermitage, Département de l'Art Occidental, Catalogue des Peintures*, 1958, II, p. 94, no. 527. (**37**) See J. O. Kronig, *A Catalogue of the Paintings at Doughty House* etc., II, 1914, no. 343. (**38**) Perhaps identical with the Cook copy. (**39**) See Dennis Farr, *William Etty*, 1958, no. 301. (**40**) According to de Piles, see Teyssèdre, *loc. cit.* (**41**) See J. Denucé, *The Antwerp Art Galleries, Inventories of the Art-Collections in Antwerp* etc., 1932, p. 246. Van Hamme was a canon of the Onze Lieve Vrouwekerk, Antwerp (see Denucé, *loc. cit.*); Denucé, *Art-Export in the 17th Century in Antwerp, The Firm of Forchoudt* 1931, p. 11 and note, quotes from Le Pays, who visited Antwerp *ca.* 1660, *Pièces choisies des Œuvres de Monsieur*, II, 1681, p. 186, 'Monsieur L. B. . . . dit qu'il n'a jamais rien veu de si beaux que les Galeries. . . du Chanoine Vanam [*sic*] . . .' He was known as a collector already by 1644, see J. Denucé, *Na P. P. Rubens*, 1949, p. 18; G. P. Bellori, *Le Vite* etc., 1672, p. 259, also refers to his collection. (42) See de Piles, *Conversations sur la Connoissance de la Peinture* etc., 1677, which is reprinted by Teyssèdre, *op. cit.*, pp. 246 ff. De Piles' description is clearly that of no. 38 or a composition closely corresponding to it. Teyssèdre, pp. 243–5, shows that de Piles' description of the pictures owned by the Duc de Richelieu, which appeared in the *Conversations* was chronologically the first of his series of four descriptions. *The Rape of the Sabines* is not mentioned in the other three. De Piles' printing privilege for the *Conversations* was registered 20 July, 1676; but the description of the pictures which he gave was out of date by the time the book was published. According to de Piles, Richelieu acquired his first Rubens'[during the French invasion of the southern Netherlands, i.e. in 1667 or 1676/8; he had disposed of some of these before 1681, see the *Epistre* to his *Dissertation sur les Ouvrages des plus fameux Peintres*, [1681], pp. iv–v. His *Rape of the Sabines* had been criticized in two anonymous pamphlets, published in Paris, *ca.* 1676, see above, under note 26. It is noteworthy that the *Rape of the Sabines* owned by Richelieu was known to Philippe Rubens, who mentions it in his *Mémoire* of 1676, addressed to de Piles (see note 4). (43) Mariette records that when Louis XV was at Antwerp he made an offer for the *Rape of the Sabines* by Rubens, which was owned by M. Goubouw, see P. J. Mariette, *Abecedario*, ed. Ph. de Chennevières and A. de Montaiglon, 1853/54, II, p. 195. Louis XV entered Antwerp 4 June, 1746, see [Lévy] *Journal Historique de Regne de Louis XV*, II, 1766, p. 456. This M. Goubouw was Georges-Alexandre Goubau (1697–1760) Seigneur de Melsen, Mespelaer de Coudenhove; he and his brother († 1733) were the sons of Alexandre and Marie-Constance-Albertine (*née* Rubens, the great grand-daughter of Peeter Pauwel Rubens), see F. V. Goethals, *Dictionnaire Généalogique et Heraldique des Familles Nobles . . . de Belgique*, 1849, II, pp. 579–80. In 1725 Georges and his brother bought a house, the Maison de Maître, rue de l'Amman, Antwerp, from Jean Steffano, 'agent van Syne Carsche Majesteyt binnen de Nederland'; the price included those of the paintings in the house; Steffano himself had bought the house from the heirs of Henri-Ignace van Buren († *ca.* 1701), see *Recueil des Bulletins de la Propriété*, published by *L'Escaut d'Anvers*, 1890, pp. 42–43. (The compiler thanks Mr. C. van der Velde of the Rubenianum for drawing his attention to this publication). Mariette, *loc. cit.*, also noted a rumour that the 1st Duke of Marlborough (see under no. 1172) had made an offer for the picture. (44) See G. P. Mensaert, *Le Peintre Amateur*, etc., I, 1763, p. 260. Mariette, *loc. cit.*, also states that at the time of writing the picture was in the possession of M. Bosschaert. He was Jacques-Joseph Bosschaert, the brother of Isabelle-Madeleine Bosschaert († 1764) who was the widow of Georges-Alexandre Goubau, see Goethals, *op. cit.*, I, 1849, p. 431. Precisely how no. 38 passed into his collection is uncertain: Goubau's inheritance may have passed to his sister, Marie-Aldegonde, who died in 1761; her possessions were divided among her brother's children, see *Recueil des Bulletins* etc., *loc. cit.* However, Mariette, *loc. cit.*, records the sale of two pictures from the Goubau collection in 1764 (the year of his widow's death); but by this time no. 38 was already in the possession of Goubau's brother-in-law. (45) J. M. F. Michel, *Histoire de la Vie de Rubens*, 1771, pp. 336–7, records that in 1766, the Chevalier Verhulst made an offer for the picture which was rejected by 'la propriétaire [=Madame la Douairière Bosschart *sic*]'. She was *née* Isabelle-Claire Melyn, the widow of Jacques-Joseph Bosschaert, and died 17 March, 1785. It was seen in her collection in 1781 by Reynolds, see *A Journey to Flanders and Holland in the year MDCCLXXXI, The Complete Works of Sir Joshua Reynolds*, 1824, II, p. 245. Reynolds, indeed, made an unsuccessful offer to buy it in 1785, see W. T. Whitley, *Artists and their Friends in England, 1700–1799*, II, 1928, p. 54. (46) The *Recueil des Bulletins* etc., 1886, p. 118, records that five months after their mother's death, her two sons Jacques and Georges divided her inheritance. But Pilaer and Beeckmans wrote informing Thomas Harvey of Norwich, 15 May, 1785, 'depuis quelques semaines La Dame [Mme. Bosschaert] vient de mourir à la quelle appartenoit l'Enlevement [*sic*] des Sabines de Rubens, ce Tableau est presentment [*sic*] a [*sic*]

vendre de la main . . .' see ms. in the Rembrandt-Huis, Amsterdam. **(47)**
According to Mols, *Rubeniana*, Bibliothèque Royale, Brussels, ms. 5735,
referred to by Rooses, under *General References*. There is no record of no. 38
in any of the Orléans importation papers, published or unpublished, nor is it
mentioned in the 1787 guide to the Orléans collection. **(48)** See ms. notes
connected with Young's *Catalogue of the Angerstein Collection* (N.G. library),
p. 12 v.: '[The Rape of the Sabines] when Laborde sold his Orleans Collection
he reserved three pictures which he could not be persuaded to sell—this was one
of them—he brought it with him to this country—but became so reduced in
circumstances that he was obliged to dispose of it.' For Laborde-Méréville, see
F. Boyer, *Bulletin de la Société de l'Histoire de l'Art Français*, 1967, pp. 141 ff.;
he states, p. 145, that Laborde finally sold his pictures from the Orléans collection in 1798, and p. 146, mentions Laborde's collecting activities before 1791,
when he bought the French and Italian pictures from the Orléans collection.
Laborde's ownership of no. 38 is perhaps in itself added evidence that it did
not come from the Orléans collection, as his holdings from this source were
the Italian and French pictures. **(49)** Burchard Documentation; see the
ms. note on the Courtauld Institute copy of the Anon. [= Galpine] sale, Greenwood, 18 [= 19] February, 1803, p. 3: 'Mr. ——d that Mr. Birch sold 2 Pict^s. by
Rubens—The Rape the Sabines for 1600 gns. to Mr. Angerstein . . .'. The same
source is recorded as having sold the *Diana and her Nymphs* by Rubens to Sir
Simon Clarke, although this picture was probably in the George Hibbert and
Sir Simon Clarke sale, Christie's 15 May (= 2nd day), 1802 (71), having been
imported by Bryan from Amsterdam and sold by him Coxe, 18 May (= 2nd day),
1798 (42). Burchard could not give a precise reading of the seller's name. It is
in fact, probably, Birch; a C. Birch was dealing in 1798, when Farington records
a visit to him, see *Farington Diary*, typescript copy, British Museum, Print
Room, p. 1390. Birch was a buyer at the Hulse sale, 21–22 March, 1806, see
N. MacLaren, *National Gallery Catalogues, The Dutch School*, 1960, p. 85
under no. 822. He was probably the Charles Birch, whose collection was sold
at Christie's, 14 June, 1828. The pictures, according to the title page of the
catalogue, had been 'collected some years ago', and were from the Orléans and
Colonna collections. **(50)** See T. Smith, *Recollections of the British Institution*
etc., 1840, p. 40.

46 MINERVA PROTECTS PAX FROM MARS (PEACE & WAR)

Minerva drives away Mars, while Pax feeds Plutus; and two girls, one
of whom is crowned by Hymen, are offered the fruits of peace by a
satyr.

Oil on relined canvas, *ca.* $80\frac{1}{8} \times 117\frac{5}{16}$ ($2 \cdot 035 \times 2 \cdot 98$).

For the make up of the support, see Appendix I. The support
bears the collection mark of Charles I on the reverse.[1]

In fairly good condition. There are many scattered, small losses, but
none is of substantial consequence. The bottom edge is retouched. The
sky, curtain and airborne *putto* on the inner pieces of canvas are worn
and retouched; the face and armour of Mars, the straps of Hymen's
cloak, the feet and lower part of the dress of the younger girl and the
inner part of the tail of the leopard are also worn. The number '398', in
white paint below the edge of the skirt of the older girl, is an inventory
number (see below) and not autograph. Cleaned, 1940.

There are several *pentimenti*, some visible only in X-ray or infra-red photography: there is a suggestion, apparent in the infra-red photograph, that Mars' shield was first placed higher and more to the left, and that it was held more upright; X-radiographs show that the right hand of Hymen was higher; and that a left and a right hand grasping at the grapes, just above and to the left of the head of the *putto*, who offers an apple, have been suppressed. Further *pentimenti* are in the right foot of the *putto* who offers the apple, in the outline of the dress of the girl on the right and in Mars' right hand. A strand of vine from the cornucopia in front of the younger girl's dress has been suppressed, but now shows up light.

No. 46 has always been accepted as an autograph work by Rubens,[2] and there is no reason to doubt this attribution. There is also little scope for dispute concerning the date of execution. It was in the collection of Charles I,[3] and van der Doort in his catalogue of the king's collection, compiled *ca.* 1637–1640,[4] recorded that it was painted by Rubens when he was in England.[5] This statement is further substantiated by the fact that two preparatory drawings for no. 46 are on the reverse of drawings, also demonstrably made while Rubens was in England (see below).

Rubens was sent to England by Philip IV of Spain, as a secretary to the Spanish king's privy council in the Netherlands, to carry on peace negotiations between the two governments.[6] A state of war had existed between England and Spain following the collapse of the Spanish match in 1623 and the naval attack on Cadiz in 1625, in which year England signed an alliance with Denmark and the United Provinces, with whom Spain was once again at war after the expiry of the twelve years' truce in 1621. The peace negotiations had been set on foot by the Duke of Buckingham and the Abbé Scaglia (see no. 4889) in 1628; Rubens was early involved (following his previous efforts), and in the autumn of 1628 was sent to Madrid as the representative of the Infanta Isabella. He left Madrid for England on 29 April, 1629, and arrived in London on 5 June, having briefly visited Brussels and Antwerp.

Separate negotiations between Spain and the United Provinces were taking place at the same time, and Rubens' instructions were in the first place to offer a truce between England and Spain that was not to involve the United Provinces. He also had instructions, set out in general terms, to discuss an exchange of ambassadors to negotiate a peace treaty; to cover the main point of contention between the two governments, the Palatinate, Rubens could offer an undertaking that the Spanish king, the Emperor and the Duke of Bavaria would do what they could to satisfy English interests.[7]

It is probable that both Charles I (and the pro-Spanish faction at the English court, headed by the Lord Treasurer, Weston and Attorney General, Sir Francis Cottington) and the Infanta Isabella (and her advisers in the southern Netherlands among whom was Rubens) were more eager for a peace settlement than was the Spanish government. As Charles had already made known his wish for peace with Spain, he could not accept Rubens' offer of a truce; Rubens, however, and the pro-Spanish faction successfully overcame opposition, fanned by the French, Dutch and Venetian governments; and was able, on 2 July, to announce to the Spanish government that Charles intended to send Cottington as ambassador; on 18 August, he was able to inform Charles that Don Carlos Coloma had been nominated Spanish ambassador in return. Cottington left for Madrid early in November, and Coloma arrived in England on 7 January, 1630. The basis of the peace treaty was to be that of 1604. Charles' *Proclamation of Peace* with Spain is dated 5 December, 1630, Cottington having signed the treaty of peace in Madrid the previous month. Rubens stayed on in England for about two months after Coloma's arrival. He left for Antwerp on 23 March, 1630, having been knighted by Charles.

Evidence which can be derived from the support, from a sheet of sketches in the Boymans-van Beuningen Museum, published by Müller Hofstede,[8] and from two drawings modelled from the life preparatory to no. 46 (see below), makes it clear that no. 46 was executed in two, main stages. The main part of the design is rendered on the two central pieces of canvas, which are joined vertically; the outer pieces of canvas, which must all have been added at the same time, account for the Harpy, the lower part of the bodies in the foreground, the leopard, the two women and for most of the *putto* bearing the olive wreath and caduceus. Intermittent convex strains, visible in X-rays, along the outer edges of the two central pieces of canvas, suggest that these edges were at one stage attached to a stretcher. And it is thus likely that some of no. 46 was worked up before the stretcher was removed and before the support was enlarged all round. The lower edge of the two inner pieces of canvas reaches down to a line which can be drawn across the back of the *putto* just beneath the join of his wings to his back. That it was Rubens' first intention not to include the lower part of the bodies of the figures in the foreground is shown by a sketch of the children at the top of the sheet in the Boymans-van Beuningen Museum, where only the top part of the bodies of the children are considered. Further, when Rubens made drawings of the two girls (see below) they were only half length studies. The motif of the children is repeated at the bottom of the Boymans-van Beuningen sheet, which has been cut down all round.[9] The chief difference between the two sketches is the presence of a confused and illegible area of drawing on the right of the sketch at the top. The bottom sketch corresponds to the group in the picture, save for the pose of Plutus, and must therefore have been made after the sketch at the top.

However, both these sketches must have been made after Rubens had begun to work up the design on the two inner pieces of canvas of no. 46, and thus also after the execution of what may have been the *modello* for it, which Vertue recorded as having been in the sale of Lord Bellemont's (*sic?*) collection in 1721/31.[10] In both sketches the pose of Hymen is established; but the presence in no. 46 of a suppressed left and right hand grasping at the grapes, just above and to the left of the *putto* who offers an apple, suggests that Rubens' first idea was either to show this boy taking the grapes to offer them to one of the girls, or to include another *putto*, who was to reach out towards the grapes from behind Hymen's back.

The fact that the two sketches differ from each other and that the second corresponds in most respects to Rubens' final solution in no. 46, which itself had begun so very differently, suggests that the *modello* preceded the sketches. And although there is no proof that the picture, recorded by Vertue, was the *modello* for no. 46, our knowledge of Rubens' working procedures makes the existence of a *modello* probable. It is likely that his first ideas were sketched out on paper and then worked out fully in oils on panel. After the execution of the *modello* he would have made detailed drawings from the life of which there are extant, studies for the heads and top half of the bodies of the two girls,[11] and of Hymen,[12] Plutus and the *putto*.[13] The first three of these studies are on individual sheets; studies of the last two are on the same sheet. The same model was probably used for the studies of the head of Plutus (essayed in two poses) and of the *putto*. Also on this sheet is a study of the head of a boy, who does not occur in no. 46. This is further evidence that Rubens first considered including a third child on the right—and that the hands suppressed in no. 46 were to belong to a child with the physiognomy drawn on this sheet.

The evolution of no. 46 was thus probably as follows: (1) sketching of the central composition; (2) working it up as a *modello* and then execution of detail studies for the children; (3) a start made at transferring the composition onto the inner pieces of canvas; (4) altering the number and/or poses of the children and re-thinking their poses on the Boymans-van Beuningen sheet; (5) execution of the central part of the design of no. 46; (6) expansion of the support and composition all round.

As Müller Hofstede has pointed out, no. 46 is inspired by Tintoretto's picture in the Doge's Palace;[14] the direct source, however, may rather have been the print after it.[15] Rubens had already shown Minerva driving away the attendants of Mars in the Marie de Médicis series.[15a] The relationship of the two girls was probably inspired by that in the centre of Titian's *Ecce Homo*,[16] at the time in York House, London, as part of the collection of the recently assassinated Duke of Buckingham. Rubens made a free copy[17] after the central figures in this painting while he was in London; a free copy of the two riders on the right is on the *recto* of the sheet in the Boymans-van Beuningen Museum, discussed above. The pose of the top half of Pax is repeated in the Dulwich *Mars and Venus*,[18] perhaps executed at about the same time.

No precise, contemporary literary source for the allegory expressed in no. 46 has been found.[19] It may be no more than an elaboration of the rubric inserted by Agostino Carracci in his print after the Tintoretto: 'Sapientia Martem depellente Pax et Abundantia cogaudent'.[20] The helmeted woman and man in armour are clearly identifiable as Minerva and Mars; the woman to the right of Mars is probably a Fury and the figure in the sky is a Harpy.[21] The *putto* in the sky, follows in Minerva's wake, and is about to bestow a caduceus and olive wreath, symbols of

Prudence or Concord[22] and Peace.[23] The seated, nude woman is probably the goddess Pax, and the child drinking her milk, Plutus, the god of wealth.[24] Müller Hofstede[25] has suggested that the woman is Ceres; but although this goddess is intimately related with peace,[26] the absence of any sheaves of corn makes his proposal unlikely. Thus his identification of the boys as *genii* of Ceres, whose gestures he claims represent Concord, need not follow.[27] More likely is the identification of the boy with a torch as the god Hymen,[28] who crowns the girl to show that marriage can flourish in peace time.[29] The satyr is offering the two girls fruit from a cornucopia, a symbol of Plenty and Happiness.[30] Müller Hofstede's[31] suggestion that the satyr and two women behind him are part of the train of Bacchus is to some extent supported by the presence of the leopard; and the woman with the tambourine and castanets recalls a Bacchante. But a woman carrying a bowl of precious objects and jewels does not normally feature in Bacchus' train. The precise allegorical significance of these two figures remains obscure, but clearly they symbolize further benefits to be derived from peace.[32]

The usual title of no. 46, *Peace and War*, is clearly inadequate.[33] No. 46 is an allegory of Rubens' aims while he was in England and of the political situation of which he was part. Rubens was seeking to create peace; and it is noteworthy that the allegory is a moving rather than a static one.[34] No. 46 was thus entirely appropriate as a gift from Rubens to Charles I;[35] the presentation may well have taken place towards the end of Rubens' stay.

The theme of no. 46 is repeated in a picture at Munich,[36] which was probably executed in Rubens' studio, after a design by the master, made soon after his return to Antwerp. Hymen, the leopard and the two female figures on the left are absent. But it is perhaps significant that the motif of the children gathering the fruits of peace is farther removed from Mars. The drawing for Hymen's face was used for one of the *genii*; indeed the face in the Munich picture follows the drawing more precisely than does the face of Hymen in no. 46. The face of one of the girls in the Munich picture appears to be the same as that on the right in no. 46.[37]

Rooses observed that several of the models in no. 46 recur in a *Family Portrait* at Windsor, which includes the coat of arms of Sir Balthazar Gerbier (1592–1667), and which may at least in part be by Rubens.[38] Gerbier, when in the service of the Duke of Buckingham, had been in contact with Rubens from 1625; after Buckingham's death, he entered the service of Charles I, remaining Keeper of the Duke's collection; and Rubens lodged with him when he was in London.[39] The Windsor picture may not be a wholly reliable document,[40] and no facts have been published concerning the dates of birth of his children. He was married before 1627[41] and had three sons, George, James and Charles (of whom George was the eldest), and five daughters, Elizabeth, Susan, Mary, Catherine and Deborah (of whom Elizabeth was the eldest). It has been assumed,[42] probably correctly, that George served as the model for Hymen, Elizabeth for the girl on the right and Susan for the young girl; it is possible also that the model for Pax was Deborah Kip, Gerbier's wife. The identity of the models for Plutus and the *putto*, and for the unused drawing of the boy on the same sheet remains uncertain.

No. 46 may have inspired Luca Giordano's *Allegory of Peace* in the Palazzo Spinola, Genoa.[43]

SKETCH (?): Earl of Bellemont (sic?) sale, between 1721–31.[44]

DRAWINGS: 1) two studies for the group of children, Boymans-van Beuningen Museum, no. V.9, the top in red and the bottom in black crayon, $13\frac{11}{61} \times 10\frac{1}{4}$ (0.348×0.261);[45] 2) head and arms (half length) of the girl with a grape (Susan Gerbier?), Weimar, Staatliche Kunstsammlungen, black and red crayon heightened with white body colour, $14\frac{5}{16} \times 9\frac{5}{8}/\frac{3}{4}$ $(0.364 \times 0.244/248)$;[46] 3) head and shoulders (half length) of the girl on the right (Elizabeth Gerbier?), Hermitage, no. 5452, black and red crayon heightened with white and a few accents in ink, $13\frac{3}{16} \times 9\frac{1}{8}$ (0.335×0.232);[47] 4) head of Hymen (George Gerbier?), Vienna, Albertina, no. 450, black and red chalk with white heightening and some brush reworking, $11\frac{5}{16} \times 8\frac{5}{8}$ (0.288×0.22);[48] 5) heads of Plutus and of the *putto*, Berlin, Staatliche Museen, no. 3997, black and red chalk heightened with white, $13\frac{11}{16} \times 19\frac{1}{2}$ (0.348×0.496).[49]

ENGRAVINGS: By J. Heath, 1815;[50] W. Greatbatch, 1839;[51] T. Garner.[52]

COPIES: By W. M. Craig, watercolour, National Gallery of Scotland;[53] J. Binns, watercolour, 1838, coll. J. W. Dyson, 1895;[54] of the girl with the grape and Plutus by W. Holman Hunt, Anon. sale, Christie's, 3 April, 1964 (55).[55]

PROVENANCE: Presented by Rubens to Charles I (1600–49) between 1629–30;[56] recorded in the Bear Gallery, Whitehall, by Abraham van der Doort, *ca.* 1639;[57] in the custody of Henry Browne at Denmark House, when valued at £100 by the Trustees for Sale on 8 September, 1649;[58] exh. for sale at Somerset House (25), for £100, May, 1650;[59] bought by Edmund Harrison for £100, 23 October, 1651;[60] perhaps already sold by him 30 December, 1652.[61] Recorded in the Giorgio Doria[62] Palazzo, Genoa in 1768[63]; bought by Irvine acting for Buchanan & Champernowne for £1,100 (incl. 5% commission) between 25 September and 1 October, 1802;[64] ownership assumed by Buchanan, offered by him to the British Government in 1803;[65] offered by Buchanan to J. J. Angerstein;[66] bought from Buchanan by Lord Gower, later Marquis of Stafford and Duke of Sutherland, for £3,000 by 13 August, 1803[67]; exh. at the British Insitution, 1815 (70); presented by the Duke of Sutherland, 1828; exh. *An Exhibition of Cleaned Pictures* etc., The National Gallery, 1947/8 (no. 49).

REPRODUCTION: *National Gallery Illustrations, Continental Schools* (*excluding Italian*), 1950, p. 303.

REFERENCES: *General:* J. Smith, *A Catalogue Raisonné* etc., 1830, II, no. 561, M. Rooses, *L'Œuvre de P. P. Rubens*, 1890, IV, no. 825; R. Oldenbourg, *Rubens, K. der K.,* [1921], p. 312.

In text: (1) See note 64. (2) See, for instance, authors listed under *General References.* (3) See under *Provenance.* (4) See O. Millar, *The Walpole Society,* 1958–60, XXXVII, p. XX. (5) See note 57. (6) This episode in Rubens' career has been frequently described. The earliest, fullest account is given by W. Sanderson, *A Compleat History of the Life and Raigne of King Charles* etc., 1658, pp. 139–40; for the most recent discussions, see R. Magurn, *The Letters of Sir*

P. P. Rubens, 1955, pp. 283–290; and C. V. Wedgwood, *History Today*, 1960, pp. 809–820. The relevant documents are published in M. Rooses & Ch. Ruelens (†), *Correspondance de Rubens*, 1907, V, pp. 33 ff. According to Sir Thomas Roe, English ambassador extraordinary to Denmark, Sweden and Poland 'Rubens was a very able man, agile and full of resource, and marvellously well equipped to conduct any great affair. He [Roe] had known him before and they were familiar at Antwerp, where he had grown so rich by his profession that he appeared everywhere, not like a painter but a great cavalier with a very stately train of servants, horses, coaches, liveries and so forth. He [Roe] said, that [the] painter had two great advantages, great wealth and much astuteness. . . .', see the letter from the Venetian ambassador in the Netherlands of 14 July, 1629 in *Calendar of State Papers, Venetian*, ed. A. B. Hinds, 1919, XXII, p. 130. (7) See Philip IV's letter to the Infanta Isabella of 27 April, 1629 and Rubens' letter to Olivares of 22 July, 1629 in *Correspondance de Rubens* etc., pp. 33–35 and 119–125. Rubens' letter, justifying his actions, was in reply to a letter of complaint from Olivares of 2 July. Letters between London and Madrid seem to have taken about three weeks; therefore Olivares' letter of 2 July must have been prompted by a despatch from Rubens made very soon after his arrival in London and probably after his interview with Charles I at Greenwich on 6 June. A résumé of this interview is given by Barocci, secretary to Duke Charles Emmanuel of Savoy, in a despatch of 6 June (*Correspondance de Rubens* etc., pp. 57–60). The substance of the résumé accords well with the report sent by Rubens to Olivares of 30 June concerning a meeting with Charles at Greenwich on 25 June (*Correspondance de Rubens* etc., pp. 74–80). It seems likely either that the interviews of 6 and 25 June covered much the same ground, or that the date of the despatch and the date of the second interview, referred to, have not been correctly transcribed, and that the despatch was in fact Rubens' first, to which Olivares took exception in his letter of July 2. (8) See J. C. Müller Hofstede, *Bulletin, Museum Boymans-van Beuningen*, 1962, pp. 104 ff., and fig. 17; and also under *Drawings*. (9) The sheet is creased across the middle in the same way as is: 1) the sheet at Stockholm that bears studies for the Augustijnerkerk altarpiece and of the *S. George and the Dragon* (Royal Collection), executed by Rubens in England, see P. Bjurström, *The Art Quarterly*, 1955, pp. 31 ff.; 2) the sheet at Berlin, which bears another study for *S. George and the Dragon*, and on the reverse studies for the head of the *putto* and Plutus in no. 46 (see above and under *Drawings*). And it is likely that they come from the same sketchbook and originally measured the same. The Stockholm sheet measures 0·348 × 0·493, the Berlin sheet 0·348 × 0·493 and the Rotterdam sheet, 0·348 × 0·261. (10) See *Vertue Note Books*, II, *Walpole Society*, XX, 1931–32, p. 57: 'in a Sale. Ld. Bellemonts. a picture. in oil. about 3 f. 2 . . . representing ye emblem of peice & war. yᵉ design of Rubens containing several figures.' The entry was made between 1721–1731, see the introduction to the volume, p. IX. No Bellemont, or Bellomont, sale is recorded in Lugt. The Lord Bellemont referred to, was probably Richard (Coote) 4th Earl of Bellomont, who succeeded in 1708 and died 1766; in 1729 he sold several of the family estates, see G. E. C., *The Complete Peerage*, 1912, II, p. 108. (11) See G. Glück and F. M. Halberditzl, *Die Handzeichnungen von Peter Paul Rubens*, 1928, nos. 179 and 181, and under *Drawings*. (12) See Glück and Halberditzl, *op. cit.*, no. 180; and under *Drawings*. (13) See L. Burchard and R. A. d'Hulst, *Rubens Drawings*, 1963, no. 146 *verso*; and under *Drawings*. (14) Reproduced by Müller Hofstede, *op. cit.*, fig. 19; and also, for instance, by H. Tietze, *Tintoretto* etc., 1948, no. 225. The connection between no. 46 and O. van Veen's *Allegory of Youth*, proposed by H. G. Evers, *Peter Paul Rubens*, trans. by K. Ruyssinck, 1946, note 163, and by Müller Hofstede, *op. cit.*, p. 110 and note 52 is no more than slight. (15) See A. Bartsch, *Le Peintre Graveur*, XVIII, 1818, p. 105, no. 118. (15A) Rep. by Oldenbourg, cited under *General References*, p. 254. (16) See O. Fischel, *Tizian, K. der K.*, p. 118; and Müller Hofstede, *op. cit.*, fig. 13. (17) See Müller-Hofstede, *op. cit.*, p. 103 ff. and fig. 16. J. S. Held, *Rubens Selected Drawings*, 1959, no. 167, is not convinced about Rubens' authorship of the drawing, and

RUBENS 123

thinks that the reworking in ink was done 'when Rubens did not have the
original by Titian before his eyes'. (18) Rep. in R. Oldenbourg, *Rubens, K. der
K.*, [1921], p. 330 left. The pose of Venus, apart from the left arm, nearly
corresponds to that of the woman in Dürer's print of the *Penance of S. John
Chrysostom*, rep. in F. Hollstein, *German Engravings Etchings & Woodcuts
etc.*, VII, ed. K. G. Boon & R. W. Scheller, p. 44. (19) C. V. Wedgwood, *The
King's Peace, 1637–1641*, 1956 (reprint), p. 62, notes a connection between no. 46
and Shirley's masque *The Triumph of Peace*, performed in 1633. (20) Ridolfi's
explanation of the Tintoretto may also be pertinent: '. . . Marte vien cacciato da
Minerva, mentre la Pace e l'Abbondanza insieme festeggiano. Minerva è quì
intesa per la sapienza di quella Republica [Venice] nel tenere le guerre lontane
dallo stato, da che ne nasce la felicità de' suddite, e ne cagiona l'amore verso il
Prencipe', see *Le Maraviglie dell'Arte . . . Descritte da Carlo Ridolfi*, ed. D. von
Hadeln, 1924, II, p. 43. (21) For renderings of the three Furies and the Harpies,
see V. Cartari, *Imagini* etc., 1626, pp. 241 and 244. (22) For the olive wreath
as a symbol of Prudence, see Rubens' explanation of the frontispiece he designed
for *Legatus Frederici de Marselaer equitis* etc., 1656, printed by Rooses, *op. cit.*,
1892,V, pp. 99 ff., note 1 (p. 100): '. . . Corona oleagina . . . huic Dea [Minerva]
peculiaris, & Themistocli olim, in publico Græciæ conventu, cum elogio Pru-
dentiæ decreta; for the olive wreath as a symbol of concord, see Cartari, *op. cit.*,
p. 262. (23) 'Caduceus Pacis symbolum est', see Rubens' explanation in Rooses,
loc. cit. (24) See Cartari, *op. cit.*, p. 264, who refers to Pausanias' description of
the statue of the Goddess Pax in Athens; and H. G. Evers, *op. cit.*, p. 190. (25)
Op. cit., p. 110. (26) See Cartari, *loc. cit.* (27) For the various meanings attached
to the symbol of a lit torch see G. de Tervarent, *Attributs et Symboles dans l'Art
Profane* etc., 1959, col. 182. (28) As indeed suggested by the National Gallery
catalogues from 1838–45. For 'antique' renderings of Hymen, see Cartari, *op.
cit.*, p. 171: 'Questi [Himeneo] da gli antichi fu fatto in forma di bel giouane
coronato di diversi fiori, & di verde perfa, che teneua una facella accesa nella
destra mano, & nel sinistra haveva quel velo rosso, ò giallo che foffe, col quale si
coprivano il capo . . . le nuove spose. . . .'. In the 1626 edition he is shown,
p. 170, with both hands holding lit torches; in the 1580 edition, opp. p. 198, and
the 1624 edition, p. 144, he is shown with the torch in his right hand and holding
the bridal veil in his left hand. It should be noted that Rubens here depicts
Hymen offering the crown of flowers, with the red veil on his own head. The god
was earlier depicted by Rubens, holding the train of Marie de Médicis in
The Marriage of Marie de Médicis by Proxy (Louvre), rep. Oldenbourg, *op. cit.*
p. 247. (29) Perhaps echoing the sentiment expressed by Erasmus: 'In time of
peace (none otherwise than as if the lusty springtime should show and shine in
men's businesses) . . . maidens are luckily married . . .', see Erasmus, *Against
War*, trans. J. W. Mackail, 1907, pp. 26–27. (30) The cornucopia was also,
among others, the attribute of Bacchus, of Public Good and Peace, see Tervarent,
op. cit., cols. 116 ff.; Rooses, *loc. cit.*, thought this figure was Pan. (31) *Op. cit.*,
p. 110. (32) They were identified as Wealth and Joy by Rooses, *op. cit.*, IV,
no. 825, who follows R. N. Wornum, *Descriptive and Historical Catalogue of the
Pictures in the National Gallery*, 1858, p. 189, and subsequent Gallery catalogues.
Cornucopias with fruit, crowns and sceptres were included by Rubens
in his frontispiece for *Legatus Frederici de Marselaer* etc., to represent 'bona
commoda e Legationibus speranda', see Rooses, cited in note 22. (33) As
pointed out by the author of the text in *The National Gallery of Pictures by the
Great Masters*, [1838], no. 31. (34) Peace, it might be added, was only achieved
after Rubens left England and after he had executed no. 46. (35) See van der
Doort, cited in note 57. It is difficult to accept Miss Wedgwood's, *loc. cit.*, thesis
that no. 46 was commissioned of Rubens by Charles I, in view of van der Doort's
statement. (36) Oldenbourg, *op. cit.*, p. 313. (37) She seems slightly older in the
Munich picture. (38) See Rooses, *loc. cit.*, For the Windsor picture see the
Catalogue of the Exhibition of the King's Pictures, Royal Academy, 1946/7, no.
103. Jaffé considers that the group portrait, coll. Colonel Fremantle, mentioned
in the R.A. catalogue, which shows only the mother, baby and the three children

nearest her is the original, see M. Jaffé, *The Burlington Magazine*, 1965, p. 381, no. 146. (**39**) For the best account of Gerbier's life see Hugh Ross Williamson, *Four Stuart Portraits*, 1949, pp. 26 ff.; see also the D. N. B. and the *Biographie Nationale . . . de Belgique*. The Venetian Ambassador, writing on 8 June, 1629, stated that Rubens was lodged with Gerbier, see *Calendar of State Papers, Venetian* etc., p. 84. A Privy Seal warrant of payment to Gerbier for his expenses, incurred while entertaining Rubens and his entourage for the period 7 December, 1629 to 22 February, 1630, is printed by W. Noël Sainsbury, *Original and Unpublished Papers illustrative of the life of . . . Rubens*, 1859, p. 146. Gerbier spent Christmas of 1629 at his house in Bethnal Green, see *Calendar of State Papers, Domestic, 1629–1631*, ed. J. Bruce, 1860, p. 121–2, where, it can thus be assumed, did Rubens and his party. Williamson, *op. cit.*, pp. 33–4, discusses where Rubens lodged with Gerbier in London; see also on this subject E. Croft-Murray, *The Burlington Magazine*, 1947, pp. 90–93. (**40**) It was probably painted in three stages, the composition of the Fremantle picture representing the first; then were added Gerbier and the two children mounting the steps and finally the section on the right, which includes the three children, see the R.A. catalogue, *loc. cit.* The last stage must have been added in, or after, 1638 when Gerbier was knighted (for which, see Sainsbury, *op. cit.*, p. 318), and was thus entitled to the coat of arms which corresponds to that on his engraved portrait of 1653, reproduced by Williamson, *op. cit.*, opp. p. 26. (**41**) See M. G. de Boer, *Oud-Holland*, 1903, p. 135, note 3. (**42**) See for instance, Williamson, *op. cit.*, p. 34. It should be pointed out, however, that while the girl with the grape certainly recurs in the Windsor picture, both the boy and the elder girl look slightly different. In the Windsor portrait, they have hooked noses; the boy, indeed is closer to Rubens' drawing for Hymen (see above and under *Drawings*) than to Hymen in no. 46, which tends to support his identification as George Gerbier. (**43**) See O. Ferrari and G. Scavizzi, *Luca Giordano*, II, 1966, p. 38 and rep., III, fig. 565. As these authors point out, it is related to Giordano's picture *Rubens painting the Allegory of Peace* in the Prado (their cat., II, p. 37 and rep. III, pl. 62). This shows Rubens at work on a small picture showing a figure of Peace in the same pose as in the Spinola picture and repeated on the right (in reverse) in the Prado picture. (**44**) See note 10. (**45**) Published by J. Müller Hofstede, see above under note 8. Further differences between the sketches and no. 46 are 1) Hymen's right arm is held higher and 2) Plutus seems to lie on Pax's lap in a pose similar to that of Christ in the Prado *Holy Family with Saints*, rep. by Oldenbourg, *op. cit.*, p. 345. (**46**) See Glück and Halberditzl, *op. cit.*, no. 179; and Burchard and d'Hulst, *op. cit.*, no. 172. The drawing was obviously made from the life preparatory to no. 46; the girl's right hand is empty. There are slight differences in costume and hair style; in the painting the head is bent further down and inclined to the left, the right hand is held higher and drapery covers the left hand and wrist. (**47**) See Glück and Halberditzl *op. cit.*, no. 181; J. S. Held, *Rubens Selected Drawings*, 1959, no. 112; and Burchard and d'Hulst, *Rubens Drawings*, 1963, no. 173. The drawing was obviously preparatory to no. 46; there are slight differences between the drawing and no. 46 in the hairstyle and costume. Held, *loc. cit.*, thinks that the girl looks older in the drawing than in the painting, but this is not the case as her body in no. 46 is equally developed. (**48**) See Glück and Halberditzl, *op. cit.*, no. 180. The drawing was obviously made preparatory to no. 46; the nose is not hooked in the painting, and the hair is shorter on the right. (**49**) See Burchard and d'Hulst, *op. cit.*, no. 146 *verso*. The *recto* bears a study for Rubens' *S. George and the Dragon* (Royal Collection, Oldenbourg, *op. cit.*, p. 311) also executed in England. Burchard's earlier view was that the heads on the *verso* were studies for the angels in the Prado *Allegory of Divine Love* (Oldenbourg, *op. cit.*, p. 296); but Burchard and d'Hulst, *loc. cit.*, rightly consider the sheet to be preparatory to no. 46. Plutus' head was essayed twice; Rubens followed the bottom drawing in the painting, although including an ear. The head of the *putto* is turned less to the right in the painting. The sheet also contains a study of a boy's head facing left in profile, that was not used in no. 46 (see above). (**50**) After W. M.

Craig in W. Y. Ottley, *Engravings of the Most Noble The Marquis of Stafford's Collection* etc., III, 1818, [no. 10]. (51) Rep. by M. Rooses, *L'Œuvre de P. P. Rubens*, 1890, IV, pl. 262. (52) In *The National Gallery of Pictures by the Great Masters*, I, [1838], no. 31. (53) 17 × 24¾ (0·432 × 0·629) see *Catalogue, National Gallery of Scotland, Edinburgh*, 1946, 50th ed., p. 117 and note 51. (54) *Ca.* 14 × 24 (0·355 × 0·609) letter in Gallery archives. (55) Canvas, 20¼ × 16 (0·514 × 0·406) ex coll. Diana Holman Hunt. (56) See note 57. (57) *Abraham van der Doort's Catalogue of the Collections of Charles I*, ed. with an introduction by O. Millar, *Walpole Society*, XXXVII, 1958–60, pp. 2 and 4: 'In the Beare Gallorie at | this present remaines the 35 *ju M* | pictures followeinge vizt: . . . [no.] 13 Done by Sr Peet^r Paule Rubins Item A Picture . . . of an Emblin wherein the differrencs | and ensuencees betweene peace and warrs is Shewed | which Sr Peeter Paule Rubins when he was here | in England did paint and *Was* presented by him to *ju* | *M. Wij* Conteys Some 9 ffigures.' See also *A Catalogue & Description of King Charles the First's Collection etc. Transcribed and prepared for the press by Vertue*, 1757, p. 86. (58) *Pictures Statues Plate and Effects of King Charles I*, Public Record Office, L.R. 2. 124, f. 4 *recto*, and *verso*. The list was signed by the Trustees for Sale on 13 September, 1649. That the picture was at Denmark House is suggested by the fact that a previous list of effects in Browne's custody, *ibid.*, f. 2, *verso* was noted there. The list, first referred to, is printed by H. G. Hewlett, *The Nineteenth Century*, August 1890, pp. 211 ff.; no. 46 is listed on p. 213. (59) This information was communicated to Mazarin by his ambassador in England, see G.-J. de Cosnac, *Les Richesses du Palais Mazarin*, 1885, p. 414 (appendix). (60) See *Inventory of the Effects of Charles I, 1649–52*, B.M., Harley MSS. 4898, f. 99 *verso*. Edmund Harrison 'and others in a Dividend' had bought goods to the value of £4,994 7s. od. by this date, which sum is not recorded as having been paid, see *ibid.*, f. 366 *recto*. (61) It was not noted by Richard Symonds when he saw Harrison's pictures at this date, see G. Redford, *Art Sales* etc., I, 1888, p. 17. (62) This is probably Giorgio Doria, 1st Count of Montaldeo, born 26 April, 1723; he was succeeded by Ambrogio Doria, see V. Spreti *et al.*, *Enciclopedia Storico Nobiliare Italiana*, 1929, p. 625. The date when no. 46 was acquired by the Doria family is not known; H. Mireur, *Dictionnaire des Ventes d'Art*, 6, 1912, p. 350 thus records a sale of 1745: 'Charles I. Les bienfaits de la paix: 2.500 fr.' This sale (?) has not been traced. The inventory number 398 on no. 46 may be a Doria inventory number. (63) [Giacomo Brusco] *Description des Beautés de Gènes* etc., 1768, p. 90, wher· called *The Family of Rubens*; see also C. Ratti, *Instruzione di quanto puo' verdersi di piu bello in Genova* etc., 1780, pp. 278–9. (64) Irvine described the transaction in his letters of 25 September, 1802, and 1 October, 1802 to Buchanan, which are printed in W. Buchanan, *Memoirs of Painting*, II, 1824, pp. 101–108. He states, p. 108, that 'It is known in Genoa by the name of Rubens's family . . . it is in the collection of George Doria.' It was Buchanan who on relining the picture found the Royal cipher on the original canvas, and who thus identified it with the picture in Charles I's collection (see Buchanan, *op. cit.*, pp. 108–9). (65) See Buchanan, *op. cit.*, pp. 109–110. Buchanan assumed full ownership after 8 March, 1803, see Buchanan, *op. cit.*, p. 124. For the date of the offer to the British Government, see p. 392. (66) See Buchanan, *op. cit.*, p. 110. (67) See Irvine's letter of this date, in W. T. Whitley, *Art in England 1800–1820*, 1928, p. 61; see also John Britton, *Catalogue Raisonné of the Pictures belonging to the Most Honourable The Marquis of Stafford, in the Gallery of Cleveland House*, 1808, no. 137; W. Y. Ottley, *Engravings of the Most Noble The Marquis of Stafford's Collection of Pictures in London* etc., III, 1818, no. 10 and pp. 71–2; and C. M. Westmacott, *British Galleries of Paintings & Sculpture*, 1824, p. 197, no. 137.

57 S. BAVO ABOUT TO RECEIVE THE MONASTIC HABIT AT GHENT

In the centre, S. Bavo is received by SS. Amand and Floribert on the steps of S. Peter's, Ghent, while a cleric holds a Benedictine habit for him. Beneath, S. Bavo's wealth is distributed to the poor. On the left-hand wing, three female witnesses, probably S. Bavo's relations, SS. Gertrude and Begga, and possibly his daughter, S. Agletrude (on the right). On the right-hand wing, Kings Clothar and Dagobert dispute with a herald from the Emperor Mauritius, who proclaims a sealed edict.

Oil on oak, left-hand support, *ca.* $42\frac{5}{16} \times 16\frac{3}{16}$ ($1 \cdot 076 \times 0 \cdot 411$), central support, *ca.* $42 \times 32\frac{5}{16}$ ($1 \cdot 067 \times 0 \cdot 821$), right-hand support, *ca.* $42\frac{5}{16} \times 16\frac{1}{16}$ ($1 \cdot 076 \times 0 \cdot 408$). The right-hand support is painted up to the edge at the top and to the right; there are irregular traces of a border on the inner edge, and a border at the bottom of $\frac{3}{8}$ ($0 \cdot 01$). The central support is painted up to a border of $\frac{3}{8}$ ($0 \cdot 01$) at the top; there are traces of a border on the other edges. The left-hand support is painted up to the right-hand and top edges; there is a border *ca.* $\frac{3}{8}$ ($0 \cdot 01$) at the bottom, and irregular traces of a border on the left-hand edge. There are small additions to the bottom of the left-hand support, the bottom of the central support and top of the right-hand support. For the make up of the supports, which are cradled, see Appendix I.

In fairly good condition. There are several vertical cracks in the supports, and many small, retouched losses along them; there are many other small losses also for the most part retouched. None is of serious consequence; but the profile of King Dagobert (the mounted figure on the far right), the hand of King Clothar, which rests on the baton, are in varying degrees modern reconstructions. Other areas, mostly the darks in the figures, have been retouched, namely: 1) in the left-hand wing, the small figures in the open corridor and the dress of the kneeling woman; 2) in the central compartment, the darks in the foreground group on the left, the feet of S. Bavo, the lower halves of the two courtiers and the dog in the foreground,[1] and the horse and rider on the extreme right;[2] 3) in the right-hand wing, the lower half of the inner edge. Seguier recorded that early in the nineteenth century a Mr. Howard 'put one of the heads in entirely' near, he thought, the inner edge of the left-hand wing.[3] This head is probably that of the youthful courtier directly to the right of the lady in the wimple.[4] All the supports have been cut down to varying extents and some of the edges have been planed, but not so much as to amputate the design.[5] Cleaned, 1939–40.[6]

There are a number of *pentimenti*, for the most part visible in X-ray or infra-red photography. On the left-hand wing, the right arm of the boy looking round the pillar was first shorter, and the right leg of the youthful courtier beneath him was first placed more to the right. On the central compartment, the deacon's face (behind S. Amand) has been altered; what may have been the head and hand of a beggar, just to the left of the treasurer distributing money, has been suppressed and the cloak of the treasurer has been widened; the child immediately to the right of the young mother originally lay with its head underneath her arm, with its right leg in deeper perspective and its body twisted to raise an arm to the right of her right arm; the arm of the child beside it was also more to the right; the topmost flight of steps, between S. Amand and S. Bavo, was first suggested in deeper perspective (this is probably the *pentimento* of a later hand (see below)); the hat of the courtier in the right foreground was first circular; and the last section of the balustrade was first set in deeper perspective (this is probably the *pentimento* of a later hand (see below)). On the right-hand wing, the reins of the horse on the right have been altered, and the arch had a steeper curve (this is probably the *pentimento* of a later hand (see below)).

In the eighteenth century the subject of no. 57 was thought to be *S. Ambrose absolving the Emperor Theodosius*;[7] by 1806 it was identified as *S. Bavo received by the Church*,[8] which is more correct than that normally used—*The Conversion of S. Bavo*.[9] The main literary source for no. 57 is Molanus' biography of S. Bavo which appeared in 1583.[10] This version of the life of the Saint is not now accepted; from at least 1703,[11] a more trustworthy, early biography was considered to be that by Abbot Theodoric, published in 1581 by Surius,[12] which differs considerably. According to Molanus, Bavo was the son of Agilulfus, Count of Hasbania; his cousin was Caroloman whose son was Pippin, Duke of Brabant. S. Bavo's first career was that of soldier, fighting under Emperor Mauritius and the Kings of France and Austrasia. Then, having been indoctrinated by S. Amand, Bishop of Tongres, 'soli Christo crucifixo militare statuit.' He had, however, to go against an edict of the Emperor Mauritius which forebade any of his soldiers to become monks. In this he was supported by Kings Clothar and Dagobert, and inspired by Gregory the Great. Bavo distributed his money and treasure among the poor. He made his penance in the monastery of S. Peter's, Ghent, where he died in 631. SS. Gertrude and Begga were inspired to lead purer lives by his example.

Thus the left-hand wing probably shows SS. Gertrude and Begga being inspired by S. Bavo's decision to enter the monastery; the central compartment shows the saint being welcomed by S. Amand and S. Floribert on the steps of the monastery, and about to receive a monk's habit, while his treasure is distributed to the poor; the right-hand wing shows Kings Clothar and Dagobert disputing with the herald from the Emperor who attempts to proclaim the edict forbidding S. Bavo to become a monk.

Molanus gives an account of S. Amand's life and his work in the Low Countries;[13] he was responsible for converting the people of Ghent to christianity and there built the monastery of S. Bavo. Molanus also gives an account of S. Floribert, S. Amand's disciple, and abbot of the monastery founded by him at Ghent; he there explains that the monastery was originally called S. Peter's.[14] The monastic rule was that of S. Benedict.[15] SS. Gertrude and Begga, who are probably the two nobly dressed witnesses on the left, were the daughters of S. Pippin, Duke of Brabant, and S. Itta. S. Gertrude is probably the woman removing her necklace; for on the death of her father, *ca.* 647, she entered the nunnery at Nivelles, founded by S. Itta, and later became its abbess; she died in 664.[16] Her sister, S. Begga, married Ansigisus, from whom Charlemagne was descended; after her husband's death, she too, founded a nunnery in which she died.[17] The two kings, Clothar and Dagobert, who dispute with the herald from the Emperor Mauritius, on the right-hand wing, were father and son.[18] According to Molanus, Clothar (II), King of the Franks, ruled for 44 years and died in 630.[19] Dagobert, his son, was made king of Austrasia in 622, succeeded his father as King of the Franks,[20] and died, according to Molanus, in 646.[21]

Molanus' biography of S. Bavo does not refer to his marriage, or to his daughter, S. Agletrude, both discussed by Theodoric.[22] According to Theodoric, S. Agletrude, brought up by God-fearing parents, was early 'a Deo praeelecta'. S. Bavo was moved to become a monk after the death of his wife and by the influence of his daughter. It is possible that S. Agletrude is included on the left-hand wing; for it is tempting to identify her as the retiring young woman in the wimple, whose hands are clasped in prayer.

Rubens' authorship of no. 57 has been doubted: Irvine, in 1806,[23] thought that only the middle part was autograph; more recently, Glück[24] and Winkler[25] have rejected the whole. Evers[26] has, in turn, rightly dismissed Glück's alternative proposal of Frans Francken II, and re-asserted the traditional and generally accepted view that no. 57 is the work of Rubens. Such a view is basically correct—the great majority of the figures and the general design being clearly authentic.

However, no. 57 has been subjected to the attention of a restorer, or restorers, who strove to convert it into a more finished looking oil sketch, mainly by strengthening and/or inventing parts of the archi-tecture.[27] The only area of architecture which is certainly as Rubens left it, is the right-hand banister, the column above it and the section of balustrade immediately to its right. Other parts of the archi-tecture on the central compartment are to varying extents retouched or repainted, notably the steps. None of the paint above the foreground figures on the right-hand wing appears to be autograph; the coarsely rendered architecture is executed in blue/grey (probably designed to match the greys on the central compartment when obscured by dirt and/or yellow varnish), which extends onto the right-hand section of the balustrade on the central compartment. The architecture above and below this section of the balustrade has also been retouched. The blue/grey paint is not much evident in the architecture at the top of the left-hand wing; but this area is also repainted to the extent that Rubens' hand is nowhere certainly discernible except in the figures, themselves probably retouched. It is noteworthy that at the last cleaning, How-ard's restorations, done in the early nineteenth century, were not removed[28]; but whether he alone was responsible for the retouching and repainting is not clear. Nor is it clear to what extent Rubens' intentions were followed. The *pentimenti* in the architecture (noted above) are probably the *pentimenti* of the restorer, but nevertheless the steps and balustrade on the central compartment more or less accord with the free copy, ascribed to Frans Francken II (1581–1642) (see below), which suggests that this area was early amplified. It is by no means sure that the architecture in the top half of both wings reflects Rubens' intentions.

Rooses[29] identified no. 57 with the 'dissegno colorito' mentioned by Rubens in a memorandum to the Archduke Albert of 1614, in which he asks him to intercede on his behalf in the matter of the commission for the high altarpiece of S. Bavo's cathedral, Ghent.[30] In this memorandum, Rubens says that the Archduke 'Ben si deve ricordar ... d'haver veduto duoi anni fà un dissegno colorito fatto di mia mano per servicio della tavola colle porte del altar maggior del duomo di Gandt ...'. Glück[31] has unreasonably questioned whether a finished (sic) oil sketch such as no. 57 could be referred to as a 'dissegno colorito'. In this context may be mentioned a record of the contract of 1620 between Rubens and the Reverend Father Jacques Tirinus for the pictures for the ceiling of the Jesuit Church.[32] Rubens there undertook to make 'de teekeninge van alle de voors. 39 Stucken ... met syn eygen handt in 't cleyn ...'. These 'teekeninge' may be reasonably identified with the coloured oil sketches recorded in the literature.[33] Further, it would have been exceptional for Rubens to set out his proposals for a prospective patron in the form of a drawing rather than an oil sketch (see no. 1865).

The identification of no. 57 with the 'dissegno colorito', mentioned by Rubens, requires dating it in or before 1612. Both Oldenbourg[34] and more recently Müller Hofstede[35] have questioned this. Oldenbourg's dating of 1622–23 is clearly too late as Müller Hofstede points out; however, he considers before 1612 to be too early, and compares no. 57 with the sketches for the altarpiece of the Jesuit Church, normally dated ca. 1619.[36] There are clear points of similarity between these sketches and no. 57; but the handling of no. 57 is different and acceptable for a date ca. 1611–12,[37] as Jaffé[38] has also recently recognized.

Such being the case, there is no reason to doubt the thesis put forward by Rooses[39] concerning the history of the commission to Rubens for the high altarpiece of S. Bavo's cathedral, Ghent. The early history of the commission is, indeed, related by Rubens in his memorandum referred to above. Rubens says there that the 'dissegno colorito' was commissioned by Bishop Maes and that it was approved by the chapter. Maes took possession of the episcopal see of Ghent on 5 November, 1610 and died on 21 May, 1612. It is possible that Rubens, armed with Maes' approval, had already gone ahead with executing the altarpiece.[40] According to Rubens, his successor, Henri van der Burch, who was confirmed as Bishop in October 1612 and transferred to the Archbishopric of Cambrai in 1616, countermanded the commission, and decided on a high altar made of sculpture. The contract between the bishop and the sculptors, de Nole, is dated 10 February, 1615, that is after Rubens' letter to the Archduke and the latter's (unsuccessful) intercession on his behalf. The altar was not completed by 1620, when van der Burch's successor, Jacques Boonen, made further changes to the commission.

Further changes were in turn made by his successor, Antoine Triest, who took possession of the see on 15 March, 1622, and who by 10 February, 1623 had decided to include a painting as the centrepiece. This painting was commissioned from Rubens, and payment for it was acknowledged on his behalf on 24 September, 1624.

The painting 'S. Bavo received by the Church',[41] still in S. Bavo's, but no longer on the high altar, differs considerably from no. 57, which was clearly not the modello for it.[42] But no. 57 was probably still to hand to provide the starting point for Rubens' new ideas, necessitated by the fact that only a single picture, rather than a triptych, was now required. Thus the general idea of the central compartment is repeated with considerable modifications: the three female saints from the left-hand wing were included, but no reference was made to the right-hand wing, perhaps because it was considered to have been historically inaccurate.[43]

Evers has suggested that Rubens executed the central compartment without the two wings in mind.[44] His comments (made without having seen no. 57 after cleaning) about the architecture of the wings can be discounted; but in further justification of his view, he brought forward the free copy ascribed by Glück to Frans Francken II, which is only of the central compartment (see below), and the fact that he considered the horse, seen in profile on the right, to be more freely executed than the rest. No records have been published concerning Rubens' discussions with Bishop Maes; but it is highly improbable that Rubens would have altered the modello for the reasons given by Evers. Although it is possible that Rubens executed the wings after completing the central compartment, the time gap was probably insignificant and is not relevant to the history of the commission.

Evers[45] has drawn attention to Rubens' effort to make the costumes historically correct, and compared them to those in the Vienna SS. Pippin and Begga.[46] Rubens' interest in 'medieval' costume is also demonstrated by the Costume Book in the British Museum;[47] none of the costumes there corresponds exactly with any in no. 57. Nevertheless the figure on page 1 of the Costume Book, inscribed 'Boudewin le debonnart Conte | de Flandre obyt ano⁰ 1067', wears a similar head-band to King Dagobert; the woman on page 21, second from the left on the bottom row, has a similar wimple to S. Agletrude's(?); and the woman, bottom centre on page 31, wears a costume similar to those worn by SS. Gertrude and Begga.

The composition of no. 57 may have been inspired by a type similar to that in Andrea Vicentino's Alessius Comnenus asking for the help of the Crusaders at Zara in the Sala del Maggior Consiglio of the Doge's Palace. Jaffé[48] has pointed out that the beggar on the extreme left derives from Raphael's cartoon of the Healing of the Lame. The poses of King Dagobert and of his horse appear, with slight variation and in reverse, in Elsheimer's Stoning of S. Stephen at Edinburgh.[49]

In his memorandum to the Archduke Albert of 1614, Rubens stated that 'quel dissegno di Gandt [=no. 57] esser la più bella cosa che facessi giamai in vita'.[50]

Some of the figures, especially in the foreground, in Jordaens' *Christ blessing little Children* (Copenhagen), may have been inspired by those in no. 57.

DRAWING: Held[51] has associated the *verso of* the Berlin *Bathsheba receiving David's Letter* with no. 57; but the connection is not close.

COPIES: By R. P. Bonington;[52] Arnold van Buren sale, A. Mak (Amsterdam), 26 May, 1925 (113);[53] Anon. sale, Christie's, 3 February, 1961 (178);[54] of the central compartment, ascribed to Frans Francken II;[55] of the figures in the right of the central compartment and in the foreground of the right-hand wing, British Museum;[56] by Fragonard of the foreground figures in the central compartment as far as the courtier with the staff, and of those in the inner half of the left-hand wing, British Museum.[57]

PROVENANCE: Commissioned by Charles Maes, Bishop of Ghent († 1612);[58] probably still in Rubens' studio *ca.* 1623.[59] Recorded in the Carrega Palace, Genoa, apparently for the first time in 1758;[60] bought from Giovan Battista (?) (b. 1760)[61] Carrega by Irvine acting for Holwell-Carr via Buchanan, 7 September, 1805;[62] lent by Holwell-Carr to the British Institution for copying, 1806;[63] exh. B.I. 1815, (116); Holwell-Carr Bequest, 1831; lent to the National Gallery of Scotland, 1921–1932; exh. *An Exhibition of Cleaned Pictures*, The National Gallery 1947/8 (no. 48).

REPRODUCTION: *National Gallery Illustrations, Continental Schools (excluding Italian)*, 1958, p. 306, top.

REFERENCES: *General:* J. Smith, *A Catalogue Raisonné* etc., II, 1830, no. 868; M. Rooses, *L'Œuvre de P. P. Rubens*, II, 1888, nos. 396 & 396 *bis*; Gregory Martin, *The Burlington Magazine*, 1968, pp. 434 ff.

In text: (1) Judging from X-radiographs, it appears that the under-modelling of the courtier on the far right has been scraped away; the under-modelling of the dog is very confused. But the poses of this foreground group correspond to those in a seventeenth-century copy in the British Museum, see below and note 56. (2) This horseman, his horse and the face behind him do not appear in the seventeenth-century copy, referred to in note 1; the horseman and his horse do appear with slight variations in the copy ascribed to Frans Francken II, see below and note 55; although the horseman and his horse are much retouched, there is thus the probability that they are not a later invention. (3) See the catalogue of *An Exhibition of Cleaned Pictures (1936–1947)*, The National Gallery, 1947 (revised ed.), no. 48. The Mr. Howard is perhaps to be identified with the painter, Henry Howard (1769–1847). (4) The catalogue cited in note 3, *loc. cit.*, suggested that Seguier misremembered where Howard made this restoration, and considered that he had put in the head of King Clothar (on the right-hand wing). The paint here is above suspicion, whereas the face of the youthful courtier is rendered in thick, opaque paint. It is possible that the head behind the horseman on the extreme right of the inner compartment is also a later invention. (5) Both the seventeenth-century copy (see below and note 56) and Fragonard's copy (see below and note 57) show more at the bottom. The presence of the borders along the bottom edges of the three supports suggests that the copies are inaccurate in this respect. The seventeenth-century copy in the British Museum shows more of the face on the far right of the right-hand support; and it is possible that a little has been lost at this edge. (6) When reconstituted as a triptych, see the catalogue cited in note 3. (7) See note 60. (8) See note 63. (9) First used in the 1854 National Gallery catalogue by R. N. Wornum. (10) See Ioannes Molanus, *Indiculus Sanctorum Belgii*, pp. 14–16, included in his edition of Usuardus' *Martyrology* of 1583. (11) It formed the basis of J. Mabillon's account of S. Bavo's conversion in *Annales Ordinis S. Benedicti*, I, 1703, pp. 398–399, where a later date for his conversion is given. For a full review of the early biographies of the saint, and a proper historically based

biography, see J. Stiltingus *et al.*, *Acta Sanctorum Octobris*, I, 1859 (ed.), pp. 205 ff.
(12) See *De Vitis Sanctorum ab Aloysio Lipomano ... nunc primum A. F.
Laurentio Surio ... emendatis & auctis*, V, 1581, pp. 166 (*verso*) ff. **(13)** *Op. cit.*,
pp. 9 (*verso*) ff. **(14)** *Op. cit.*, pp. 29 ff. **(15)** See Mabillon, *loc. cit.* **(16)** For the life
of S. Gertrude, see Molanus, *op. cit.*, p. 31 (*verso*) ff. **(17)** For the life of S. Begga,
see Molanus, *op. cit.*, pp. 16 ff. **(18)** See Les Petits Bollandistes, *Vie des Saints*
etc., II, 1882, p. 610. **(19)** *Op. cit.*, p. 82. **(20)** See note 18. **(21)** *Op. cit.*, p. 82
(*verso*). **(22)** His biography is also reprinted in Stiltingus *et al.*, *Acta
Sanctorum Octobris*, I, 1859 (ed.), pp. 241 ff. **(23)** See W. Buchanan,
Memoirs of Painting etc., II, 1824, p. 177. **(24)** His essay of 1918 reprinted by G. Glück, *Rubens, van Dyck und ihr Kreis*, 1933, pp. 198 ff.
(25) His view is referred to by Z. v M. in *ibid.*, p. 403. **(26)** See H. G. Evers,
Rubens und sein Werk, I, 1944, pp. 144 ff. **(27)** See Martin, *loc. cit.* **(28)** See the
catalogue of *An Exhibition of Cleaned Pictures, 1936–1947*, The National
Gallery, 1947 (revised ed.), p. 48. **(29)** See under *General References*. **(30)** See
M. Rooses and Ch. Ruelens (†), *Correspondance de Rubens*, 1898, II, pp. 69–
70. **(31)** *Op. cit.*, pp. 201–202. **(32)** Printed by M. Rooses, *L'Œuvre de P. P.
Rubens*, 1886, I, pp. 43 ff. **(33)** See, for instance, L. van Puyvelde, *Les Esquisses de
Rubens*, 1940, nos. 30–40 (one of which is a preliminary grisaille). **(34)** See R.
Oldenbourg, *Rubens, K. der K.*, [1921], p. 272. **(35)** See J. Müller Hofstede,
Pantheon, 1967, no. 1, pp. 41–2, note 9. **(36)** See *Katalog der Gemäldegalerie
Kunsthistorisches Museum, Vienna*, II, 1958, nos. 310 and 312; there is no
reason why these sketches should not be earlier, see Martin, *op. cit.*, note 6,
and F. Baudouin in *Miscellanea Jozef Duverger*, I, 1968, pp. 301 ff. **(37)** The
handling is comparable to that in the Dulwich *modelli*, executed *ca.* 1610,
for the outsides of the wings of the *Erection of the Cross* for S. Walburgis, for
which see M. Rooses, *L'Œuvre de P. P. Rubens*, 1888, II, nos. 278–279 *bis*.
(38) See *Studies in Renaissance and Baroque Art presented to Anthony Blunt*,
1967, p. 104. **(39)** See under *General References*. **(40)** His work in this respect
could be identified with the two pictures mentioned by Rooses, *op. cit.*, 1888,
II, under no. 396 *bis*, as having been destroyed, or partly destroyed
in 1659, when in the collection of Canon van Halmale, Antwerp: 'een
... groot stuck van Rubbens [*sic*] ... 't gene oytbeldt de bekeeringhe van
sinte Bavo. ... Een stuck van Rubbens [*sic*], uytbellende het leven van sinte
Bavo ...', see A. Pinchart, *Archives des Sciences* etc., 1863, I, p. 187. But there
is no proof for this; indeed the apparent non-existence of any studies by Rubens
from the life, made preparatory to the execution of the altarpiece in order to
amplify the poses sketched in no. 57, makes this unlikely; thus the relevance
of these two pictures to the commission for the high altarpiece of Ghent cathedral remains obscure. **(41)** Rep. in Oldenbourg, *op. cit.*, p. 275. **(42)** Oldenbourg, *op. cit.*, p. 466, note p. 272, considered no. 57 to be the *modello* for the
altarpiece, and advanced its date, because he felt that Rubens would not have
used a *modello* made over ten years previously. The actual *modello* may have
been the sketch in Bryan's Exhibition, 27 ff. April, 1795 (13). Rooses, *loc. cit.*,
refers to the sketch in the Baron de B[eurnonville] sale, Drouot, 21/22 May, 1883
(85) which came from the M. A. Febure sale, Drouot, 17–20 April, 1882 (81).
The measurements were, $26\frac{3}{4} \times 18\frac{1}{2}$ (0·68 × 0·47); and it is probably identical
with that in the J. Friedlander sale, Sotheby's, 27 October, 1943 (109), as the
measurements correspond. Judging from a photograph, this appears to be a copy
of a sketch (?). The same, or another similar copy, called by Burchard Documentation 'a copy of a lost sketch for the altarpiece', was in the collection of
Jacques Guerlain, Paris, 1953, and, in 1957, in the Tomas Harris collection.
(43) See Martin, *loc. cit.* **(44)** *Loc. cit.* **(45)** *Ibid.* **(46)** Rep. in Oldenbourg, *op. cit.*,
p. 106. **(47)** See A. M. Hind, *Catalogue of Drawings by Dutch and Flemish
Artists ... in the British Museum*, 1923, II, pp. 36 ff., under no. 119. **(48)** *Loc. cit.*
(49) See I. Jost, *The Burlington Magazine*, 1966, fig. 1. **(50)** See note 30. **(51)** See
J. S. Held, *Rubens Selected Drawings*, I, 1959, p. 108 under no. 32. **(52)** Oil on
panel, $10\frac{1}{2} \times 16$ (0·267 × 0·406); Anon. sale, Sotheby, 20 November, 1968 (55);
see also the Hon. A. Shirley, *Bonington*, 1940, pl. 62, and page 97, by whom

dated 1825. (53) Oil on panel, $17\frac{15}{16} \times 23\frac{11}{16}$ (0·455 × 0·605); Burchard Documentation. (54) 31 × 48 (0·787 × 1·22). (55) See G. Glück, *Rubens, van Dyck und ihr Kreis*, 1933, pp. 198 ff., and fig. 113, when (1918) in coll. Count Karl Lanckoronski, Vienna. (56) Pen and black and grey ink, and grey wash, heightened with white, $11\frac{3}{8} \times 15\frac{13}{16}$ (0·29 × 0·40); British Museum, Department of Prints & Drawings inv. no. 1950, 5.8.1; presented by C. Briscoe, ex coll. J. McGowan († 1803), see F. Lugt, *Les Marques des Collections* etc., 1921, no. 1496. This copy is of the seventeenth century; the figures correspond, but the copy lacks the horseman, horse and face, behind him, on the far right of the inner compartment, of which the first two appear in Francken's copy. The drawing shows more at the bottom and was probably made before the supports were joined together as there is a gap in the relevant area. The compiler thanks Mr. J. Gere for his help in discussing the drawing and dating it. (57) Pencil, $7\frac{1}{2} \times 11\frac{1}{4}$ (0·19 × 0·286), British Museum, Department of Prints and Drawings, inv. no. 1936, 5.9.57. Inscribed in Fragonard's hand: 'Rubens. Palais Corregha [sic]. Gesnes'. The drawing was probably made in 1761, as another from the same series, of the Château Multado, belonging to Doge Lomellini, is so dated. The copy shows that the supports had already been joined together by this time; it shows more at the bottom and less skirt at the back of the beggar woman, seen in profile on the left. Either because of a dirty varnish or because of a capricious delicacy, Fragonard invented a wall between the courtiers and the beggars. The compiler thanks Mr. J. Gere for his help in discussing this drawing (58) See above. (59) On the assumption that no. 57 was the starting point for Rubens' idea for the altarpiece commissioned by Bishop Triest, see above. (60) See C. N. Cochin, *Voyage d'Italie*, III, 1758, pp. 262–3: 'Palais Caregha [sic] ... Un petit tableau de Rubens ... C'est une grande composition: il paroît que le sujet est un Evêque qui reçoit un Empereur'; see also [Giacomo Brusco] *Description des Beautés de Gènes* etc., 1768, pp. 91–92; and C. G. Ratti, *Instruzione di quanto puo' vedersi ... in Genova* etc., 1780, pp. 279–281: 'Palazzo del Giacomo Filippo Carrega. ... Un quadro sorprendente del *Rubens* in piccole figure, e d'una gran finitezza. Mostra S. Ambrogio, che assolve l'Imperador Teodosio'. This Giacomo Filippo Carrega was born in 1714 and was succeeded by Giovan Battista Carrega, born 1760, see V. Spreti *et al.*, *Enciclopedia Storico-Nobiliare Italiana*, 1929, II, pp. 340–1. (61) See note 60. (62) See W. Buchanan, *Memoirs of Painting* etc., II, 1824, pp. 168–170. (63) See W. T. Whitley, *Art in England 1800–1820*, 1928, p. 111.

59 THE BRAZEN SERPENT

Moses, with Eleazar beside him, summons the people of Israel, who are being attacked by serpents, to look at the brazen serpent which he has set up on a pole.

Oil on relined canvas, $77\frac{3}{8} \times 104\frac{1}{2}$ (1·864 × 2·645). The canvas edge is concealed by binding paper. The support is made up of a single piece of canvas.

Probably in fairly good condition; an unevenly discoloured varnish obscures the paint, and makes estimates concerning condition difficult. Small losses and some wearing in the darks are likely. Partly cleaned, 1946.[1]

There are several *pentimenti*, some visible to the naked eye: the thumb of the female Israelite in black was longer; the child to the left first looked out of the picture and rested its chin on its right hand, while its left arm lay along the thigh of the woman in front of it; the outline of the old woman's hand was higher; the face of an old man has been painted out just beneath the baby held aloft by the woman, who was first depicted in a white head dress.

The subject is taken from Numbers, XXI, 6–9.

No. 59 was generally accepted as an autograph work by Rubens,[2] until ascribed to the School of Rubens in the 1947 catalogue of *An Exhibition of Cleaned Pictures*.[3] The level of quality remains to some extent obscured by the uneven and discoloured varnish, not removed in 1946. The view of the 1947 catalogue may be thought to be too harsh, for Rubens' hand is evident in many areas, and there is no doubt that the design is his. Nevertheless it must be admitted that the nude foreground figures are not well integrated with the others, and even if no. 59 were cleaned, the colours and finish might not be as brilliant as should be expected. No. 59 has been dated in the 1630's (see below), and its short-comings are evident if it is compared with the *Ildefonso Altarpiece*, the King's College *Adoration of the Kings* and the Brussels *Ascent to Calvary* —three large works whose dates of execution range from *ca.* 1630 to 1637.[4] Thus it seems likely that the design of no. 59 was blocked in by a studio hand working from a *modello* by the master,[5] and that a good deal, but not all, of the composition was then to some extent worked up by Rubens.

The difficulty in defining the precise status of no. 59, is paralleled by a difficulty in dating it. It is evidently a work of the 1630's; Rooses[6] and Rosenberg[7] have proposed the first years of the second half of the decade, while Oldenbourg[8] and Burchard/d'Hulst[9] have dated it *ca.* 1630. The latter date seems too early: the handling of the head of Moses is comparable with that of the attendant in the far left of the *Adoration of the Kings* (King's College Chapel) completed in 1634.[10] The handling of the woman in black deserves comparison with that of the Sabine woman in the centre of no. 38 *q.v.*—a work probably executed early in the second half of the 1630's. It is possible that the execution of no. 59 was spread over a number of years; but a date in the second half of the 1630's seems most acceptable for its execution.

The composition of no. 59 may be a development of the idea expressed in the foreground of the sketch at Berlin of *Henri IV subjugating the City of Paris*,[11] executed *ca.* 1628–31 as a *modello* for one of the series to decorate the Henri IV gallery in the Luxembourg Palace.[12] It may thus owe something to Antonio Veneziano's print after Raphael of *The Gathering of Manna*.[13] Several poses may also ultimately derive from other artists: Moses presumably derives from the apostle in Raphael's cartoon of *The Death of Ananias*;[14] the Israelite in the background, who plunges forward, is a quotation from Michelangelo,[15] whose *Tityus* was probably the source for the Israelite lying in the centre foreground;[16] the Israelite, in armour, was probably inspired by the top part of *Laöcoön*.[17] Three motifs are connected with ideas, elaborated by Rubens himself: the woman holding up a child is repeated from his earlier *Brazen Serpent* (coll. Count Seilern);[18] the pose of the woman struggling with a serpent is connected with the idea for a seated Dejanira in a sketch in the Louvre;[19] while the pose of the woman looking at the

Israelite on the ground recalls that of the woman second from the left in *The Garden of Love* (Prado).[20]

The model for the woman in black may well have been Rubens' second wife, Helena;[21] that of the child in front of her could have been Frans, born in 1633—his eldest son by Helena.[22] The model for the old woman occurs frequently in Rubens' œuvre; that of the old man in the top right-hand corner occurs in the earlier *Christ with the penitent Sinners* (Munich),[23] while the woman holding up the baby seems to be the same as that in the Albertina drawing, which Burchard/d'Hulst[24] consider was a study for a female saint intended for the centre compartment of the *Ildefonso Altarpiece.*

SKETCH (?): Ex coll. the Earl of Derby, Knowsley Hall, panel, 24 × 33 (0·61 × 0·838);[25] the following sketches are perhaps to be connected with no. 59: Anon. sale, Amsterdam, 13 April, 1695 (7);[26] Anon. sale, The Hague, 15 July, 1749 (1);[27] Queen of Spain and Anon. sale, Stewarts (London), 15 April, 1813 (86).[28]

ENGRAVINGS: Schelte à Bolswert (in reverse) first published by G. Hendricx;[29] Corneel Galle II;[30] F. Ragot;[31] A. Gobert;[32] M. Aubert, 1725;[33] 2 Anon.[34]

COPIES:[35] Potsdam, Sanssouci;[36] Gateshead, Shipley Art Gallery;[37] Sacramento, California, E. B. Croker Art Gallery; Coll. Madame Xavier de Pret, Antwerp, ca. 1888;[38] coll. L. Birtschansky, Paris, 1946;[39] coll. Baron T. Gabriel, Stockholm, 1947;[40] coll. Panducci, Florence 1950; Anon. sale, Brussels, 4/5 May, 1956 (105) as by T. van Thulden;[41] Anon. sale, Sotheby's, 16 May, 1962 (65);[42] Anon. sale, Christie's, 8 February, 1963 (81);[43] coll. Govers, Eindhoven, 1963;[44] in reverse, Lord Doverdale sale, Sotheby's, 8 November, 1950 (106);[45] a reduced copy or version appears on the wall in N.G. no. 844, by C. Netscher.[46]

PROVENANCE: Coll. Lorenzo Marana (1735–1809), Genoa,[47] from whom bought by Andrew Wilson for 17,500 lire on 27 March, 1805;[48] Andrew Wilson sale, Coxe, 6 May, 1807 (36) bt. in at £1,260.[49] With Buchanan, 1808.[50] William Champion sale, Phillips, 23 March 1810 (47) sold for £1,000.[51] Coll., J. Graves, 1815, when exh. at the B.I. (7). Coll. T. B. H. Owen by 1824;[52] exh. for sale by J. B. Bulkeley Owen, at George Yates' Gallery, London, 1837,[53] where bought by the National Gallery; exh. *An Exhibition of Cleaned Pictures,* The National Gallery, 1947 (no. 57).

REPRODUCTION: *National Gallery Illustrations, Continental Schools (excluding Italian),* 1950, p. 304.

REFERENCES: *General:* J. Smith, *A Catalogue Raisonné,* 1830, II, no. 769; M. Rooses, *L'Œuvre de P. P. Rubens,* 1886, I, no. 112; R. Oldenbourg, *Rubens, K. der K.,* [1921], p. 315.

In text: (1) See the catalogue of *An Exhibition of Cleaned Pictures,* The National Gallery, 1947/8 (57). (2) See for instance the authors listed under *General References.* (3) See note 1. (4) See Oldenbourg, *op. cit.,* pp. 325, 419. The Kings College *Adoration of the Magi* is illustrated in the catalogue of the Duke of Westminster sale, Sotheby's, 24 June, 1959. (5) This *modello* is not known to exist; see under *Sketch*(?). (6) See under *General References.* (7) A. Rosenberg, *Rubens, K. der K.,* 1905, p. 390. (8) See under *General References.* (9) See L. Burchard and R. A. d'Hulst, *Rubens Drawings,* 1963, p. 33, under no. 15. (10) See Rooses, *op. cit.,* 1886, I, no. 176. (11) See Oldenbourg, *op. cit.,* p 318. (12) For the most recent discussion of this commission, see I. Jost, *Netherlands Yearbook for History of Art,* 1964, pp. 175 ff. (13) See M. Jaffé, *Van Dyck's Antwerp Sketchbook,* I, 1966, fig. LXXXIX. (14) See G. Gronau, *Raffael, K. der K.,* 1923,

p. 140. For a recent discussion of Rubens' interest in the Raphael cartoons, see J. Müller Hofstede, *Wallraf Richartz Jahrbuch*, 1965, pp. 274 ff. (15) As pointed out by Ursula Hoff, *Old Master Drawings*, 1938, p. 14. She shows that the drawing by Rubens of the *Brazen Serpent* in the British Museum, which Hind related to no. 59 (see A. Hind, *Catalogue of Drawings by Dutch and Flemish Artists . . . in the British Museum*, 1923, II, no. 4, p. 7) by virtue of the occurrence of a man in the same pose but in reverse, derives from Michelangelo's *Brazen Serpent* on the Sistine Chapel ceiling. (16) For Michelangelo's drawing, see A. E. Popham and J. Wilde, *The Italian Drawings of XV and XVI Centuries . . . at Windsor Castle*, 1949, no. 429, and pl. 21. The influence of the Tityus on Rubens was first pointed out by R. Oldenbourg, see *P. P. Rubens . . . Abhandlungen über den Meister*, ed. by W. von Bode, 1922, pp. 75 ff. For a further discussion, see Count Antoine Seilern, *Flemish Paintings & Drawings* etc., 1955, pp. 32–3 under no. 19; and Burchard/d'Hulst, *op. cit.*, p. 71 under no. 39. The pose of the Tityus was also used by Coxcie for an Israelite in the centre of his print of the *Brazen Serpent* for which see F. W. H. Hollstein, *Dutch & Flemish Etchings, Engravings and Woodcuts* etc., V, p. 62. The variation of it in no. 59 was first suggested in Rubens' *modello* of *The Fall of the rebel Angels* for a compartment of the Jesuit Church (see Oldenbourg, cited under *General References*, p. 214, bottom); as Rooses, *op. cit.*, 1888, II, under no. 800, has pointed out, it is a repetition of the figure in the centre foreground of the *Martyrdom of S. Ursula* (Montpellier). Burchard/d'Hulst, *op. cit.*, p. 33, suggest not convincingly that the legs of the figure in no. 59 derive from those of one of the sons in the Laocoön group. (17) See Burchard/d'Hulst, *loc. cit.* For Rubens' interest in the Laocoön group, see also G. Fubini and J. S. Held, *Master Drawings*, 1964, pp. 123 ff. (18) See Seilern, *op. cit.*, no. 15. (19) See Burchard/d'Hulst, *op. cit.*, no. 189v. (20) See Oldenbourg, *op. cit.*, p. 348. (21) Compare with Venus in no. 194 *q.v.*, and see under the entry for the latter. (22) Compare with the portraits of Frans in the pictures at Munich and Paris, for which see Oldenbourg, *op. cit.*, pp. 346 and 383; if this is correct, he would appear to be older than in the latter. (23) See Oldenbourg, *op. cit.*, p. 176. (24) *Op. cit.*, no. 175. (25) See G. Scharf, *A . . . Catalogue of the Collection of Pictures at Knowsley Hall*, 1875, p. 70, no. 127; apparently not now traceable at Knowsley. (26) Described as 'Daer Mosis de Slang opregt van P. P. Rubens synde een schets', see G. Hoet, *Catalogus* etc., 1752, I, p. 25. (27) Copper, 16 × 22 duimen, see G. Hoet, *Catalogus* etc., 1770, III, p. 53; and Smith under *General References*. Described in the sale catalogue as an 'Eeen extra schoon stuk' etc., that is not specifically as a sketch. (28) Described as 'Moses with the Brazen Serpent, the finished study for the large picture'. No such sketch is described in the Buen Retiro inventory of 1701 (ms. coll. The Duke of Wellington), and it seems probable that this lot was part of the property offered anonymously. (29) See C. G. Voorhelm Schneevoogt, *Catalogue des Estamp Gravées* etc., 1873, p. 5, no. 33, dedicated to François Goubau (b. 1611), Lord of Mespelaer etc., for whom see the entry in the *Biographie Nationale . . . de Belgique*. The print shows more at the top and at the left, and on the horizon there is a port beneath a hill. What is thought to be Schelte à Bolswert's drawing for it in the Louvre (for which see F. Lugt, *Inventaire Général des Dessins des Ecoles du Nord*, II, 1949, no. 1128) follows no. 59 more or less exactly; this is the drawing that Smith, see under *General References*, considered to be by Rubens. (30) See F. van den Wijngaert, *Inventaris der Rubeniaansche Prentkunst*, 1940, no. 251, where listed as a copy of Schelte à Bolswert's print. (31) Schneevoogt, *op. cit.*, p. 5, no. 34. (32) *Ibid.*, p. 5, no. 33 *bis*. (33) *Ibid.*, p. 5, no. 36. (34) *Ibid.*, p. 6, nos. 37 and 38. These and the three preceding prints are in the opposite direction to Schelte à Bolswert's print. (35) Rooses, see under *General References*, states that there was a copy in the Akademie der Bildenden Küntse, Vienna, where no such copy is recorded in the 1927 catalogue by Eigenberger. Smith, see under *General References*, recorded a copy in the Prado, but this is probably the picture by van Dyck. (36) Canvas, 72 × 87⅜ (1·83 × 2·22), see E. Henschel-Simon, *Die Gemälde . . . in der Bildergalerie von Sanssouci*,

1930, no. 112, p. 34. (37) Canvas, 46 × 36 (1·168 × 0·915), see *The Shipley Art Gallery, Catalogue of the Paintings* etc., 1951 (ed.), no. 362, p. 27. (38) See Rooses, under *General References*. (39) 63⅜ × 92½ (1·61 × 2·35); Burchard Documentation. (40) Panel, 22⁷⁄₁₆ × 27¹⁵⁄₁₆ (0·57 × 0·71); Burchard Documentation, which also records a copy coll. L. van Cruyssen, Dijon, oak, 20⅞ × 29½ (0·53 × 0·75). (41) Copper, 17⁵⁄₁₆ × 23¼ (0·44 × 0·59) and rep. XXXIV in catalogue. (42) Canvas, 24½ × 32 (0·62 × 0·81). (43) Copper, 27 × 33¼ (0·686 × 0·845), ascribed to T. van Thulden. (44) Copper, 16¹⁵⁄₁₆ × 23¼ (0·43 × 0·59), photo. in RKD; perhaps identical with the picture sold at Brussels 1956, see note 41. (45) Canvas, 33¾ × 45½ (0·857 × 1·156). (46) See N. MacLaren, *The National Gallery Catalogues, The Dutch School*, 1960, p. 269. (47) He was the son of Antonio Maria (1710–1796) and grandson of Giovanni Lorenzo (1673–*ca.* 1742), who was admitted to the Genoese nobility in 1733, see V. Spreti *et al.*, *Enciclopedia Storico Nobiliare Italiana*, 1931, IV, pp. 344–5. No record has been traced concerning the Marana collection in the eighteenth century. (48) Details from Andrew Wilson's account book, kindly supplied by Professor Ellis Waterhouse, 1951. (49) W. T. Whitley, *Art in England 1800–1820*, 1928, p. 125. (50) See the letter from Sir Thomas Lawrence to Mr. Penrice, 5 July, 1808, printed in *Letters addressed to the late Thomas Penrice Esq.... 1808–14*, (n.d.), p. 1; also printed by Whitley, *op. cit.*, p. 132. (51) Price in marked catalogue in N.G. library. (52) See W. Buchanan, *Memoirs of Painting*, II, 1824, p. 201. (53) See W. T. Whitley, *Art in England, 1821–1837*, 1930, p. 313.

66 AN AUTUMN LANDSCAPE WITH A VIEW OF HET STEEN IN THE EARLY MORNING

A farm wagon leaves the house, Het Steen, on the left; in the centre, a sportsman stalks partridges, while in the right middleground, women milk a herd of cows.

Oil on oak, 51⅝/¾ × 90¼/½ (1·312/1·318 × 2·292/2·299). There is an addition *ca.* ⁷⁄₁₆ (0·012) down the left-hand edge, and an addition *ca.* 1¾ (0·045) along the bottom.

For the make up of the support, see Appendix I.

Generally in good condition. The support is painted up to the edges; but some streaks of blue in the sky may have been added after the support was framed. Parts of the foreground appear to be unsatisfactory because of the unevenness of a black wash, which is worn in certain areas, notably round the horses' feet, among the trunks of the trees on the far left and the hedgerow in the bottom right-hand corner. Parts of the horses, wagoner and cart (especially the wheel) are worn. There are some small areas of damage to the right of the sportsman, and some losses along the joins and cracks, which are retouched. The addition at the bottom extends as far as, and includes the toe of, the sportsman's right boot; it is likely that the edge of the support was planed to facilitate joining up the addition. Cleaned, 1940/1 and 1950.[1]

There are several *pentimenti*, for the most part visible only in X-rays: the foliage of the tree directly behind the cart first extended more to the left; the tower was first placed more to the right; the trunk of the dead tree in the centre foreground was first taller and twisted up to the right; an open barn was originally placed in the area of the clump of trees in the middle distance, directly behind the dead tree; a young sportsman, stalking with a gun, and two dogs to his right, in the centre foreground beneath the dead tree, have been suppressed; the sportsman's right arm was first higher and his hand was placed round the nearside of the barrel of the gun, which was held at a higher angle, and there was a streak of sunlight towards the top of the hedgerow. There is a long, thin modelled object in white paint, beneath the dark wash to the right of the cart wheel.

The house was apparently first identified as Rubens' own by Smith,[2] and named as (Het) Steen by Mrs. Jameson.[3] The main part of the façade, which dates probably from the sixteenth century, has remained largely unaltered; the building which now stands to the left of the entrance dates from the eighteenth century.[4] The tower has disappeared; Rooses[5] states that it stood about three metres to the north-west of the house.

The property, which formed the fief of Steen, near Elewijt, between Vilvorde and Malines and 'fuori della strada maestra',[6] was thus described when it was put up for sale in 1682: 'A manorial residence with a large stone house and other fine buildings in the form of a castle, with garden, orchard, fruit trees and draw-bridge, and a large hillock on the middle of which stands a high square tower, having also a lake and a farm . . . the whole surrounded by moats.'[7] The stream running across the middle ground is probably the Barenbeek.[8]

Het Steen lies just off the road from Elewijt to Eppegem. Between it and the road are farm buildings, referred to above. The view of the house is that seen from the road coming from Elewijt, although the farm buildings have not been included. The road runs almost due West, and the view in the distance is thus to the North, which is confirmed by Rooses' statement concerning the position of the tower. The sun is thus in the East, and the time of day is early morning, as was generally thought in the nineteenth century,[9] rather than early evening as has been supposed more recently. The laden farm wagon is going to market. The town on the horizon is probably Antwerp,[10] and the smaller town before it, could have been intended as a reminiscence of Malines.

The hedgerow in the foreground is mostly made up by a rambling blackberry bush, partly in flower and partly bearing fruit. Immediately behind it, is a species of chrysanthemum, to the right of which are species of achillea and arctium—all autumn flowering plants.[11] Behind the flowers is a covey of partridges; on the branch in the right foreground are two goldfinches—the other four birds there are not identifiable; a kingfisher flies in front of the hedgerow and there are two magpies in the sky.[12]

Rubens' authorship of no. 66 has not and need not be doubted.[13] However, not all the dark wash round and behind the wagon may be autograph. The group of figures seen just in front of the house are painted over this dark wash; they are rendered in a way which is not convincingly reminiscent of Rubens,[14] and may be a later addition. The tree trunks behind them and some of the foliage of these trees may also not be reliable.

Rubens was the owner of the fief of Steen—his purchase of it was

acknowledged by the Council of Brabant in May, 1635;[15] but apparently
he did not take possession of the house until November of the same
year.[16] This provides a likely *terminus post quem* for the date of execution
of no. 66, as it was probably painted there. The flowers indicate that
the time of year is autumn (see above), but the greenness of the leaves
indicate that it is not as late as November.

The evolution of Rubens' late landscape style remains somewhat
obscure; but the handling makes it seem probable that no. 66 was not
painted in Rubens' very last years—rather the autumn of 1636 seems the
most likely time for its execution.[17] Rubens had been staying at Het
Steen for some months when he wrote to Pieresc from there on 4
September, 1636;[18] he was probably back in Antwerp by about the
middle of November.[19]

The size and complex construction of the support make it clear that
the execution of no. 66 took quite an amount of time. There is nothing
to suggest that the process was interrupted, or that Rubens embarked
on significant alterations during it. Nevertheless, the way the support
was put together makes it likely that there were definable stages in the
process of execution, although the homogeneity of the handling makes
such a definition uncertain. The main part of the composition is made up
of three separate groups of panels (see Appendix I); and it is probable
that Rubens began with this, main section, working from left to right,
beginning with the house and expanding the support to take in the
landscape (probably first drawn in with a dark wash), and finally the
sun. Then he enlarged the support to the top and bottom, adding
the horse-drawn cart, reducing the foliage above and to the right of the
house, and painting in the reflections of the rising sun on the water,
rocks and finally the window panes of the house, which he also probably
re-worked. The partridges and main group of flowers—the chief
evidence with regard to the time of year—were already present. But after
the inclusion of the sportsmen on the bottom members, he amplified
the hedgerow (suppressing a streak of sunlight there) and in the course
of so doing also suppressed the younger sportsman and the two dogs.

No. 66 is approximately the same size as the Wallace Collection
Landscape with a Rainbow;[20] it came from the same collection in Genoa
and the two pictures may have been regarded as pendants at Rubens'
death (see under *Provenance*). Although it has been generally assumed
that the two pictures were painted as pendants, there is nothing to prove
it beyond doubt. The compositions would not argue against it, and the
similarity in size may be significant and not coincidental. The subject of the Wallace Collection picture recurs in a smaller picture at
Munich;[21] it is uncertain which of the two is the repetition. The
handling of the Wallace Collection picture is very similar to that in no.
66, but the support (as far as can be made out) seems to be more simply
constructed, and the season is high summer, before the wheat harvest.
If the two pictures were painted as pendants, the more complex support
of no. 66 suggests that the Wallace Collection picture was painted as the
pendant to it. If such was the case, the order of execution would have

been: the Munich picture in the summer of 1636, no. 66 in the autumn, and then the Wallace Collection picture. But this must remain conjecture until the Munich and Wallace Collection pictures are properly studied.

MacLaren[22] considered that the landscape in no. 66 was based on a rapid, preliminary oil sketch taken from countryside not round Elewijt, which, as he observed, is flat. This seems unlikely; it is not certain that it was Rubens' practice to execute oil sketches, as opposed to drawings, out of doors (see under no. 157). It seems more likely that Rubens took the view of the house and landscape from one of the farm buildings, which would explain their absence, the high view point, and the far horizon depicted. No doubt there was a good deal of extemporization on his part while executing the landscape view. Popham has associated Rubens' study of a wild cherry tree with brambles and weeds (coll. Count Seilern)[23] with no. 66, but the flora do not correspond.[24]

MacLaren[25] has observed that the sportsman 'is not without a resemblance to Rubens himself'; so little of the face is visible that it is impossible to establish an identification with certainty. The idea is however attractive, especially as it is likely that Rubens would have reserved the game on his estate for himself and his family. The wagoner has the same features as the one in the Wallace Collection picture.

No. 66 was greatly admired by John Constable;[26] and is the subject of a poem by the obscure William Lisle Bowles.[27]

ENGRAVINGS: By George Cook;[28] J. B. Allen;[29] F. J. Havell.

COPIES: By George Arnald, signed and dated 1804 on the reverse;[30] by Constable;[31] derivative by Lucas van Uden;[32] in imitation: *Fighting Bulls* by James Ward, Victoria and Albert Museum.[33]

PROVENANCE: Perhaps P. P. Rubens (†) sale, Antwerp, 1640 (135).[34] Coll. Giacomino [= (?) Giacomo] Balbi, Genoa, by 1758;[35] sold by Costantino Balbi to Irvine and Arthur Champernowne, acting for and with Buchanan, 1802;[36] in England by April, 1803, when seen at Buchanan's by Joseph Farington;[37] complete ownership assumed by Buchanan, by whom offered to the British Government and J. J. Angerstein;[38] sold to Lady Beaumont by 25 May, 1803[39] for £1,500,[40] and given by her to Sir George Beaumont by 23 June, 1803;[41] seen by John Constable at Benjamin West's in February 1804;[42] exh. B.I. 1815 (10) and 1823 (120); presented by Sir George Beaumont to the British Museum for the proposed National Gallery, 1823; transferred to the National Gallery, 1828; exh. *An Exhibition of Cleaned Pictures*, The National Gallery, 1947/8 (54).

REPRODUCTION: *National Gallery Illustrations, Continental Schools (excluding Italian)*, 1950, p. 305.

REFERENCES: *General:* M. Rooses, *L'Œuvre de P. P. Rubens*, 1890, IV, no. 1204; G. Glück, *Die Landschaften von P. P. Rubens*, 1940/5, no. 30; N. MacLaren, *Peter Paul Rubens, The Château de Steen*, 1946.

In text: (1) See the catalogue of *An Exhibition of Cleaned Pictures 1936–1947*, The National Gallery, 1947 (revised ed.), under no. 54, for a discussion of the first cleaning; at the second cleaning, a later addition along the left-hand edge was removed. (2) See J. Smith, *A Catalogue Raisonné* etc., 1830, II, no. 767. (3) See Mrs. Jameson, *A Handbook to the Public Galleries of Art in and near London*, I, 1842, p. 90. (4) See M. Rooses, *Rubens*, trans. by H. Child, II, 1904, pp. 571–572; he reproduces a photograph of the front of the house, which, but for the wing to the left of the entrance, corresponds with the house in no. 66; see also *Catalogue Rubens Diplomate*, Château Rubens, Elewijt, 1962, pp. 45–48; Lauters' view of the house, of 1841, reproduced on p. 47, seems not to have been exact. (5) See Rooses, cited under *General References*. The tower also occurs in the Louvre *Tournament* (Glück, *op. cit.*, no. 36), and in the sketch at Berlin (Dahlem), Rooses, *op. cit.*, no. 1204 *bis*. (6) See Rubens' letter to Piersc of the 4 September, 1636, in M. Rooses and Ch. Ruelens (†), *Correspondance de Rubens*, 1909, VI, p. 164. (7) See Rooses, *Rubens* etc., p. 571; and under note 34. (8) *Ibid*. (9) For the nineteenth-century view, see, for instance, National Gallery catalogues from 1838–1906. Rooses, see under *General References*, seems first to have suggested that the sun was setting. (10) The tower being that of the Onze Lieve Vrouwekerk. (11) Dr. Melderis of the Natural History Museum kindly identified the plants. (12) See MacLaren under *General References*; Mr. Goodwin of the Natural History Museum kindly advised about the birds. He did not think that linnets also featured on the hedgerow as MacLaren, *op. cit.*, p. 8, supposed. (13) See Smith, cited in note 2; and the authors listed under *General References*. (14) They do not compare favourably with the figures in the left foreground of the Louvre *Landscape with a Bird Catcher*, executed about the same time as no 66 (see Glück, no. 35). It is also peculiar that the little girl seems to be picking up fruit from the ground, although there are no fruit trees nearby. (15) See note 7. (16) See H. G. Evers, *Rubens und sein Werk*, 1944, p. 82. (17) It almost certainly precedes no. 157, *q.v.* Glück, see under *General References*, has tentatively suggested that no. 66 can be dated by the age of the youngest child seated before the house, on the attractive hypothesis that the group may represent members of Rubens' family. He considered that this child is less than a year old and stated that no. 66 could thus date from the summer of 1635 or 1637. But the child seems to be older than that, and the group may well be a later addition, not by Rubens (see above). (18) See M. Rooses and Ch. Ruelens (†), *Correspondance de Rubens*, 1909, VI, pp. 164 ff. (19) In a letter of the 20 November, 1636, the Cardinal Infant Ferdinand told Philip IV that Rubens had begun work on the pictures for the Torre de la Parada, having just received the commission, see M. Rooses and Ch. Ruelens (†), *Correspondance de Rubens*, VI, 1909, p. 170. It thus seems probable that Rubens was back at Antwerp by this time. (20) See *Wallace Collection Catalogues, Pictures and Drawings*, 1928 (ed.), p. 259, no. 63. (21) See Glück, *op. cit.*, no. 29. (22) *Op. cit.*, p. 9. (23) See Count Antoine Seilern, *Flemish Paintings and Drawings* etc., 1955, no. 63 and plate cxx. (24) Count Seilern, *loc. cit.*, cites Mr. Wilfrid Blunt's view that the species helicampene occurs in both Count Seilern's sheet and in no. 66; but Dr. Melderis of the Natural History Museum thinks that it does not feature in no. 66. Nevertheless this kind of drawing, with colour notes added by Rubens, should obviously be associated with no. 66. (25) *Op. cit.*, p. 8. (26) See, for instance, his lecture delivered to the Royal Institution 3 June, 1836, printed C. R. Leslie, *Memoirs of the Life of John Constable*, 1845, p. 346: 'Constable described the large picture in the National Gallery, in which a fowler is seen watching a covey of partridges, as a fine specimen of Rubens' power of landscape . . .'; see also Farington's diary entry, referred to in note 33. (27) Mentioned by Farington under his entry for 10 August, 1803, see *The Farington Diary of Joseph Farington, R.A.*, ed. J. Grieg, 1923, II, p. 132. (28) See Smith, *loc. cit.* (29) See *The National Gallery of Pictures*, II, [1838], no. 64. (30) Panel, 23 × 41½ (0·584 × 1·054); Anon. sale, Sotheby's, 9 February, 1955 (109); ex Sir G. A. M. Beaumont sale, 20 February, 1952 (75). The inscription on the back runs: 'Copied from the Original picture by Rubens | in the year 1804. for Sir George Beaumont Bar*. | by G. Arnald'. Farington noted in his diary (typescript copy in the British Museum, Print Room) for 23 June, 1803, that 'Arnald is making a copy of Sir G. Beaumont's Rubens [*sic*] landscape.' (31) See *Memoirs of the Life of John Constable, R.A. by C. R. Leslie, R.A.*, ed. and enlarged by the Hon. Andrew Shirley, 1937, p. 156 and p. 158, note: 'During his visit [Constable's] to Cole-Orton [Cole-Orton Hall, Leicestershire, the Beaumont's country house, where his collection had been housed since 1808] besides his admirable copies of the Claudes, he made a sketch from a landscape by Rubens.' (32) Panel, $20\frac{1}{2} \times 33\frac{7}{16}$ (0.52×0.85), Jules Porgès sale, Paris, 7 December, 1925(?), see Glück, *op. cit.*, under no. 30. (33) See *The Farington Diary by Joseph Farington, R.A.*, ed. by J. Grieg, 1923, II, p. 189–90, entry under 10 February, 1804; He [Constable] had also seen the picture painted in imitation of it [no. 66] by Ward which Mr. West told him was the best picture of the kind executed since the days of Rubens ... Constable thought such praise extravagant & sd. the picture shewed How inferior a production made upon a picture is to one that is founded on original observation of nature.' See also W. T. Whitley, *Art in England, 1800–1820*, 1928, p. 71, for the identification of Ward's picture and other details concerning his execution of it. Wilkie also records being influenced by no. 66 while staying at Cole-Orton in 1809, see A. Cunningham, *The Life of Sir David Wilkie* etc., I, 1843, p. 247. (34) Glück, *loc. cit.*, first proposed this identification. It rests on the supposition that no. 66 and the Wallace Collection *Landscape with a Rainbow* were painted as pendants. Lot 135 of the catalogue of the sale is 'Un grand Paysage au naturel avec des petites figures, sur fond de bois'; no. 136 is 'Un grand paysage avec une pluye', see J. Denucé, *Inventories of the Art-Collections in Antwerp* etc., 1932, p. 62. The Wallace Collection picture is reasonably identified with no. 136; and it seems likely that its pendant should have been catalogued immediately before it. The Wallace Collection picture (rather than no. 66 as Glück, *op. cit.*, under no. 30; and MacLaren, *op. cit.*, p. 10, supposed) seems to have been bought by Rubens' eldest son, Albert (1614–1657), see item LXXIIII of the *Staetmasse ende Rekeninge* etc. of Rubens' estate, in Denucé, *op. cit.*, p. 79: 'De voors. Joncker Albert [= Albert Rubens], heeft noch gehadt een groote landschappe, de wedergaey van dat tot Steene is, hem aengeschat voorde somme van 1250 [guilders].' This landscape is probably that recorded in Albert Rubens' house in Brussels after his death, see M. Rooses, *Rubens-Bulletijn*, V, 1910, p. 28 and note: 'Item een groot landschap wesende een schouwstuck'. The phrase in the *Staetmasse ende Rekeninge* etc., perhaps relevant is 'de wedergaey van dat tot Steene is'—which could be translated to mean 'the equal (i.e. pendant) of that is at Steen'. Thus if nos. 136 and 135 of the catalogue of Rubens' sale after his death are correctly identified as the Wallace Collection picture and no. 66, and/or if the entry no. LXXIIII does refer in part to the latter, it means that no. 66 was at the time at Het Steen, having been presumably bought by Rubens' widow Helena († 1673) who, along with her children, had been left the property, see P. Génard, *Rubens-Bulletijn*, 1890, IV, pp. 133–4 and p. 138. The accounts of the *Staetmasse ende Rekeninge* etc., of the pictures are not complete; they begin with no. XX, and the entry, relevant to no. 66, may have been in the missing section. Het Steen was sold by Rubens' heirs in 1682, see M. Rooses, *Rubens-Bulletijn*, 1910, V, p. 151. (35) See C. N. Cochin, *Voyage d'Italie* etc., III, 1758, pp. 268–269; Palais de Giacomino Balbi ... Deux grands Paysages de Rubens ... 'une représente une plaine, dans l'autre on voit un arc-en-ciel.' See also [G. Brusco], *Description des Beautés de Gènes* etc., 1768, p. 57. For Giacomo Balbi see note 42 under no. 278. How no. 66 and the Wallace Collection picture were reunited(?) is not as yet clear. (36) See Arthur Champernowne's letter of 25 September, 1802, printed by W. Buchanan, *Memoirs of Painting* etc., II, 1824, pp. 101–2. (37) See *The Farington Diary by Joseph Farington, R.A.*, ed. J. Grieg, 1923, II, p. 94, entry for 29 April 'Called upon Lawrence and recd. from him a direction to No. 18 Oxendon St. to see two Landscapes by Rubens brought from the *Balbi* Palace at Genoa ...'. (38) See Buchanan, *op. cit.*, pp. 109–110. (39) See *The Farington Diary* etc., 1923, II, p. 102, under entry for 25 May. (40) See Buchanan, *op. cit.*, p. 110. (41) See Farington's diary entry of this date, cited in note 30. (42) See *The Farington Diary* etc., 1923, II, p. 189, under entry for 10 February.

157 A LANDSCAPE WITH A SHEPHERD AND HIS FLOCK

Oil on oak, $19\frac{7}{16}/19\frac{9}{16} \times 32\frac{7}{8}$ ($0.494/0.497 \times 0.835$).

The support is made up of 2 [1] members, see Appendix I.

In good condition. There are some marks in the sky (see below), and some long, but very thin, cracks in the paint which have been retouched. An area of sky above the highest tree (on the right) is thinly painted, perhaps worn, and is now retouched. Cleaned, 1946.

There is a *pentimento* in the lower part of the roof of the outhouse, which originally was not so low.

X-radiographs reveal a vertical line drawn in the ground down the length of the support, *ca.* $1\frac{9}{16}$ (0·04) to the left of the join. Infra-red photography confirms the presence of some writing in black chalk(?) just to the left of this line, and *ca.* $\frac{3}{8}$ (0·01) from the top edge. The inscription, which is *ca.* $3\frac{3}{4}$ (0·095) long, has been deciphered to read: *sonder rand*(??) *jede*(?) *malen*(?).[2] About $1\frac{1}{8}$ (0·03) beneath the inscription is an arrow also in black chalk(?) *ca.* $4\frac{3}{4}$ (0·12) long, pointing to the left. Just to its left is a vertical line also in black chalk(?), which starts at the top edge and is *ca.* $3\frac{1}{8}$ (0·08) long; just to its left and a little beneath the line of the arrow is another horizontal line in black chalk(?) *ca.* 2 (0·05) long. Along the right-hand edge are marks, scratched into the paint by the end of the brush. They begin just above the top of the house and are extremely difficult, or even impossible, to decipher: perhaps they read '15'(?), followed by some dots, dashes and squiggles, 'XI', followed by further squiggles, '8'(?).

The landscape and much of the sky is painted all the way up to the edges; but the light blue in the sky (which covers the inscription) is painted up to a margin, which is *ca.* $\frac{1}{4}$ (0·006) wide; the same applies to the outhouse and trees behind and before it (although the fence seems to go to the edge).

It is not possible to be certain whether no. 157 depicts a sunset or sunrise.[3] The compiler inclines to accept the traditional[4] view that it depicts a sunset.

No. 157 is evidently by Rubens, and is unanimously considered to be a late work.[5] It is probably later than no. 66, *q.v.*, and a date *ca.* 1638 seems acceptable for it.[6]

It is evident from the make up of the support and from the guide lines, which Rubens set out for himself on the left-hand panel, that he executed much of this panel first. The evolution of no. 157 seems to have been the following: selection of the left-hand panel and, at an early stage, the decision to expand it to the right (thus the scoring in of the vertical line just to the left of the right-hand edge to mark how far he should paint up to that edge); execution of much of the sky and landscape, adding the trees against the sky last; at a stage after the vertical line had been obscured by paint, writing a reminder that he should 'paint everything' (to the left of the right-hand edge) 'without a border [=frame [7]]', since as he was going to expand the picture, it was pointless to frame the support; addition of the right-hand panel; painting much of it, probably beginning with the two tallest trees and then the streaks of sunlight; painting in the tower and adjacent building and blocking in the outhouse; introduction of the shepherd and his flock; framing the support; painting in the details of the outhouse and adding the smaller tree and perhaps the church tower behind; painting out the inscription in the sky.

The course of the evolution of no. 157 suggests that there was a definite time lapse (however short) in its execution. It is evident that at an early stage Rubens intended to enlarge the support, and the time lapse was probably due to a temporary lack of an additional panel.

The evolution of no. 157 does not disprove the thesis that Rubens had a composition in mind for the whole picture before he began it. But the connection between the picture in the Ashmolean,[8] first considered to be a sketch for no. 157 by Kieser,[9] should be re-examined. The quality of the Ashmolean picture does not appear to be high. The composition differs in some respects from that of no. 157; the shape of the outhouse roof in the Ashmolean picture rather inclines to follow Rubens' final idea for it in no. 157. Thus it seems more likely that it derives from no. 157.

Puyvelde considered that the Ashmolean picture was made 'after nature'.[10] It is not at all certain that Rubens painted out of doors;[11] however, Norgate recorded that the principal landscape by Rubens at York House (in the collection of the Duke of Buckingham, † 1628) had been 'an Aurora . . . as done by the Life as him selfe [= Rubens] told me un poco ajutato'.[12] Evidently one of Rubens' concerns in no. 157 was to record the affect of the sun on the horizon and the reflection of the trees in the stream. In this he probably bore in mind a late drawing, probably done on the spot, of the reflection of trees in a pond before a red sky, in the British Museum.[13] Although there is no red in the sky in no. 157, the reflection of the trees is more strongly rendered than the trees themselves, and this follows his written observation on the drawing.[14]

The buildings which Rubens added on the right-hand panel are probably not wholly imaginary. Scholars[15] who have accepted the Ashmolean picture consider that it depicted a view in the environs of Elewijt, where Rubens' house, Het Steen, was situated (see no. 66). The view in no. 157 has not been identified;[16] the thesis that the tower and adjacent buildings is Het Steen itself is not acceptable.[17] However, taking into account the facts that no. 157 was almost certainly executed after Rubens bought Het Steen in 1635 and that his interest in landscape painting increased during the time he spent there,[18] it is likely that no. 157 was inspired by the countryside round Elewijt and that it was executed there. This could explain the temporary lack of the panel, needed to make the enlargement. Rubens indeed wrote from Het Steen on 17 August, 1638 (the year in which no. 157 is normally dated, see above) asking Fayd'herbe to send or bring a picture on panel from Antwerp.[19] This shows that Rubens was active in the autumn of 1638, and no. 157 may have been executed then, before his illness which occurred in October.[20]

Gerson[21] has drawn attention to the sketchy quality of no. 157; he considers it to be a fully worked-out sketch. It seems more likely that no. 157 was painted as an end in itself and that Rubens considered it finished.

Hermann[22] has suggested that no. 157 was inspired by Titian; this has been rejected by Glück.[23] However, the bucolic tone, with the presence of the shepherd, may owe something to Titian.[24]

ENGRAVING: By Schelte à Bolswert, in reverse, published by Gillis Hendricx with a dedication to J. P. Happart.[25]

COPIES: Ashmolean Museum, no. 386;[26] Pastrana Collection, Madrid;[27] Cook Collection, no. 330;[28] by Sir Timothy Eden, 1934;[29] of the right-hand half with slight variations: Dulwich College Art Gallery, no. 218;[30] the following lots may be in some way related to no. 157: Sir Peter Lely sale, 18 April, 1682 (old style);[31] Dr. Bragge sale, Prestage, 4 March, (=2nd day), 1763 (50);[32] Anon. sale, Christie's, 27 July, 1821 (67);[33] Sir J. C. Robinson sale, Drouot, 7/8 May, 1868 (38).[34]

PROVENANCE: Perhaps P. P. Rubens (†) sale, Antwerp, 1640 (112).[35] Perhaps coll. J. P. Happart, Antwerp († 1686).[36] Perhaps coll. Everhard Jabach, Paris (1610–1695),[37] and, by descent, coll. his widow and thence his grand-daughter, Mme. Fourment, 1724.[38] Coll. Dutartre, Paris, by 1787;[39] Dutartre (†) sale, Paillet (Paris), 19 ff. March, 1804 (21)[40] sold for 3,400 francs.[41] Probably coll. the Hon. C. Long (later Lord Farnborough) by 1810;[42] exh. by him at the B.I., 1815 (18); Lord Farnborough Bequest, 1839; exh. *An Exhibition of Cleaned Pictures*, The National Gallery, 1947/8 (55).

REPRODUCTION: *National Gallery Illustrations, Continental Schools (excluding Italian)*, 1950, p. 306, bottom.

REFERENCES: *General*: J. Smith, *A Catalogue Raisonné*, II, 1830, no. 1212; M. Rooses, *L'Œuvre de P. P. Rubens*, 1890, IV, no. 1193; G. Glück, *Die Landschaften von P. P. Rubens*, 1940–1945, no. 31.

In text: (1) The catalogue of *An Exhibition of Cleaned Pictures (1936–1947)*, The National Gallery, 1947, no. 55, states that the support is made up out of three panels—with two of the panels joined horizontally. Although a jutting out edge beneath a strip of canvas, stuck to the back of the support, suggests a horizontal join, this is not confirmed by an examination of X-rays and of the left-hand edge, where there is no sign of a join. (2) The compiler is most grateful to Miss Pamela Willetts of the Department of Manuscripts, The British Museum, for suggesting 'with considerable hesitation' this reading of the inscription, which she translated as 'Without border paint everything.' (3) If de Mayerne is thought to record the general visual language of the time, then no. 157 seems not likely to depict a sunset, as there is no red in the sky; of de Mayerne's formulae for depicting sunrise and sunset, no. 157 comes closer to the former, for which, see J. A. van Graf, *Het de Mayerne Manuscript* etc., 1958, p. 163; De Mayerne's ms. is dated 1620. But see also the discussion of the British Museum drawing below. (4) See, for instance, the description in the Dutartre sale catalogue, referred to in note 40; and Smith, under *General References*. (5) See R. Oldenbourg, *Rubens, K. der K.*, 1921, p. 409; A. Rosenberg, *Rubens, K. der K.*, 1905, p. 397; and G. Glück, cited under *General References*. (6) It is tempting to read the 'inscription', scratched along the right-hand edge (see above), as a possible date, but this would be rash. (7) See note 2. It is reasonable to assume that 'rand' may have meant frame. (8) See *Catalogue of Paintings in the Ashmolean Museum*, [1961], p. 139, no. 386; and Oldenbourg, *op. cit.*, p. 414, bottom. (9) See E. Kieser, *Münchner Jahrbuch*, 1931, p. 291, footnote 8. His view has been accepted by Glück, *loc. cit.*; L. van Puyvelde, *Les Esquisses de Rubens* 1940, no. 91; and the author of the catalogue of *Olieverfschetsen van Rubens*, Museum Boymans, 1953, no. 115. (10) *Loc. cit.* (11) Philippe Rubens, in his *Mémoire* of 1676 addressed to de Piles, stated that Rubens, after he bought the 'seigneurie de Steen' in 1630 [*sic*], took pleasure in a solitary life to 'plus vivement dépeindre au naturel les montaignes plaines, vallées et prairies d'alentour, au lever et au coucher du soleil avec leur orizons', see *Rubens-Bulletijn*, 1883, II, p. 167. These words should not be taken too literally, as, for one reason, Rubens could not have painted any mountains 'au naturel' round Elewijt. (12) See E. Norgate, *Miniatura*, ed. M. Hardie, 1919, p. 46. (13) See J. S. Held, *Rubens Selected Drawings*, 1959, p. 146, no. 135 (and colour plate facing p. 80); Held, probably rightly, thought the drawing was made at sunset; he associated it with no. 157, *inter alia*, and dated it *ca*. 1635. (14) Held, *loc. cit.*, gives a translation of Rubens' inscription. (15) That is for instance Puyvelde, *loc. cit.*; and the author of the catalogue of *Olieversfschetsen van Rubens, loc. cit.* (16) It is perhaps worthy of note that the easternmost church spire near the horizon in no. 66 *q.v.* also has an onion-shaped top. (17) It seems first to have been advanced in the *National Gallery Catalogue* of 1913 and was retained until the 1958 *Summary Catalogue*, having already been rejected by Glück, *loc. cit.*; for a view of Steen, see no. 66. (18) See Philippe Rubens, *loc. cit.* (19) See M. Rooses and Ch. Ruelens (†) *Correspondance de Rubens* etc., VI, 1909, pp. 222–223. (20) The Cardinal Infant Ferdinand wrote to Philip IV on 13 October, 1638 saying that Rubens had been ill, and on 11 December, 1638, saying that he had heard that Rubens had received the Last Unction, see Rooses and Ruelens (†), *op. cit.*, pp. 226–227. (21) H. Gerson, *Art and Architecture in Belgium*, 1960, p. 108. Rooses, *loc. cit.*, also described no. 157 as a sketch. (22) H. Hermann, *Untersuchungen über die Landschafts— gemälde des P. P. Rubens*, 1936, pp. 24–5; he suggested that a drawing attributed to Titian at Besançon is the source. Hermann, here, makes specific Kieser's view, *op. cit.*, p. 291, that no. 157 is indirectly connected with Titian. (23) *Loc. cit.* (24) Compare the engravings by Giulio and Domenico Campagnola, rep. by A. M. Hind, *Early Italian Engraving*, VII, 1948, plates, 773 and 776. (25) See F. van den Wijngaert, *Inventaris der Rubeniaansche Prentkunst*, 1940, p. 37, no. 106. The engraving shows more birds above the highest tree on the right, the tower of the house is slightly different, and the steeple of the church in the distance is taller. Rooses records an anonymous copy of this print, which, as Wijngaert points out, was published by F. de Wit, and showed Cain killing Abel in the foreground. (26) Panel, 10⅝ × 15¾ (0·27 × 0·39), see under note 8. (27) See Rooses, *loc. cit.* (28) Panel, 19¾ × 36⅜ (0·50 × 0·925), see J. O. Kronig, *A Catalogue of the Paintings . . . in the Collection of Sir Frederick Cook* etc., II, 1914, p. 84; exh. *Five Centuries of European Painting*, Whitechapel Art Gallery, 1948 (47)—certainly not a preliminary study as is suggested there. Burchard Documentation suggests that the Cook collection picture is ex coll. Sir J. C. Robinson, but the sizes do not accord (see note 34). Glück, *loc. cit.*, suggests that the Cook picture was ex coll. Pastrana. (29) Photograph in N.G. archives. (30) Panel, 18 × 16¾ (0·457 × 0·425), see *A Brief Catalogue of the Pictures in Dulwich College Picture Gallery*, 1953, p. 35; and Smith, *loc. cit.*, who makes a confused reference to his no. 725. (31) For the Sir Peter Lely sale, see *The Burlington Magazine*, 1943, pp. 186–187; on page 187 is the entry 'of Paul Ruebens A landskip 1ft. 7ins. × 2ft. 8½ins. bt.' by J. B. Hoys a Dutch dealer for £27. Burchard Documentation affords a fuller description from a catalogue in French (not seen): '*Inventaire des . . . Tableaux du Cabinet de Feu Monsieur Lely. Imprimé à Londres. . . . De Paul Rubens Un Pais. d'après nature avec des Bergers & des Brebis 1′7″ × 2′8½″.*' It would be tempting to identify this lot with no. 157 but the entry refers to shepherds rather than to one shepherd; and if no. 157 is indeed the picture described in Happart's inventory, see under *Provenance*, the identification is even more unlikely. (32) Described as: 'Rubens. One of his landscapes, a setting Sun with Shepherds &c, the coloring [*sic*] very strong (more so than usual) the Reflection so great, as to make the Trees near almost appear to have red Flowers' (typescript of the Phillipps ms., in the N.G. library). Here again the description refers to shepherds rather than to one shepherd. Landscapes by Rubens also featured in the Bragge sale of 1755 (55) and 1759 (59). (33) Described as 'A Shepherd watching his sheep in a bold landscape warmed by the setting sun'.

(34) Panel, $19\frac{11}{16} \times 31\frac{1}{2}$ (0·50 × 0·80). (35) Described as 'Un paysage avec des brebis, sur fond de bois', see J. Denucé, *Inventories of the Art-Collections in Antwerp* etc., 1932, p. 61. The description of this lot could equally well fit, *inter alia*, no. 2924 *q.v.* (36) See Denucé, *op. cit.*, pp. 333–4: 'Inventaris van . . . Joannes Philippus Happart, Canonick vande Cathedrale kerk van onse Lieve Vrouwe alhier . . .' He owned 7 landscapes by Rubens, 4 undescribed, one with a wagon, one of a view in Spain, and one with an 'opcomende sonne . . .' It seems probable that this Happart was the dedicatee of Bolswert's print after no. 157; thus it is tempting to identify no. 157 with one of the 2 undescribed landscapes or the sunrise in his inventory. However, it should be pointed out that the fact that Happart was the dedicatee of the print, does not necessarily mean that he owned the prototype. In only one instance is the dedicatee of one of Bolswert's prints in the 'small landscape series' (of which this is one) known to have been the owner; and then the inscription on the print (= Wijngaert, *op. cit.*, no. 91) makes it clear. (37) See the inventory of Jabach and his widow's collection, in *Mémoires de la Société de l'Histoire de Paris*, 1894, p. 257: no. '150 Paysage; sur le devant un berger assis jouant de sa flûte, sur bois, de Rubens, 300 livres.' For biographies of Jabach and his family, see L. Clément de Ris, *Les Amateurs d'Autrefois*, 1877, pp. 125 ff.; and F. Lugt, *Les Marques de Collections*, 1921, I, pp. 550–3, 1956, II, pp. 416–417. (38) See the notarial note at the head of the inventory, in *Mémoires de la Société de l'Histoire de Paris*, 1894, p. 249; Mme. Fourment is described as 'la fille de la dite dame Fourment'; Jabach's daughter, Marie Anne († 1706) married Nicholas Fourment of Paris who predeceased her, see Clément de Ris, *op. cit.*, p. 135. Clément de Ris, *op. cit.*, p. 182, stated that Jabach's house in Paris, was sold by his grandchildren, *ca.* 1721. (39) See Thiéry, *Guides des Amateurs . . . à Paris*, I, 1787, pp. 584–5: '*L'hôtel de la Tour du Pin* . . . est occupé par M. *du Tartre* [*sic*], Trésorier des Bâtimens du Roi . . . cinq tableaux de *Rubens* . . . un charmant paysage éclairé d'un soleil couchant . . .' M. Dutartre was already active in the affairs of the Treasurer of the Bâtiments du Roi in 1737, see *Correspondance des Directeurs de l'Académie de France à Rome* etc., ed. A. de Montaiglon and J. Guiffrey, 1899, IX, p. 319. (40) As on panel, 18 × 31 pouces (= $19\frac{1}{8} \times 33$). The description corresponds to no. 157, save for the fact that the houses, sheep and shepherd are said to have been on the left (a mistake in part repeated by Smith, see under *General References*) and for the mention of distant mountains. (41) See the marked copy in the R.K.D. (42) See *The Farington Diary* etc., ed. J. Grieg, 1926, VI, p. 82 (30 June, 1810): 'From Greenwich we [Farington and West] proceeded to Mr. Long's at Bromley Hill . . .. Before dinner we were occupied in looking at a small landscape by Rubens which Mr. Long had purchased.'

187 MINERVA AND MERCURY CONDUCT THE DUKE OF BUCKINGHAM TO THE TEMPLE OF *VIRTUS*(?)

George Villiers, 1st Duke of Buckingham, is borne upwards by Minerva and Mercury, who holds a wreathed crown above him, to a marble temple before which are personifications of *Virtus* and Abundance(?). To the left, the three Graces offer him a crown of flowers, while the personification of Envy seeks to pull him down, and a lion challenges him.

Oil on oak, $25\frac{1}{16}/25\frac{3}{16} \times 25/25\frac{1}{8}$ (0·637/0·64 × 0·635/0·637).

Painted area (roughly circular), $24\frac{7}{16} \times 24\frac{5}{8}$ (0·62 × 0·625). The spandrels are also coated with a ground and filled in with black paint.

For the make up of the support, see Appendix I.

In good condition. There are some small, scattered losses in the *putto* to the right of the lion, in the drapery above it, a long the left-hand join, and in the two outer Graces. There is a vertical crack, *ca.* 5 (0·127) long, across the legs of the central Grace; the dark paint beneath her is a little worn and retouched. Cleaned, 1939/40, and 1946.

Several *pentimenti* can be made out by the naked eye; others are evident in X-ray photographs. The painted area may originally have been intended to be smaller, as a dark, preliminary oil wash (?) shows up as ending *ca.* $1\frac{1}{8}$ (0·03) from the top left-hand spandrel. Envy's left hand was first placed above the Duke's foot. A *putto*, flying to the left just above the lion, has been suppressed. The position of Minerva's shield was first higher and more to the right; she originally held the shaft of her spear in her left hand as well. A large figure, blowing a trumpet and facing left, just above and to the right of Mercury, has been suppressed. The area above this figure is confused in the X-radiograph, but there may have been a mass of drapery there. It seems that the pose of the *putto* directly above was different. The trumpet of the figure immediately below this *putto* was first shorter. The inner columns, above left, remain somewhat undefined and confused; on the left, a narrow column on a simple base has been suppressed; what may have been another column, behind the figure with the cornucopia, has also been suppressed; the perspective of the base of the plinth was first less steep.

George Villiers (1592–1628), created a Knight of the Garter in 1616, and the acknowledged favourite of James I from 1617 and then of Charles I, was made 1st Duke of Buckingham (of the second creation) in 1623. In 1625 he was made General of the Fleet and Army. His dominant role in English politics was brought to a violent end at Portsmouth, where he was assassinated by John Felton.

Minerva is identified by her shield and helmet, etc.; she is the goddess of Wisdom.[1] Mercury is identified by his helmet; he is the god of Eloquence.[2] The three Graces Eufrosine, Aglaia and Thalia, personify the joyful life.[3] The woman with snakes in her hair, who tries to pull the Duke down, can be identified as the personification of Envy.[4] The lion is a symbol of Anger.[5] The female figure in a helmet, holding a sword and partisan, standing before the central column, is probably the goddess *Virtus*.[6] The seated female figure, seated beside her and holding a cornucopia, probably personifies Abundance and by extension 'ogni humana felicità'.[7] It seems likely that the marble building was intended to be a temple, probably the temple of the goddess *Virtus*.[8]

No. 187 has been generally considered to be the work of Rubens;[9] and there is no reason to doubt this attribution.

Wornum[10] rightly associated no. 187 with the picture then at Osterley Park in the possession of the Earl of Jersey,[11] which was destroyed in 1949. Rooses[12] identified the central figure in this picture as the Duke of Buckingham by virtue of the existence in Rubens' estate of a copy 'deen daer den Hertoge van Bocquingam ten hemel opgeheven wort.'[13] The ex Jersey picture has been reasonably identified with 'A great piece for the ceiling of my Lord's Closett [*sic*]' by Rubens, listed in the inventory of pictures at the Duke of Buckingham's palace, York House, made in 1635.[14]

An engraving by Panneels, who left Rubens' studio early in June, 1630, shows that the ex Jersey picture was in existence by this year.[15] Chiefly on the basis of a poem commemorating Felton's act, a transcript of which dating from Charles I's reign is in the British Museum, the compiler[16] has sought to show that this picture was executed for the Duke of Buckingham, and that it was known in England before his assassination in August, 1628. The Duke first met Rubens in Paris in 1625; they remained in regular contact, often through the Duke's agent, Balthazar Gerbier, until the Duke's death.[17] Their discussions were on two topics: diplomacy and the sale by Rubens of some works of art to the Duke.[18] The year 1625 therefore provides a reasonable *terminus post quem* for the commission of the ex Jersey picture; it may well have been ready for despatch from Rubens' studio in September, 1627.[19] Stylistic evidence supports a dating of between 1625–27, and suggests that, if anything, it was executed in the latter half of this time bracket.[20]

In its form known to us, the ex Jersey picture was octagonal, but as Jaffé has recently pointed out, it was originally probably circular.[21] Because of the differences between it and no. 187, it is evident that no. 187 was not the working *modello*, which is not known to exist. A drawing of a *Harpy* in the British Museum, which occurs in the ex Jersey picture, and which Hind,[22] followed by Jaffé,[23] accepted as the work of Rubens, certainly represents or echoes a stage in the evolution of the execution of the commission subsequent to no. 187. It is probable that a copy by Watteau[24] after a lost drawing[25] or oil sketch[26] by Rubens for the two outer Graces, also records a stage subsequent to no. 187.[27]

Burchard drew attention to what he considered to be a copy of a lost oil sketch by Rubens for the same commission.[28] His view that the original preceded the execution of no. 187 is confirmed by the suppression in the latter of Rubens' first idea for the position of Minerva's shield and her spear, and the trumpet-blowing figure (Fame).

Recent authorities have accepted Rooses'[29] suggestion that the commission was to depict the Apotheosis of the Duke of Buckingham; in fact it was probably intended as an allegorical commentary on Buckingham's aims and aspirations, and on the forces that sought to impede him.[30]

Rubens' first known idea was to show the Duke climbing up to a festooned, classical temple, assisted by Minerva and heralded by Fame. *Putti* offered him a victor's palm and crown, as did the three Graces, while a lion (Anger) challenged him and a figure tried to pull him down. No. 187 differs considerably. Rubens began by altering the pose of the Duke, so that he was lifted up by Minerva, with his left hand (which was probably to hold a flag) above his shoulder; he retained Fame, but the Graces had to lean farther in to offer their crown. The position of the lion was retained and Envy was made clearly recognizable. Rubens also elaborated on the Duke's aspirations, by introducing the figures before the temple, one of which is probably the goddess *Virtus* (see above). He then abandoned Fame, introduced Mercury (who assists the Duke and, with a *putto*, offers him a crown), and moved down the Duke's left arm in the process. He also depicted the Duke in a costume more like contemporary fighting costume. Fame was probably intended to be represented by one of the subsidiary figures above and to the right of Mercury. In the final picture, Rubens added a dragon and a Harpy to the forces of opposition; modified the left-hand figure before the column to depict the god, *Honos*;[31] and changed the number and disposition of the *putti* above the Duke, so that the crown offered him by Mercury and the *putto* was closer to his head, but the victor's palm was farther from him.

The poses of the three Graces in Rubens' first known idea for the commission occur in his oil sketch of *Mercury conducting Psyche to Olympus* (coll. the Prince of Liechtenstein);[32] they are probably repeated from it.[33]

The poses of the two inner Graces probably derive from those in Raphael's *Marriage of Psyche* in the Farnesina; that of the outer Grace may have been inspired by the *putto* with flowers above the table in the same fresco series.[34] The final idea for the central group in no. 187 is re-worked in the spirit of *The Apotheosis of Henri IV* in the Marie de Médicis series.[35] The pose of the Duke is inspired by that of Christ in Correggio's ceiling fresco in S. Giovanni Evangelista, Parma.[36] The pose of Mercury is a conflation of that of Mercury in the Liechtenstein sketch and of Fame in Rubens' first known idea for the commission, which in itself may have derived from Giulio Romano.[37] Several ideas developed in the commission were used again by Rubens in the decorations for the ceiling of the Banqueting Hall, Whitehall.[38]

COPIES: Coll. Sir Ilay Campbell (brush drawing);[39] by William Etty, City Art Gallery, York;[40] by Delacroix, Akron Art Institute, Ohio;[41] ascribed to Bonington, Comte A. de G[anay] sale, Drouot, 11 June, 1904 (3);[42] Anon. sale, Sotheby's, 24 January, 1962 (30).[43]

PROVENANCE: Perhaps in a French collection in the eighteenth century.[44] Apparently recorded for the first time[45] in the Hon. John Clerk of Eldin (Lord Eldin (1757–1832)) sale, Edinburgh, 14 March (= 2nd day), 1833 (109)[46] bt. Renius(?) for 90 gns.;[47] given in exchange by the purchaser's family to Sir David Wilkie (1785–1841);[48] Sir David Wilkie sale, Christie's, 30 April (= 6th day), 1842 (680) bt. Tiffin for £84;[49] by whom sold to the National Gallery for £200 in 1843; exh. *An Exhibition of Cleaned Pictures*, The National Gallery, 1947/8 (no. 50).

REPRODUCTION: *National Gallery Illustrations, Continental Schools (excluding Italian)*, 1950, p. 309, top.

REFERENCE: *General:* Gregory Martin, *The Burlington Magazine*, 1966, pp. 613 ff.; a different title is proposed in this entry.

In Text: (1) See for instance, V. Cartari, *Imagini de gli Dei delli Antichi*, 1626 (ed.), pp. 295 ff., and his translation of Ovid's description of Minerva: 'Fà sè con l'hasta, e con lo scudo, e s'arma | Il capo d'elmo, e di corazza il petto'. (2) See, for instance, Cartari, *op. cit.*, pp. 260 ff. (3) See, for instance, Cartari, *op. cit.*, pp. 454 and 455; on the latter page beneath the cut is the rubric: 'Imagini delle tre Gratie Dee della bellezza, & gratia; Dee ancora della gratitudine, & del benefico, nominate Eufrosina o giocondità, Aglaia ò venustà, Thalia ò piacevolezza; Dee della conversatione, sociabilità, & amicitia, & di quella allegra vita, che gli huomini desiderano di vivere.' (4) See, for instance, Cartari, *op. cit.*, p. 384. (5) See G. de Tervarent, *Attributs et Symboles dans l'Art Profane* etc., 1959, col. 245, no. VII. (6) This figure is similar to that in a drawing by Rubens in the Musée Plantin Moretus, for which see J. Held, *Rubens Selected Drawings*, 1959, no. 138 and pl. 148, which is identified by Rubens as *Virtus*; see also Otho van Veen *Historia Septem Infantiam de Lara*, 1612, fig. 3 (for example) which may have influenced Rubens. A similar figure, but not identical, occurs in van Dyck's sketchbook at Chatsworth, see M. Jaffé, *Van Dyck's Antwerp Sketchbook*, II, 1966, 33 *recto*, which as Jaffé shows, p. 228, note to 33 *recto*, derives ultimately from a figure on the *Arch of Constantine*, that was included in an engraving by Marcantonio Raimondi, his fig. CIII. The drapery and pose in no. 187 differ from the Plantin Moretus drawing, and in particular it is not clear whether one breast is bare; nevertheless the identification of this figure as *Virtus* seems probable. (7) The precise meaning of this figure is somewhat obscure. The absence of a staff prevents a safe identification of the figure as *Honos*, which could be rendered by either a male or female figure, see Cartari, *op. cit.*, p. 305; for a male figure, see the second figure on the sheet by Rubens in the Plantin Moretus Museum, for which, see Held, *loc. cit.* (the two statues, made from the studies on the Plantin Moretus sheet, are also in the Plantin Moretus Museum). Cartari, *loc. cit.*, explains that 'dalla virtù & attioni virtuose provenir l'honore' & con l'honore l'abondanza del tutto, & ogni humana felicità.' Thus the figure in no. 187 may, because of the cornucopia, signify Abundance etc. (8) Cartari, *op. cit.*, p. 304, stated: 'La quale [Virtù] fu da gli antichi parimente creduta Dea, & adorata, & a lei come à gli altri Dei posero i Romani un(?) tempio davanti à quello dell' Honore . . .' (9) See, for instance, M. Rooses, *L'Œuvre de P. P. Rubens*, 1890, IV, no. 820; R. Oldenbourg, *Rubens, K. der K.*, [1921] p. 413; and L. van Puyvelde, *Les Esquisses de Rubens*, 1940, no. 52, p. 81. For the traditional attribution, see under *Provenance*. (10) See R. N. Wornum, *Descriptive & Historical Catalogue of the Pictures in the National Gallery*, 1858, p. 191. (11) The picture is reproduced by C. R. Cammell, *The Great Duke of Buckingham*, 1939, opp. p. 371; and by Martin, see under *General Reference*, fig. 21. It was bought by Sir Francis Child during a tour of the Low Countries in 1679–99 for £400 and was recorded at Child's house in Lincoln's Inn Fields in 1706; about 1765 it was installed at Osterley Park by Robert Child, and passed by descent to the Earls of Jersey (information kindly provided in a letter of 1935 in the Gallery archives from J. B. Hunt, Secretary to the Earl of Jersey). Copies of three details are in the Rubens Cantoor in the Print Room of the Royal Museum of Fine Arts, Copenhagen, see Burchard Documentation and Martin, *op. cit.*, note 3. (12) *Op. cit.*, under no. 819. (13) For the *Staetmasse ende Rekeninge* etc., of Rubens' estate, see J. Denucé, *Inventories of the Art-Collections in Antwerp* etc., 1932, pp. 71 ff.; the relevant entry is no. LII on p. 77 and was sold to Herman Denyt [*sic*]; the copy was also recorded in the inventory of Herman de Nyt's collection of 15–21 October, 1642, see Denucé, *op. cit.*, p. 110. (14) See Randall Davies, *The Burlington Magazine*, 1906/7, p. 379. (15) The engraving, entitled *Pictura, Sculptura et Statuaria*, is reproduced in F. Hollstein, *Dutch and Flemish Etchings* etc., XV, by K. G. Boon and J. Verbeek, p. 126. It shows a knowledge of the three Graces as they appear in no. 187, of the woman and Envy, with Minerva substituted for the woman, and of one of the *putti* in the final picture. (16) See under *General Reference*. (17) See, for instance, R. Magurn, *The Letters of Peter Paul Rubens*, 1955, pp. 161 ff. (18) For the fullest discussion of this latter negotiation, see M. Rooses and Ch. Ruelens (†), *Le Correspondance de Rubens*, 1904, IV, pp. 23–26. (19) See under *General Reference*, p. 614. (20) See *ibid.* It might also be pointed out that Sandrart stated that Rubens' work for Buckingham was done after Rubens' visit to the northern Netherlands (in July 1627), see *Joachim von Sandrarts Academie der Bau-, Bild-, und Mahlerey-Künste von 1675*, ed. A. R. Peltzer, 1925, p. 157. (21) See Michael Jaffé in *Studies in Renaissance* and *Baroque Art presented to Anthony Blunt*, 1967, p. 104, under note 64. (22) See A. M. Hind, *Catalogue of Drawings by Dutch and Flemish Artists . . . in the British Museum*,

1923, II, p. 12, no. 20. (23) See Jaffé, *op. cit.*, p. 104 and fig. 10. (24) See K. T. Parker and J. Mathey, *Antoine Watteau, Catalogue Complet de son Œuvre Dessiné*, 1958, II, no. 946. (25) As suggested by Parker and Mathey, *loc. cit.* (26) It is possible that it derived from an oil sketch similar to those for details in the Whitehall Ceiling, for which see O. Millar, *Rubens: The Whitehall Ceiling*, (Charlton Lectures on Art), 1958, *passim*. (27) That the original succeeded no. 187 is suggested by the presence of drapery, present in the ex Jersey picture but absent in no. 187; although the architecture does not follow either that in no. 187 or the ex Jersey picture, it accords better with that in the latter. (28) First noted in coll. A. E. Reyre, London; exh. *Peter Paul Rubens, Loan Exhibition*, Schaeffer & Brandt, New York, 1942 (26), (rep. in cat.), and *Loan Exhibition of Forty-three Paintings by Rubens* etc., Los Angeles County Museum, 1946 (40); Anon. sale, Palais des Beaux-Arts, 9 March, 1953 (78) (rep. in cat.); see also under *General Reference*, p. 617, and fig. 26. (29) *Loc. cit.* (30) See under *General Reference*, pp. 617–8; the achievement of *Virtus* could give a man immortality and make him equal with the Gods, see O. Van Veen, *Q. Horati Flacci Emblemata*, 1607, p. 14. (31) Compare the figure thus inscribed by Rubens in the sheet in the Musée Plantin Moretus, see note 6. It should also be noted that *Virtus* no longer holds a staff. In the final picture the Temple becomes that of *Honos* and *Virtus*, although Cartari, *op. cit.*, p. 304, recorded that Valerius Maximus refers to the fact that the Romans had decided that there should be separate temples for the two deities. (32) See Puyvelde, *op. cit.*, no. 53 and fig. (33) See under *General References*, p. 614. (34) Rep. in G. Gronau, *Raffael, K. der K.*, 1923, pp. 158 and 164; see also under *General Reference*, p. 617; and Jaffé, *op. cit.*, p. 106. (35) Rep. in Oldenbourg, *op. cit.*, p. 252; the design may have been inspired by Otho van Veen's print, *A Musis Aeternitas*, in his *Q. Horati Flacci Emblemata*, 1607, p. 159. (36) Rep. in G. Gronau, *Correggio, K. der K.*, 1907, p. 60. (37) Compare the topmost figure in Giulio Romano's study for *The Allegory of the Virtues of Federigo Gonzaga*, in the British Museum, discussed and reproduced by Philip Pouncey and J. A. Gere, *Italian Drawings in the Department of Prints and Drawings, Raphael and his Circle*, 1962, no. 79 and pl. 72. (38) Minerva and the Duke recur with slight variation and in steeper perspective as Justice and James I in the *Apotheosis of James I*. The pose for the outer Grace, which previously had been used for the large *putto* in the *Birth of Marie de Médicis*, recurs in steeper perspective in the Boymans-van Beuningen sketch of *England and Scotland crowning the Infant Charles*, and with increased variation in the final canvas. Finally, the pose of the lion recurs with slight variation in the leopard. (39) Diameter 13 (0·33); inscribed: 'Tableau de Rubens qui prèsente l'Apotheose [*sic*] de Jacques Premier Roi d'Angleterre | Ce tableau a etè [*sic*] fait pour servir de modèle du plat-fond d'un cabinet du Palais Royal de S. M. le Roi d'Angleterre, peint par le même Rubens [last letter cut] tel qu'on le voit encore à present'; on loan to the Glasgow Museums and Art Galleries, 1967. (40) No. 371/1952; see D. Farr, *William Etty*, 1958, no. 298 and pl. 41B. (41) Canvas, diameter 25 (0·635), see B. E. White, *The Art Bulletin*, 1967, p. 49, no. 28 and fig. 6, by whom dated 1825, although it was not then in the collection of Sir David Wilkie as she supposed (p. 38). (42) Canvas, 14⅛ × 11 (0·36 × 0·28), rep. in catalogue; Burchard Documentation. (43) Diameter, 23½ (0·597). (44) Sir Ilay Campbell's copy, see above, seems, to judge from the inscription, to have been made in France, and probably in the eighteenth century. (45) The 1929 Gallery catalogue suggested that no. 187 was in the Nathaniel Bayly sale (=Anon.=Lord Hampden) sale, Christie's, 31 May, 1799, (102). The owner's name (given as Hampton) is written beside the lot in Christie's copy of the catalogue; the lot was bought in and must be the Glynde Place sketch having passed by descent to Mrs. Brand from Lord Hampden († 1824 and buried at Glynde). (46) Frank Simpson (letter in Gallery archives) kindly drew attention to a report in *Art-Union*, V, (1843) p. 122: 'A small Rubens has also been added to the collection [of the National Gallery]; it is the original sketch for the ceiling at Whitehall. The little picture was in the possession of the Scottish family of Clerk, of

Eldin. It was sold at a public auction, on which occasion some part of the building wherein it was held gave way—an accident that caused the death of several persons present, among whom was the purchaser of this picture. The friends of the gentleman thus unfortunately killed took a dislike to the sketch, from the associations and reminiscences it called forth: in consequence of which it came into the possession of Sir David Wilkie, who presented the family, in return for it, a very beautiful picture of his own. It was disposed of at the sale of Sir David Wilkie's pictures for £80, and subsequently purchased for the Gallery for £200. It seems to be painted on panel, and is in the highest state of preservation, but is seen to disadvantage in a hanging position'. It was described in the sale catalogue of 1833 as 'A finished study of the Apotheosis of James I being part of the Ceiling of the Chapel of Whitehall . . .'. (47) This is the name and price in Professor Waterhouse's marked copy of the sale catalogue according to Frank Simpson, *loc. cit.*, who also stated 'but this name does not appear amongst the dead, listed in a pamphlet tucked in the catalogue'. (48) See note 46. (49) Marked catalogue in the National Gallery library.

194 PARIS AWARDS THE GOLDEN APPLE TO VENUS (THE JUDGMENT OF PARIS)

Paris hands the golden apple to Venus who stands between Minerva and Juno. Mercury stands behind Paris. Above is the Fury, Alecto.

Oil on oak, $57 \times 76\frac{1}{4}$ (1·448 × 1·937).

For the make up of the support, see Appendix I.

In fairly good condition. The ground extends to the edges; the paint extends to the left-hand edge, but there is a border of *ca.* $\frac{3}{8}$ (0·01) at the bottom, and traces of a border of the same width on the right and at the top. The part of Venus' cloak which is in front of her has been retouched to reduce the craquelure, and may not be reliable. There are many scattered losses, notably in the breasts of Minerva, the buttocks of Venus and the small of Juno's back, which are retouched. In some areas the top layer of paint was either thinly applied and/or is worn, or has become translucent with time such that many *pentimenti* (see below) now show up light. The most prominent, i.e. Mercury's right arm, the two doves and the *putto* pulling down Venus' cloak, have been retouched to reduce them. The foliage in the top left-hand corner, much of the dog and Minerva's hair are worn. Cleaned, 1940/1.[1]

The *pentimenti* referred to above show that beneath no. 194 is a somewhat different composition. The evolution of no. 194 can be traced by the picture of *The Judgment of Paris* at Dresden[2] (referred to below as the Dresden picture), because the majority of the differences between the Dresden picture and no. 194 can be seen either by the naked eye, infra-red or X-ray photography in no. 194. A further group of *pentimenti*, similarly revealed, show a preliminary, and otherwise unrecorded stage of the composition. On the basis of the Dresden picture, it is possible to divide the *pentimenti* into three groups. Group I consists of motifs which do not occur in the Dresden picture; group II consists of those made to complete the first stage of the composition as recorded in the Dresden picture; group III consists of alterations made to complete no. 194 as it now stands.

Group I is made up thus: Minerva's right leg was placed farther away from her left leg; a pair of doves were placed to the left of Venus' head; her right foot was much closer to her left and pointed nearly in the same direction, her cloak hung lower—more amply in front—and lay on the ground round her feet, and may have extended over her right hand;[3] Juno's right leg was originally farther away from her left; her cloak was less wide so that nearly all her right buttock and both her legs up to her knees were visible.

Group II is made up thus: in the top left-hand corner, three satyrs watched the scene from behind the rock and foliage, which may have extended down in front of Venus' head; Minerva's left elbow was higher; a *putto* to the left pulled off her shift; a *putto* (Cupid)[4] standing in front of Venus and looking back over his shoulder pulled down her cloak and shift; Juno's hair was done up at the back in a single bun and was more disarranged; Mercury's right arm was extended and he pointed down with his right hand; more of his left thigh was visible above Paris' leg; the wings on his helmet were connected by two strands of metal, joined by a clasp at the front; Paris' right leg jutted almost straight out (nearly parallel with Mercury's right arm); he held the golden apple in his right hand which rested on his left wrist; his left foot was placed near the dog's head; he wore a round, broad-rimmed straw hat, his shirt covered both his shoulders and as much of his left arm as his right.

Group III is made up thus: apart from the suppression and alterations of motifs described in II, the base of the Medusa shield was filled in and Minerva's helmet was enlarged; wings and a quiver were added to the kneeling *putto* on the left, thus converting him into Cupid and the drapery covering Paris' thighs was amplified.

The legend of the Judgment of Paris is frequently alluded to in classical literature, and obviously was commonly known in the seventeenth century. Of all the descriptions of the legend, no. 194 seems to follow most closely that given by Lucian in his *Judgment of the Goddesses*, where he described how, after Mercury had taken the three goddesses to Paris and handed him the golden apple, Paris asked 'But first I want to know whether it will satisfy the requirements to look them over just as they are or must I have them naked for a thorough examination?' Hermes: 'That is your affair, you are the judge. Give your orders as you will.' Paris: 'As I will? I want to see them naked.' Hermes: 'Undress, goddesses. . . .'[5] The first stage of no. 194 as recorded in the Dresden picture depicts the moment when Mercury orders the goddesses to undress.[6] The final stage of no. 194 shows Paris awarding the golden apple to Venus. In this context the suppression of the two *putti* disrobing Minerva and Venus is acceptable, but not necessary. Cupid was probably present as the son of Venus.

The attributes of the deities: owl, helmet, Medusa shield and spear for Minerva; roses and doves (suppressed) for Venus; peacock for Juno; quiver for Cupid; and caduceus and winged helmet for Mercury, were all widely known and used by the seventeenth century.[7] The Fury, Alecto, is identifiable by the flaming torch she carries and the serpents covering her head.[8]

No. 194 is unevenly finished; the definition of apparent degrees of finish is complicated by the uneven condition. Venus' head is the most highly finished and best preserved area. Much of the Medusa shield, Cupid, the peacock, flowers in the foreground and Minerva's cloak appear to be fully worked up and well preserved. The bodies of the goddesses and the drapery of Venus were also probably fully worked up, but are less well preserved. Alecto, much of the sky, foliage, landscape and Juno's drapery are more freely rendered and generally well preserved. The foliage in the top left-hand corner is sketchily rendered, but it is now to all intents indecipherable; the dark paint between Minerva and Venus, and the sky on either side of Juno is retouched and somewhat featureless, while the drapery over Paris, the landscape and some of the sky just over the horizon behind him seems not necessarily reliable. The base of the Medusa shield is more sketchily rendered than the rest of it; and the area of black beneath it is also very sketchy. Paris and much of Mercury, apart from his cloak and hand to the right of the tree, are unevenly retouched and re-worked. The presence of the border at the bottom, and traces of one on the right and at the top of the support, suggests that Rubens added the flowers at the bottom and re-worked the foliage in the top right-hand corner after the support was framed.

Both tradition[9] and recent authorities[10] agree that no. 194 is by Rubens; and in general there is no good reason to doubt this attribution. However, the re-working of Paris and Mercury, referred to above, is not of the quality to be expected of him. In particular, the fingers and toes are weakly drawn; the alteration to Mercury was unsuccessfully carried out in so far as his right shoulder has not been reduced; finally the alterations to Paris have made him seem to be too large in proportion to the other figures. Cross sections, taken from these altered areas show some, albeit irregular, traces of what could be dirty varnish beneath the top layer of paint. These observations suggest that Paris and Mercury may have been altered some time after no. 194 left Rubens' studio. If such was the case, no. 194 could have been a picture fully described by de Piles in 1676–7; de Piles noted the satyrs, but only one *putto*.[11] Thus it is possible that the satyrs were suppressed at the same time as the alterations were made to Paris and Mercury, all of which must have been carried out by 1727, when no. 194 was described in the catalogue of the collection of the Duc d'Orléans.[12] It is also possible that the other alterations, mostly involving suppression, noted above in group III, are not by Rubens, but by an artist working closely in his style and not long after his death. Examination of these areas show that while they are closely in Rubens' manner, they are not wholly convincing.[13] These qualifications concerning the authorship of no. 194 are also connected with problems concerning its early provenance, discussed below.

No. 194 has always been dated to the last decade of Rubens' life.[14]

Burchard/d'Hulst[15] have provided an indication for the date of execution by pointing out that a rapid sketch for the three goddesses occurs on a sheet of studies, associated by them with *The Mystic Coronation of S. Catherine*, which was delivered by Rubens in 1633.[16] It is not known, however, when Rubens received this commission. But a date *ca.* 1632–1635 seems acceptable for the execution of no. 194, as Oldenbourg suggested.[17]

No. 194 differs considerably from the six other known renderings of the subject by, or probably deriving from, Rubens.[18] Of these, it most closely resembles the composition recorded in Jan Brueghel I's *Sight and Smell* in the Prado, where the pose of Paris bears some connection with that of the first idea for Paris, while the top half of the pose of Mercury is connected with the final idea for this figure in no. 194.[19] To some extent no. 194 resembles the composition of Rottenhammer's *Judgment of Paris* at Munich;[20] and it is probable that Rubens had a composition such as this in mind when evolving no. 194.

The pose of the suppressed *putto* disrobing Venus, and to a lesser degree the pose of Venus herself, derive from those of Hebe and a *putto* in Raphael's *Psyche received into Olympus* (Farnesina).[21] As Burchard/d'Hulst[22] have pointed out, studies of a female figure on a sheet at Leningrad, are also connected with the pose of Venus; but it seems not certain that the studies were made specifically for no. 194. The same sheet contains a study of a *putto* in the same pose as that of the suppressed *putto* who disrobes Minerva in no. 194, and the pose may have been inspired by that of the *putto* disrobing Venus in Marcantonio Raimondi's engraving of *The Judgment of Paris* after Raphael.[23] The pose of Minerva may derive from the classical type of *Venus Anadyomene*;[24] it was earlier used by Rubens in an exaggerated form for Bellona in the *Apotheosis of Henri IV* in the Marie de Médicis series,[25] and later in the Berlin *Andromeda* and the Prado *Perseus and Andromeda*.[26] The pose of Juno occurs twice in a sheet of studies for a *Bath of Diana* at Berlin,[27] and could derive from the Farnese *Flora* at Naples.[28]

The model for Venus is not unlike Rubens' second wife, Helena Fourment,[29] and that for Minerva is not unlike the sitter in no. 852 *q.v.*, who was, perhaps, her sister, Susanna.

DRAWING: Pen and ink sketch essaying the juxtaposition of the three goddesses in the top left-hand corner of a sheet of studies for the *Mystic Coronation of S. Catherine*, Boymans-van Beuningen Museum, Rotterdam, V.92 (*verso*), $10\frac{1}{8} \times 16\frac{7}{16}$ (0·258 × 0·418).[30]

SKETCHES: What was described as an 'esquisse très arrêtée' for the composition engraved by Adriaen Lommelin (i.e. perhaps no. 194, see under *Engravings*) was in the Charles Spruyt sale, Ghent, 3 ff. October, 1815 (120), panel, 20 p. × 19 p. ($= 21\frac{1}{4} \times 20\frac{1}{4}$);[31] what was claimed to be the 'original idea' for no. 194 was offered by B. Novaro in 1845.[32]

ENGRAVINGS: Perhaps after the Dresden picture: by P. F. Tardieu and P. E. Moitte, 1750, in *Recueil d'Estampes gravées d'aprez les tableaux de la galerie et du Cabinet ... Comte de Bruhl*, I, 1754, no. XXVI;[33] perhaps after no. 194: by Adriaen Lommelin;[34] after no. 194: by J. Couché and J. Dambrun in *Galerie du Palais Royal gravée d'après les Tableaux des différentes Écoles. ... Avec* *un abrégé de la Vie des Peintres par M^r. L'Abbé de Fontenai*, 1786, II, 1808; R. Woodman, in *Kinnaird Collection* etc., published by Edward Orme, 1809.[35]

COPIES: Numerous copies or pictures claimed to be versions of the first stage of no. 194 are recorded; the best of these, apparently, is that in the Gemäldegalerie, Dresden, no. 962B, oak, $19\frac{5}{16} \times 24\frac{13}{16}$ (0·49 × 0·63), which is catalogued as by Rubens in the latest Dresden catalogue (1962);[36] the following, of varying degrees of quality and accuracy, are recorded: Musée d'Art et d'Histoire, Geneva, no. 2, 1933 panel, $19\frac{7}{8} \times 31\frac{11}{16}$ (0·505 × 0·805);[37] coll. M. J. H. Burt, London, 1877, support and measurements not known;[38] Cook coll., 1914, panel, $18\frac{11}{16} \times 25$ (0·475 × 0·635);[39] C.–L. Cardon sale, Brussels, 27/30 June, 1921 (102), copper, $19\frac{11}{16}(?) \times 27\frac{11}{16}$ (0·50(?) × 0·70);[40] Melzi sale, Milan, 19/23 March, 1928 (554), support not given, $19\frac{11}{16} \times 28\frac{5}{16}$ (0·50 × 0·72); coll. J. Schmidt, Paris,[41] 1930, panel, $18\frac{1}{2} \times 23\frac{1}{2}$ (0·47 × 0·597); coll. Sam Hartveld, Antwerp, 1934, panel, $19\frac{1}{4} \times 25\frac{3}{16}$ (0·49 × 0·64);[42] Baron C. A. de Cosson sale, Sotheby's, 30 June, 1948 (112), [panel] measurements not given; Lord Queenborough sale, Christie's, 28 April, 1950 (69), panel, $21 \times 29\frac{1}{2}$ (0·533 × 0·750); Lord Gretton sale, Christie's, 27 June, 1952 (107), [canvas], 20×25 (0·508 × 0·635); Anon. sale, Christie's, 3 June, 1954 (166), canvas, $18 \times 24\frac{1}{2}$ (0·457 × 0·622); Anon. sale, Sotheby's, 2 November, 1955 (68), [canvas], 32×42 (0·813 × 1·68); Anon. sale, Charpentier, 16 March, 1959 (150,) panel, $18\frac{15}{16} \times 25\frac{13}{16}$ (0·48 × 0·64);[43] Anon. sale, Charpentier, 10 December, 1959 (90), panel, $18\frac{15}{16} \times 24\frac{3}{16}$ (0·48 × 0·63); Anon. sale, Galerie Georges Giroux, Brussels, 20/22 June, 1960 (941), copper, $23\frac{3}{16} \times 34\frac{1}{4}$ (0·59 × 0·87);[44] coll. John Leapman until 24 August, 1960;[45] Anon. sale, Christie's, 28 January, 1966 (64), canvas, 44×74 (1·118 × 1·88); Anon. sale, Sotheby's, 4 May, 1966 (29), panel, $14 \times 22\frac{1}{2}$ (0·386 × 0·571).

COPIES of no. 194: W. M. Craig, watercolour, Anon. [= Lord Kinnaird] sale, Phillips, 21 May, 1811 (19);[46] Countess of Holderness [*sic*] sale, Christie's, 6 March, 1802 (74);[47] Major J. M. Askew sale, Christie's, 17 May, 1946 (85), support not given, 53×72 (1·347 × 1·829); Duke of Westminster (†) sale, Sotheby's, 8 July, 1959 (68), [canvas], 57×76 (1·448 × 1·93) (arched at top) as by the Rev. W. M. Peters (after Rubens); Anon. sale, Christie's, 26 March, 1964 (174), canvas, 54×73 (1·73 × 1·75); of Juno and Cupid: Anon. sale Christie's, 9 February, 1968 (59), $29 \times 24\frac{1}{2}$ (0·737 × 0·61).

CARICATURE COPY of no. 194: By Norman Mansbridge in *Punch*, 11 November, 1959, with the Chancellor of the Exchequer, the Rt. Hon. D. Heathcoat Amory (Lord Amory) as Paris.

DRAWING COPY of Paris's dog and Cupid: Attributed to Watteau, coll. Lady (Jane) Cook, London, sanguine, $4\frac{1}{2} \times 7\frac{1}{4}$ (0·115 × 0·184).[48]

The following may derive or be connected with no. 194: coll. P. P. Rubens (†), Antwerp, 1640;[49] coll. Jeremias Wildens (†), Antwerp, 30 December, 1653;[50] coll. Erasmus Quellinus (†), Antwerp, 24 March, 1678;[51] coll. Joannes Philippus Happart (†), Antwerp, 1686;[52] Anon. [= Wm. Hubert] sale, Ford, 24 April (2nd day), 1751 (121); Samuel Palmer sale, Langford, 9 March, 1775 (63); Anon. sale, Speare, Edinburgh, 14–15 (2nd day) March, 1828 (74), as by Watteau and claimed to be from the Prince of Conti's collection; Dr. Nevinson sale, Christie's, 3 June, 1850 (28); Aston Hall sale, 6 August, 1862 (20), $18\frac{1}{2} \times 24\frac{1}{2}$ (0·409 × 0·609).

PROVENANCE: Perhaps coll. Diego Duarte, Antwerp,[53] before 1649;[54] perhaps sold through the agency of the dealers Picart and Musson, to the Duc de Richelieu (1629–1715) for 4,000 guilders in 1675;[55] perhaps coll. the Duc de Richelieu, Paris, until *ca.* 1676.[56] Recorded with certainty for the first time by Dubois de Saint-Gelais in 1727 at the Palais Royal, Paris, as having been in the collection of Philippe, Duc d'Orléans (1674–1723),[57] though not apparently listed in the inventory made at his death;[58] recorded at the Palais Royal in 1733;[59] bought from Louis-Philippe-Joseph, Duc d'Orléans (1747–1793), by a syndicate consisting of George, Lord Kinnaird (1754–1805), William Morland

and Mr. Hammersley, and imported by its agent Thomas Moore Slade in 1792;[60] exhibited in the same year in Mr. Slade's house in Chatham;[61] for sale by private contract at the exhibition of *The Orleans Gallery . . . at . . . no. 125, Pall Mall*, April–mid June, 1793 (120) not sold; for sale by private contract at the exhibition of *The Orleans Gallery . . . at no. 16, Old Bond St.*, May, 1795 (75) not sold; still not sold, 30 March, 1796;[62] ownership assumed by Lord Kinnaird for 2,000 guineas before 1805;[63] inherited by Charles, Lord Kinnaird (1780–1828); for sale, by private contract, 21 May, 1811;[64] Lord Kinnaird sale, Phillips, 4–5 March (10th [sic]? = 2nd day) 1813 (87) withdrawn and sold by private contract to A. Delahante for 2,500 guineas;[65] by 19 June, 1813 Delahante was negotiating its sale with the Rev. Mr. Bageley (sic?) at which date Ralph Cockburn told Joseph Farington that it was actually in Bageley's possession;[66] the sale must have collapsed for by 29 September, 1813 Delahante had sold it to Thomas Penrice;[67] John Penrice sale, Christie's, 6 July, 1844 (17) bought by the National Gallery for 4,000 guineas;[68] exh. *An Exhibition of Cleaned Pictures*, The National Gallery, 1947/8, (53).

REPRODUCTION: *National Gallery Illustrations, Continental Schools (excluding Italian)*, 1950, p. 307.

REFERENCES: *General:* J. Smith, *A Catalogue Raisonné* etc., 1830, II, no. 748; M. Rooses, *L'Œuvre de P. P. Rubens*, 1890, III, no. 663; R. Oldenbourg, *Rubens, K. der K.*, [1921], p. 344.

In text: (1) See the catalogue of *An Exhibition of Cleaned Pictures (1936–1947)*, The National Gallery, 1947 (revised edition) (53), where a detailed history of the treatment of no. 194 since 1844 is given. The three goddesses were again cleaned and retouched in 1952. (2) For a discussion of the status of the Dresden painting, see under *Copies*. (3) The dark blue paint round Venus's right hand would appear to be a good deal retouched. X-ray photography confirms that at one stage her cloak did extend over her right hand. It may have been strengthened more recently to give the impression that she is holding up her cloak. (4) Lommelin's engraving, for which see below under *Engravings*, and the Dresden picture show a quiver hanging beside the *putto's* leg; what is probably a quiver can be made out beneath the repaint in no. 194 which allows the identification as Cupid. (5) See *Lucian*, with an English translation by A. M. Harmon, (The Loeb Classical Library), 1921, III, p. 397. According to Harmon, *op. cit.*, I, p. xi, the principal edition of Lucian's work was published in 1496. (6) De Piles, describing a composition like that recorded in the Dresden picture (perhaps no. 194, see below), interpreted Mercury's gesture as one of ordering the goddesses and in particular Venus to approach, see his *Conversations sur la connoissance de la Peinture* etc., 1677, reprinted by B. Teyssèdre, *Gazette des Beaux-Arts*, 1963, p. 270: '. . . et Venus qui est entre Pallas et Junon est veuë de profil, et s'avance d'un air coquet et assuré au signe que luy en fait Mercure . . .'. Rooses, *op. cit.*, no. 664, following de Piles, interpreted the gesture as one ordering all the goddesses to approach. Teyssèdre, *op. cit.*, pp. 270–1, reprints the whole of de Piles' description. (7) See, for instance, V. Cartari, *Imagini de gli Dei delli Antichi*, 1626 ed., pp. 302–04, 312–13, 315–16 for Minerva; pp. 435 and 436 for Venus; pp. 151 and 153–54 for Juno; p. 404 for Cupid, and p. 260 for Mercury. (8) Previously identified as Discord, see for instance, Rooses, cited under *General References*; but see Cartari, *op. cit.*, pp. 239–43. (9) See under *Provenance*. (10) See the authors cited under *General References*, and/or in note 14. (11) See under note 6. (12) See note 57. (13) At the second stage of its evolution, no. 194 agreed in all essentials with the print by Lommelin; therefore the alterations, if not by Rubens, would have to have been made after it was published. For a further discussion, see under *Engravings* and note 34. (14) See, for example, Rooses, cited under *General References*, ca. 1636; A. Rosenberg, *Rubens, K. der K.*, 1905, p. 383, ca. 1635–6; Oldenbourg, cited under *General References*, 1632–5. Philippe Rubens in his *Mémoire*, sent to de Piles in 1676, see *Rubens-Bulletijn*, 1883, II, p. 166, stated that the *Judgment of Paris* (in the collection of the Duc de Richelieu, thus perhaps no. 194, see below under *Provenance*) was painted between 1630–40. **(15)** See L. Burchard and R. A. d'Hulst, *Rubens Drawings*, 1963, p. 309, no. 194 *verso*. **(16)** See Rooses, *op. cit.*, no. 400. The painting, which is now at Toledo, is Oldenbourg, *op. cit.*, p. 343. **(17)** Cited under *General References*. **(18)** These are in chronological order: 1. Vienna, Akademie der bildenden Künste, Vienna, no. 39, for which see under no. 6379; 2. no. 6379 *q.v.*; 3. Prado, no. 1731, for which see L. Burchard, *Pinacotheca*, 1928–1929, pp. 14–16 and fig. 8; 4. the composition recorded in *Sight and Smell* by Jan Brueghel I, Prado, no. 1403, see also Burchard/d'Hulst, *op. cit.*, p. 128; 5. coll. H. Wilhelmson, 1930, see Michael Jaffé, *The Burlington Magazine*, 1968, p. 175, note 3 and fig. 13; 6. the design for the silver ewer recorded in J. Neeffs' engraving, for which see under no. 1195, a design which was repeated in all essentials in the picture in Prado, no. 1669, which Rubens had completed by 27 February, 1639, see M. Rooses and Ch. Ruelens (†), *Correspondance de Rubens*, VI, 1909, p. 228. **(19)** The artist responsible for the alteration to Mercury—if not Rubens as is here suggested—may have had a knowledge of the picture depicted. **(20)** Munich, Staatsgemäldesammlungen, no. 750, copper, signed and dated 1605, see R. A. Peltzer, *Jahrbuch der Kunsthistorischen Sammlungen des allerhöchsten Kaiserhauses*, 1916, p. 346, no. 40. **(21)** Rep. by G. Gronau, *Raffael, K. der K.*, 1923, p. 163; see also Michael Jaffé in *Studies in Renaissance & Baroque Art presented to Anthony Blunt*, 1967, p. 104, footnote 70. **(22)** *Op. cit.*, no. 142, pp. 220–222. **(23)** Reproduced by O. Fischel, *Raphael*, trans. by B. Rackman, II, 1948, fig. 294. A nearly identical pose, though seen from the back, occurs in a study of a woman in black and white crayon and sanguine in the Louvre, see F. Lugt, *Inventaire Général des Dessins des Écoles du Nord*, II, 1949, p. 19, no. 1031 and pl. XXIX, who attributes it only with reservations to Rubens. It is accepted as by Rubens by G. Glück and F. M. Halberditzl, *Die Handzeichnungen von P. P. Rubens*, 1928, no. 238, who dated it 1635–40 and, following a suggestion from Burchard, proposed that it was a drawing for an ivory carving. Held considered that 'even if not an original it may record a Rubens drawing, especially as the pose is identical—though seen from the back—with that of Pallas in the London Judgment of Paris', see J. S. Held, *Rubens Selected Drawings*, I, 1959, p. 28. In fact the pose seems not to be identical, for apart from the drapery, Minerva's right arm in no. 194 juts well forward while in the drawing the arm is nearly parallel with shoulder. **(25)** See Oldenbourg, cited under *General Reference*, p. 253. **(26)** *Ibid.*, pp. 430 and 431. **(27)** Burchard Documentation; the drawing is Glück & Halberditzl, *op. cit.*, no. 186, by whom dated *ca.* 1630. The identification of the subject is due to Burchard. **(28)** A copy of which by Rubens was engraved by C. Galle, see Rooses, cited under *General References*, under no. 1299. **(29)** Compare the features with those in, for instance, the picture at Munich (Oldenbourg, cited under *General References*, p. 328). Helena Fourment, was the model for Venus in the picture in the Prado (no. 1669) according to the Cardinal Infant Ferdinand, see his letter of 1639 to his brother cited under note 18. **(30)** See note 15. The *putto* disrobing Venus is placed behind her; he faces to the front, and his head and right arm are also visible. **(31)** See also Rooses, cited under *General References*, no. 664. **(32)** Letter of 24 March, 1845 in the Gallery archives. **(33)** The engraving is rep. by Rooses, cited under *General References*, pl. 204. It differs in several respects from the Dresden picture, notably by including a spiked collar round the dog's neck; further the Bruhl picture was on canvas, and measured 18 × 23 p. (= 19½ × 24½), see the *Recueil d'Estampes gravées d'aprez [sic] les tableaux . . . de . . . Comte Bruhl*, no. XXVI, while the Dresden picture is on oak, and differs slightly in size (see below under *Copies*). The early Dresden catalogues, see for instance the French translation of Hübner's catalogue, 1856, p. 194, no. 802, give no provenance; later catalogues, from at least 1887, see K. Woermann, *Katalog der Königlichen Gemäldegalerie zu Dresden*, p. 319, no. 977 give a provenance from the Bruhl collection. However, because of the differences noted above, this seems at least open to doubt. The author of the notes to the *Recueil d'Estampes gravées* etc., stated that no. XXVI came from the 'succession' of

Rubens and was also engraved by A. Sommelin (*sic*), which last is stated by later writers, and Rooses, cited under *General References*, no. 664. Lommelin's engraving, for which see below, differs both from Tardieu & Moitte's engraving, and the Dresden picture. (34) As after Rubens, published by Gillis Hendricx, Antwerp. The first state is inscribed: *Detur Pulcherrimæ.*; the second state is inscribed: *Detur Pulcherrimæ. D. Iacobo Düarte nobili domestico Regis Angliæ singulari pictoriæ artis cultori, huius archetypi tabulam inter plurima possidenti L. M. D. C. Q. Aegidius Hendricx.* The third state, with same inscription, was published by G. B. Merlen, Antwerp. So far as the date of the first state is concerned, Hendricx became a master in the Antwerp guild of S. Luke in 1643/44, see Ph. Rombouts and Th. van Lerius, *De Liggeren* etc., [1864–1876], p. 144; Lommelin, born in Amiens *ca.* 1616, is first recorded in the southern Netherlands—in Bruges—in 1639/40; he was in Antwerp before 1654–55, see F. van den Wijngaert, *Inventaris van der Rubeniaansche Prentkunst*, 1940, p. 70. The description of Duarte as 'nobili domestico Regis Angliæ' makes it likely that the second state was published by 1649, see under note 54. The print closely connects (in reverse) with the design of no. 194 as recorded in the Dresden picture, although the peacock and goddess are further away from Paris and Mercury. It was criticized in 1675 by the Antwerp dealer, Musson, who was engaged in selling Duarte's picture, see J. Denucé, *Na P. P. Rubens*, 1934, p. 425. His criticism is contained in a letter probably to Picart, engaged in the same business, to answer Picart's criticism of the picture, when judging from the print, see Denucé, *op. cit.*, p. 417. Musson stated that the print was wrong in the rendering of all the parts of the figures and bore no resemblance to the picture, so that he himself wondered why so good a picture had never been better engraved. He explained the difference by recounting that he had known Rubens to retouch his paintings. However, as the print, which follows the second stage in the evolution of no. 194 was probably made after Rubens' death, the differences cannot be explained by any retouching by Rubens. Musson must have exaggerated the differences, as in many respects the print follows the description of the picture given by de Piles after the sale, for which see note 6. The differences, Lommelin's clumsiness apart, may have amounted to no more than what may have been the earlier group of later alterations made to no. 194, as described above, unless of course, Lommelin's print was not after no. 194. It is noteworthy that after the successful sale of Duarte's picture, it was criticized in Paris, see under note 56. (35) This and the previous engraving follow the sense of the picture. That by Couché and Dambrun shows two trees in the middle distance on the extreme right and two sheep both seen from the front. Woodman's shows the sheep as they are in no. 194, but even more foliage in the middle distance. These trees were removed during the recent cleaning, see note 1. A difference which appears in Couché and Dambrun's engraving, but not in Woodman's is in Juno's hairstyle which with Couché is done up in one bun with more hair twisted into it from the back. (36) Rooses, cited under *General References*, no. 664, considered that the Dresden picture was retouched by Rubens and dated from *ca.* 1625; Rosenberg, *op. cit.*, p. 266, concurred with this view. If this was the case the first stage of no. 194 would be a repetition of it. In view of the first group of *pentimenti*, this hypothesis can be rejected. The extent of Rubens' actual participation in the execution of the Dresden picture is open to doubt (it is rejected by Oldenbourg); that it is an old picture in Rubens' manner seems evident. For its provenance see under note 33. The author of the notes to the *Recueil des Estampes gravées d'aprez [sic] les tableaux . . . de . . . Comte Bruhl*, stated that no. XXVI was already a much copied picture. (37) Bequeathed by Mlle. Adrienne Guillaument in 1933, photographs and information provided by Mme. Anne de Herdt of the Musée d'Art et d'Histoire, Geneva. (38) When lent to the *Exposition de Vieux Maîtres*, Antwerp, see Rooses, cited under *General References*, under no. 664. (39) See J. O. Kronig, *A Catalogue of the Paintings at Doughty House . . . in the Collection of Sir Frederick Cook Bt.*, 1914, 11 (335), bt. from Sir J. C. Robinson, 1874.

(40) By whom it had been lent to the *Exposition d'Art Ancien, L'Art Belge au XVIIᵉ Siècle*, Brussels, 1910 (368) and the *Exposition du Musée d'Anvers*, 1914. The sale catalogue inverts the measurements, see the Brussels exhibition catalogue where the height is given as 0·52. (41) When lent to the exhibition *Trésor de l'Art Flamand*, Antwerp, (*Mémorial de l'Exposition d'Art Flamand . . . 1930*, I, 1932 (256)); ex coll. Lord Chesham by whom lent to the *National Exhibition of Works of Art*, Leeds, 1868 (820), Lord Chesham sale, Christie's, 31 January, 1930 (78). (42) Ex a Fiévez sale, Brussels, 16 December, 1933 (16). (43) Ex colls. L. B. Baudot, Dijon and Paul Court, Dijon. (44) Ex coll. Louis Schellink. (45) See national newspapers for 25 ff. August, 1960. (46) Craig's copies were 'from the above pictures'; the Rubens is not listed in the catalogue. (47) See W. Buchanan, *Memoirs of Painting*, I, 1824, p. 307–8, as inherited from the Greffiers Fagel; for the buyer and price see *ibid.*, p. 318; for the status of the picture, see J. Smith, *loc. cit.* (48) See K. T. Parker and J. Mathey, *Catalogue de l'Œuvre dessiné d'Antoine Watteau*, 1958, II, no. 941. Presumably the drawing was done in Paris. (49) See J. Denucé, *Inventories of the Art-Collections* in *Antwerp* etc., 1932, p. 79; but see also note 33. (50) *Ibid.*, p. 157 and p. 166. (51) *Ibid.*, p. 290. (52) *Ibid.*, p. 334. (53) Diego Duarte's collection was a famous one; it was visited by Evelyn in 1641: '. . . Signor Duerts [*sic*], a Portuguese by nation, an exceeding rich Merchant, whose Palace I found to be furnish'd [*sic*] like a Princes [*sic*]', see *The Diary of John Evelyn*, ed. E. S. de Beer, II, 1955, p. 67; by Le Pays, *ca.* 1660, see J. Denucé, *Art-Export in the 17th Century. . . . The Firm of Forchoudt*, 1931, p. 11 and note; by M. de Monconys in July 1663, see *Journal de Voyages des Monsieur de Monconys*, II, 1666, pp. 101–2; by Sir Edward Browne in 1673: 'At Antwerp, Mr. Duart carried me to his house, and showed me the best collection of pictures that any man hath in these parts . . .' see *Sir Thomas Browne's Works* etc., ed. S. Wilkin, 1836, I, pp. 206–7 (reference from de Beer, *op. cit.*, note 6, pp. 67–8); by Constantijn Huygens' son on on 11 June, 1676, see *Musique et Musiciens au XVIIᵉ Siècle, Correspondance et œuvres musicales de Constantin Huygens*, ed. W. J. A. Jonckbloet and J. P. N. Land, 1882, p. CLXXXI, note 3 (reference from de Beer, *loc. cit.*); by Nicodemus Tessin, in 1687, see *Oud Holland*, 1900, pp. 20–1. An inventory of his collection in 1682 was published by F. Muller, *De Oude Tijd*, 1870, pp. 397 ff. It was known to Bellori, see *Le Vite* etc., 1672, p. 259. For details concerning Diego Duarte's life and family, see note 54; *Le Journal L'Escaut d'Anvers*, 1880, pp. 144–6; and Jonckbloet and Land, *op. cit.*, pp. clxxiv ff. (54) When engraved by Lommelin, see above; the *terminus ante quem* for Duarte's ownership rests on the inscription on the print which states that Duarte was 'nobili domestico regis Angliæ'. James or Jacques Duarte is recorded as Charles I's jeweller from 1636–38, see *Calendar of State Papers, Domestic Series . . . 1636–8*, ed. J. Bruce, 1868–69, *passim*. He does not feature in subsequent volumes of the *Calendar of State Papers*; hence the *terminus ante quem* of 1649—Charles I's date of death. The suggestion that no. 194 was in Duarte's collection rests primarily on the supposition that no. 194 suffered two alterations, at different times, after Rubens' death. The first made after Lommelin's engraving and the second after *ca.* 1676, see above. The visual evidence is not against this; both alterations would have been effected by artists with a knowledge of Rubens, see above and under note 19. It also rests on the otherwise extraordinary coincidence of the existence of a superb Rubens in a famous Antwerp collection sold to a famous French collection—the Duc de Richelieu's—and then disappearing from sight, and the sudden appearance of no. 194 in another famous French collection—the Duc d'Orléans' (see below)—which at one stage in its evolution (as we now see it) corresponded with the other picture. A further, slight factor in favour of this thesis is the mistake made by Dubois de Saint-Gelais in 1727 concerning the provenance of no. 194, for which see under note 57. (55) See J. Denucé, *Na P. P. Rubens*, 1934, pp. 412–427, who prints letters between Picart in Paris and Musson in Antwerp, and one other, which cover the whole negotiation of the sale. The painting arrived in Paris on 13 December, 1675, see p. 424; Musson in an undated letter of 1675, see p. 425, referred to the reputation

of the picture: '. . . het stuck alhier genoech gerenomeert is ende bekent voor een van de alderbeste, gluyenste, hoochsten top gevoert dat Rubens oyt heeft gemaeckt . . .'. (56) When described by de Piles, see under note 6; for the dating of the relevant catalogue, see Teyssèdre, *op. cit.*, pp. 242–45. See also Rooses, cited under *General References*, whose suggestion was rejected by L. Burchard, *loc. cit.* Reasons for reviving Rooses' thesis are given in note 54. The Duc de Richelieu's picture was described as 'le Jugement infame de Paris' in an anonymous pamphlet, published in Paris, and dated 12 April, 1676, see J. Thuillier, *Archives de l'Art Français*, 1968, p. 185. The *Judgment of Paris* does not occur in the other descriptions of Richelieu's collection, which were written subsequently to the *Conversations* of 1677, see Teyssèdre, *op. cit.*, pp. 243–5; for Richelieu's disposal of some of his Rubens' before 1681, see de Piles, p. v *recto*, of the *Epistre* to his *Dissertation sur les Ouvrages des plus fameux Peintres*, [1681]. (57) See Dubois de Saint-Gelais, *Description des Tableaux du Palais Royal*, etc., 1727, pp. 415–17 and pp. ii–iv, where he states that the collection was formed by the Duke in twenty years. An earlier record of no. 194, however, would appear to be the copy attributed to Watteau (†1721) (see under *Drawing Copy*). Dubois de Saint-Gelais states, p. 415, that no. 194 came from the collection of Cardinal de Richelieu († 1642), see also E. Bonaffé, *Gazette des Beaux-Arts*, 1882, no. 2, p. 97; and L. Burchard, *Jahrbuch der preuszichen Kunstsammlungen*, 1928, p. 63. However, C. Stryienski, *La Galerie du Régent Philippe, Duc d'Orléans*, Paris, 1913, p. 112, stated that Dubois de Saint-Gelais was wrong, as no *Judgment of Paris* by Rubens is listed in the inventories of Cardinal de Richelieu. Dubois de Saint-Gelais was also wrong (p. 417) in stating that the *Landscape with S. George* (Royal Collection) came from Cardinal de Richelieu's collection; it came in fact from the Duc de Richelieu's collection. See also the author of the introduction to the exhibition catalogue of *The Orleans Gallery*, 1793, pp. iv–v. (58) See Stryienski, *op. cit.*, no. 464, p. 188. The significance of this is doubtful, as apparently the *Landscape with S. George*, which came from the Duc de Richelieu's collection, was not listed in this inventory either, see Stryienski, *op. cit.*, no. 470, p. 188. (59) See [M.L.R.], *Les Curiositez de Paris* etc., I, new ed., 1733; and subsequent guide books to Paris: it is listed in the inventories after death of Louis, Duc d'Orléans (1703–1752) and Louis-Philippe, Duc d'Orléans (1725–1785), see Stryienski, *op. cit.*, no. 464, p. 188; and V. Champier, *Le Palais-Royal*, I, 1900, p. 519. (60) See Slade's letter describing the negotiations and importation in W. Buchanan, *op. cit.*, pp. 159–164. Slade stated, p. 160, that he arrived in Paris on his first trip 'the very day the King had fled', which was on the 20 June, 1791, see also Stryienski, *op. cit.*, pp. 135–6. It seems therefore that Slade was mistaken when he wrote that he was first approached by the syndicate in May, 1792 (Buchanan, *op. cit.*, p. 159). He probably meant May, 1791; the date of his second trip and the actual importation could still have taken place in 1792. It should be noted that Thomas Alldridge writing on 27 February, 1813 to Thomas Penrice claimed that he had brought no. 194 over from France, see *Letters addressed to the late Thomas Penrice, Esq., while engaged in forming his collection of pictures, 1808–1814*, no. XIX, p. 26. (61) See Buchanan, *op. cit.*, pp. 163–64. (62) See the report in the *Oracle* for this date (*Whitley Papers*, X, p. 1333, British Museum, Print Room); 'The Judicium Paridis of the same master [Rubens] remains for the Royal Academy to Purchase as a beginning towards a gallery for this country'. (63) That Lord Kinnaird bought the picture some time after the exhibition of May, 1795 seems probable by comparison of the lists of exhibits in the two exhibitions of 1793 and 1795 and the lists kept for the benefit of the syndicate which are preserved in Barclays Bank, Pall Mall East. It was obviously before Lord Kinnaird's death in 1805, as it is described as bought by the late Lord Kinnaird when engraved in the *Kinnaird* [=Charles, Lord Kinnaird] *Collection* in 1809 (see under *Engravings*). For the price see Buchanan, *op. cit.*, p. 167. (64) Recorded by an ms. note on the sale catalogue in the National Gallery library of an Anon. [=Kinnaird] sale, Phillips, of this date.

(65) Recorded by an ms. note on the sale catalogue in the National Gallery library, which states that no. 194 was sold to Delahante or La Fontaine. The actual identity of the buyer and the sum is given by Buchanan, loc. cit. (66) See The Farington Diary etc., ed. J. Grieg, 1927, VII, p. 183. On 7 July, 1813 Delahante wrote to Thomas Penrice; 'Lord Kinnaird's Rubens [=no. 194] is actually sold to Mr. Baseley [sic?] for £4,200; but I have it in my power to dispose of it as I like, until he has given me proper security for the said sum . . .' see Letters addressed to the late Thomas Penrice etc., no. XX, pp. 30–31. (67) On which date a Mr. Harvey wrote to congratulate Thomas Penrice on his Rubens, which he had seen at Yarmouth, see Letters addressed to the late Thomas Penrice etc., no. XXIV, pp. 34–35. No. 194 was the only Rubens owned by Thomas Penrice, see the sale catalogue of 1844 below. No. 194 is recorded in Thomas Penrice's collection at Yarmouth by Buchanan, op. cit., p. 167; John Stacy, History of Norfolk, I, 1829, p. 304; and Smith, cited under General References. (68) Marked sale catalogue in the National Gallery library.

278   A ROMAN TRIUMPH

A crowd on a grass embankment watch the procession, which is headed by women with flowers and men blowing pipes, who accompany priests with sacrificial animals and their executioners, followed by a troop of elephants.

Oil on canvas, stuck on oak, $34\frac{1}{8} \times 64\frac{1}{2}$ (0.868×1.639).

The support is made up of three pieces of canvas stuck down on oak. The pieces of canvas are joined vertically; the edges of the centre piece are ragged, thus the measurements of the widths is only approximate; these are (reading from the left) ca. $17\frac{1}{2}$, 11 and $35\frac{1}{2}$ (0.445, 0.28, 0.902) wide; narrow remains of a fourth canvas, at the widest ca. $\frac{5}{16}$ (0.008), are visible in X-radiographs down the right-hand edge. The pieces of canvas are stuck down on a support made up of 12 oak members. For the make up of the canvas and wood supports, see Appendix I.

Generally in good condition. Some small paint losses along a series of horizontal cracks in the canvas (now closed up), which were caused by stress from the wooden support, and larger losses down the vertical canvas joins have been retouched. Cleaned, 1966, when eighteenth century[1] wooden additions ca. $3\frac{1}{4}$ (0.083) wide at the top, $4\frac{3}{4}$ (0.12) at the bottom, $1\frac{1}{8}$ (0.03) at each side, on which the design was coarsely finished, were removed.

For a discussion of the numerous pentimenti on the right-hand canvas, see below; there are a number of minor pentimenti on the other two canvases visible for the most part with the naked eye: these are that the basket of flowers on the extreme left was originally wider; that a trumpet(?) has been painted out to the right of the innermost basket of flowers; that the axe was originally shorter; and that the temple, left centre, was first smaller. Not all the pentimenti in the right-hand canvas have been resolved and the grass embankment to the right of the temple has not been fully worked up, nor does the paint continue with equal degrees of finish down the right-hand edge. Part of a man's foot under the dancing woman's raised left leg in the left-hand bottom corner was revealed during cleaning and has been touched out.

The procession includes *camillae* (maidens of unblemished birth who were thus allowed to serve in sacred rites), *hostiae* (animals for sacrifice), *tubicines* (trumpeters), *tibicines* (pipe players), *popae* (slaughterers), and in the centre a *pontifex* (priest with the laurel wreath round his head), and on his right an *augur* (soothsayer), who carries a *lituus* (augural wand); the elephants carry incense burners.[2]

The design of no. 278 has long[3] been recognized as in part deriving from no. V of Andrea Mantegna's series of the *Triumph of Julius Caesar* (Royal Collection, Hampton Court).[4] X-radiographs of the right-hand canvas suggest that originally Mantegna's design was exactly, but perhaps not *in toto*, followed. No trace is evident in them of the incense burner towards the centre or of the ears of the elephant which supported it. Infra-red photography and the naked eye suggest that the other elephants probably originally followed Mantegna's invention; the dogs on the right were also possibly copied. Evidently the copy was never fully worked up; rather, it was substantially altered by Rubens who added an extra elephant's head on the right and an extra cow(?), and made substantial alterations to the remaining elephants and their riders (converting them appropriately into negroes). The re-working and alterations were never fully completed by him, as is made clear from the muddled sequence of the elephant's trunks and fore-legs, the unresolved *pentimenti* in the leopard's feet and the grass embankment, where a dark green/brown glaze covers the tower of Mantegna's invention. This dark glaze is also apparent on the embankment on the other two canvases. Apart from the general idea of the line of elephants, carrying incense burners, the only part of Mantegna's invention which Rubens did not alter is the youth in white and the calf(?) whose rein he holds, the head of the youth to his right and the old man behind him.

The youth holding the reins of the two rams on the left is a variation of the youth leading the cow(?) in no. IV of Mantegna's series; the presence of musicians, who follow in both instances, may not therefore be coincidental. The head of the man to the right of the soothsayer derives from a head in no. VII of the series (see below).

That Rubens executed no. 278 has never been doubted; however, widely varying proposals have been made as to when he did so. These proposals, which are based on attempts to tie the execution of no. 278 to periods (*sic*) when Rubens would have had direct access to Mantegna's series are not convincing.

Rooses[5] and Puyvelde[6] suggested that no. 278 was executed during Rubens' time in Mantua, as do Burchard/d'Hulst[7] so far as the right-hand canvas is concerned. Undoubtedly Rubens would have known the series when he was at Mantua in the service of the Duke, between 1600–08, for the Duke then owned it; and Burchard/d'Hulst's dating of a drawn copy after a detail in no. VII to this time has not been disputed.[8] But there is nothing in the style of no. 278 which suggests that it was executed in these years.

Indeed such a dating has been questioned by Glück,[9] Bode[10] and Oldenbourg,[11] who all consider that it was executed in or after 1629, as a result, so their argument runs, of Rubens seeing the series for a second time in England. To this there may be joined the thesis of Burchard/d'Hulst who consider that the left-hand portion(s) of no. 278 was (were) then executed. Burchard/d'Hulst's dating of a copy by Rubens of a detail of no. VI of the series to 1627–30 is on stylistic grounds undoubtedly correct;[12] but the fact is that documents, printed by Sainsbury, make it clear that, although Nys had bought the series by early 1629, it did not arrive in England until after Rubens' departure, which took place towards the end of March, 1630.[13]

Jaffé[14] has rejected Burchard/d'Hulst's thesis of a chronological hiatus in the date of execution of no. 278. It is not possible to date the copy on the right-hand canvas from X-radiographs; and the copy has been too thoroughly re-worked to form an opinion from ordinary visual evidence. Jaffé considers that no. 278 is 'uniformly painted c. 1630', and thus is in general agreement with the views of Glück, Bode and Oldenbourg.

Leaving aside the problems raised by the first state of the composition on the right-hand canvas, there is no evidence on stylistic grounds to support Burchard/d'Hulst's contention. The re-working of the right-hand canvas seems to be contemporary with the execution of the foreground figures on the other two pieces of canvas. Any differences are due to the lack of finish in the re-working of the right-hand canvas. In this sense Jaffé's use of the adverb 'uniformly' to some extent blurs the issue, as the make up of the wooden support makes it clear that there was a definite sequence in the execution of no. 278.

However, its evolution cannot be fully understood unless Rubens' intentions are explained. There can be little doubt that no. 278 was not so much intended as a re-interpretation of no. V of the series, but of nos. IV and V. The right-hand canvas which bears the re-interpretation of no. V is ca. 35½ (0·902) wide; the left-hand canvas is ca. 17½ (0·445) wide, i.e. just under half as wide as the right-hand piece. The youth on the left-hand canvas is clearly a re-interpretation of the youth on the right of no. IV; the foot revealed in cleaning must therefore be that of the vase bearer in no. IV, because this foot occurs just to the right of the centre of Mantegna's canvas. This being so, it seems likely that no. 278 has been cut down by at least ca. 18 (0·457) to the left. Rubens' final re-working of the copy of no. V was no more extensive than his re-interpretation of no. IV; the only difference is that his re-interpretation of no. IV did not occur as a result of re-working.

The sequence of the execution of no. 278 is now evident. It is: (1) the execution of the copy of no. V; (2) Rubens' realization that Mantegna's nos. IV and V could not be joined comfortably together and his decision to invent a link passage; (3) construction of a wooden support to enable him to make the canvas join; (4) sticking down the copy and the canvas for the link passage onto the wooden support, which allowed for a difference of about 1 (0·025) between the end of the wooden support and the canvas support;[15] (5) execution of the main figures of the link passage, beginning by altering of the figures on the extreme left of the right-hand canvas into priests and soothsayers; (6) further enlargement of the wooden support, and sticking down the left-hand piece of canvas; (7) continuation of the link passage onto the left-hand canvas; (8) re-interpretation on the left-hand canvas of no. IV; (9) brushing on a dark green/brown glaze on the background; re-working the right-hand canvas and painting in the background landscape with figures—working from the left, leaving the re-working of the right-hand canvas and landscape unfinished.

So far as dating is concerned, the thesis that no. 278 was executed sometime round 1630 is on stylistic grounds correct. Since it has been established that no. 278 does not result from a second, direct contact with Mantegna's series, the question arises as to whether it was executed before Rubens' departure from Antwerp in 1628, in Spain, or in England, or again soon after his return to Antwerp in 1630. It seems that no. 278 belongs in spirit more to the 1620's than the 1630's; in particular the type of woman depicted in the left-hand canvas is not the type that Rubens evolved in 1630's. Bode[16] has drawn attention to the influence of Titian in no. 278; but this seems incorrect, for the women are not very Titianesque.

Several features in no. 278 can be related to the *Triumph of the Eucharist* series, which was executed by Rubens in the years just before his departure from Antwerp in 1628.[17] The woman with the basket of flowers on her head occurs in the design for the *Israelites gathering Manna*;[18] the bull(?) in the centre invites comparison with the bull(?) in *The Triumph of the Eucharist*,[19] and the handling of its slaughter with that of the attendant in the bottom right-hand corner of the *Abraham and Melchizedek*.[20]

In 1628, before he left Antwerp, Rubens began work on the series commissioned by Marie de Médicis for the second gallery in the Luxembourg Palace.[21] The work was interrupted by his diplomatic journeys, but some months after his return to his studio in 1630, work on one of the canvases—the *Triumph of Henri IV*—was nearing completion.[22] That the design for this painting was worked out before his departure is established by the existence of copies after it by Willem Panneels, who left Rubens' studio in June 1630.[23] The sketch at Bayonne[24] is clearly influenced by no. IX of Mantegna's series; in it also occurs a quotation from no. II and a variation of a pose in no. IV.[25] It is perhaps relevant that Rubens quoted Caesar's words on the occasion of his Pontine Triumph (the subject of Mantegna's series) in a letter to Dupuy of 29 April, 1629.[26]

There is no reason why Rubens should not have turned to Mantegna's series for inspiration for the *Triumph of Henri IV* without direct contact with it: he had his own recollections, and may have owned Andreani's woodcuts after it. Finally he may already have owned the series of copies on three pieces of canvas stuck on panel recorded in the inventory of the paintings in his collection which were for sale at his death.[27] Thus a dating for no. 278 to the last months spent in Antwerp before his diplomatic journeys seems best. However, there is the possibility that part of it may be have been executed in England, and that the rest was completed in Antwerp soon after his return in 1630, but this is unlikely.

This possibility rests on two factors: (1) the outer pieces of canvas are of the same weave and have the same count of 15 as the canvas used for the *Landscape with S. George* (Royal Collection),[28] which was painted by Rubens while he was in England and despatched by him to Antwerp before his return;[29] (2) Mantegna's series would no doubt have been a talking point in the English court after the news had reached the court, early in 1629, that Nys had bought it to sell to the king. It may have been as a result of this interest and of contact with Andreani's woodcuts, sent to Viscount Dorchester by Nys early in 1629,[30] that Rubens executed the copy on the right-hand canvas. Certainly Rubens appears to have favoured the use of canvas rather than panel (for it was more easily transportable) as a support when he was away from his studio. The similar canvas weave count between the two outer canvases of no. 278 and the *Landscape with S. George* is not necessarily significant. It may mean no more than that Rubens took with him to England part of a stock of canvas which he had in Antwerp. That this stock was available in Antwerp after his return, if we accept that the right-hand canvas was executed in England, is evident from the fact that he used some of it after he began to extend the composition. Extension involved the type of carpentry in making a wooden support which we associate with Rubens in his studio.

It is by no means certain that Rubens was responsible for executing the copy on the right-hand canvas; areas visible, which are not fully re-worked by him, are not of the highest quality; the inner part of the bottom of the tunic worn by the youth, who holds the rein of the cow, the cow's left foreleg, the elephants' legs and trunks and the tower on the hill are not particularly distinguished in handling. It is therefore a possibility that the copy was executed in Rubens' studio, but not by the master.

That no. 278 has been cut down to the left has already been pointed out. The gesture of the spectator on the centre canvas makes it clear that a hero is following somewhere along the line behind the elephants; and the small remains of a fourth canvas on the right-hand edge establish that it has been cut down to the right. The fourth canvas may have depicted a link passage between nos. V and VI of Mantegna's series. Evidence that Rubens may have gone some way in creating a variation, which was cut up by the late 1660's, of perhaps the whole of Mantegna's series, is provided by the accounts of the firm of Forchoudt. These accounts refer to two separate *Triumphs of Julius Caesar* by Rubens, the first received in Vienna from Antwerp in 1668 and the second in 1671, and two 'Triumphs of Andrea Mantegna perfected by Rubens being the Triumphs of Julius Caesar' which reached Vienna in 1673.[31] These two pictures may or may not be two of the three *Triumphs of Julius Caesar* referred to by Forchoudt in his letter to his sons in Vienna of 14 August, 1672.[32] The two pictures received in Vienna in 1673 and later sold to a Count Berka[33] are relevant to no. 278.

Hind first drew attention to the influence of Giulio Romano in Rubens' concept of the background figures of no. 278; he also thought that the left-hand figures might derive from him, but this cannot be established.[34] Jaffé[35] considers that the elephant on the right may also have been inspired by Giulio Romano. The woman with the basket of flowers on her head derives ultimately from Raphael.[36]

DRAWING: Study (?) for the re-working of the right-hand elephant, Coll., Paul Wallraf.[37]

COPY: Potsdam, canvas, $23\frac{5}{8} \times 39\frac{3}{8}$ (0·60 × 1·00).[38]

PROVENANCE: Perhaps exported from Antwerp by the dealer Forchoudt to his two sons, Alexander and William, in Vienna, 7 May, 1673 when valued at 100 guilders,[39] and sold in Vienna by them to Count Berca[40] (? = Franz Anton Hovora, Graf Berka von Duba and Lipa († 1706)).[41] Perhaps bought in Vienna by Costantino Balbi (1676–ca. 1741) when Genoese ambassador there from 1706–1710.[42] Recorded in the collection of Giacomino [? = Giacomo] Balbi, Genoa, 1758;[43] sold by Costantino Balbi to Irvine and Arthur Champernowne, acting for and with Buchanan, in 1802;[44] ownership assumed by Buchanan, who after an offer to the British Government and to J. J. Angerstein, sold it to Champernowne for 800 gns.;[45] exh. B.I. 1815 (129); A. Champernowne (†) sale, Christie's, 30 June [= 2nd day], 1820 (83) bt. Brockedon [= ?Champernowne family] for £351 15sh.[46] Coll. Samuel Rogers by 1824;[47] exh. B.I. 1854 (42); Samuel Rogers (†) sale, Christie's, 3 May, 1856 (726) bt. Bentley for the National Gallery for 1050 gns.[48]

REPRODUCTION: *National Gallery Illustrations, Continental Schools (excluding Italian)*, 1950, p. 308, top.

REFERENCES: *General:* J. Smith, *A Catalogue Raisonné*, 1830, II, no. 803; M. Rooses, *L'Œuvre de P. P. Rubens*, 1890, III, nos. 715–17; R. Oldenbourg, *Rubens, K. der K.*, [1921], p. 310.

In text: (1) See Champernowne's letter to Buchanan of 25 September, 1802 in W. Buchanan, *Memoirs of Painting*, II, 1824, pp. 101–102. (2) O. Panvinio († 1568), *De Triumpho*, describes a triumphal procession with similar detail, which included 'bovis ... cornibus auratis ... ab adolescentibus popis succintis ad immolandum ducebantur'; *De Triumpho* is printed in *Thesaurus Antiquitum Romanum*, IX, 1699, ed. J. G. Graevius; the quotation given here is from p. 1364; see also p. 6 of the first edition printed by Gerard de Jode, where the description is less detailed. (3) See *General References*; and the Champernowne sale entry of 1820 under *Provenance*. (4) Reproduced in F. Knapp, *Andrea Mantegna, K. der K.*, 1910, pp. 50–68. (5) See under *General References*. (6) See L. van Puyvelde, *Les Esquisses de Rubens*, 1940, no. 63; see also A. Rosenberg, *Rubens, K. der K.*, 1905, p. 8 and note; and National Gallery catalogues from 1915. (7) See L. Burchard and R. A. d'Hulst, *Rubens Drawings*, 1963, p. 41 under no. 21. (8) See Burchard/d'Hulst, *loc. cit.* The copy includes the captive with the goitre, whose face was used by Rubens for the figure to the right of the soothsayer in no. 278. Michael Jaffé has kindly drawn the compiler's attention to an eighteenth-century reference to Rubens' interest in Mantegna's series when he was in Italy. This is in the ms. *Anecdotes sur la vie de Rubens*, Bibliothèque Royale, Brussels, no. 5726, p. 3: '1. Quand Rubens séjourna à Mantoue il y dessina entre autres la fameuse frise d'André Mantenga [*sic*] cela parroit par deux dessins, fait auquel'on croit, sur les originaux de Rubens: aussi que par une Esquisse coloriée peinte a l'Huile sur papier aussi d'après cette frise. Cette esquisse se trouve dans le cabinet de M. Verlinden, Sécretaire de la ville de Malines'. Further details concerning Rubens' interest in the series may well be given by H. Kauffman in an article in *Beiträge zur Geschichte Wirtschaft und Kultur des Rhein,—Mass und Schelderaumes, Köln und der Nordwesten* 1941, which, unfortunately, has not been seen by the compiler. (9) See G. Glück, *Rubens, van Dyck und ihr Kreis*, 1933, p. 157 (reprint of an article of 1905). (10) See W. Bode, *Zeitschrift für bildenden Kunst*, 1905, p. 201. (11) See under *General References*; and the National Gallery catalogue of 1929. (12) The detail is of one of the corselet bearers, see Burchard/d'Hulst, *loc. cit.*; and L. Burchard, *The Burlington Magazine*, 1956, p. 415. (13) See W. Noël Sainsbury, *Original and Unpublished Papers* etc., 1859, pp. 327 ff. The sequence of events is the following: Nys writes to Viscount Dorchester, 2 February, 1629, that he has bought the Mantegna's; 9 February, 1629, he writes again to say that he has sent prints after the Mantegna's; 28 July, 1630, he writes to Charles I to say that he has sent his servant to explain the position about the Mantegna's to him; one of the servant's instructions, set out by Nys, was to make it known 'that the statues [which had also been bought, some of which had already been sent to Charles I, see Nys' letter to him of 26 July, 1630] and pictures of his majesty are daily visited here in Venice.' Rubens left England on 23 March, 1630. (14) M. Jaffé, *The Burlington Magazine*, 1965, p. 380 under no. 21. (15) The canvas join was thus strengthened by the underlapping wooden support, see Appendix. (16) *Loc. cit.* (17) The *modelli* for the tapestries were probably executed 1627–28; see the introductory entry to nos. 73–77 in the catalogue of *Olieverfschetsen van Rubens*, Museum Boymans, 1953, with references to previous literature. (18) *Ibid.*, no. 73 and rep. no. 63. (19) *Ibid.*, no. 77 and fig. no. 65, and the Prado picture. (20) The National Gallery of Art, Washington; ex coll. Stoye. (21) See Rooses, *op. cit.*, III, p. 277, where the relevant passage of Rubens' letter to Dupuy of 27 January, 1628, in which he states that he has begun the 'dissegni' for the other gallery, is quoted. For the whole letter see M. Rooses and Ch. Ruelens (†), *Correspondance de Rubens*, 1904, IV, p. 356–57. (22) See M. Rooses, *L'Œuvre* etc., III, pp. 277–78; and M. Rooses and Ch. Ruelens (†), *op. cit.*, V, 1907, p. 340. (23) See Burchard/d'Hulst, *op. cit.*, pp. 228–9, under no. 146. (24) See *Musée Bonnat, Catalogue Sommaire*, 1930, p. 157, no. 954. (25) That is in the top left-hand group where the central standard bearer seen from the back, recalls the foot soldier in the centre of no. II, and the man bending downwards to his left (who also occurs in the sketch at Berlin for the *Landscape with S. George*, see Burchard/d'Hulst, *op. cit.*, no. 146) recalls the bearer, also copied by Rubens, in no. IV. (26) See Rooses and Ruelens (†), *op. cit.*, V, 1907, pp. 29–31. (27) See J. Denucé, *Inventories of the Art-Collections in Antwerp* etc., 1932, p. 70. It is tempting to identify this entry in the inventory with no. 278, see Smith under *General References*; and R. N. Wornum, *Descriptive ... Catalogue of the Pictures in the National Gallery*, from 1857; but after reconsideration, the identification is improbable because (1) the entry does not specify that Rubens was responsible for the copies and (2) the entry suggests that the copies were after the whole of Mantegna's series. (28) Rep. by Oldenbourg, cited under *General References*, p. 311. (29) Rooses, *L'Œuvre* etc., 1888, II, no. 435. (30) See under note 13. (31) See J. Denucé, *Art-Export in the 17th Century in Antwerp, The Firm of Forchoudt*, 1931, pp. 122 and 133. (32) *Ibid.*, p. 185. (33) *Ibid.*, p. 165. Count 'Berckel' also bought the *Triumph of Julius Caesar* by Rubens which reached Vienna in 1671, see p. 159. (34) See A. M. Hind, *Catalogue of Drawings ... in the British Museum*, 1923, II, p. 21, no. 50. The influence of Giulio Romano is in fact more evident in the Bayonne sketch. (35) *Loc. cit.* (36) That is from the woman carrying the jug on her head in *The Fire in the Borgo*, rep. by G. Gronau, *Raffael, K. der K.*, 1923, p. 121. (37) Black chalk with traces of red, $8\frac{5}{8} \times 7\frac{7}{8}$ (0·22 × 0·20), see Jaffé *loc. cit.* The drawing now in the collection of G. M. Gathorne-Hardy and discussed in the *Descriptive Catalogue of Drawings ... in the possession of the Hon. A. E. Gathorne-Hardy*, 1902, no. 69, p. 33, is clearly not a study for no. 278 as is claimed there. MacLaren, ms. notes, has connected it with the picture in the Prado (no. 91) now ascribed to A. Falcone (see *Museo del Prado, Catálogo de las Pinturas*, 1963, p. 206, and reproduced by M. Soria in the *Art Quarterly*, 1960, p. 32, fig. 7, who ascribed it to Andrea di Leone). The drawing obviously derives from no. V of Mantegna's series. Any relation that the drawing has to no. 278 is in the province of no. 278's provenance; but it is not necessary to suppose that the artist responsible for it was influenced by no. 278. If the Prado picture is indeed by a Neapolitan artist and if the drawing is preparatory to it, the indications are that he could not have been influenced by no. 278 (see under *Provenance*). (38) See J. G. Puhlmann, *Beschreibung des Berliner Schlosses*, 1790; and G. Poensgen, *Die Gemälde in den Preussischen Schlössern, Das Neue Palais*, 1935, no. 224; noted as in a Prussian private collection before the reign of Frederick II (1740–86); information and references kindly provided by Dr. Rüdiger Klessmann, of the Staatliche Museen, Berlin. (39) See note 31. These two pictures were received in Vienna on 4 July, 1673; no. 278 could also be identified with the *Triumphs of Julius Caesar* by Rubens despatched in 1668 and 1671 respectively. (40) See note 33. (41) See J. Siebmacher's *Grosses und allgemeines Wappenbuch*, 1886, IV, no. 9, by G. F. Meraviglia, p. 54. This Count Berka was Oberstlandmarshall and Statthalter 'im Königreiche Böhmen.' C. G. F. Heyer von Rosenfeld in the same series, 1873, IV, no. 2, p. 28, records a previous Count Berka, Heinrich Wolf Berka von Hovora, created in 1640, who was 'kaiserl. Rath' and 'böhmisher Kammerdirecktor.' (42) There is no evidence that Costantino Balbi bought no. 278; but his movements, for which see the *Dizionario Biografico degli Italiani*, 1963, V, p. 360, make his acquisition of it an attractive hypothesis. (43) See C. N. Cochin, *Voyage d'Italie*, III, 1758, pp. 268–269. Cochin considered that the hero of the Triumph should be Bacchus. Giacomino Balbi is probably Giacomo Balbi, Costantino's son; he was senator in 1746, 1766, 1770 and 1783, see V. Spreti, *et al.*, *Enciclopedia Storico Nobiliare Italiana*, 1928, I, p. 476. (44) See W. Buchanan, *Memoirs of Painting*, I, 1824, pp. 175–177. Costantino was a son of Giacomo Balbi, in 1790 he was one of the *protectori dei Banco di S. Giorgio*, and ambassador to Vienna in 1791; he later set up house in Venice, see *Enciclopedia Storico Nobiliare Italiana*, loc. cit. Balbi's certificate concerning the sale to Irvine dated 24 September (?), 1802, is in the N.G. archives, see also Champernowne's letter cited in note 1. (45) See Buchanan, *op. cit.*, I, pp. 175–177 and II, pp. 109–10. (46) Buyer's name and price given in Christie's marked copy of the sale catalogue. According to Buchanan, *op. cit.*, I, p. 177, the picture was bought in. (47) See Buchanan, *op. cit.*, II, p. 388, under Balbi. (48) Buyer's name and price in the N.G.'s marked copy of the sale catalogue.

680 THE MIRACULOUS DRAUGHT OF FISHES

Simon Peter kneels before Christ, while his fellow fishermen draw in a net miraculously full of fish from Lake Gennesaret.

Pencil, pen and oil, on paper, stuck on canvas, $21\frac{7}{16}/\frac{5}{8} \times 33\frac{1}{4}/\frac{9}{16}$ (0·545/0·55 × 0·845/0·85).

The paper support is made up out of three sheets, whose widths measure approximately (from left to right), $7\frac{11}{16}$ (0·195), $17\frac{13}{16}$ (0·453), $8\frac{1}{16}$ (0·205). The canvas lining dates from 1862.[1]

Generally in good condition. The bottom and right-hand edges of the paper are ragged and torn in places. There are several minor, scattered losses in the paint especially round Christ, and there is a little wearing in the sea. The paper has discoloured through having absorbed varnish. Cleaned, 1964.

The media differ on each sheet. On the central sheet, the figures, fish, net and shells were first drawn in chalk or pencil, with probably some modelling in thin, greyish washes, both now very faint and evident only in certain areas; the outlines and some details (notably the fish, net and heads, except Christ's which is executed in black washes) are heightened with pen and ink; the sheet was then in varying degrees re-worked in oil (some areas being left uncovered). The right-hand sheet is executed wholly in oil, as is the left, but for the fisherman, who was first drawn in pencil.

For *pentimenti*, see below.

The subject is taken from Luke, V, 1–10.

Wornum[2] first pointed out that no. 680 was the working sketch for Schelte à Bolswert's engraving.[3] Bolswert's engraving is also on three sheets (the joins do not exactly correspond with the joins in the paper support of no. 680). The engraver's 'drawing out' lines can be made out here and there on no. 680. There are some minor differences between the working sketch and the engraving: Christ's nose is straighter in the engraving; several of the fishermen's heads (notably Simon Peter's) are more articulated in the print and differ slightly; no. 680 lacks the two birds immediately to the right (in the engraving) of Christ and the pin on the port (in the engraving) side of the nearer boat.

The composition on the central sheet derives from the central panel of Rubens' triptych in Notre Dame au delà de la Dyle, Malines,[4] from which it differs in several details: the horizon is higher; the left thumb of the fisherman standing in the far boat is not included; the face of the fisherman about to get into the water is turned more to the right and his features have been simplified; the waistline of the fisherman leaning on the pole in the near boat is lower; the hand of the fisherman beckoning is open; the fisherman in the boat, holding the net, looks more upwards; Simon Peter's left knee is lower; Christ's right hand is lower, his cloak has been given more movement so that his legs are visible; his profile and hair are slightly different; the costume of the fisherman standing in the water is different and his left leg has been widened; shells have been painted out between his feet; the fall of the rope and two of the fish are also different.

Some of the differences result from *pentimenti* in no. 680, which are visible to the naked eye: in one of the fish, the rope and the shells; there is also a faint suggestion in infra-red photography that the fall of Christ's cloak may first have been straight and that Simon Peter's left knee was higher. Many of the differences result from the working in oil paint or oil wash (including those in Christ's face).[5]

Schelte à Bolswert's engraving bears the privileges of the King of France, the States General, and the joint privilege of the Archduke Albert and Archduchess Isabella. It must therefore pre-date the Archduke's death on 13 July, 1621, which provides a sure *terminus ante quem* for the date of execution for no. 680.[6]

Rubens probably began to consider the commission for the triptych for Notre Dame au delà de la Dyle from 9 October, 1617;[7] but work on the actual triptych could not have started until the panels had been sent to him, which was sometime after 5 February, 1618,[8] when the terms of the commission may have been finalized. The triptych was completed by 11 August, 1619.[9] The direct dependence of the 'copy' on the centre sheet of no. 680 requires either that the central panel of the triptych was finished or nearly finished or that the *modello* for it (apparently not extant) was completed. Whichever was the case, this would have been after *ca.* 5 February, 1618 and before 11 August, 1619 (depending on when the terms commission were finalized and when Rubens painted the *modello*).

The later of these two dates is unlikely as the *terminus post quem* for the execution of no. 680. For it is probable that the engraving had already been made before 28 May, 1619—the date of a letter from Rubens to Sir Dudley Carleton at The Hague, in which we learn that two engravings: a 'caccia de tanti animali formidabili' and 'la pescagione delli apostoli' had already been received by Carleton.[10] The identity of the engraver is open to doubt;[11] but the inscription on Bolswert's print, from Luke, V, 10 (see below under *Engravings*) provides a much better basis for Carleton's play on words, acknowledged by Rubens in his letter to him, than does the inscription on Soutman's print of the same subject.[12] If Carleton had received a copy of Bolswert's engraving by 28 May, 1619, it shows that both the working sketch and the engraving were made while the triptych, destined for Malines, was still in Rubens' studio, in which case no. 680 would date from *ca.* 5 February, 1618 and before 28 May, 1619. It seems improbable (though not impossible) that Rubens should have decided to engrave the composition of the central panel while he was actually evolving the latter. Thus a date late in 1618 or early in 1619 appears to be the most acceptable for no. 680.

The authorship of working drawings for engravings produced by Rubens, particularly round 1619, is disputed. Bellori[13] records that van Dyck produced such drawings, and Lugt[14] has suggested that a group in the Louvre may be by van Dyck in the main. So far as one of the series is concerned, Burchard and d'Hulst[15] consider it to be retouched in ink by Rubens, while Jaffé[16] specifies that it is by van Dyck and corrected by Rubens. Held[17] considers the attribution of the series to van Dyck 'to be a matter of conjecture' but states that, except in exceptional cases, the working drawings were entrusted to pupils, Rubens confining himself to making 'final corrections'.

No. 680 has been catalogued as by van Dyck,[18] Rubens,[19] and more recently ascribed to him.[20] Recent cleaning has shown that the brushwork in oils is clearly by Rubens; the pencil drawing of the fisherman on the far left is also exceptionally vigorous, and is almost certainly his work as well. This leaves the problem of the authorship of the underdrawing and modelling, and the heightening with pen and ink on the central sheet. The underdrawing and modelling is so faint that it is not possible to form an opinion concerning its authorship; Jaffé[21] believes that the heightening in pen and ink is also by Rubens.

The underdrawing etc., was confined to a transposition of the original design; and it is possible that Rubens changed his mind concerning the format of the print after this had been done. Only if it was his original intention to confine the print to a single sheet, would his responsibility for the pen drawing be explained, on the grounds (which was not always the case in his print making) that he would wish

to make the finishing touches to the working drawing. The handling of
the pen and ink on the faces and hair is similar to that in several of the
working drawings in the Louvre. And it is notable that the faces,
rendered in pen and ink, in no. 680 lack the eloquence of expression of
those in the painting and the articulation of those in the print. Furthermore the re-working in oil often corrects the pen drawing, which could
not have been considered essential as a guide line for the engraver as its
presence is confined to the central sheet. These observations suggest
that the pen and ink work (and thus the underdrawing etc.) was done by
an assistant. It must remain a matter for conjecture, but unlikely, that
this assistant was van Dyck.

The evolution of no. 680 seems thus to have been: the execution of a
copy, heightened in pen and ink, of the original design on the centre
sheet, probably by an assistant; Rubens' decision (perhaps after a start
had been made at engraving the design, see under *Copies*) to enlarge the
working drawing by the addition of a sheet to either side; his execution
of the fisherman on the far left in pencil, and then his elaboration of the
composition in oils, combined with his re-working of much of the centre
sheet, in oils to take this enlargement into account (the alterations to
Christ are only explicable in this way) and to correct or change some
details in the copy. Further alterations and corrections (notably to the
faces and hair styles on the centre sheet) must have been made by him
on proof copies of the print.

COPIES: After no. 680: oil on panel, Major Ynyr A. Burges sale, Christie's,
17 February, 1956 (14): perhaps after an early proof engraving of the central
design: drawing, Weimar Museum, 1892;[22] after the engraving: oil on copper,
approx. same size, Sacristy of Granada Cathedral; detail, by J. Baudin(?),
S. Alban's Church, Namur.[23]
ENGRAVINGS:[24] Schelte à Bolswert (in reverse) with the inscription: *ait
ad Simonem, Jesus, Noli timere: ex hoc iam, homines eris capiens, Lucæ cap.
V.*; Anon. (published by Gillis Hendricx) (in reverse); F. Ragot (in reverse);[25]
G. Edelinck;[26] C. Galle III (?) (in reverse);[27] Anon. (published by Cornelis
Danckerts);[28] R. H. J. Delvaux (in reverse).
PROVENANCE: Perhaps coll. Cav. Gizzi, Palazzo Gizzi, Naples, 1815.[29]
Bought from Cav. Raffaelle Carelli, Naples, 1861; lent, through the Arts Council,
to the City Museum and Art Gallery, Birmingham, 1958–63.
REPRODUCTION: *National Gallery Illustrations, Continental Schools (excluding
Italian)*, 1950, p. 309, bottom.
REFERENCE: *General:* Gregory Martin, *The Burlington Magazine*, 1966, pp.
239 ff.
In text: (1) The paper was stuck on a thin piece of canvas which in turn was
insecurely fixed to a panel on acquisition. (2) R. N. Wornum, *Descriptive and
Historical Catalogue of the Pictures in the National Gallery*, 1862, p. 270. (3) F.
van den Wijngaert, *Inventaris der Rubeniaansche Prentkunst*, 1940, no. 39.
(4) M. Rooses, *L'Œuvre de P. P. Rubens*, II, 1888, no. 245; rep. Oldenbourg,
Rubens, K. der K., [1921], p. 172. (5) The compiler, see under *General Reference*,
there thought that the outline of Christ's face was heightened with pen and ink;
but, the black is richer in texture than the dark brown of the ink, and similar
to the wash on the outlines of Christ's legs. (6) As pointed out by Rooses,
op. cit., 1888, II, p. 28. (7) See Rooses, *op. cit.*, 1888, II, p. 25. (8) *Ibid.* (9) *Ibid.*
(10) M. Rooses and Ch. Ruelens (†) *Correspondance de Rubens*, 1898, II, pp. 215–
216. (11) H. Hymans, *L'Histoire de la Gravure dans l'École de Rubens*, 1879, p.

124; and R. S. Magurn, *The Letters of Peter Paul Rubens*, 1955, p. 444, have suggested that the engraver was Pieter Soutman. Rooses has argued that he was Schelte à Bolswert, see M. Rooses and Ch. Ruelens (†), *op. cit.*, p. 218; followed by the compiler, cited under *General Reference*. (12) The inscription, on Soutman's print, which is Wijngaert, *op. cit.*, no. 629, is 'Impletum Loeti, ducunt ad littore rete: Dum sic, In Incerto gurgite, Piscis Adest'. Rubens, in his letter to Carleton, see Rooses and Ruelens (†) *op. cit.*, p. 215, wrote 'Certo che fu opportuna la cacçia . . . chella diede à quei sig^{ri} (=members of the States General at The Hague) si come ancora la pescagione delli apostoli che da vero sono riusciti per noi piscatores hominum, come V. E. argutamente mi accenna . . .' (13) G. P. Bellori, *Le Vite* etc., 1672, p. 284. (14) F. Lugt, *Musée du Louvre, Inventaire Général des Dessins des Écoles du Nord*, II, 1949, pp. 36 ff. H. Vey, *Die Zeichnungen Anton van Dycks*, I, 1962, nos. 160–167, accepts the attribution in the majority of instances. (15) L. Burchard and R.-A. d'Hulst, *Rubens Drawings*, I, 1963, p. 150. (16) Michael Jaffé, *The Burlington Magazine*, 1965, p. 376. (17) J. S. Held, *Rubens Selected Drawings*, II, 1959, p. 37. (18) See notes 2 and 3; Rooses, *op. cit.*, 1888, II, p. 28 considered the ascription 'fort possible.' (19) See *An Abridged Catalogue of the Pictures in the National Gallery*, 1911, p. 283; and, if correctly, identified, D. Romanelli (see note 29). (20) In *The National Gallery Catalogues, The Summary Catalogue*, 1958. (21) Letter to the compiler. (22) M. Rooses, *L'Œuvre* etc., 1892, V, no. 1344 and pl. 385; ex coll. the Duchess of Weimar, 1888, see Rooses, *op. cit.*, II, p. 28. Rooses considered it to be by Rubens and preparatory to the engraving. But judging from the photograph reproduced by him it appears to be of poorish quality. As reproduced, the drawing shows a little more to the right and left than does the prototype but corresponds in height with it. It follows the direction of the engraving and apart from the alterations shown in the pose of Christ, follows the engraving where it differs from the working sketch, though it does not show the two sea gulls, just to the left of Christ in the engraving. Christ's drapery fully covers his legs; but He is shown stepping towards Simon Peter and the two positions of his right (in the working sketch) hand and his flowing cloak are shown. There is also a *pentimento* in the position of his head which is difficult to relate to either the working sketch or the prototype. In view of these facts the drawing's status is problematic: as it follows the direction of the engraving (and shows a knowledge of the extension to left and right of the original composition) it should derive from it. It may be that it is a copy of a proof of a first attempt at engraving the centre sheet. (23) Photograph with attribution in the R.K.D. (24) See C. G. Voorhelm Schneevoogt, *Catalogue des Estampes gravées d'après P. P. Rubens* etc., 1873, pp. 28–9, nos. 141–47. (25) With a different inscription. (26) Without the inscription, and cut to the left. (27) Presumably made by C. Galle III, as the publisher was Cornelius de Bondt [*sic*] (active 1687/8–*ca.* 1730). The print is cut to the left. (28) The name of the engraver is illegible. (29) See D. Romanelli, *Napoli antica e moderna*, 1815, III, p. 112, as 'La pesca degli Apostoli del Rubens'.

852 PORTRAIT OF SUSANNA LUNDEN (*NÉE FOURMENT*) (?)

The sitter wears a plumed, beaver hat; her left hand holds a grey shawl, which is draped round her shoulders.

Oil on oak, $31\frac{1}{16} \times 21\frac{1}{4}/21\frac{1}{2}$ (0·79 × 0·54/0·546).

The support is made up of 4 members,[1] see Appendix I. On the reverse of the central member is the brand of the coat of arms of the city of Antwerp, and the incised initials, *M V* (in monogram).[2]

In good condition. There are some small losses along the joins. The bottom and right-hand edges are painted up to a border, *ca.* $\frac{1}{4}$ (0·006) wide, as is the lower part of the left-hand edge (= that part of it made up by the fourth member) and the right-hand part of the top edge (= that part of the support made up by the third member, joined vertically); the paint goes up to the rest of the left-hand and top edges. Cleaned, 1946.[3]

There are several *pentimenti*, visible for the most part to the naked eye: the hat was first sketched in slightly higher and more to the left; only the thumb and forefinger of the sitter's left hand were first depicted; the thumb of her right hand was originally higher; part of her left cuff was shown; one of the gold tips to the bow on her left sleeve has been painted out; the shawl originally billowed out more to the right, and part of the white chemise on her right shoulder has been painted out.

Susanna Fourment (1599–1643) was the third daughter of Daniel Fourment and Clara Stappaert, of Antwerp. She married Raymond del Monte in 1617 and then, in 1622, Arnold Lunden. Her youngest sister, Helena, married Peeter Pauwel Rubens in 1630. Rubens described the parents as 'honesti pero cittadini' (= bourgeois);[4] Daniel Fourment was an Antwerp silk and tapestry merchant.[5]

Rubens' authorship of no. 852 has not and need not be doubted.[6]

The make up of the support and certain of the *pentimenti* suggest that no. 852 was executed in three stages. Rubens began with the two (counting from the left) members that are joined vertically. He sketched in the hat nearer the top and left-hand edges. He then moved the hat down and worked up the portrait. When this was completed, he enlarged the support to the right and bottom; he then re-worked the dark crimson sleeves in a lighter orange. The first two stages were painted with the support unframed, which may suggest that Rubens had an enlargement in mind from early on (see under no. 157). The disposition of the borders makes it clear that the support was framed after the enlargement, but before the execution of the third stage.

The earliest printed reference to what is probably no. 852 refers to the sitter as Demoiselle Lundens (*sic*);[7] Génard[8] appears to have been the first to identify the sitter as Susanna Fourment. This thesis has since been generally accepted,[9] despite its rejection by Glück.[10]

There is no certain portrait of Susanna Fourment. The *Staetmasse* of Rubens' estate shows, however, that she sat for him and that Rubens had at least four[11] of his portraits of her at his death. No. 852 is not certainly identifiable with any of these.[12] It was in the possession of the Lunden family in the eighteenth century.[13] Extracts by Mols of two Lunden inventories, one dating from 1639–1649[14] and the other perhaps from the second half of the century,[15] show that the only portraits of women by Rubens then owned by the family were of Susanna.[16] However, no. 852 is not certainly identifiable with any of these portraits.[17]

The sitter in no. 852 is probably in her twenties and she is wearing what is perhaps a betrothal or marriage ring.[18] No. 852 has been generally dated between 1620–25;[19] Glück's[20] proposal of after 1630 is unacceptable both on grounds of style and costume.[21] Oldenbourg's juxtaposition of no. 852 with the *Double Portrait of Albert and Nicholas Rubens* (coll. the Prince of Liechtenstein) of *ca.* 1625[22] is valid; the difference between the two works can be explained by the fact that the Liechtenstein picture is more fully worked up. The first half of the 1620's, which is the probable date of execution of no. 852, supports rather than rules out the identification of the sitter as Susanna Fourment, who married Arnold Lunden in 1622, when she was twenty-three.

The same sitter appears in other works by Rubens—notably in a drawing in the Albertina which is inscribed in an old hand 'suster van Heer Rubbens [sic]'; this is some indication that the sitter was related to Rubens.[23]

None of these observations prove that Susanna Fourment is the sitter in no. 852; but taken cumulatively they make it probable. And it seems likely that no. 852 was painted a year or two after her marriage to Arnold Lunden.[24] If such was the case, the painting in the Louvre[25] and the drawing in the Albertina were probably made a little earlier, and the full length (Gulbenkian coll.) about six years later—ca. 1630.[26]

For nearly two hundred years, no. 852 has been burdened with the sobriquet 'chapeau de paille.' Evers[27] believed that it was given to no. 852 by Rubens himself. This cannot be proved and is most improbable, not least because it appears to have become attached only round 1780.[28] Several theories have been advanced to explain it; none is convincing.[29] The explanation lies in a confusion which evolved from round 1770–1780,[30] when no. 852 was beginning to attract the attention of amateurs. The sobriquet is entirely inappropriate; it seems to have no historical justification, and is therefore, here, rejected and abandoned.

The hat is similar to others worn by both men and women in the Netherlands already by the early 1620's.[31]

ENGRAVINGS: G. Maile, 1818;[32] R. Cooper, 1823; S. W. Reynolds, 1823; M. Steyaert;[33] A. Cornilliet;[34] C. Marr; P. A. Rajon;[35] F. Daems (lithograph);[36] Jobard (lithograph).

COPIES: Antonius Ysendyck;[37] pen drawing by Antonius Overlaet, 1768;[38] miniature by Madame de Neuville;[39] gouache by M. de Meulemeester;[40] drawing by J. M. W. Turner;[41] pastel by Andrew Geddes.[42]

DERIVATIONS: Self Portrait by Madame Vigée Lebrun;[43] Portrait of Lady Julia Peel by Sir Thomas Lawrence;[44] Portrait of Miss Charlotte Nasmyth ('Summer') by Andrew Geddes;[45] Portrait of Miss McDougall by Henry Wyatt.[46] A number of other paintings show the sitter with the face half shaded from the sun, or in straw hats, but they cannot be called derivations of no. 852.[47]

PROVENANCE: Perhaps coll. Lunden (? = Arnold Lunden († 1656) by 1639–49,[48] and, by descent, coll. Arnold Lunden's grandson, Arnold-Albert Lunden (1646–†ca. 1682);[49] coll. his grandson Arnold-Albert Lunden (1707–1733), Antwerp, who left it as 'propriété indivise' to his descendants;[50] recorded in the collection of M. Lundens (sic), Antwerp, (? = his son, Arnold-Guillaume—Joseph (1732–1782)), by Descamps in 1753;[51] according to Mensaert to be seen 'chez les Demoiselles de Lunde' (sic), Antwerp (? = the nieces of Arnold-Albert Lunden, Marie-Thérèse (1722–1794) and Helène-Joséphine (1725–1780)) in 1763;[52] in the collection of Jean-Michel-Joseph van Havre (1730–1804), Antwerp, who, in 1763, married Arnold-Albert Lunden's daughter Catherine-Anne-Marie, in 1771;[53] perhaps seen in this collection in 1774,[54] and certainly seen in it by Reynolds in 1781;[55] apparently for sale in 1803[56] but withdrawn; and in the collection of van Havre's son, Jean-Michel-Antoine-Joseph (1764–1844), Antwerp, with whom seen in 1813;[57] advertised for sale, 1817,[58] but sold privately by van Havre to his father-in-law, Henri-Joseph Stier (1743–1821) in November, 1817(?) for 50,000 francs;[59] Henri-Joseph Stier (d'Aertselaer) (†) sale, Antwerp, 29 July, 1822 (1) bought by L. J. Nieuwenhuys, J. Foster and J. Smith for 5,970 fl.;[60] deposited with George IV at Carlton House, London, February, 1823;[61] exhibited in Mr. Stanley's Rooms, Old Bond Street, London, March–June, 1823;[62] sold by Smith to the Rt. Hon. Robert Peel (later Sir Robert Peel, Bart.) for £2,725 in 1824;[63] purchased with the Peel Collection, 1871; exh. *An Exhibition of Cleaned Pictures*, The National Gallery, 1946/7 (no. 52).

REPRODUCTION: *National Gallery Illustrations, Continental Schools (excluding Italian)*, 1950, p. 310.

REFERENCES: *General:* J. Smith, *A Catalogue Raisonné* etc., 1830, II, no. 811; M. Rooses, *L'Œuvre de P. P. Rubens*, 1890, IV, no. 949; R. Oldenbourg, *Rubens, K. der K.*, [1921], p. 280.

In text: (1) See P. Coremans, *The Burlington Magazine*, 1948, fig. 18. There is the possibility that the support is made up by five members as is to be inferred from the catalogue of *An Exhibition of Cleaned Pictures*, National Gallery, 1947 (no. 52). But the parting in the paint on the left is more likely to be a crack than a join that has opened. (2) This monogram is that of the Antwerp panel maker Michiel Vriendt, see G. Gepts, *Jaarboek koninklijk Museum voor schone Kunsten*, Antwerp, 1954–60, pp. 83 ff. (3) The cleaning led to a certain amount of controversy referred to in the catalogue of *An Exhibition of Cleaned Pictures*, *loc. cit.*; and by Coremans, *loc. cit.* Earlier accusations that it had been damaged by cleaning are refuted by Geo. Stanley, *Memorandum of the Picture called the Chapeau de Paille*, 1823, 5th edition, postscript to the 4th edition, p. 10. He stated there that the picture had not been in fact cleaned. Northcote, at any rate, did not think that the rumours that it had been injured by cleaning, were true, see, *Conversations of James Northcote, R.A.* etc., ed. by E. Fletcher, 1901, pp. 60–61. (4) See *Correspondance de Rubens*, ed. M. Rooses, and Ch. Ruelens (†), 1906, VI, p. 82. (5) See M. Rooses, *Rubens*, trans. by H. Child, I, 1904, p. 301. (6) The critic of the *Times*, 15 March, 1823, did not believe that Rubens was responsible for the lower portion including the hands, see W. T. Whitley, *Art in England 1821–1837*, 1930, p. 38. (7) See J. B. Descamps, *La Vie des Peintres Flamands* etc., 1753, I, p. 324. (8) As is to be inferred from *P. P. Rubens Aanteekeningen over den groten Meester* etc., I, 1877, pp. 42 and 47–9. (9) For instance by M. Rooses, see under *General References*; A. Rosenberg, *Rubens, K. der K.*, 1905, p. 224; H. G. Evers, *Rubens und sein Werk*, 1944, pp. 281–84; J. S. Held, *Rubens Selected Drawings*, I, 1959, p. 137 under no. 104; L. Burchard and R. A. d'Hulst, *Rubens Drawings*, I, 1963, p. 214 under no. 136. R. Oldenbourg, see under *General References*, accepted the identification with qualification; qualifications are more strongly expressed in the *National Gallery Summary Catalogue*, 1958, p. 210 under no. 852. (10) G. Glück, *Rubens, van Dyck und ihr Kreis*, 1933, p. 144. J. T. Smith, *A Book for a Rainy Day*, 1845, p. 245 of 1905 ed., stated that 'the popular report . . .is, that it [no. 852] was the portrait of Elizabeth Lunden'. MacLaren, ms. notes, suggested that the sitter was Elizabeth Fourment (b. 1609) who married Nicholas Picquery in 1627 'if a date of 1630 or later is accepted', but this dating seems too late (see above). MacLaren went on to state, in support of his view, that 'Elizabeth is the only one [of the Fourment sisters] besides Helena and Susanna of whom a portrait by Rubens is recorded' (=no. LXIII of the *Staetmasse ende Rekeninge* of Rubens' estate, printed by J. Denucé, *Inventories of the Art-Collections in Antwerp* etc., 1932, p. 78). (11) That is nos. LXIII [= LXIV], LXIX, LXX, see Denucé, *loc. cit.*, Génard and Rooses, *loc. cit.*, included no. LVI: 2 portraits sold to Arnold Lunden of 'syne huysvrouwe'; but Burchard has shown that the phrase 'syne huysvrouwe' in the *Staetmasse* refers to Rubens' wife, Helena Fourment or to Isabella Brant, see Glück, *op. cit.*, p. 388. (12) Génard and Rooses, *loc. cit.*, claimed that no. 852 is probably identifiable with no. LXIV, which was sold to Helena Fourment, but this is probably rightly rejected by Evers, *op. cit.*, p. 280–282. (13) See under *Provenance*. (14) This extract is headed 'Extrait d'un Catalogue de Tableaux fait entre les années 1639 a [*sic*] 1649 avec les prix qu'ils ont coutés . . .' with a note by Mols: 'Le Catalogue est dressé certainement par *un Lunden* qui avoit été marié ou bién alié avec une Rubens'; and the relevant entries are printed by both Rooses, *loc. cit.*, and Evers, *op. cit.*, p. 281, but in both cases inaccurately. This and the following extract (see note 15) are inv. no. 5730 of the Cabinet des Manuscrits, Bibliothèque Royale de Belgique. Rooses states that there were only 3 portraits of Susanna mentioned; Evers prints only two entries. He omits no. 106, on page 43 of the ms.: '2 portraits sujets de Susanne fl. 120'; the entry above contains the words 'par le même' (= Rubens) and although there are no ditto marks for no. 106, the implication is that Rubens was the author of no. 106 as well. No. 106 has the comment by Mols 'c'est la même sans doute que dessus', that is the same Susanna as referred to in nos. 54 and 78 of the inventory (printed by Evers). (15) This extract is headed: Extrait d'un Inventaire de Tableaux . . . dans la Famille du Sieur Arnold Lunden' with a note by Mols: 'Mr. Arnold Lunden étoit le fils ou le petit fils, de celui qui a été marié avec une des filles de Rubens'. The relevant entries are printed by Evers, *loc. cit.*, he argues, p. 283, that this Arnold Lunden was Arnold-Albert Lunden (1646–ca. 1682), the grandson (by the female side) of Arnold Lunden and Susanna Fourment; for as he makes clear no Lunden married a daughter of Rubens. (16) Rooses and Evers, *loc. cit.*, are probably right in supposing that the Susanne Rubens in the extract of the 1639–49 catalogue refers to Susanna Fourment. A simple error may have been made in transcribing the original inventory (so far as nos. 54 and 78 are concerned) and that is the omission of the word 'par'. (17) Given our present state of knowledge of archival sources concerning pictures owned by the descendants of Arnold Lunden and Susanna Fourment the identification of no. 852 with any of the portraits mentioned in the *Staetmasse* and the two extracts of catalogues of pictures (referred to above) owned by the Lunden family, is not certain. (18) See G. F. Kunz, *Rings for the Finger*, 1917, p. 224, 'That the betrothal ring was occasionally worn on the index finger is shown in two celebrated seventeenth century pictures, the Betrothal of 'Marie de' Medici', by Rubens, and the 'Betrothal of St. Catherine' by Murillo.' It is perhaps worthy of note that only one portrait by Rubens of either of his wives shows a ring being worn: that is the Munich *Portrait of Rubens and Isabella Brant* (Oldenbourg, *op. cit.*, p. 35) where the ring is also worn on the index finger of the right hand. As this portrait obviously refers to the marriage of Rubens and Isabella Brant, it seems likely that the ring in no. 852 means that the sitter was also married or about to be married, especially as the ring is given prominence. (19) Rooses, *loc. cit.*, ca. 1620; Rosenberg, *loc. cit.*, ca. 1620; Oldenbourg, *loc. cit.*, ca. 1625; Burchard Documentation ± 1621; J. S. Held, *Rubens*, 1963, p. 12, 1622; J. M. Müller Hofstede, *Rubens*, 1964, pl. XVII, ca. 1625. (20) *Loc. cit.* (21) The flesh in no. 852 is tightly drawn and the brush strokes of the face do not have the feathery looseness that Rubens evolved in the last decade under the influence of Titian. (22) *Op. cit.*, p. 281. Held, *Rubens, Selected Drawings*, I, 1959, p. 139, under no. 108, accepts this dating; Burchard and d'Hulst, *op. cit.*, p. 215 under no. 138, date it ca. 1630–31, which is too late. (23) G. Glück and M. Halberditzl, *Die Handzeichnungen von P. P. Rubens*, 1928, no. 162, as Susanna Fourment, dated by them 1626–27. Rooses, *op. cit.*, V, no. 1205, and Held, *op. cit.*, I, 1959, p. 137, under no. 104, consider that the inscription supports the identification; Held, *op. cit.*, p. 138, under no. 106, argues that the inscription must date from after 1630 when Rubens married Susanna's sister, Helena. (24) Rubens was related to Susanna before his marriage with her younger sister, through his first wife's sister, Clara, who married their brother Daniel Fourment, see M. Rooses, *Rubens*, trans. by H. Child, I, 1904, p. 301. (25) See Oldenbourg, *op. cit.*, p. 279. (26) Glück and Halberditzl, *op. cit.*, no. 161; Held, *op. cit.*, no. 104; and Burchard/d'Hulst, *op. cit.*, no. 136, consider that the

drawing in the Boymans-van Beuningen Museum, inv. no. V.58, also depicts
Susanna. But the eye and ear are different from those in no. 852. That the
sitter in the Boymans-van Beuningen drawing is not Susanna is suggested by the
fact that the same model appears on the right in Waddesdon *Garden of Love*
beside the lady, who is very like the lady in the Gulbenkian portrait (Oldenbourg, *op. cit.*, p. 329) which is accepted as depicting Susanna Fourment.
(**27**) *Op. cit.*, pp. 287–288. (**28**) Reynolds is the first author to refer to no. 852
by the title 'chapeau de paille': he saw it in 1781, see *A Journey to Flanders and
Holland in the year MDCCLXXXI* . . . in *The Complete Works of Sir Joshua
Reynolds*, II, 1824, p. 244. Paquet-Syphorien appears to have been the first to
point out the inappropriateness of the sobriquet, see *Voyage Historique* . . .
pendant les années 1811, 1812 et 1813, II, 1813, p. 83, 'le portrait si fameux et si
généralement connu sous le nom de Chapeau de Paille . . . Je ne sais trop d'où
lui est venu le nom de Chapeau de Paille, puisqu'en effet la femme est coîffée
d'un vrai chapeau de feutre orné d'un plumet blanc.' (**29**) The explanation most
popular in the nineteenth century was that apparently first advanced in the
Journal d'Anvers, 30 September, 1822: 'il [no. 852] est improprement appellé
Chapeau de Paille; il représente . . . une jeune fille . . . la tête couverte d'un
chapeau de feutre à l'espagnole . . . il est vraisemblable qu'on l'aura d'abord
appelé [*sic*] en flamand: Spaensch-Hoedeken, et par corruption: Spaen-
Hoedeken, qu'on aura traduit par chapeau de paille; c'est-à-dire fait de copeaux
(spaenen) de cette tige végétable', quoted by H. G. Evers, *op. cit.*, p. 279. This
explanation was adopted by, *inter al.*, Smith (see under *General References*);
G. F. Waagen, *Treasures of Art* etc., I, 1854, p. 398: 'the picture was formerly known
in Belgium by the name of "Het Spaansch Hoedje", which, in very recent times
has been corrupted into the unsuitable denomination of Chapeau de Paille'; and
Rooses, *op. cit.*, 1890, IV, no. 949. C. F. H. writing in *The Times*, 29 April,
1847, ventured 'the opinion that its [no. 852] French title, Chapeau de Paille,
is but a corruption of Chapeau de Poil, which would be its real designation'.
The 1911 and 1912 National Gallery catalogues stated that no. 852 was known
as 'Chapeau de Poil'. The poil/paille corruption was later revived by P. Jamot,
Annuaire des Musées Royaux des Beaux-Arts, 1938, pp. 157 ff, who thought the
corruption took place after no. 852 reached England; see also *National Gallery
Summary Catalogue*, 1958; MacLaren, ms. notes, suggested that the
confusion came from the change of the old French spelling *oi* to *ai*.
Dr. Bloch, *The Sunday Times*, 7 March, 1948, proposed 'the confusion
of feutre to feurre which means straw and a later substitution of feurre by the
more usual word paille'. Evers, *op. cit.*, pp. 276–279 rejected, rightly, the first
two theories. He proposed a fourth explanation which is based on the assumption that 'paille' is not used in the sense of meaning 'straw', but as a word
current in French up to the eighteenth century at least, which derived from the
latin 'pallium' rather than 'palea'. This 'paille' had a series of different
meanings, as he points out. One current in the seventeenth century, spelt as
'poille', meant 'parasol' of the kind used in processions (p. 286). Evers may well
be right to have diverted attention from 'paille' meaning straw to other meanings
of 'paille'; thus chapeau de paille in this context may mean simply a hat that
provides shade from the sun. See below under note 30 (2). (**30**) The confusion may
have resulted from one of two. (1) Burchard Documentation suggested that
there might in fact have been a portrait of a woman wearing a straw hat in the
Lunden collection along with no. 852, and that descriptions of the former came
to be taken to refer to no. 852. No. 852 is first mentioned in print as being in the
collection of Arnold-Wilhelm-Joseph Lunden (1732–1782); it passed with other
pictures by Rubens into the possession of Jean-Michel-Joseph van Havre
(† 1804) perhaps through his wife, Catherine, a sister of Arnold W. J. Lunden,
whom he married in 1763 (see under *Provenance*). G. P. Mensaert, *Le Peintre
Amateur* etc., I, 1763, pp. 196–98, stated that the Lunden collection consisted of
The Farm at Laeken and four portraits, three (?) of which were of one of Rubens'
wives. However, J. F. M. Michel, *Histoire de la Vie de P. P. Rubens*, 1771,
p. 360, and G. Forster, in 1790, *Briefe und Tagebücher Georg Forsters* etc., ed. A.

Leitzmann, 1893, pp. 62–3 noted only three portraits of women by Rubens in the brother-in-law's collection. In fact in 1785 (as Burchard Documentation notes), Pilaer and Beeckmans wrote to Thomas Harvey (ms. in the Rembrandt-Huis, Amsterdam) to say that they had just acquired a portrait of Helena Fourment in a straw hat; Burchard suggests that this portrait came from the Lunden collection, that it is in fact one of the four pictures noted by Mensaert and the one that was not made over to the brother-in-law, van Havre. It is not difficult to understand why visitors to the van Havre collection armed with a recently published guide book and/or biography of Rubens should have assumed that the description of the most notable portrait in the old Lunden collection, in which a straw hat was worn, in fact referred to no. 852. For the mention of a straw hat apart, the words of praise and comment were appropriate to no. 852. This was partly because the two authors who singled out for praise the portraits in the Lunden collection in which, by their descriptions, a straw hat was mentioned, were influenced in their use of phrases by an earlier laudatory critique of no. 852. The laudatory critique is that by Descamps, *loc. cit.*, that was published in 1753. Descamps noted 'le Portrait d'une Demoiselle *Lundens* [*sic*]: La tête est couverte d'un chapeau qui y porte l'ombre, ensorte que cette tête n'est éclairée que par la réflexion des lumieres [*sic*] qui l'environnent. On a dit . . . qu' il [Rubens] avoit voulu epousér cette aimable personne'. Mensaert, *op. cit.*, p. 197, ten years later, noted the portrait of a woman who 'est coeffé d'un chapeau de paille, mais de façon que le visage est en réverberation de la clarté du soleil . . .' Michel, *op. cit.*, p. 339, in 1771, noted a portrait of a young 'Demoiselle, qui dans son tems [*sic*] passa pour la plus belle personne des 17. Provinces, elle y est représentée le chapeau de paille plumé en tête, qui met le visage dans un clair ombrage, & le grand jour donnant tout son éclat sur la belle poitrine découverte . . . produit l'effet le plus enchantant . . .'. Although Mensaert and Michel may have been describing a different portrait from that described by Descamps, all write in praising the shadow cast by the hat on the face. Indeed Mols commenting on no. 852 when in the van Havre collection also mentioned this: 'La tradition veut que c'est le portrait d'une personne de condition, très belle; mais qui a toujours vécu dans le célibat . . . . Elle est présentée de face ayant la tête couverte d'un chapeau gris orné de plumes, qui lui tombent sur les Epaules . . . Comme elle paroit peinte en grande jour, son visage est moitié ombré par son chapeau . . .' It seems perfectly possible, given the books of reference to hand in the late eighteenth century, that visitors saw at once the appropriateness and inappropriateness of Mensaert's and Michel's comments when applied to no. 852 in the van Havre collection. Indeed, this must have become a talking point for visitors. And it is noticeable that the sobriquet which came to be attached to no. 852 was the very phrase which made the comments by Mensaert and Michel inappropriate—chapeau de paille. Reynolds, *loc. cit.*, in 1781, considered that no. 852 was thus called because the sitter had on 'her head a hat and feather airily put on'. Nearly thirty years later, and after the death of van Havre, Paquet-Syphorien, *loc. cit.*, pointed out the entire inappropriateness of the sobriquet; but by this time it had stuck. The theories in justification only came in the 1820's, nearly forty years after the confusion had first arisen. (2) Mensaert, *loc. cit.*, is the only author to state in plain French that he had seen a portrait of a woman, dressed in a straw hat, in the Lunden collection. Michel's, *loc. cit.*, actual words 'elle y est représentée le chapeau de paille plumé en tête . . .' are ungrammatical and untranslatable. At the time 'représenter' could, *inter alia.*, mean 'donner une vive idée de quelque chose', see P. Richelet, *Dictionnaire de la langue Française*, III, 1759, new ed., p. 440. Straw hats have generally been used as sun hats, and, *pace* Evers, Michel may have intended to say 'the sitter is depicted in a way that evokes the idea of someone wearing a sunhat, for the sun shines on her body, but her face is in the shade because of it'. Later, amateurs using Michel, may have misunderstood what he wrote, and thought he meant 'she is represented (as) the chapeau de paille' or 'she is known as the chapeau de paile' etc. (31) Compare the hat worn by the man in the *Group Portrait*

by van Dyck, rep. by G. Glück, *Van Dyck, K. der K.*, [1931] p. 112; and
those in the later works of Willem Buytewech († 1624), for which see E.
Haverkamp Begemann, *Willem Buytewech*, 1959, nos. 8, 9, 45, 47 & 48. **(32)**
After Goubaud; a free rendering of the head and shoulders only. There
is a similar print by Vauthier and engraved by J. Mécon. **(33)** See
Messager des Sciences et des Arts, 1824, p. 325. **(34)** See Rooses, under
General References,. **(35)** *Ibid.* **(36)** *Ibid.* **(37)** Made from memory in 1821, owned
by Mme. Boursault, Paris, 1843, see J. Immerzeel Jr., *De Levens en Werken des
Hollandsche en Vlaamsche Kunstchilders* etc., 1843, III, p. 256. This may be the
copy noted by MacLaren as being in the collection of Col. J. T. Lutley, Brom-
yard, Herefordshire, 1941, which was labelled '(Ysen or Van) Dyck after
Rubens.' **(38)** Lord Northwick sale, Christie's, 26 May (= 3rd day), 1838 (166),
probably bought in, for see *Hours in the Picture Gallery at Thirlestane House,
Cheltenham* etc., 1846, p. 82, no. DI. According to this and the 1838 sale catalogue, it was purchased from the van Haveren [*sic*] family. **(39)** See *Messager
des Sciences et des Arts*, 1824, p. 325. **(40)** *Ibid.* **(41)** See A. J. Finberg, *The Life
of J. M. W. Turner, R.A.* 1939, p. 281. **(42)** See K. Andrews and J. R. Brotchie,
National Gallery of Scotland, Catalogue of Scottish Drawings, 1960, p. 93, no.
1073a. **(43)** Coll. Baron Maurice de Rothschild, Paris; copy: N.G., no. 1653,
see M. Davies, *National Gallery Catalogues, French School*, 1957, p. 133. Mme.
Vigée Le Brun recorded the circumstances of her execution of the *Self
Portrait*: '... à Anvers [in 1782] je trouvai chez un particulier le fameux
chapeau de paille qui vient d'etre vendu dernièrement à un Anglais pour une
somme considérable [see under *Provenance*]. Cet admirable tableau représente
une des femmes de Rubens: son grand effet réside dans les deux différentes
lumières que donnent le simple jour et la lueur du soleil. ... Ce tableau
me ravit et m'inspira au point que je fis mon portrait ... en cherchant
le même effet ...' see *Souvenirs de Madame Louise Elisabeth Vigée Le
Brun*, I, 1835, p. 83. **(44)** Frick Collection, New York; exhibited at the
Royal Academy, 1827, see K. Garlick, *The Walpole Society*, 1962–64, 39, p. 159.
D. E. Williams, *The Life ... of Sir Thomas Lawrence Kt.*, II, 1831, p. 475,
stated: 'it is obvious that Sir Thomas designed it as a companion to the
celebrated Chapeau de Paille of Rubens.' **(45)** National Gallery of Scotland,
no. 191, exhibited at the Royal Institution, Edinburgh, 1828, see *National
Gallery of Scotland Catalogue of Paintings* etc., 1957, p. 100; for the preparatory
study, see Andrews & Brotchie, *op. cit.*, p. 93, no. 1073b. **(46)** Signed and dated
183(.); Anon. sale, Christie's, 2 April, 1965 (89). **(47)** The Hon. Mrs. Howe in a
letter of 24 December, 1785 (in the collection of the Earl Spencer) wrote: Sir
Joshua [Reynolds] is about an excessive pretty portrait of Nannette [Anne
Bingham] in a straw hat, and, as Rubens painted one which was called the
'Chapeau de Paille' this is to be called Sir Joshua's.' In fact Reynolds' *Portrait
of Lavinia, Countess Spencer* (coll. Lord Spencer) seems closer in spirit to no.
852 than his *Portrait of Lady Anne Bingham*, referred to by Mrs. Howe. G. F.
Waagen, *Galleries and Cabinets of Art in Great Britain, Supplement*, 1857, p. 91,
considered that Reynolds' *Portrait of Nelly O'Brien*, (Wallace Collection, no.
38) was painted 'after the manner of Rubens' Chapeau de Paille ...'. But as
this portrait was painted before 1781, see *Wallace Collection Catalogues, Pictures
and Drawings*, 1928, p. 242, when Reynolds saw no. 852, its influence should
be ruled out. **(48)** See above and notes 14, 16 and 17. That no. 852 is one of the
portraits in the Lunden inventory of this date is a possibility which cannot be
proved; that the possessor of the pictures was Arnold Lunden is based on Mols'
observation and the fact that Arnold was the only Lunden to be connected with
Rubens. According to Mensaert, *op. cit.*, p. 198, he was told by M. Lunde
(? = Arnold-Guillaume-Joseph Lunden (1732–1782)) that 'ses ancêtres étant de
la famille de *Rubens*, ils avoient hérités de ces tableaux (including no. 852) après
sa mort'. The *Staetmasse ende Rekeninge* of Rubens' estate shows that Arnold
Lunden did not buy a portrait of his wife from Rubens' estate. Smith's, *loc.
cit.*, view that no. 852 was to be identified with no. 122 of Rubens' pictures put up
for sale after his death (Denucé, *op. cit.*, p. 61: 'Un pourtrait d'une damoiselle,

ayant les mains l'une sur l'autre '), which was perhaps based on Mensaert's words seems unlikely. At all events the identification cannot be proved as the entry is so vague. Génard's and Rooses' view that no. 852 was the portrait sold to Helena Fourment (= LXIV of the *Staetmasse*) would rule out its identification with any of the portraits mentioned in the 1639–49 inventory. And although this latter identification cannot be proved, it is the more reasonable one because the line of descent from Helena Fourments' heirs to the Lunden family cannot be established. (**49**) See note 15. Arnold-Albert Lunden's last child was born in 1682, see F.–V. Goethals, *Dictionnaire Généalogique* etc., 1849, 2, pp. 705–07. (**50**) See Rooses, *loc. cit.*, quoting from van Havre papers. (**51**) Descamps, *loc. cit.* (**52**) See Mensaert, *op. cit.*, p. 260: ' Il me reste à vous dire . . . que les tab- leaux dont j'ai parlé . . . qui se voyoient dans le cabinet de M. de Lunde (= *The Farm at Laeken* and four portraits of women by Rubens, see above) sont présente- ment chez les Demoiselles de Lunde.' According to Goethals, *op. cit.*, pp. 708 ff., Marie-Thérèse Lunden and Helène-Joséphine Lunden were the only unmarried women in the family in 1763. Their uncle, Arnold-Albert's will has not been seen, but he may have left his collection, which included no. 852, with his house in Antwerp. Thus, Mensaert's correction may not signify so much a change of ownership—no. 852 was *propriété indivise*—but merely a change of occupants of Arnold-Albert's house. In 1763 both his children were married and may have been living on their spouse's property. (**53**) See Michel, *op. cit.*, p. 360: ' Anvers . . . chez M. van Haveren [*sic*] un excellent Paysage par Rubens, item 3, portraits dudit Peintre, dont celui représentant une jeune Demoiselle, est d'une beauté ravissante '. Van Havre's wife was the daughter of Arnold-Albert— not the grand-daughter as Evers, *op. cit.*, p. 283, suggests; van Havre was her second husband, see Goethals, *op. cit.*, p. 707. Michel had previously noted, pp. 338–39, the *Farm at Laeken* and the portrait ' d'une jeune Demoiselle ' etc. (which may or may not have been no. 852) in the possession of the Lunden fam- ily. This suggests either that the transfer from the Lunden family to the van Havre family of, at any rate, four of the Rubens' left by Arnold-Albert Lunden, or that the return of his daughter, Catherine-Anne-Marie van Havre, with her husband to her parental house, where the pictures had remained, occurred while Michel was assembling material for his book. (**54**) See [B. Holland], *A Tour of Spa* etc., 1774, p. 45, ' Mr. Vanofre [*sic*] Where Reubens [*sic*] wives are painted by himself;—the expression great;—Veins fine;—shape of the Hat, most re- markable . . .' (**55**) See note 28. (**56**) See a letter from Seymour de Ricci, *Burling- ton Magazine*, XXII, 1912–13, p. 170, where he draws attention to a letter from Empress Joséphine, dated 12 Floréal an XI [1803], sold by Gilhofer and Ranschburg, Vienna, 26 October, 1908 (27); where described as ' relative a une vente publique de tableaux dont L'Impératice [*sic*] désire d'acquérir le *Chapeau de paille* de Rubens . . . et une paysage du même maître '. (**57**) See Paquet—Syphorien, *loc. cit.* (**58**) See *Description des quatres superbes tableaux . . . par . . . Rubens à vendre à l'aimable*, 1817 (1). (**59**) J. M. A. J. van Havre married H. J. Stiers' eldest daughter in 1790, see Goethals, *op. cit.* pp. 712–13. For the date of sale, see Rooses, *loc. cit.*; and for the price, see Smith, *loc. cit.*; see also C. J. Nieuwenhuys, *A Review of the Lives and Works of some of the most Eminent Painters* etc., 1834, pp. 204 ff., for the dispersal of the van Havre collection. His account, p. 210, suggests that the sale of no. 852 to Stiers took place in 1818; according to him, Stiers was one of the heirs for whom van Havre was acting. (**60**) See Nieuwenhuys, *op. cit.*, pp. 211–12. (**61**) See Smith, *loc. cit.* (**62**) See Nieuwenhuys and Smith, *loc. cit.* (**63**) See Smith's receipt, Goulburn ms., Surrey County Record Office, which is dated 19 June, 1824.

853P   A LION HUNT

Three mounted huntsmen attempt to kill a lion, which is attacking their companion. A fifth huntsman kills a lion on the ground, while a sixth lies dead. The main motif—of a lion attacking the mounted huntsman—recurs in the top right-hand corner.

Oil on oak, $29/29\frac{1}{8} \times 41\frac{1}{2}/\frac{5}{8}$ ($0.736/0.74 \times 1.054/057$).

For the make up of the support, see Appendix I. The reverse bears the brand of the coat of arms of the city of Antwerp, and an incised six pointed star.

Grisaille, in fairly good condition. There are a good number of re-touchings along the top join and an adjacent crack: in particular in and around the head of the horse on the right, the head of the lion in the centre, and to a lesser extent on the arms of the huntsman on the bucking horse. The left-hand half of the lower join is also retouched. The varnish is yellow.

No. 853P is executed basically in brown and black oil washes with many areas of the main design filled in with thick white to black oil paint and a few touches of red. It is painted up to all the edges, except the right-hand edge where there is a border of *ca.* $\frac{1}{8}$ (0.003). The brown wash has run over the right hind leg of the horse on the left. Over the motif in the top right-hand corner are traces of the top half of a horse's head (slightly larger than those in the main design), executed in white oil paint.

Rubens' authorship of no. 853P has not and need not be doubted; however, there should be some caution in accepting the horse's head executed in white paint in the top right-hand corner, where the handling is obscured by the yellow varnish.

No. 853P has been little discussed[1]; and its position in the sequence of Rubens' rendering of lion hunts has not been clarified. To do this, it is necessary to review the relevant works.

Rubens seems to have evolved three main lion hunt compositions; these are the Munich,[2] ex Bordeaux[3] and Dresden/Rennes[4] pictures. The Munich picture was probably executed in the very early 1620's.[5] Burchard has pointed out that the ex Bordeaux and Rennes pictures were part of the set painted for the Duke of Bavaria (= the Elector Maximilian)[6] which was finished at least by 1617.[7] Burchard/d'Hulst,[8] have dated the set 1615–1616; Held[9] dates it 1615–1617. The difference between the two compositions is the heightened danger of the huntsman assailed by the lion; the motif of the huntsman brought off his horse by the lion reached perfection in the Munich picture. Such being the case it is legitimate to suppose that the Dresden/Rennes pictures came first in the sequence.

Smith[10] considered that no. 853P was the sketch for the Dresden picture; this is clearly not correct, in so far as no. 853P is obviously not the *modello* for it. The 1929 catalogue introduced an irrelevancy, by suggesting that no. 853P was a sketch for a picture in the Crabbe sale of 1892,[11] which seems to be no more than a work deriving indirectly from Rubens.[12]

Burchard's[13] view was that no. 853P was perhaps the earliest 'version' of a lion hunt by Rubens, preceding the Dresden picture. This seems probable for the same reason for dating the ex Bordeaux picture before the Munich picture: a comparison of the motifs in no. 853P and the Dresden/Rennes pictures shows a heightening of danger in the latter.

In no. 853P the main motif also occurs in the top right-hand corner; it is likely that this quick sketch preceded the execution of the main design, and that it was made as a guide line for further elaboration. Elaboration involved injecting more movement and articulation into the poses to heighten the sense of conflict: as a result of elaboration, the lion bites into the now braced arm of the huntsman, and although the embrace of the claws is wider, the lion's body twists from the threat of the lances. In the Dresden/Rennes compositions the lances were abandoned, and while the hold of the lion on the horse is less secure, it bites more firmly into the huntsman. Two of the other motifs in no. 853P are further refined in the three large scale compositions, of which the Dresden/Rennes pictures were the first, and one is abandoned. The huntsman attacking the lion with a sword appears in the Dresden/ Rennes and ex Bordeaux pictures, and only in the oil sketch[14] for the Munich picture. The huntsman seen from the front on a bucking horse is very altered and reversed—as is the horse—in the Dresden/Rennes and ex Bordeaux pictures; and only the horse remains, obviously related, in the Munich picture. The huntsman with the lance and his horse on the left of no. 853P do not appear in any of the large scale pictures.

The earliest mention of a picture depicting a hunt by Rubens is in October 1616;[15] this was in all probability a *European Hunt of Wolves and Foxes*,[16] similar perhaps in composition to that now in the Metro-politan Museum of Art,[17] which has been dated *ca.* 1615.[18] It seems probable that no. 853P was executed about the same time, or soon after, as a *modello* for the studio to follow when executing a larger picture. However, it was clearly abandoned, unfinished;[19] and thus it became no more than a discarded idea in a train of thought that culminated in either the Dresden *Lion Hunt* or the Rennes *Lion and Tiger Hunt*.[20]

Several ideas in no. 853P occur in other compositions by Rubens, executed about the same time: the huntsman about to strike with his sword and the horse galloping to the right occur in the Munich *Battle of the Amazons*;[21] the rearing horse and its rider recur in the Munich *Defeat of Sennacherib*;[22] and the bucking horse seems first to occur in Count Seilern's *Conversion of S. Paul*.[23] Of these Count Seilern's picture was probably executed first.[24]

Two of the motifs in no. 853P may derive ultimately from the antique: the lion leaping on a horse's back,[25] and the back handed blow of the huntsman;[26] but the composition as a whole probably derives from Stradanus' design of a *Lion Hunt*, published by Cock in 1570.[27] Rubens achieved coherence in no. 853P by drawing on Leonardo's design for the *Battle of Anghiari*.[28] The horse on the left, and the face and right arm of the huntsman on the bucking horse appear to be quotations from Leonardo's design. The reason for Rubens' abandoning the composition may have been dissatisfaction with the pose of this rider and his horse. It is also noticeable that none of the huntsmen on the ground recurs later.

No. 853P can be placed in Rubens' category of a lion hunt with knights 'alla moresca e turcesca'.[29] The literary source for the scene may perhaps go back to Plutarch's account of how Craterus caused a representation to be made of his coming to Alexander's assistance in one of his encounters with a lion.[30] But equally it could be no more than the equivalent to one of the descriptive rubrics included in engravings of lion hunts made after designs by Stradanus.

PROVENANCE: Coll. Johann Engelbert von Jabach, Cologne († before 1754);[31] left by him to his executor Baron Heinrich von Mering;[32] coll. Freiherr Everard Oswald, Baron von Mering (1755–1820);[33] Everard Oswald von Mering (†) sale, Cologne, 25 August, 1820, (86).[34] Sold by Smith to the Rt. Hon. Robert Peel (later Sir Robert Peel, Bart.), 1826, for 100 gns.;[35] bought with the Peel Collection, 1871.[36]

REPRODUCTION: *National Gallery Illustrations, Continental Schools* (*excluding Italian*), 1950, p. 312, top.

REFERENCES *in text:* (1) David Rosand's article *Rubens' Munich Lion Hunt* etc., *The Art Bulletin*, 1969, pp. 29 ff., came to hand after this entry went to press; he provides a full review of Rubens' treatment of the theme. (2) Canvas, $92\frac{1}{4} \times 148$ (2·47 × 3·755), see *Alte Pinakothek München kurzes Verzeichnis*, 1957, p. 90, no. 602; rep. by R. Oldenbourg, *Rubens, K. der K.*, [1921] p. 154. (3) Canvas, 7 ft. 8 p. × 10 ft. 1 p. ($= 97\frac{3}{4} \times 128\frac{1}{2}$ or 2·483 × 3·264), see H. de la Ville de Mirmont, *Histoire du Musée de Bordeaux* I, 1899, p. 93; destroyed in 1870. Engraved by P. Soutman, rep. in M. Rooses, *L'Œuvre de P. P. Rubens*, 1890, IV, pl. 322. Copies in the Gainsborough House National Appeal Fund sale, Christie's, 29 November, 1957 (56), and in the Northwick Park sale, Christie's, 29 October, 1965 (39). (4) Canvas, $92\frac{1}{8} \times 125\frac{3}{4}$ (2·40 × 3·17), see *Picture Gallery Dresden, Old Masters*, 1962, p. 91, no. 270, rep. by Oldenbourg, *op. cit.*, p. 113. The picture at Rennes, canvas $99\frac{5}{8} \times 125\frac{1}{2}$ (2·53 × 3·19) is a variant of the Dresden picture, and includes leopards and tigers; rep. by H. Gerson, *Art and Architecture in Belgium 1600–1800*, 1960, pl. 146A. (5) The two main reasons for this are: (a) The preliminary oil sketch is on the reverse of a sketch for the *Marriage by proxy of Henri IV to Marie de Médicis* (coll. the Marquess of Cholmondeley) which could not have been executed much before 1622, see L. Burchard, catalogue of *A loan Exhibition of Works by Peter Paul Rubens, Kt.*, Wildenstein's, London, 1950 (20). Although J. S. Held, *Rubens Selected Drawings*, I, 1959, under no. 96, dates this sketch for the hunt to a few years before the sketch on the other side; (b) Schelte à Bolswert's engraving of the composition, rep. by Rooses, *op. cit.*, pl. 321, bears the privileges of the King of France, the States General and the Archduchess Isabella, which shows that it was published after the Archduke's death in 1621. The Munich *Lion Hunt* should perhaps be connected with the *Lion Hunt* commissioned by John Digby (created Earl of Pembroke in 1622) to present to the Marquess of Hamilton, which Rubens had nearly finished on 13 September, 1621, see his letter to William Trumbull (ed. M. Rooses & Ch. Ruelens), printed in *Correspondance de Rubens*, 1898, II, p. 286. No *Lion Hunt* is recorded in the Hamilton inventories. A *Lion Hunt* was, however, owned by the Duke of Buckingham († 1628), see R. Davies, *The Burlington Magazine*, 1906/7, p. 380. (6) See Burchard, *loc. cit.* The only difficulty concerning this identification of the ex Bordeaux picture is that the engraving and copies do not agree with Toby Matthews' description of a copy being executed in Rubens' studio, 25 November, 1620, when he wrote to Sir Dudley Carleton: 'The Caccia is of an excellent desseigne. Ther [*sic*] ar [*sic*] Lyons [*sic*] & Tygars [*sic*], and three men on horse backe [*sic*] (some in halfe [*sic*] figures) huntinge [*sic*], & killinge [*sic*] beastes [*sic*] and beinge [*sic*] killed by them. The originall [*sic*] was ... sold to yᵉ Duke of Bavaria ...', see *Correspondance de Rubens*

etc., 1898, II, p. 261. (7) This *terminus ante quem* is provided by the copy of the
Rennes picture in Jan Brueghel I's *Sight* in the Prado (Prado catalogue, 1963,
no. 1394) of 1617, rep. by M. de Maeyer, *Albrecht en Isabella en de Schilderkunst*, 1955, pl. I. (8) *Rubens Drawings*, I, 1963, p. 87, under no. 50. See also
Oldenbourg, *op. cit.*, pp. 114 and 115. (9) *Op. cit.*, p. 133, under no. 89; and
proposing a date round 1615, p. 110, under no. 39. (10) See J. Smith, *A
Catalogue Raisonné* etc., 1830, II, no. 251; his view is repeated by,
inter al., G. F. Waagen, *Art Treasures* etc., I, 1854, p. 415; and M. Rooses,
op. cit., 1890, IV, under no. 1154. (11) Prosper Crabbe sale, Sedelmeyer,
12 June, 1892 (14), canvas, $16\frac{15}{16} \times 24\frac{3}{8}$ (0·43 × 0·62); rep. in catalogue. (12) Three
other records of the composition are known: Oslo, National Museum, panel,
$17\frac{1}{8} \times 24\frac{1}{4}$ (0·435 × 0·615), ex coll. Lord Darnley, see Rooses, *op. cit.*, under
no. 1155; Spridlington Hall, nr. Lincoln, *ca.* 76 × 144 (1·93 × 3·658) (photo. in
National Gallery archives); Vienna, Kunsthistorisches Museum, tapestry by
Daniel Eggermans, which was one of a set bought in 1666, see L. Baldass, *Wiener
Gobelinsammlung*, 1920, pl. 187. The composition seems to be a clumsy combination of two separate designs, one certainly by Rubens and the other possibly
so. (13) Burchard Documentation. (14) See under note 5. (15) See *Correspondance de Rubens* etc., 1898, II, p. 85. (16) See M. Rooses, *L'Œuvre de P. P.
Rubens*, 1890, IV, p. 342, under no. 1157. (17) *Ibid.*, and no. 1156; see also
B. Burroughs, *Metropolitan Museum of Art, Catalogue of Paintings*, 1922,
p. 264; and J.–A. Goris & J. S. Held, *Rubens in America* [1947], no. 94. Engraved
by P. Soutman, see Rooses, *op. cit.*, 1890, IV, pl. 324. (18) See Oldenbourg,
op. cit., p. 112; and Held, *op. cit.*, p. 110, under no. 39. (19) The head of the horse
in white paint, which was to suppress the sketch in the top right-hand corner,
was never completed. How this head, assuming it to be by Rubens, was to be
integrated with rest is uncertain; maybe it was not intended to be. (20) If this is
the case, the sketch with P. de Boer, 1938 (*Catalogue de Tableaux Anciens*,
1938 (22), panel, $19\frac{1}{2} \times 25\frac{3}{8}$ (0·495 × 0·645)), may be a record of a slightly later,
but also discarded, idea of the master's in the same train of thought. Burchard,
see the catalogue, who accepted the sketch, dated it just after 1620. The drawing
of a *Tartar Huntsman, about to give the coup de grace*, coll. M. Jaffé, by whom
lent to *Art Historians and Critics as Collectors*, Agnew's, 1965 (30), would have
been made after the design of the ex Bordeaux *Hunt* had been worked out in an
oil sketch. (21) Rep. by Oldenbourg, *op. cit.*, p. 196. (22) Rep. by Oldenbourg,
op. cit., p. 156. (23) Rep. by Oldenbourg, *op. cit.*, p. 157; see also Count Seilern,
Flemish Paintings and Drawings etc., 1955, I, no. 21, & II, plates XLVII–
LI. (24) Oldenbourg, *op. cit.*, p. 196, dates the *Battle of the Amazons*
1618–20; but Held, *op. cit.*, under no. 40, citing Philippe Rubens'
Mémoire, sent to de Piles in 1676 (printed in the *Rubens-Bulletijn*,
1883, II, p. 166), dates it 1615. Oldenbourg, *op. cit.*, p. 156, dates the *Defeat of
Sennacherib*, 1616–1618; Burchard/d'Hulst date it *ca.* 1612–14, see *Rubens
Drawings*, I, 1963, pp. 86–8, under no. 50; Held, *op. cit.*, p. 107, under no. 31,
dates it before *ca.* 1617. So far as *The Conversion of S. Paul* is concerned, Held,
loc. cit., and Burchard/d'Hulst, *loc. cit.*, date it *ca.* 1612–14; while Count Seilern,
loc. cit., favours a date *ca.* 1615 +. The compiler believes that it may have been
executed in the main *ca.* 1611, with some areas altered *ca.* 1614–15 (for these
pentimenti see Seilern, *loc. cit.*). (25) See H. Stuart Jones, *A Catalogue of the
Ancient Sculptures in the Municipal Collections in Rome*, 1926, pl. 69; that the
theme had some currency in ancient times, see the bronze of a lion attacking a
bull (Vienna), rep. in Dr. E. F. v. Sacken, *Die Antiken Bronzen des K. K. Munz
und Antiken Cabinetes in Wien*, I, 1871, pl. LI (5). In fact Jacopo Bellini's
drawing in the British Museum sketch book comes closest in spirit to Rubens'
rendering here, although the rider is still absent. (26) A huntsman about to
strike a lion with his sword, similar in pose to that in no. 853P, 'was quite common on Roman monuments' (information kindly supplied by Professor
D. Strong of the Institute of Archaeology, London University), one such Roman
monument may have influenced Rubens here, although a more direct source
could have been Raphael's *S. George* (Louvre), rep. by G. Gronau, *Raffael*,

K. der K., 1923, p. 7, left. **(27)** See F. W. H. Hollstein, *Dutch and Flemish Etchings, Engravings* etc., IV, p. 190; rep. by Rosand, *op. cit.*, fig. 18. **(28)** Rubens' copy of Leonardo's composition, as recorded in Zacchia's engraving, is in the Louvre, see F. Lugt, *Musée du Louvre, Inventaire Général des Dessins des Écoles du Nord* etc., II, 1949, no. 1084. For Rubens' interest in this design, see J. Müller Hofstede, *The Burlington Magazine*, 1964, pp. 95 ff. The influence of Leonardo's design on the hunts painted for the Duke of Bavaria has been claimed by Burchard/d'Hulst, *Rubens Drawings*, I, 1963, p. 87, under no. 50. **(29)** See Rubens' letter to Sir Dudley Carleton of 12 May, 1618 in *Correspondance de Rubens* etc., 1898, II, pp. 149–150. **(30)** See *Plutarch's Lives*, with an introduction by A. H. Clough, II, 1910, p. 500. **(31)** Burchard Documentation. See J. Merlo, *Die Familie Jabach zu Köln* etc., 1861, p. 65; and O. H. Forster, *Kölner Kunstsammler*, 1931, p. 55. Johann Englebert von Jabach was a grandson of Everhard III Jabach (1610–1695), but no. 853P does not feature in the inventory of Everhard III's collection made after his death, printed in *Mémoires de la Société de l'Histoire de Paris*, 1894, pp. 249 ff. **(32)** See Merlo, *op. cit.*, p. 65, note 2. A book plate of the Mering family, identified by A. van de Put (letter in N.G. archives) is stuck on the reverse of the panel. **(33)** See Merlo, *op. cit.*, p. 65; and Forster, *loc. cit.* **(34)** information and details concerning this sale, which is Lugt no. 9864, kindly supplied by Dr. Blum, Oberbibliotheksrat of the Universitäts und Stadtbibliothek, Cologne, where the catalogue is preserved. The sale took place at von Mering's house. The entry for lot 86 reads: 'Eine grosse Skizze in grauer Farbe, eine Löwenhetze vorstellend; verschiendene Soldaten zu Pferd mit Spiesen streiten sich gegen wüthende Löwen . . . auf Holz, hoch 2 Fuss 6 Zoll, breit 3 Fuss 7 Zoll, von Peter Paul Rubens'. **(35)** See Smith, *loc. cit.* No. 853P is no. 372 of the Smith and Successors Stockbook, XII (ms., Victoria and Albert Museum Library), where noted as having been sold to Peel on 24 November, 1825(?). **(36)** But not catalogued until 1891.

1195 THE BIRTH OF VENUS

Venus, centre left, steps from her shell onto the island of Cyprus or Cythera. At the top, centre, Neptune and Amphitrite; at the bottom, centre, Cupid and Psyche. At the centre of the two sides, *putti* blowing conch shells on sea-horses; above them, *putti*, one holding a lit torch and another a bow and arrow, with swans; and, below them, two Nereids holding pearls, on dolphins.

Black chalk and oil on oak, 24 × 30¾ (0·61 × 0·78).

For the make up of the support, see Appendix I. The reverse bears the brand of the coat of arms of the city of Antwerp.

Grisaille, generally in very good condition. There are some small losses in the ground which are retouched; these are along the topmost join from the left edge to the outside edge of the conch shell blown by the *putto* on the left, just below the right armpit of the Nereid on the left and just above the head of the Triton in the centre.

The ground extends to the edges; the measurements of the design are *ca.* 23 × 29½ (0·58 × 0·75). The precise limits of the design are not possible to define as the inner edges of the spandrels have been coarsely defined here and there by a later hand in grey paint. The spandrels are covered with a muddy brown paint, which goes up to the top and bottom edges but not to the sides, where there are borders showing the ground. Beneath the brown paint is a layer (or layers?) of gold leaf—minute traces of which are visible within the design.[1]

The central point of the design was established by ruling, in black chalk, vertical and horizontal lines, which are both slightly off the centre of the support. The outlines of the inner and outer rims were also drawn in black chalk. The composition was first sketched in brown wash, which was then heightened in black, grey and white (and in the sky, light blue) oil paint. The rocks were painted in black oil paint, probably after the sketching in brown wash was completed elsewhere.

There are a number of *pentimenti*: the right leg of Venus was first placed farther back; the *putto* (= Cupid?, see below) holding the palm above Venus, was first placed farther to the left, and seen from behind, flying upwards to the right; at the lower edge, Cupid's left leg was first placed slightly higher up and his right wing was larger; Psyche's wings were originally placed lower down. There is some indecipherable drawing in brown wash beneath the winged female figure (= Suada?, see below) whose left knee was first placed further forward; there is also some indecipherable drawing in brown wash below the *putto* with the torch on the left. The *putto* on a barrel drawn by a swan, in the top left, was abandoned as it is not heightened in oil paint.

The subject of no. 1195 was apparently first identified as the birth of Venus by Smith.[2] The design, as reproduced in a print (see below), was previously thought to depict *The Triumph of Galatea*,[3] a view expressed as late as 1934.[4] The subject of no. 1195 is not, in fact, the birth of Venus, but rather the arrival of Venus at Cyprus or Cythera. However, the events were so closely connected that the title *The Birth of Venus* has been retained here.

There are few lengthy descriptions of the birth of Venus by classical authors; the basic sources are Hesiod's *Theogony* and the *Homeric Hymns*.[5] These, along with other accounts in classical literature and descriptions of antique paintings and sculptures of the subject, are for the most part mentioned by Cartari and Natale Conte.[6] No. 1195 does not appear to follow any one source uniquely, and thus the identity of some of the figures is open to doubt.

The three women helping Venus from her shell could be intended to be Nereids,[7] the Horae, who, as Hesiod stated, welcomed her to Cyprus,[8] or, as Smith probably correctly suggested, the three Graces.[9] It may be that the woman on the Triton is intended to personify Desire.[10] The National Gallery catalogues, 1889–1906, identified the two figures crowning Venus as Persuasion and Cupid;[11] this may well be correct as Pausanias stated that Phidias' rendering of the birth of Venus on the base of his statue of Zeus at Olympus showed Venus about to be received by Cupid and being crowned by Suada (Persuasion).[12] The wind god is probably Zephyrus.[13] Apelles' picture of Venus rising from the sea was normally thought to show her wringing the foam from her hair with both hands; Politian,[14] however, wrote that she wrung the foam from her hair with her right hand, as she does in no. 1195.

So far as the outer rim is concerned, Smith rightly identified the two figures at the top as Neptune and Amphitrite.[15] Neptune is present as the god of the sea from which Venus rose. Rooses rightly identified the two figures at the bottom as Cupid and Psyche;[16] Cupid is present as the son of Venus. According to Cartari,[17] swans are appropriate to Venus, but the source for their presence here is probably Philostratus the Elder's *Imagines*.[18] Apuleius[19] included *putti* holding lit torches and arrows as part of the train of Venus.

It has been generally accepted that the grisaille in no. 1195 is by Rubens; and there is no reason to doubt this attribution. The paint on the spandrels is clearly by a later hand.

The grisaille is in the shape of a basin. An inscription on a print, made probably after 1660 by Jacob Neeffs (see under *Engraving*), of a basin showing the same decoration and of an accompanying ewer, states that they were painted by Rubens for Charles I, and made into silver by Theodore Rogiers (or Rasières) (1602–1654?). This is perfectly possible, and no doubt the inscription is true. However, it should be pointed out that although Charles I did own work by Rogiers,[20] there is no mention of no. 1195 or of a basin and ewer, similar to those depicted in Neeffs' print, in van der Doort's catalogue of the King's works of art, or in the most complete record of the sale of the King's possessions.[21] The basin and ewer are not known to exist, nor is there any record of their having existed, other than the inscription on Neeffs' print. Furthermore, the inscription on Neeffs' print apart, there is no published evidence of collaboration between Rubens and Rogiers. Génard has published another silver basin and ewer, which on stylistic grounds he attributed to Rogiers working under the 'inspiration' of Rubens, and identified them with the silver basin and ewer recorded in Rubens' estate; but his thesis does not carry conviction.[22]

No. 1195 is generally[23] thought to have been Rubens' *modello* for the silver basin depicted in the print; and, if the inscription on the print is accepted as true, there is no reason to doubt this view. The *modello* for the ewer is not known to exist. It is noteworthy that the great majority of extant *modelli* by Rubens for wood, stone or ivory carvings are drawings;[24] Burchard/d'Hulst[25] have recently suggested that another grisaille associated with a carving, the *Triumph of sea born Venus* (coll. the Duke of Portland),[26] was made after the carving for the engraver.[27] It is unlikely that this is the case as far as no. 1195 is concerned, if its size and *pentimenti* are taken into account.

On the basis of the inscription on Neeffs' print, no. 1195 has been dated *ca.* 1630,[28] i.e. to the time when, or just after, Rubens was in England in direct contact with Charles I (see under no. 46). Rooses has also associated Gerbier's letter to Arundel of 29 October/8 November, 1636, with the commission.[29] Gerbier speaks there of obtaining for Arundel 'certaine drawings of the said Sr. P. Reubens for carving of cups.' This, it is argued, could refer to Rubens' proposals for the ewer, which as Neeffs' etching shows, had the Judgment of Paris as its central motif. The same design, but including only the main participants, was used by Rubens for the Prado *Judgment of Paris*,[30] which was completed by early 1639.[31] This fact need not effect the

dating of no. 1195. Nor is it necessary to associate Gerbeir's letter with
the commission (if it existed) from Charles I, for it is unlikely that
Rubens' proposals would have been sent to Arundel rather than to the
King himself.

The central part of the composition of no. 1195 is related to Rubens'
design for an ivory salt-cellar,[32] which is also recorded in the grisaille
owned by the Duke of Portland. The two nymphs on either side of
Venus and Venus herself in the Duke of Portland's grisaille, are closely
related in pose to Venus and two of the Graces in no. 1195. In no. 1195,
Rubens lowered the arms and face of the nymph on the right and
transferred the left-hand nymph's action of wringing out her hair to
Venus. Venus' pose in no. 1195 was also altered by showing her body
more in profile. A third nymph was depicted in the Portland grisaille
riding a Triton, her pose has been transformed into that of the third
Grace (on the right) in no. 1195 and the Triton was retained as the bearer
of Desire(?).

The handling of the paint in the Portland grisaille is different from
that in no. 1195. Burchard/d'Hulst have dated the salt-cellar to just
before Rubens' departure on his diplomatic journeys.[33] Held[34] however, supports Feuchtmayr's[35] view that it should be dated just after his
return—i.e. 1630/1. The grisaille is acceptably earlier in handling than
no. 1195.

There is nothing in Rubens' œuvre, however, which is strictly comparable in handling with no. 1195. The forms are not as generous as those
in the sketches for decorations of the Torre de la Parada of ca. 1636 (see
no. 2598). But taking into account the fact that Rubens would have
had to control and tighten his brush-work, so that his intentions could
be easily read by the silversmith, a date about the middle of the first
half of the 1630's is acceptable for no. 1195.[36] Theodore Rogiers became
a master in the Antwerp guild in 1630/1.[37]

The central part of the design of no. 1195 is repeated and extended in
rectangular form in a sketch at Bayonne;[38] it has been suggested[39] that
this sketch is preliminary to no. 1195. This is improbable because the
pentimenti in the relevant area of no. 1195 show that Rubens was there
working out the composition. As the Bayonne sketch follows and repeats
Rubens' main and final proposals, as set out in no. 1195, it is probable
that it was made after no. 1195, possibly as a modello (unused) for an
engraver. Its status would thus be similar, pace Burchard/d'Hulst, to
that of the Duke of Portland's grisaille.

The pose of Venus in no. 1195 is a variant of that of Psyche in Marco
da Ravenna's engraving after Raphael of Juno, Ceres and Psyche.[40] The
pose of Desire(?), seated on the Triton, was repeated by Rubens with
slight variation in a sketch for one of the decorations of the Torre de la
Parada;[41] it probably derives from types on Roman sarcophagi. It
seems evident that the group made up by Venus and the three Graces (?)
is an adaptation of the motif of drunken Silenus supported by satyrs,
evolved by Rubens during the second decade of the century, and given
its final expression in Jegher's woodcut of ca. 1635.[42] Fischel has

suggested that the decoration on the rim of no. 1195 was inspired by Raphael's design for a rim of a dish, for Agostino Chigi.[43]

COPY: Of the left hand *putto* on the seahorse, Mrs. M. Fowler sale, Sotheby's, 11 July, 1962 (28).[44]

ENGRAVING: Etched in reverse by Jacob Neeffs.[45]

PROVENANCE: Coll. the 10th Duke of Hamilton (1767–1852), Lennoxlove, by 1830;[46] 12th Duke of Hamilton sale, Christie's, 17 June, 1882 (44) bt. Denison for £1,680;[47] Christopher Beckett Denison (†) sale, Christie's, 13 June (=7th day), 1885 (924) bt. by Agnew for the National Gallery for £672 (purchased out of the Clarke Fund).

REPRODUCTION: *National Gallery Illustrations, Continental Schools (excluding Italian)*, 1950, p. 312, bottom.

REFERENCES: *General:* J. Smith, *A Catalogue Raisonné* etc., 1830, II, no. 848, and Supplement, 1841, no. 282, pp. 321–2; M. Rooses, *L'Œuvre de P. P. Rubens*, 1890, III, no. 688; R. Oldenbourg, *Rubens, K. der K.*, [1921], p. 314.

In text: (1) These remains are on top of the original paint, and probably result from messy gilding of the spandrels, done when the support was first framed, leaving the spandrels uncovered. (2) See under *General References*. (3) See F. P. Basan, *Catalogue des Estampes gravées d'après P. P. Rubens*, 1767 (new ed.), p. 96 under no. 31; and M. Huber and C. G. Martini, *Manuel . . . des Amateurs* etc., VI, 1803, p. 217 under Jac. Neefs [*sic*]. (4) See the entry in Thieme-Becker, *Künstler Lexikon*, XXVIII, 1934, p. 22, for Théodore Raisères (=Rogiers); F. Donnet, *Biographie Nationale . . . de Belgique*, 1901, XIX, cols. 814–15, considered the subject of no. 1195 to be the *Triumph of Amphitrite*. (5) See *The Homeric Hymns and Homerica*, trans. by H. G. Evelyn-White, 1914, p. 93 and p. 428. (6) See V. Cartari, *Imagini* etc., 1626 ed., pp. 429 ff.; and Natale Conte, *Mythologiae*, 1616, pp. 202 ff. (7) Cartari, *op. cit.*, p. 210, records Pausanias' description of the statue of Neptune at Corinth, which showed, on its base, Venus leaving the sea accompanied by 'bellissime Neriede'; see also *Pausanias' Description of Greece*, trans. by J. G. Frazer, 1898, I, p. 72. (8) Hesiod, *op. cit.*, p. 428. (9) See Smith, cited under *General References*; the Graces were the companions of Venus; Cartari, *op. cit.*, pp. 458–59, gives a translation of a latin poem on the statue of *The Three Graces* in the palazzo Colonna where they are called ' . . . ministre liete e grate | A l'alma Citherea . . .'. (10) See Hesiod, *op. cit.*, p. 93; 'comely Desire followed her [Venus] at her birth at first'. (11) Smith, see under *General References*, wrongly identifies these figures as Cupid and Psyche. (12) See *Pausanias' Description of Greece* etc. p. 252. This description is mentioned by Cartari, *op. cit.*, p. 441. (13) See Natale Conte, *op. cit.*, p. 202, who quotes Homer. (14) *Stanze*, I, 1494 (ed.), excerpts of which are printed by H. Horne, *Sandro Botticelli*, 1908, p. 149: . . . 'La Dea premendo colla dextra il crino . . .'. Antipater of Sidon had previously imagined Venus in Apelles' picture 'grasping her dripping hair with her hand', see *The Greek Anthology*, trans. by W. R. Paton, 1918, V, no. 178. (15) See Smith, cited under *General References*. Neptune is identifiable by his trident; Rooses, cited under *General References*, did not identify the goddess; but Amphitrite rather than any other nymph, was usually depicted with Neptune, see Cartari, *op. cit.*, p. 203 and p. 210. Rubens included her and Neptune in the *Birth of Venus* at Sanssouci, rep. by R. Oldenbourg, *Rubens, K. der K.*, [1921], p. 107. (16) See Rooses, cited under *General References*; Psyche is identifiable by her butterfly wings. For the story of Cupid and Psyche, see Apuleius, *The Golden Ass*, trans. W. Aldington, 1935 ed., pp. 185 ff. (17) Cartari, *op. cit.*, p. 435. (18) See Philostratus the Elder, *Imagines*, I, 9, trans. by A. Fairbanks, 1931, p. 37: 'No wonder that the swans are ridden by Cupids, for these gods are mischievous and prone to sport with birds.' (19) Apuleius, *op. cit.*, book X, 32, p. 531, of the 1935 ed. of Aldington's translation: 'Then came Venus. . . . She was accompanied with a great number of little boys, whereby you could have judged them to be all Cupids, so plump and fair were they, and either to have flown from heaven or else from the river of the sea for they had little wings and little arrows . . . and they have in their hands torches lighted.' See also Cartari, *op. cit.*, p. 428. (20) See *The Walpole Society*, XXXVII, 1958–60, pp. 149, 150, and 221. (21) A typed ms. exists in the Lord Chamberlain's office, which Mr. Oliver Millar kindly let the compiler examine. It should be added that there are no published records of payments made to Rogiers by Charles I. (22) See P. Génard, *Rubens-Bulletijn*, 1882, I, pp. 224 ff.; reproduced by P. Génard, *Anvers à travers les Ages*, II, [1888], pp. 408 and 409. Génard based his attribution on a comparison with Neeff's print; Neeff's print, however, is of too poor quality (see below) to be a satisfactory yardstick. The basin has on it the initials of the Archduke Albert and Archduchess Isabella; Génard repeated the family tradition, recounted by the owners, that the basin and ewer were given to Rubens by the Archduchess sometime after 1630. Such a gift, were Génard's attribution correct, would be tantamount to carrying coals to Newcastle. Further, the fact that the owners were descendants of Rubens does not prove that the basin and ewer is identical with that recorded in Rubens' estate, for which see Génard *Bulletin des Archives d'Anvers*, II, p. 72. (23) See the authors cited under *General References*; see also L. van Puyvelde, *Les Esquisses de Rubens*, 1940, no. 61. No. 1195 was first published by Goeler von Ravensburg, *Rubens und die Antike*, 1882, pp. 113–14. (24) For the drawings for the enrichment of Jesuit Church, Antwerp, see L. Burchard and R. A. d'Hulst, *Tekeningen van Rubens*, Antwerp, 1956, nos. 67–71; M. Jaffé, *Burlington Magazine*, 1956, p. 314, note 5; J. S. Held, *Rubens Selected Drawings*, I, 1959, nos. 144–45, and 172, pl. 149–50 and fig. 58; L. Burchard and R. A. d'Hulst, *Rubens Drawings*, 1963, nos. 116 and 117. For a design for a tomb, see Held, *op. cit.*, no. 171, fig. 36. For designs of other individual figures or small reliefs: see G. Glück, *Rubens, van Dyck und ihr Kreis*, 1933, pp. 188 ff., and fig. 106; Held, *op. cit.*, no. 138, pl. 148; and Burchard and d'Hulst, *op. cit.*, nos. 149 and 160. An oil sketch prepared as a *modello* for a sculptor was with Heim (1967); Jaffé's note in the catalogue of the *Summer Exhibition*, 1967 (12), refers to another similar *modello*. (25) See Burchard/d'Hulst, *op. cit.*, pp. 234–35, under no. 149. (26) Oil on panel, $14\frac{1}{2} \times 19\frac{1}{2}$ (0·368 × 0·495); it is Rooses, *op. cit.*, no. 687. (27) It should be pointed out that Rooses' reservations about the thesis that the Portland grisaille was the *modello* for the ivory carving, see *L'Œuvre de P. P. Rubens*, 1890, III, under no. 687 (which is the thesis rejected by Burchard), may also be used against Burchard's proposal. For as Rooses points out the dedication on the engraving, made by Peeter de Jode II, states that Rubens' idea had been expressed 'ac vivibus coloribus'. (28) See the authors cited under *General References*; L. van Puyvelde, *Les Equisses de Rubens*, 1940, no. 61; and Burchard Documentation. (29) See *Correspondance de Rubens*, ed. M. Rooses and Ch. Ruelens (†), 1909, VI, pp. 168–69. (30) Canvas, $78\frac{5}{8} \times 149\frac{1}{4}$ (1·99 × 3·79), see *Museo del Prado, Catálogo de las Pinturas*, 1963, p. 581, no. 1669. (31) See M. Rooses, *L'Œuvre de P. P. Rubens*, 1890, III, no. 662; and Oldenbourg, *op. cit.*, no. 432. (32) Stockholm, Statens Historiska Museum; published by G. Glück, whose essay is reprinted in G. Glück, *Rubens, van Dyck und ihr Kreis*, 1933, pp. 188 ff.; the salt-cellar is fig. 110. For the attribution of the salt-cellar to G. Petel, see K. Feuchtmayr, in Glück, *op. cit.*, pp. 399 ff. These authors point out that the salt-cellar is one of the objects listed in the catalogue of the sale of works by Rubens after his death, see J. Denucé, *Inventories of the Art Collections in Antwerp* etc., 1932, p. 70. Feuchtmayr, *op. cit.*, p. 400, footnote 7, suggested a connection between the salt-cellar and Rubens' marriage with Helena Fourment; and recalled that Gevartius in his *Epithalamium* likened Helena to sea born Venus. By the same score, the design of no. 1195 is equally appropriate to their marriage. And were the inscription on Neeff's etching to be rejected, an alternative, but unprovable, theory would be to suggest that no. 1195 was the *modello* for a basin, which along with the ewer was made in allusion to, or commemoration of, Rubens' marriage, and that it was the basin recorded in Rubens' estate, for which see note 22. (33) Burchard/d'Hulst, *loc. cit.* The dating was first proposed by Burchard in his catalogue of *A Loan Exhibition of Works by . . . Rubens*, 1950, Wildenstein's, London (16). (33) J. S. Held, *Rubens Selected Drawings*, I, 1959, pp. 120–21. (35) Feuchtmayr, *loc. cit.* (36) A comparable note of sweet delicacy, evident in the faces of the two Nereids on the rim, is to be found in the drawing of the head and shoulders of a girl(?) in the bottom centre of the drawing of *Christ shown to the People* and *The Bearing of the Cross*, reproduced and discussed by Burchard/d'Hulst, *op. cit.*, no. 191 *verso*, and dated by them *ca.* 1634. (37) See Ph. Rombouts and Th. van Lerius, *De Liggeren* etc., [1864–1876], II, p. 16. (38) Panel, $17\frac{11}{16} \times 23\frac{7}{16}$ (0.45×0.595); *Ville de Bayonne, Musée Bonnat, Catalogue Sommaire*, 1930, p. 155, no. 947, seems to give the support, wrongly, as canvas. (39) See Puyvelde, *op. cit.*, nos. 61 and 62; also dated by Burchard Documentation, *ca.* 1630. (40) A. Bartsch, *Le Peintre Graveur*, 1813, XIV, p. 247, no. 327. (41) Panel, $5\frac{11}{16} \times 5$ (0.145×0.14), Boymans Museum, see *Olieverfschetsen van Rubens*, Rotterdam, 1953, no. 111; and Puyvelde, *op. cit.*, no. 100. Rubens also designed a *Birth of Venus* for the same series, Brussels, Musées Royaux des Beaux-Arts, *Catalogue de la Peinture Ancienne*, 1957, p. 88, no. 815, where the pose of Venus recalls that in the Sanssouci picture (rep. by Oldenbourg, *op. cit.*, p. 107, bottom) but which in fact derives from Giulio Romano, as M. Jaffé, *The Art Bulletin*, 1958, p. 326, has pointed out. (42) For a review of Rubens' rendering of drunken Silenus, see H. G. Evers, *Rubens und sein Werk*, 1944, pp. 238 ff.; and under no. 853 *q.v.*, Jegher's woodcut is F. van den Wijngaert, *Inventaris der Rubeniaansche Prent-kunst*, 1940, no. 318; Rubens' drawing for it is reproduced in M. Rooses, *L'Œuvre de P. P. Rubens*, V, 1892, pl. 380. (43) See O. Fischel, *Raphael*, trans. B. Rackham, I, 1948, p. 325, and pls. 300 and 301 in vol. II. (44) Oak, $10\frac{1}{2} \times 5\frac{3}{4}$ (0.27×0.146). (45) See van den Wijngaert, *op. cit.*, no. 465; reproduced by H. Hymans, *Histoire de la Gravure dans l'École de Rubens*, 1879, opposite p. 418. The etching also shows a ewer and the central design on it—the Judgment of Paris—separately. The etching is inscribed: *P. P. Rubens pinxit | pro Carolo I magnæ | Britaniæ Franciæ | et Hiberniæ Rege | Theodorus Rogiers | celavit Argento | Jacobus Neffs [sic] fecit | aqua forti | Gillis Hendricx excudit Ant-verpiæ.* Hymans, page 417, comments on the weakness of the etching. As Rooses, *L'Œuvre de P. P. Rubens*, 1820, III, no. 688, has pointed out, the wind god, Zephyrus, has been omitted; there are several other misunderstandings of Rubens' design and differences between it and no. 1195. This makes it clear that the plate was not made under Rubens' supervision. Hendricx began pub-lishing prints between 1641–45, according to Hymans, *op. cit.*, pp. 343–44, although he did not become a master in the Antwerp guild until 1643/44; he died 1676/1677, see Rombouts and van Lerius, *op. cit.*, pp. 144 and 457. Neeffs became a master in the Antwerp guild in 1632/33 and died after 1660/1, see Rombouts and van Lerius, *op. cit.*, pp. 36 and 318. The inclusion of 'I' after Charles in the inscription strongly suggests that the etching was published after the accession of Charles II in 1660 (see note 4 of no. 1172). (46) See Smith, cited under *General References*. No. 1195 seems not to be recorded in any of the ms. inventories of pictures (coll. the Duke of Hamilton, Lennoxlove) owned by the Hamilton family, the earliest of which date from the first half of the seven-teenth century. (47) See Christie's marked copy of the sale catalogue.

1865 THE 'COUP DE LANCE'

Christ between the robbers is pierced by S. Longinus; at the foot of the Cross, S. Mary Magdalene; a soldier is breaking the legs of the robber on the right, beneath are S. John the Evangelist, the Virgin and S. Mary of Cleophas(?).

Oil on oak, $25\frac{1}{2} \times 19\frac{5}{8}$ (0.648×0.499).

The support is made up of 2 members joined vertically. The reverse bears the brand of the coat of arms of the city of Antwerp.

Grisaille with some touches of red; generally in good condition. The support is painted up to the edges. There are numerous, small, discoloured retouchings overall. Yellow varnish.

The subject is from John, XIX, 31–34. The identification of the soldier, who pierced Christ, as S. Longinus was made by S. Bonaventura and S. Augustine.[1]

Although recorded as early as 1753 (see under *Provenance*) as the sketch by Rubens for the 'Coup de Lance',[2] the status of no. 1865 has been disputed.

The 'Coup de Lance' was commissioned from Rubens as the high altarpiece for the church of the Récollets, Antwerp; the altar, at least, was paid for by Nicolaes Rockox.[3] No. 1865 is more complex than the altarpiece as a composition, and differs from it in several respects: it lacks the two spears to the left; the head of the horse on the left is higher; S. Longinus' horse is farther from the Cross and is placed in deeper foreshortening; a soldier stands between the two horses, with a shield at his feet; the cross on the left is not so high; Christ does not wear the crown of thorns and a piece of his loin cloth falls free; a man carries a ladder in front of a soldier behind Our Lord's Cross; the Magdalen is further from the Cross and her left arm is raised upright; a woman stands behind her; there is a soldier on horseback behind the ladder against the right-hand cross, which is placed at a more acute angle, so that the soldier (who does not wear a helmet) breaking the robber's legs, is farther from Christ; S. John lifts his cloak to his face with both hands; there is a tree on high ground in the right background; S. Mary of Cleophas(?) is seen in profile and does not wring her hands. In the altarpiece, the crosses are placed on high ground, and the heads of two spectators are depicted immediately behind and to the left of the Cross.

A sheet of studies (see under *Drawings*)—now generally agreed to be by Rubens and preparatory for the 'Coup de Lance'[4]—has on the *verso* a study for Christ and, on the *recto*, the disposition of the three Crosses and the poses of Christ and the robbers. Here the Magdalen is placed to the left of the Cross; Christ was pierced from the right, and the pose of the soldier on the ladder, breaking the robbers legs, is considered. On the right is a figure seen from the back, which Burchard/d'Hulst[5] suggest is an alternative pose for this soldier, but which may rather be an idea for the pose of S. Longinus. It is clear from the depiction of the Magdalen and the figure at the base of the ladder that Rubens envisaged the three Crosses on a high terrain such as they were to be in the altarpiece.

No. 1865 has been ascribed to the School of Rubens[6] and to van Dyck;[7] more recently strong arguments have been advanced for its re-attribution to Rubens, thus vindicating the opinion of Smith.[8] The reasons put forward for its authorship by van Dyck are mutually exclusive: Glück[9] believed no. 1865 to be preparatory for the 'Coup de Lance', while Burchard/d'Hulst[10] stated that it is the only example of the procedure, recorded by Bellori, of van Dyck producing a sketch for the engraver after a composition by Rubens.

Held[11] has argued that the basis of both the attribution to the School of Rubens and to van Dyck assumes the absurd—that Rubens was prepared to entrust to an anonymous studio assistant or to van Dyck the task of a share in both evolving and executing an important commission. It has been suggested, not convincingly, that van Dyck had a part in executing the 'Coup de Lance';[12] even if this were so, it does not follow that he was responsible for a preparatory sketch. It is by no means certain that he knew of no. 1865, as opposed to the altarpiece.[13] Held considers that the differences between no. 1865 and the altarpiece are characteristic of Rubens' preparatory sketches; this view is in itself a strong argument against the basis for Burchard/d'Hulst's attribution of no. 1865 to van Dyck. It is hardly necessary to add to Jaffé's[14] reasons for rejecting their opinion; but if no. 1865 is the only example of the procedure, not necessarily reliably recorded by Bellori,[15] then it is odd that no engraving follows no. 1865,[16] and that there is no prototype by Rubens from which no. 1865 directly derives.

Vey[17] first challenged the attribution of no. 1865 to van Dyck; Held and Jaffé both consider it to be by Rubens. Held included in his persuasive line of reasoning, the drawing of a young man carrying a ladder (see under *Drawings*), which motif appears apparently uniquely in Rubens' œuvre in no. 1865. Rubens' authorship of this drawing has never been questioned and thus, as Held has pointed out, 'one would have to assume a very complex manner of collaboration (such as Rubens making studies from nature for a composition sketched by van Dyck) if the London sketch [=no. 1865] were by van Dyck'. In fact, it is not absolutely necessary to associate this drawing with no. 1865; at the most it would appear to be an elaboration of the motif first sketched in no. 1865. If such was the case the manner of collaboration would be equally complex, if not ridiculous (such as Rubens elaborating a pose invented by van Dyck).

Rooses[18] stated that a picture at Aachen was Rubens' sketch for the 'Coup de Lance', but he confused the provenance of the Aachen picture with that of no. 1865 (see below under *Provenance*). The Aachen picture first doubted in 1883[19] is now recognized to be a copy of no. 1865.[20] Rooses considered that the provenance (*sic*) of the Aachen picture supported his attribution, by the same token the provenance of no. 1865 must support its attribution to Rubens. Indeed the use of brown and black oil washes, combined with white oil paint with touches of red and grey, is typical of Rubens, while the handling compares with that in his grisaille sketches for the ceiling paintings for the Jesuit Church, Antwerp, of 1620.[21]

No. 1865 could not have been the final *modello* for the 'Coup de Lance', executed for the studio to follow, because of the differences between the two. It is first recorded in the monastery of the Récollets, Antwerp (see below under *Provenance*), which suggests that it may represent Rubens' first, completed and general idea for the altarpiece, which was shown and/or presented to the recipients of Rockox's donation, to give them an idea of the composition he had in mind.

It is not known when the details of the commission were finalized; the stone for the high altar was ordered in September, 1619,[22] and the altarpiece was installed in 1620.[23] It seems not improbable to assume, granted the length of time necessary to execute such a large picture, that the commission had been settled at least by the time the stone for the altar was ordered. A date *ca.* 1619 would thus appear acceptable for no. 1865.

The composition of the 'Coup de Lance' connects (in reverse) with an unused design by Rubens for the *Breviarum Romanum* and *Missale Romanum*, published by the Plantin Press in 1614.[24] A source for the composition may be the relevant area in Veronese's *Calvary* (Accademia, Venice);[25] the soldier on the horse on the left may derive from a composition such as Veronese's *Calvary* (Louvre).[26]

DRAWINGS: (1) *recto*: preliminary idea for the composition; *verso*: study for the pose of Christ, Boymans-van Beuningen Museum, Rubens 4, pen and brown ink, $8\frac{1}{8} \times 6\frac{7}{16}$ (0·206 × 0·164);[27] (2) study for the young man carrying a ladder, or, alternatively, an elaboration of this motif: Albertina, no. 8298, black chalk heightened with white body colour, $13\frac{7}{16} \times 10\frac{5}{8}$ (0·342 × 0·27).[28]

COPY: Aachen, Städtisches Suermondt Museum, panel, $25\frac{9}{16} \times 19\frac{11}{16}$ (0·65 × 0·50).[29]

PROVENANCE: Apparently first recorded in the 'Chambre des Hôtes' of the monastery of the Récollets, Antwerp (suppressed, 1794), 1753;[30] perhaps acquired from the monks by M. Schamp, d'Aveschoot, 1794;[31] certainly his coll., Ghent, by 1830;[32] Schamp d'Averschoot sale, Regermorter, 14 ff. September, 1840 (235) bt. Smith for Blamire for 2330 francs;[33] George Blamire sale, Christie's, 7 November, 1863 (69) bt. Smith 23 gns;[34] sold presumably by Smith to George Mitchell; bequeathed by George Mitchell to the South Kensington Museum, 1878; lent to the National Gallery, 1895.

REPRODUCTION: *National Gallery Illustrations, Continental Schools (excluding Italian)*, 1950, p. 317, bottom.

REFERENCE: *General:* J. Smith, *A Catalogue Raisonné* etc., 1830, II, no. 28.

In text: (1) See Ch. Rouault de Fleury, *Mémoire sur les Instruments de la Passion* etc., 1870, pp. 273; and Les Petits Bollandistes, *Vie des Saints* etc., 3, 1882, pp. 425–26. (2) Musée Royal des Beaux-Arts, Antwerp, no. 297 (in 1958 catalogue referred to in note 12); rep. by R. Oldenbourg, *Rubens, K. der K.*, [1921], p. 216. (3) See M. Rooses, *L'Œuvre de P. P. Rubens*, 1888, II, no. 296. (4) See note 27. (5) *Ibid.* (6) See the National Gallery catalogue, 1929. (7) See G. Glück, *Van Dyck, Klassiker der Kunst*, [1931], p. 519, under no. 19; and the *National Gallery, Summary Catalogue*, 1958. (8) See under *General Reference.* (9) *Loc. cit.* (10) L. Burchard and R.-A. d'Hulst, *Rubens Drawings*, I, 1963, p. 190 under no. 120. (11) J. S. Held, *Rubens Selected Drawings*, I, 1959, pp. 135–36, under no. 99. Further references to Held are to these pages. (12) See Rooses, *loc. cit.*; Glück, *loc. cit.*; and W. Vanbeselaere, *Catalogue Descriptif, Maîtres Anciens*, Musée Royal des Beaux-Arts, Antwerp, 1958, p. 198, no. 297. (13) The *Crucifixion* in the Louvre, which Glück, *op. cit.*, p. 19, believes to be by van Dyck, includes a tree on high ground on the right as in no. 1865; but whether Glück's attribution is accepted or not, it is not necessarily significant, as the design clearly derives from Rubens. (14) See *The Burlington Magazine*, 1965, p. 376. Further references to Jaffé are to this page. (15) G. P. Bellori, *Le Vite*, etc. 1674, p. 254. For van Dyck's relationship with Rubens, see further under nos. 50, 680, & 853. (16) Rubens' working drawing for Boetius' à Bolswert's engraving of the *Coup de Lance* (see Frank van den Wijngaert, *Inventaris der Rubiaansche Prentkunst*, 1940, no. 30) is N.G. no. 853G, on loan to the British Museum. In spite of differences, the drawing is closer to the finished picture than to no. 1865, although Christ's drapery recalls that in no. 1865 and the soldier on the ladder is helmet-less. (17) H. Vey, *Bulletin Musées Royaux des Beaux-Arts*, Brussels, 1956, p. 174. (18) *Op. cit.*, no. 296 bis. (19) J. Meyer, *Beschreibendes Verzeichniss der Gemälde, Königlichen Museen zu Berlin*, 1883, p. 395, no. 798A. (20) See Held, *loc. cit.* (21) Compare for instance the grisaille in the Ashmolean, for which see L. van Puyvelde, *Les Esquisses de Rubens*, 1940, no. 33. (22) See Rooses, *op. cit.*, no. 296. (23) *Ibid.* (24) For a discussion of the drawing, which is in the British Museum, see Burchard/ d'Hulst, *op. cit.*, no. 68; see also J. Muller Hofstede, *Pantheon*, 1969, p. 139, who prefers an earlier dating. He there publishes, pp. 136 ff., an oil sketch which he believes to be by Rubens, that shows Christ on the Cross in a pose similar to that in the 'Coup de Lance'. He points out that a thief in a similar pose (but in reverse) occurs in the background of Rubens' sketch (Louvre) for the Antwerp *Erection of the Cross* (Rooses, *op. cit.*, nos. 275–85). The top part of the thief in the Louvre sketch should be treated with caution, as the central compartment of the *modello* was originally designed to show an arched top in the centre; the two wings were also designed to match this, as is clear from what are probably the backs of the two wings of the Louvre *modello*, showing *SS. Amandus & Walburgis* and *SS. Elegius & Catherine*, at Dulwich. (25) See S. Moschini Marconi, *Gallerie dell'Accademia, . . . Opere . . . del Secolo XVI*, 1962, no. 142, & fig. (26) See G. Fiocco, *Paolo Veronese* etc., 1928, fig. LXXXIII. (27) See Burchard & d'Hulst, *op. cit.*, no. 118. They note what they consider to be a second study for Christ, coll. Ernst Proehl, Amsterdam; exh. *Rubens-Tentoonstelling*, Amsterdam, 1933 (75) and rep. (28) See Held, *op. cit.*, no. 99; and Burchard/d'Hulst, *op. cit.*, no. 120. (29) See F. Kuetgens, *Städtisches Suermondt Museum . . . Gemälde-Katalog*, 1932, p. 149, no. 442. Ex coll. Graf von Kesselstadt, Mainz, 1828 (see below); coll. J. P. Weyer, Cologne, 1852 with a provenance from Graf Kesselstadt, see M. Unger, *Beschreibung des Inhaltes der Sammlung von Gemälden älterer Meister des Herrn Johann Peter Weyer in Coeln*, [1852], p. 67, no. 217; by whom sold, apparently in 1857; certainly in coll. Barthold Suermondt, Aachen, in 1859, see G. F. Waagen, *Raisonnirender Catalog der Gemälde-Sammlung des Herrn Barthold Suermondt zu Aachen*, 1859, pp. 6–7, no. 8 (with a provenance from Graf von Kesselstadt, 1828, and J. P. Weyer, 1857); bequeathed by Suermondt to the Königlichen Museen, Berlin, 1874, and recorded there in 1883 (see note 19); transferred to Aachen, 1884. Rep. by Held, *op. cit.*, I, fig. 51. (30) See J. B. Descamps, *La Vie des Peintres* etc., 1753, I, p. 322; see also *Description des Principaux Ouvrages de Peinture . . . de la Ville d'Anvers*, 1763 [4th ed.], à Anvers chèz Gerard Berbie, p. 62; G. P. Mensaert, *Le Peintre Amateur* etc., I, 1763, p. 204; and J. F. Michel, *Histoire de la vie de P. P. Rubens* etc., 1771, p. 96. (31) The introduction to the Schamp d'Aveschoot sale catalogue of 1840, see below, p. V, stated: 'Le cabinet de tableaux, légué à M. Schamp par ces ancêtres, s'est enrichi, depuis un demi-siècle environ, d'une grande quantité d'œuvres de premier ordre. La plupart de ces acquisitions ont été faites des moines eux-mêmes, à l'époque de la sup-pression des couvens . . .' No. 1865 does not appear to have been looted by Napoleon. (32) See Smith, cited under *General Reference*. (33) See Smith and Successors *Day Book*, 1837–48 (mss. Victoria and Albert Museum Library), entry for 18 September, 1840. The name 'G. Blamire' is written on the reverse of no. 1865. (34) Marked copy of the sale catalogue in the National Gallery library.

2598 AURORA ABDUCTING CEPHALUS

Aurora steps from her chariot to embrace Cephalus, who is on Mount Hymettus.

Oil on oak, $12\frac{1}{8} \times 19/19\frac{1}{8}$ ($0.308 \times 0.48/0.485$).

The support is made up of 2 members joined vertically. Remains of the brand of the coat of arms of the city of Antwerp are on the reverse.

In very good condition. There is a border drawn in black chalk: *ca.* $\frac{3}{16}$ (0.005) wide at the bottom, *ca.* $\frac{1}{4}$ (0.006) at the top and *ca.* $\frac{1}{8}$ (0.004) on the left and the right. There are some small losses along the edges, and a few small blobs of blue paint (not Rubens') scattered about.

On the drawn borders are various marks to assist in the execution of the design on a larger scale (see below).

For the subject, see Ovid, *Metamorphoses*, VII, 849–854. Aurora was the goddess of daylight; her chariot was drawn by Campius and Phaeton. Cephalus, the husband of Procris, was seduced by Aurora; he then sought to try the fidelity of his wife, whom later he was accidentally to kill while hunting.

No. 2598 has been generally accepted as the work of Rubens,[1] and there is no reason to doubt this attribution.

No. 2598 is similar in style and subject matter to a group of sketches by Rubens (and has a provenance in common with many of them, see below under *Provenance*), which were executed as *modelli* for paintings (not all to be by his hand), commissioned by Philip IV of Spain to decorate a royal hunting lodge, the Torre de la Parada, outside Madrid.[2] The lodge was sacked in 1710, and in the following years the series was in part further broken up.[3] The commission amounted to probably not more than 112 paintings,[4] but the exact number is not known. No painting of *Cephalus and Aurora* is known to exist, or is recorded in the inventories of the Spanish Royal Collection available in England. However, granted this, and the lack of any detailed knowledge of the commission, it seems reasonable to accept the generally held assumption that no. 2598 was one of Rubens' *modelli* for this commission.

Rubens had begun work on the commission by November, 1636.[5] The paintings were probably nearing completion by September, 1637.[6] A date late in 1636 or early in 1637 is thus acceptable for no. 2598.

For at least a hundred years (see below under *Provenance*), the subject of no. 2598 was thought to be *Diana and Endymion*; the correct identification is due to Michael Jaffé.[7]

COPIES: Panel, $12\frac{5}{16} \times 18\frac{11}{16}$ (0.313×0.475), private collection, Paris, 1965;[8] copper, $16 \times 8\frac{3}{4}$ (0.406×0.223), London Art Market, 1969.[9]

PROVENANCE: Owned by the Infantado family, and probably noted in the palace, in Madrid, of the 12th Duque, 1776;[10] after the death of the 13th Duque in 1841, inherited by the 11th Duque de Osuna († 1844); seen in the collection of the 12th Duque de Osuna (1814–1882) by Eastlake in 1859;[11] Casa Ducal de Osuna sale, Madrid, 11 ff. May, 1896 (135)[12] bought by George Salting for £300;[13] exh. *The Collection of Pictures and Drawings owned by the late Mr. George Salting*, Agnew's, 1910 (141); George Salting Bequest, 1910.

REPRODUCTION: *National Gallery Illustrations, Continental Schools (excluding Italian)*, 1950, p. 313, top.

REFERENCES: *General:* M. Rooses, *L'Œuvre de P. P. Rubens*, 1890, III, no. 516; R. Oldenbourg, *Rubens, K. der K.*, [1921], p. 395.

In text: (1) See the authors cited under *General References*; and for instance, L. van Puyvelde, *Les Esquisses de Rubens*, 1940, no. 98. (2) The outlines concerning the commission were first drawn by C. Justi, *Zeitschrift für bildende Kunst*, 1880, pp. 229 ff; see also Rooses, *op. cit.*, 1890, III, pp. 5–35; and more recently the catalogue of *Olieverfschetsen van Rubens*, Rotterdam, 1953, nos. 100 ff; and M. Jaffé, *La Revue du Louvre* etc., 1964, pp. 313 ff. (3) A number of pictures from the Torre de la Parada feature in the inventory (copy coll. the Duke of Wellington) of the pictures in the Nuevo Palacio, Madrid, of 1772. For a description of the Torre de la Parada towards the end of the eighteenth century, see A. Ponz, *Viage de España*, 1782 ed., VI, pp. 183–4. (4) See Serrano's letter of 1 May, 1638 stating that 112 pictures had arrived in Madrid accompanied by 'un Aiutante di Camᵃ dell Infante di Fiandra', which Philip IV had commissioned for 'il Ritiro [*sic*], et per la nuova casa della Parada, che si fabbrica nei Boschi del Pardo ...', printed by M. Rooses and Ch. Ruelens (†), *Correspondance de Rubens*, 1909, VI, p. 214. (5) See the Cardinal Infant Ferdinand's letter to Philip IV of 20 November, 1636, printed by Rooses and Ruelens (†), *op. cit.*, 1909, VI, p. 170. (6) See the Cardinal Infant Ferdinand's letter of 11 August, 1637 to Philip IV, printed by Rooses and Ruelens (†), *op. cit.*, 1909, VI, p. 183. Their despatch was held up by Snijders' slowness in completing paintings, also commissioned by Philip IV; on 21 January, 1638 the Cardinal Infant reported that Rubens required another 20 days for the paintings to dry before they could be rolled up for transport, see Rooses and Ruelens (†), *op. cit.*, 1909, VI, pp. 191–92. (7) *Op. cit.*, pp. 318–19. (8) Exhibited at *Le Siècle de Rubens*, Musées Royaux des Beaux-Arts de Belgique, Brussels, 1965, (234), where accepted as autograph. (9) Acceptably the work of a minor, contemporary Flemish artist; it shows more sky, and has a pendant *Mercury and Argus* (not Rubens' composition for the Torre de la Parada). (10) See A. Ponz, *Viage de España*, V, 1782 ((2nd ed.) 1st ed., 1776), p. 301: 'En casa [in Madrid] de Duque del Infantado hay algunos asuntos fabulosos executados por Rubens'; see also J. A. Ceán Bermúdez, *Diccionario Historico* etc., IV, 1800, pp. 272–3, note 1: the collection of the Duque del Infantado, Madrid, 'que contiene quarenta y seis bocetos originales de Rúbens en diferentes tamaños, cuyos asuntos pertenecen á la mitologia...'. N. Sentenach y Cabañas, *La Pintura en Madrid* etc., 1907, pp. 78 ff., prints an undated excerpt of an inventory, entailed to the Pastrana title and estate (the 8th Duquesa del Infantado married the 4th Duque de Pastrana († 1675); the two titles remained united, and both passed to the 11th Duque de Osuna in 1841; after a lawsuit, the natural son of the last Duque del Infantado obtained the dukedom of Pastrana from the 12th Duque de Osuna). The inventory contains a picture by Giaquinto, and thus could post date 1753 when he arrived in Spain. It includes 44 sketches by Rubens, all of which seem to have been *modelli* for the Torre de la Parada commission, see Sentenach, *op. cit.*, pp. 77–8. Among these are two called *Diana and Endymion*; it seems most improbable that Rubens would have treated the same subject twice, and likely that one of the *modelli* in the inventory was mis-named. The first (see p. 80) measured 'a tercia [vara] en quadro' (=*ca.* 11 square), which is about the same size as the *modello* of *Diana and Endymion* at Bayonne, recently published by Jaffé, *op. cit.*, p. 314 and fig. 5; the second (p. 82), measured 'tercia y un dedo de alto y media vara y tres dedos de ancho' (=*ca.* 11¾ × 18¾), which is about the same size as no. 2598. No. 2598 was thought to represent 'Diana and Endymion' in 1859, see below; and it seems more likely that no. 2598 should be thus identified with this entry in the inventory, rather than with the pendant 'Yo registrando á Narciso' as attempted by Sentenach, *op. cit.*, p. 82, notes 6 and 7. The earlier provenance of this group of *modelli* is obscure. Sentenach, *op. cit.*, p. 78, was incorrect to claim that they passed from the Alcazar after the death of Charles II to D. Franchisco Casimiro Pimentel as 'legatorio de todas los alhayas que habia en la pieza llamada de las Furias [in the Alcazar]', and thence, with the Benavente estate, by marriage into the Infantado family, as no such marriage took place. The 11th Duque de Osuna inherited the

Benavente titles and estates from his grandmother in 1835, and the Infantado estates and titles in 1841 from his uncle. **(11)** Eastlake's notebook for 1859 in the National Gallery library. He saw only nine sketches; of these one was called *Diana and Endymion* and measured $12 \times 19\frac{1}{2}$. At least six of these sketches feature in the inventory, published by Sentenach, *op. cit.*, pp. 78 ff. **(12)** As 'Venus encontrando á Adonis dormido', $12\frac{1}{4} \times 18\frac{1}{2}$ (0.31×0.47). **(13)** Salting's notebook in the National Gallery library.

2924 A SHEPHERD WITH HIS FLOCK IN A WOODY LANDSCAPE

A stream runs towards open country out of a wood. On the right bank is a shepherd with nineteen sheep nearby; in the distance is a huntsman coursing and a cottage. In the far left is the sun on the horizon.

Oil on oak, $25\frac{1}{8}/\frac{5}{16} \times 37\frac{1}{8}$ ($0.639/644 \times 0.943$).

For the make up of the support, see Appendix I.[1]

Generally in good condition. The support is painted up to the edges. Some of the joins have opened and cracks have appeared elsewhere, but this has resulted in very little paint loss. There is some wearing in the sky in the centre top, in the foliage above the bridge, in the lowest branch of the tree in the left foreground and in the small tree trunk to its right, both of which have also become translucent with time. There is probably some retouching in black towards the top left, above the bridge on the right, among the trees behind the shepherd, in the water in front of him, and beneath the dead, forked branch in the left foreground. Surface dirt.

A number of *pentimenti* can be made out by the naked eye, infra-red, or X-ray photography. X-radiographs indicate that there may perhaps first have been a small group of cottages beyond a bridge in the left centre, just below where the cottage now is.[2] The sun was first placed more to the right—just to the left of the tree in the middle of the group in the left foreground.[3] A swan in the stream also just to the left of this tree has been suppressed. The alley in the centre middle ground may have first been wider, and there may have been more streaks of sunlight evident among the trees behind the shepherd. There are also some minor *pentimenti* in the shepherd, the rim of whose hat was first flat, and in the sheep.

The handling of the paint in no. 2924 gets looser towards the edges of the support; detail on the right, above the bridge, has not been worked up.

No. 2924 was engraved by Schelte à Bolswert as one of the series of small, engraved landscapes after Rubens (see under *Engravings*); and although not included by either Rosenberg or Oldenbourg in their Klassiker der Kunst editions of Rubens' oeuvre, no. 2924 has otherwise been generally accepted as by Rubens.[4] There is no reason to doubt this attribution; but it is possible that some of the dark foliage in the trees behind the shepherd soon suffered amplification by another hand.[5]

What might be read in X-ray photography as a small group of cottages, in the centre of the support, would suggest that Rubens began no. 2924 with quite a different landscape in mind. There is no other evidence to support this; and this apart, it is clear that no. 2924 was evolved in two main stages, as Evers suggested.[6] The first stage was confined to the two central members; and showed the sun above the horizon at the left-hand edge. The support was then enlarged all round: the wood was extended to the right, and the group of trees in the left foreground was enlarged and elaborated, partly to conceal the first position of the sun, which was moved down to the horizon at the new edge of the support.[6a]

It is not possible to be certain whether Rubens intended to depict a sunset or sunrise in no. 2924; the fact that he moved the sun downwards is perhaps an indication that he had a sunset in mind, but the presence of the huntsman makes it more likely that the time of day is dawn.[7]

A shepherd in a comparable pose appears in the distance of the *View of the Palatine Hills*,[8] and a huntsman 'coursing across an alley of trees is the subject of another landscape by Rubens,[9] both of which were engraved by Schelte à Bolswert. The composition of no. 2924 recurs with slight variation in no. 4815 *q.v.*, and for a further discussion, see under the latter.

ENGRAVINGS: By Schelte à Bolswert (in reverse);[10] Anon.[11]

COPIES: Leipzig, Museum der bildenden Kunst, canvas, $26 \times 38\frac{3}{16}$ ($0·66 \times 0·97$);[12] The Earl of Pembroke, Wilton House, canvas 27×32 ($0·685 \times 0·813$);[13] Anon. sale, Christie's, 28 March, 1947 (117), panel, 25×39 ($0·635 \times 0·99$); Anon. sale, Sotheby's, 27 May, 1964 (169), canvas, $11\frac{1}{2} \times 17\frac{1}{4}$ ($0·293 \times 0·438$);[14] of the right-hand half: private collection, Pennsylvania, panel, $18\frac{7}{8} \times 16\frac{3}{8}$ ($0·479 \times 0·417$);[15] drawing: Graphische Sammlung, Munich, ascribed to Lucas van Uden;[16] derivation; ascribed to J. d'Arthois, Achillito Chiesa sale, American Art Association, New York, 27 November, 1925 (8), panel, $19 \times 36\frac{1}{2}$ ($0·483 \times 0·922$).

PROVENANCE: Perhaps P. P. Rubens sale (†), Antwerp, 1640 (112).[17] Perhaps coll. the dealer Gersaint, Paris, *ca.* 1721.[18] Perhaps coll. the artist and dealer Peeter Snijers, Antwerp, 1747.[19] Certainly in the Cressent sale, Paris, 15 ff. January, 1749 (79).[20] Coll. the Earl of Carlisle (1748–1825), by whom lent to the B.I. (71) in 1819;[21] presented by Rosalind, Countess of Carlisle, 1913.

REPRODUCTION: *National Gallery Illustrations, Continental Schools (excluding Italian)*, 1950, p. 316, bottom.

REFERENCES: *General:* G. Glück, *Die Landschaften von P. P. Rubens*, 1940/5, no. 4; Gregory Martin, *The Burlington Magazine*, 1966, pp. 180 ff.

In text: (1) See also Martin, cited under *General References*, fig. 14. (2) For a reproduction of the X-ray see *ibid.*, fig. 17. If these are cottages (and the proposal is not pressed here) they would have to be thought of as in the distance, like those in Rubens' *Landscape with a Rainbow* (Hermitage), rep. by R. Olden-bourg, *Rubens, K. der K.*, [1921], p. 356. (3) For a reproduction of the X-ray, see Martin, cited under *General References*, fig. 16. (4) See Glück, cited under *General References*; and, for instance, J. Smith, *A Catalogue Raisonné* etc., 1830, II, no. 1206; M. Rooses, *L'Œuvre de P. P. Rubens*, 1890, IV, no. 1177; and other authors cited in note 4 under no. 4815. (5) The foliage agrees with that in Schelte à Bolswert's engraving, for which see under *Engravings*. (6) See H. G. Evers, *Peter Paul Rubens*, 1946 [Dutch ed.], pp. 398–400; and Martin, cited under *General References*, pp. 180–83. (6a) Michael Jaffé has recently argued, see his forthcoming article in the July (1969) number of *The Burlington Magazine*, which he kindly showed the compiler before publication, that the second stage consisted merely in the addition of the left-hand member. From the point of view of the structure of the support there is no reason why this should not be so. But the aesthetic grounds he mentions are unspecified and thus meaningless; and the 'preliminary study', which determined his proposal, is not acceptable as an autograph work by Rubens (see below under *Copies*). (7) Both subjects were treated by Rubens before 1628, see note 21 under no. 4815. For the hunter at dawn and a description of the rising sun, see C. van Mander, *Het Schilder-Boeck* etc., 1604, p. 34 *recto* and *verso*. (8) See Glück, *op. cit.*, no. 11. Compare also the shepherd on the sheet in the Rubens' sketchbook, engraved by Pontius, for which see F. van den Wijngaert, *Inventaris der Rubeniaansche Prentkunst*, 1940, no. 557 (16), who also occurs in the Royal Collection *Winter*. (9) See Glück, *op. cit.*, no. 28. (10) See van den Wijngaert, *op. cit.*, no. 92. (11) See C. G. Voorhelm Schneevoogt, *Catalogue des Estampes Gravées d'après P. P. Rubens* etc., 1873, p. 235, no. 53(4); published by Gaspar Huberti (Huybrechts) (1619–1684), Antwerp. Rooses, *op. cit.*, under no. 1177, records a second anonymous engraving. (12) According to the R.K.D.; ex coll. Frieherr Speck von Sternberg, Lützchena, see Oldenbourg, *op. cit.*, p. 445 (from whom the measurements are taken); and Glück, cited under *General References*. (13) See Sidney, 16th Earl of Pembroke, *A Catalogue of the Paintings and Drawings ... at Wilton House*, 1968, no. 155, where thought to be by Rubens; recorded at Wilton in 1758. (14) Ex coll. Dr. Burd. (15) Probably ex Anon. sale, Christie's, 27 February, 1948 (157); and Anon. sale, Christie's, 18 February, 1955 (169); recently published by Jaffé, see note 6a, as Rubens' preliminary study, partly after nature, for no. 2924. The owner generously brought his painting to the National Gallery for study purposes. The compiler is as sure as is possible that it is not an autograph work by Rubens for the following reasons: 1) although the absence of major *pentimenti* in the centre of no. 2924 suggests that Rubens may have been working from a study made after nature, there is nothing to prove this; indeed the evolution of no. 4815 (see below) suggests that he was apt to rely a good deal on his imagination for the elaboration of the foliage; 2) whatever connections Jaffé may find in the handling of the pen work with that in drawings considered to be by Rubens, the pen work itself is unspecific in the very areas unspecified or in very dark shade in no. 2924; 3) there is no other extant example of Rubens working with a pen & ink on panel after nature; 4) there is no reference in the sketch to the streaks of sunlight suppressed above the shepherd in no. 2924; 5) the handling of oil paint is weak and the colour range has none of the brilliance to be associated with Rubens. (16) See E. Kieser, *Die Rubenslandschaft*, 1926, p. 42, note 2. (17) Described as 'Un paysage avec des brebis, sur fond de bois', see J. Denucé, *Inventories of the Art-Collections in Antwerp* etc., 1932, p. 61; but see also under no. 157. (18) No. 2924, or a copy of it, appears, in the top left-hand corner of Watteau's *Enseigne de Gersaint* (Charlottenburg Palace), datable to 1721, see E. Dacier and A. Vuaflart, *Jean de Julienne et les Graveurs de Watteau au XVIIIᵉ Siècle*, 1922, III, no. 115, p. 56. It is reasonable to assume that the pictures there depicted by Watteau were part of Gersaint's stock. (19) No. 2924, or a copy of it, appears in a picture, perhaps a self portrait by P. Snijers (1681–1752), signed and dated Antwerp, 1747, which was in an Anon. sale, Sotheby's, 30 November, 1966 (51). No. 2924 does not feature in any of the Snijers' sales. (20) Information supplied by Dr. L. Burchard (see also Burchard Documentation). Smith followed by Rooses, see under note 4, wrongly stated that no. 2924 was in the Orléans collection, 1749; this was due to a misreading of the title page of the Cressent sale catalogue: *Catalogue des Differens [sic] Effects Curieux du Sieur Cressent Ebeniste des Palais de feu S. A. R. Monseigneur le Duc d'Orleans [sic]*. The description of lot 79 agrees with no. 2924, but the measurements are slightly different. They are given as 26 p × 36 p ($= 27\frac{11}{16} \times 38\frac{5}{16}$); the entry also states that the picture was engraved 'de trois pouces ($= 3\frac{3}{16}$) par le haut, et d'un pouce ($= 1\frac{1}{16}$) par le bas moins large que la Peinture dans le quele [sic] on remarque cette augmentation'. Bolswert's engraving follows no. 2924 exactly in the area depicted. The catalogue states that the additions were evident on the painting; a subtraction of them from the overall measurement of the height makes the size as $23\frac{7}{16}$, i.e. *ca.* 2 less than that of no. 2924. (21) It is not known when no. 2924 was bought by the Earl of Carlisle; it does not feature in guide books which cover Castle Howard before 1819, or for instance in [John Henry Manners, 5th Duke of Rutland] *Journal of a Tour to the Northern Parts of Great Britain*, 1796, in *Travels in Great Britain*, 1813.

2968 PORTRAIT OF THOMAS HOWARD, 2ND EARL OF ARUNDEL

The sitter wears a fur-lined cloak and the lesser George hung from a blue ribbon.

Oil on relined[1] canvas, $26\frac{3}{8} \times 21\frac{1}{4}$ (0·67 × 0·54); the left-hand edge of the canvas is ragged; the canvas is irregularly bent over the stretcher by as much as *ca.* $\frac{3}{4}$ (0·020) all round.

Generally in good condition. The head and collar are well preserved; the paint is thinner elsewhere. The area where the hair joins the centre of the forehead is not filled in. Cleaned, 1959.

Thomas Howard, 2nd Earl of Arundel and Surrey (1585–1646) married Alathea, daughter of Gilbert Talbot, Earl of Shrewsbury, 1606. He was created a Knight of the Garter, 1611; Earl Marshal of England, 1621, and general of the army against the Scots, 1638. He left England in 1642 and died in Padua. One of the first and most famous of English connoisseurs; according to an anonymous correspondent of the Earl's, he was regarded by Rubens as 'un évangéliste pour le monde de l'art, et comme le grand protecteur de notre état'.[2]

No. 2968 has previously been considered to be wholly by Rubens.[3] However, the treatment of the background and costume, except the collar, is too feeble for him. There is no reason to doubt that Rubens painted the head and collar. The handling of the background and much of the costume seems to have few of the characteristics of Rubens or his studio.

The sitter is clearly the same person as that in other accepted depictions of Arundel.[4] There are two other painted portraits of him by Rubens: the three-quarter length as Earl Marshal in the Isabella Gardner Museum[5] and the bust length study for it at the National Portrait Gallery.[6] No. 2968 is comparable to the latter picture, which Piper has dated 1629.[7] He considered no. 2968 to be 'rather later'; Rooses suggested that it could have been painted *ca.* 1636 during Arundel's journey to Ratisbon;[8] while Miss Hervey has dated no. 2968 '*c.* 1638?'.[9] Rooses' view is in part contradicted by the inscription on an etched portrait by Krafft[10] after Rubens; the drawing[11] from which this print derives is connected with, but not a study for, no. 2968. There is no evidence that Arundel and Rubens ever met after Rubens' departure from England; further, Arundel does not appear as old in no. 2968 as he does in his portrait with his grandson by van Dyck (coll. the Duke of Norfolk),[12] which was completed certainly before November, 1636.[13] But he does have more white hair in no. 2968 than in the National Portrait Gallery picture; thus the head and collar in no. 2968 can reasonably be dated towards the end of Rubens' stay in England, that is early in 1630. In support of this dating is the fact that Rubens may well have left no. 2968 unfinished.

Because no. 2968 may have been left unfinished, it is not possible to state what Rubens had in mind. It should not be associated with the commission which resulted in the Gardner Museum portrait. The pose in no. 2968 is peculiar as Arundel does not look at the spectator; it suggests that it was done from the life but not for a single portrait, at least in the accepted sense. It may be that Arundel had in mind to commission from Rubens a double portrait with himself and his wife as he was later to commission from van Dyck,[14] or a *modello* for a sculptor to make a *bas-relief* from[15]—possibly comparable to that painted by van Dyck of Charles I.[16] The ragged left-hand edge of no. 2968 may not therefore be entirely fortuituous, for it may have resulted from removing the area of canvas which Rubens had earmarked for either Arundel's wife's head or just conceivably for frontal and left-hand views of Arundel. The drawing from which Krafft made his etching could derive from a later study for the latter.

It seems reasonable to suppose that if this drawing does derive from Rubens, the original showed the lesser George hanging from the ribbon. If this was the case the assistant, who completed no. 2968, may have had this drawing in mind especially as Arundel also wears a fur-lined cloak; the alternative is that he had a knowledge of Vorsterman's print after van Dyck(?) where Arundel is shown bust length and full face, wearing the lesser George and/or of D. Mytens' earlier rendering of Arundel (coll. the Duke of Norfolk) where he is shown seated, full length, wearing a fur-lined cloak and the lesser George.

ENGRAVINGS: By J. Houbraken, 1743 (in reverse, roundel);[17] T. Chambers (roundel);[18] J. Goldar, published 1786 (roundel);[19] J. Record (roundel).

COPIES: London Art Market, 1930, oil on relined canvas, $28\frac{1}{8} \times 21\frac{5}{8}$ (0·72 × 0·55) inscribed 'Thomas Howard Arundell Comes';[20] coll. R. F. de Roos, 1961, paper stuck on panel, $8\frac{1}{16} \times 6\frac{1}{8}$ (0·205 × 0·155);[21] drawing by Wilkin Jnr., Anon. sale, Phillips, 20 April, 1813 (36).

PROVENANCE: Perhaps P. P. Rubens (†) sale, Antwerp, 1640 (97).[22] Possibly in the Earl of Melfort (ca. 1650–1715) sale, The Banqueting House, 21(?) June, 1693, bt. Glanvill for £20.[23] Recorded with certainty in coll. Dr. [Richard] Mead, 1743;[24] Dr. Mead sale, Langford's, 20 March, 1754 (40) bt. the Earl of Carlisle (1694–1758) for £36 15sh.;[25] seen at Castle Howard, 12 August, 1772 by Horace Walpole,[26] and recorded in the Blue Dining Room there by R. J. Sullivan, 1785;[27] exh. B.I. 1824 (89); New Gallery 1899 (133): presented by Rosalind, Countess of Carlisle, 1914.

REPRODUCTION: *National Gallery Illustrations, Continental Schools (excluding Italian)*, 1950, p. 313, bottom.

REFERENCES: *in text:* (1) 'P.P.R.Nº. 186' is inscribed on the back. See note 7. (2) See M. Rooses and Ch. Ruelens (†), *Correspondance de Rubens*, 1898, II, p. 250. (3) See under *Provenance*; and for instance, J. Smith, *A Catalogue Raisonné* etc., 1830, II, no. 1130; and M. Rooses, *L'Œuvre de P. P. Rubens*, 1890, IV, no. 889. (4) Sir Edward Walker, *Historical Discourses* etc., 1705, p. 221, described him thus: 'He was tall of stature, and of Shape and proportion rather goodly than neat; his Countenance was Majestical and grave, his Visage long, his Eyes large black and piercing; he had a hooked Nose, and some Warts or Moles on his cheeks; his countenance was brown, his hair thin both on his Head and Beard . . .' Walker accompanied Arundel as Secretary on his embassy to Ratisbon in 1636. (5) Wrongly identified as Count Hendrick van den Bergh by R. Oldenbourg, *Rubens, K. der K.*, [1921], p. 288; see P. Hendy, *The Isabella Stewart Gardner Museum, Catalogue of the Exhibited Paintings and Drawings*, 1931, pp. 307–11 (& rep.). (6) No. 2391. (7) See D. Piper, *Catalogue of the Seventeenth-Century Portraits in the National Portrait Gallery*, 1963, p. 15. The picture measures 27 × 21, and has inscribed on the back: 'le comte d'arondel anglois | par Van Dijk' and 'N 169 PPR'. (8) See M. Rooses, *L'Œuvre* etc., 1892, V, under no. 1497. (9) See Mary Hervey, *The Life of Thomas Howard* etc., 1921, pl. XIX. (10) Which reads 'A P. P. Rubenio memoriter designatum non coram'. (11) See Rooses, *loc. cit.*, and pl. 418. (12) Exh. R. A., 1953/4 (136).' (13) See Oliver Millar, catalogue of *Flemish Art, 1300–1700*, R. A., 1953/4 (136); and Arundel's letter to William Petty of 8 November, 1636, printed in Hervey, *op. cit.*, p. 391: 'I send by Francesco a Picture of my owne [*sic*] and my little Tom bye [*sic*] me; and I desire it may be done at Florence in ... Basso relievo ...'. (14) That is the version of the so-called Madagascar Portrait, discussed by Hervey, *op. cit.*, pp. 418–19. (15) Arundel was clearly interested in having *bas-relief* portraits carved as is shown by his letter to Petty of 8/18 November, 1636 (see note 13). (16) See Oliver Millar, *The Tudor, Stuart and Early Georgian Pictures in the Collection of H.M. the Queen*, 1, 1963, pp. 96–7, no. 146 and rep. vol. II, pl. 20. (17) As in the collection of Dr. Mead; published 1744. (18) In T. Smollett, *A Complete History of England* etc., 1759 (3rd ed.), 6, opp. p. 393. (19) Engraved for Harrison's edition of P. de Rapin-Thoyras, *The History of England* (note in the library of the National Portrait Gallery) as still in the collection of Dr. Mead. (20) Note in the National Gallery archives. (21) Photo. in R.K.D. (22) See J. Denucé, *Inventories of the Art-Collections in Antwerp* etc., 1932, p. 60. (23) See *The Diary of John Evelyn*, ed. E. S. de Beer, V, 1955, pp. 144–45. 21 June: 'I saw a greate [*sic*] Auction of Pictures exposed to be sold in the Banqueting house, White-Hall; they had been my Lord Melfords [*sic*] ... Divers ... bought ... 'pictures ... my Nephew Glanvill the old Earle [*sic*] of Arundels [*sic*] head of Rubens for 20 pounds'. The pictures had belonged to John Drummond, 1st Earl of Melfort; they were seized by the Crown after he was outlawed, 10 February, 1690. The Master of the Great Wardrobe was authorized to take possession of a number of the pictures, 13 June, 1693; the authorization and list is printed in the *Calendar of Treasury Books, 1689–92*, 1931, IX, part IV, ed. W. A. Shaw, pp. 1678–1681; a further number of pictures were ordered to be handed over on 20 June, 1693, see *Calendar of Treasury Books 1693–96*, 1935, X, part 1, ed. W. A. Shaw, pp. 248–9. No portrait by Rubens or of Arundel is mentioned; no. 54 in the first consignment was called 'a head in armour' and was valued at £2. 10sh. This could be identified with the National Portrait Gallery picture, which as Piper, *loc. cit.*, has also pointed out could have been the picture recorded in Rubens' inventory and in the picture bought by Glanvill. De Beer, *op. cit.*, pp. 144–45, note 3, has suggested that the date given by Evelyn is probably wrong. (24) When engraved by Houbraken. (25) See the collection of ms. sale catalogues in the Victoria & Albert Museum. (26) See Paget Toynbee, *The Walpole Society*, 1927–8, XVI, p. 73. (27) R. J. Sullivan, *A Tour through Parts of England . . . in 1778*, 1785 (2nd ed.), II, p. 110.

4815 PEASANTS WITH CATTLE BY A STREAM IN A WOODY LANDSCAPE ('THE WATERING PLACE')

A stream runs to open country between the edge of a wood on the right and a bank cluttered with logs, at the bend of which are three trees. In the foreground two horses, one ridden by a young farmhand, drink in the stream; to the left an older farmhand forces a cow out of the water with a long pole. Behind is a milkmaid who walks along the path beside the stream, carrying a bucket in her right hand and a churn on her head; around her are four cows. To the right at the edge of the path, a young goatherd sits playing on a pipe with four goats scattered behind him. Farther to the right are two more cows, one with a suckling calf. In the middle distance by the stream is a flock of sheep with a dog. In the far distance, centre, a huntsman coursing; and to the left, two cottages, a windmill and the sun on the horizon.

Oil and black chalk on oak, $38\frac{7}{8}/39\frac{1}{8} \times 52\frac{15}{16}$ ($0 \cdot 987/\cdot 994 \times 1 \cdot 35$).

The support is made up of 11 members see Appendix I. A twelfth member, $ca.$ $\frac{11}{16}$ ($0 \cdot 018$) wide, which runs along the bottom of the support, is probably a later addition.

In good condition. There are traces of a border $ca.$ $\frac{5}{16}$ ($0 \cdot 008$) along the right-hand edge, and $ca.$ $\frac{3}{16}$ ($0 \cdot 005$) along the top. Some of the joins have opened, and cracks have appeared in the support, but this has resulted in very little paint loss. A yellow varnish to some extent obscures the state of preservation of the foliage especially towards the right.

A number of *pentimenti* can be made out by the naked eye, others in infra-red and X-ray photography. The *pentimenti* can be divided into those connected with the landscape and those connected with the staffage.[1] So far as the landscape is concerned, the sun was first placed farther to the right along the horizon, the trunk of the left-most tree was thinner, and a branch grew up to the right from the base of its inner edge, while the dead forked branch, leaning against the tree beside it, was longer. *Pentimenti* in the staffage are of two types: (a) the suppression of a shepherd leaning on a staff, just to the left of the bridge in the centre middle ground (the shepherd may first have been placed a little to the left with his staff at a different angle), and minor alterations to the sheep nearest him; and (b) underdrawing, revealed by infra-red photography, which shows that several poses were essayed for the milkmaid and the cow immediately to her right; minor alterations are also evident in the outline of the neck and belly of the cow immediately in front of the milkmaid, in the mounted farmhand and in the nearside legs of the suckling calf.

There are signs of underdrawing in the dead wood in the left foreground, the farmhand and cow in the reeds, the next cow to the right, the forepart of the cow on the bridge, the rear part (only?) of the cow in front of the milkmaid, in the goatherd and perhaps in the mounted farmhand.

The handling of paint gets looser towards the top and the right-hand edges, where the path and hill are executed for the most part in thin oil washes.

The status of no. 4815 is confused by the etching by Lucas van Uden that derives in reverse from it (see under *Engravings*): the early states credit Lucas van Uden with the authorship of the prototype, the last credits it to Rubens. Rooses[2] probably thus (*sic*) considered no. 4815 to be a work of collaboration between Rubens and Lucas van Uden, the latter being responsible for the landscape; and no. 4815 does not appear in either of the Klassiker der Kunst editions of Rubens' œuvre. The etching includes the branch of the tree in the left middleground, which was suppressed in no. 4815; there are other minor differences, including an extension to the left (in the etching) that cannot be connected with the evolution of the painting. No wholly satisfactory explanation has been advanced to explain the changed inscriptions on the etching;[3] but they certainly do not support Rooses' contention. Further, as the signature and/or inscription on the first three states were not retained in the final state, they need not be considered reliable evidence concerning the authorship of no. 4815. Recent authors[4] are in fact agreed in accepting the traditional[5] attribution of no. 4815 to Rubens, which there is no reason to doubt.

The view depicted in the left middle ground of no. 4815 occurs with minor differences[6] in no. 2924 q.v. On the basis of a comparison of X-rays, the compiler[7] has shown that this area in no. 4815 must be a reduced repetition of no. 2924, because there are no signs of the evolution of no. 2924 in it. This is as Raczyński[8] and Evers[9] supposed.

The make up of the support of no. 4815 suggests that it was not the result of a single, uninterrupted creative effort; there may have been as many as four stages in its evolution.[10] The first stage would have consisted in executing the reduced repetition of no. 2924 on a single panel that measures ca. $14\frac{1}{8} \times 22\frac{5}{16}$ (0.359×0.567). It is not possible to be dogmatic concerning the number or limits of the following stages. But that there were at least two further stages is also suggested by the difference in execution of the staffage: there is no underdrawing in the group of cattle in the right, while there is certainly underdrawing for the milkmaid and cattle round her.

A further indication in support of a third (intervening stage), already suggested by the make up of the support, is afforded by a drawing in the Städelsches Kunstinstitut, Frankfurt,[11] probably executed by a Bolognese artist early in the seventeenth century; Dr. Adler[12] was the first to observe that the man forcing the cow out of the reeds and the farmhand watering the two horses in no. 4815 derive in reverse from this drawing or a prototype from which it also derives. It is not of course necessary that the staffage in each stage of no. 4815 (after the first) was completed before the support was further enlarged.

The evolution of no. 4815 may thus have been: (1) execution of the reduced repetition of no. 2924; (2) expansion of the support and composition all round, and inclusion of the milkmaid and cattle round her, with perhaps the hindquarters of the cow in front of her painted up to the new edge of the support; (3) expansion of the support to the top, bottom and right, inclusion of the two farmhands derived from the Frankfurt drawing (or a prototype in common), and the goatherd, and completion of the cow in front of the milkmaid; (4) final expansion (and then framing) of the support to the top and right, and inclusion of the cattle on the right over the join. The sun was probably moved farther to the left in the second stage; the suppression of the base of the dead branch and of the shepherd (and inclusion of the sheepdog in his place) took place, probably, later; and, if the evidence of van Uden's etching is considered reliable, it seems likely that the branch of the left-most tree in the middle ground was not suppressed until the end of the evolution of no. 4815.[13]

The relationship between no. 2924 and no. 4815 is unique among Rubens' landscapes; and the support of no. 4815 may also be one of his most complex. The make up of the support of no. 2924 is comparable to, but not the same as, that of the *Farm at Laeken* (Royal Collection)[14] and the *Charrette Embourbée* (Hermitage).[15] Traces of a border at the top and right-hand edges of the *Farm at Laeken* show that Rubens completed it in its frame, as he did no. 4815. By the same token, the absence of any borders in no. 2924 shows that Rubens may have contemplated a further enlargement of the composition while he was executing the second stage. Only after he had completed it did he realize that the support was already too large to consider further ex-pansion; hence his execution of the reduction of no. 2924 as the starting point of no. 4815. But whether he had the composition of the whole of no. 4815 in mind at any stage of his execution of no. 2924 is uncertain; the evolution of the two pictures suggests that whatever prototypes or studies for the staffage or studies of nature (none extant) which were at hand, he evolved the composition as he worked. To what extent the foliage was worked up at each intervening stage must remain uncertain; it is noteworthy that the foliage to the right in no. 4815 is less worked up than the rest.

The thesis of MacLaren[16] and Raczyński[17] notwithstanding, it seems probable that there was no significant time lapse between the inception of no. 4815 and its completion, and that nos. 2924 and 4815 were executed about the same time, as Glück[18] and Burchard[19] supposed.

There is no secure means of dating Rubens' landscapes before 1629/30.[20] That Rubens executed landscapes before this date is estab-lished by those mentioned in the inventory of the Duke of Buckingham who died in 1628.[21] It is clear that a group of landscapes was executed well before this, but when and in what order, there are as many theories as authors. It is generally agreed that nos. 2924 and 4815 are part of the early group, and thus the bracket *ca.* 1615–1622 is acceptable, in so far as it represents the common denominator of the dates advanced by more recent authors.

It seems likely that nos. 2924 and 4815 were among the first to be executed in the early group. Three observations suggest this. First, three of the poses of the cows occur with variation in a sheet of sketches, engraved by Pontius.[22] MacLaren[23] associated the sheet with no. 4815, *The Farm at Laeken* (Royal Collection) and *The Marshy Landscape with Cattle* (Munich).[24] It seems probable, however, that Rubens executed the staffage in no. 4815 without the sketches in mind, because in one instance two other poses were first essayed, in the second minor *penti-menti* in the outline also suggest that the pose was evolved in no. 4815, while in the third the pose is closer to that in the Frankfurt drawing (though inverted). Second, of the early group, nos. 2924 and 4815 seem most comparable to the *Charrette Embourbée* (Leningrad)[25] and the *Landscape with Farmgirls and Cattle* (Prince of Liechtenstein).[26] Burchard and d'Hulst[27] dated the Leningrad picture *ca.* 1617, while Glück[28] considered the Liechtenstein picture to be the earliest of all Rubens' pure landscapes, that is executed before 1617. Third, while nos. 2924 and 4815 show the general influence of Bril and Elsheimer, as MacLaren has pointed out,[29] no. 4815 in its final form has connections with the landscapes of Jan Brueghel I, whose art is likely to have been an important influence when Rubens turned to landscape painting.

It is not possible to be certain whether Rubens intended a sunset or sunrise in nos. 2924 and 4815; the presence of the huntsman suggests that he intended a sunrise (see under no. 2924). The theme of no. 4815 was taken up again by Rubens in the Wallace Collection *Landscape with a Rainbow.* The farmhand watering two horses, the milkmaid with a churn on her head, and the goatherd and group of cattle on the right occur (the first three in reverse) in the second state of an engraving by Schelte à Bolswert.[30]

No. 4815 was admired by Gainsborough (see below under *Provenance*), and had a certain influence on his landscapes.[31]

SKETCH : What was claimed to be 'the counterpart or first thought' of no. 4815 was in an Anon. [= Hart Davis] sale, Peter Coxe, 1 June, 1814 (42).[32]

ENGRAVINGS: By Lucas van Uden, etching (in reverse);[33] John Browne, 1770 (in reverse);[34] R. Brookshaw, 1773 (in reverse and in aquatint.)[35]

COPIES: Perm Art Gallery, Perm, U.S.S.R., panel, $21\frac{1}{16} \times 28\frac{15}{16}$ (0.535×0.735);[36] Leger and Son, London, 1929, panel, 25×31 (0.635×0.788);[37] the Ehrich-Newhouse Galleries, New York, 1936, panel, $37 \times 48\frac{13}{16}$ (0.94×1.24);[38] dealer, Sam Hartveld, Antwerp, 1938, canvas, $39 \times 52\frac{1}{8}$ (0.99×1.325);[39] Consul C. E. Schlyter, Stockholm, 1947;[40] Anon. sale, Sotheby's, 7 June, 1950 (107), canvas, $28\frac{1}{2} \times 41\frac{1}{2}$ (0.724×1.055); London Art Market, 1950, canvas, $26\frac{5}{8} \times 34\frac{3}{4}$ (0.677×0.883);[41] Anon. sale, Palais des Beaux-Arts, Brussels, 17 November, 1954 (329), canvas, $38\frac{3}{16} \times 57\frac{9}{16}$ (0.97×1.31);[42] Anon. sale, Christie's, 18 October 1957 (60), panel, $26 \times 34\frac{1}{2}$ (0.66×0.877); Anon. sale, Sotheby's, 10 June, 1965 (162), canvas, $17\frac{1}{2} \times 22\frac{1}{2}$ (0.445×0.572) as by J. Ward; Coll. Señor Juan Escoda, Barcelona, 1965, panel, $25\frac{5}{16} \times 35$ (0.65×0.89);[43] Anon. sale, Sotheby's, 2 February, 1966 (162), canvas, $22\frac{1}{2} \times 29$ (0.572×0.737) in reverse as by J. Ross; Anon. sale, Sotheby's, 18 October, 1967 (163) panel (?), $23\frac{3}{4} \times 33\frac{1}{2}$ (0.604×0.851) as by J. d'Arthois; coll. H. A. E. Day, canvas, 18×24 (0.46×0.61);[44] the group of cattle on the right are repeated in a picture, coll. the dealer Dr. Wendland, Berlin, 1929, where ascribed to Lucas van Uden, canvas, $46\frac{5}{16} \times 64\frac{5}{16}$ (1.177×1.65);[45] perhaps after no. 4815: coll. the Jabach family, Paris, 1696;[46] Anon. sale, Langford, 26 March, 1778 (10).[47]

PROVENANCE: Coll. M. d'Armagnac, 'grand Ecuier'[48] (? = Charles, Comte d'Armagnac (1684–1753))[49] by whom sold for 1650 francs.[50] Coll. the Duc de Tallard (= Marie-Joseph, Duc d'Hostun et de Tallard (1683–1755)) by 1753;[51] Duc de Tallard (†) sale, Remy & Glomy, Paris, 22 ff. March, 1756 (141)[52] bt. by Remy for 9905 francs.[53] Perhaps in the Peilhon (†) sale, Remy, Paris, 16 ff. May, 1763 (16), sold for 1,410 francs.[54] Coll. the Duke of Montagu (= George Montagu, 3rd Duke of Montagu († 1790)), London, probably at least by the summer of 1768;[55] inherited by his daughter, Elizabeth († 1827) wife of Henry, 3rd Duke of Buccleuch († 1812); exh. B.I. 1815 (17);[56] B.I., 1836 (12);[57] B.I., 1851 (61); R.A., 1872 (195); R.A., 1927 (263); bought from the 8th Duke of Buccleuch, out of the Grant-in-Aid and the Mackerell, Scott,

and Temple-West Funds, with the aid of a contribution from the National Art-
Collections Fund, 1936; exh. *Exhibition in Honour of Sir Robert Witt*, The National
Gallery, 1945/6 (5).

REPRODUCTION: *National Gallery Illustrations, Continental Schools (excluding
Italian)*, 1950, p. 314.

REFERENCES: *General:* G. Glück, *Die Landschaften von Peter Paul Rubens*,
1940/5, p. 23, no. 5; Gregory Martin, *The Burlington Magazine*, 1966, pp. 180–
183.

In text: (1) The *pentimenti*, along with X-ray and infra-red photographs, were
published and discussed by Martin, see under *General References*. (2) See
M. Rooses, *L'Œuvre de P. P. Rubens*, 1890, IV, no. 1196. (3) See note 33. (4) See,
for instance, K. Kieser, *Die Rubenslandschaft*, 1926, p. 42, note 2; N. MacLaren,
The Burlington Magazine, 1936, pp. 207–213 (publishing no. 4815); H. Hermann, *Untersuchungen uber die Landschaftsgemälde des P. P. Rubens*, 1936, p. 15;
J. A. Graf Raczyński, *Die Flämische Landschaft vor Rubens*, 1937, p. 80; G.
Glück, cited under *General References*; and H. G. Evers, *Peter Paul Rubens*,
trans. into Dutch by K. Ruyssinck, 1946, pp. 398–400. (5) See under *Provenance*;
and J. Smith, *A Catalogue Raisonné* etc., 1830, II, no. 630. (6) The outline of the
far bank and the foliage of the smaller tree on the left in no. 4815 differs; there
are also more sheep in no. 4815, further the huntsman does not seem to be
accompanied by any dogs, the shepherd was shown in shorter trousers, and the
cart in front of the cottage was omitted. (7) See under *General References*.
(8) *Loc. cit.* (9) *Ibid.*; MacLaren, *op. cit.*, p. 208, and Burchard Documentation considered that no. 2924 was an enlarged repetition of the embryo panel
of no. 4815. (10) See Martin, cited under *General References*, and in particular
fig. 20 that shows the suggested extents of the stages. (11) $9\frac{1}{2} \times 15\frac{3}{4}$ (0·242 ×
0·40), inventory no. 4427, ascribed to Titian. (12) The compiler is most grateful
to Dr. Alder for drawing his attention to, and sending him a photograph of, this
drawing in 1968. His attribution to a Bolognese artist of the early 17th century
is accepted by Denis Mahon, from the sight of a photograph. Dr. Adler considers that it derives from a sketch executed in the circle of Titian. The motif
of a man watering a pair of horses also occurs in earlier Netherlandish painting,
see, for example, the detail in *The Virgin and S. Joseph arriving at Bethlehem* by
Cornelis Massys at Dahlem, rep. in M. J. Friedländer, *From Van Eyck to
Bruegel*, 1956, fig. 188. (13) The compiler, see under *General References*, first
thought that these alterations, apart from the moving of the sun, took place
earlier. (14) See Glück, *op. cit.*, under no. 2; and the catalogue of the exhibition
of *The King's Pictures*, The Royal Academy, 1946/7 (289), which omits the
right-hand join; all the additions are evident in the colour plate in Glück.
(15) The parting of joins of the original wood support, now replaced by canvas,
has affected the paint surface, and are evident in the black and white plate in
Glück, *op. cit.*, no. 7. Both supports differ from no. 2924 in that the top members
runs across the whole support. (16) MacLaren, *loc. cit.*, proposed a definite
time lapse of years between (a) the first and final stages of no. 4815,
and (b) the first stage of no. 4815 and no. 2924. (17) Raczyński, *loc.
cit.*, thought that a time gap of a few years separated no. 4815 from no. 2924.
(18) See under *General References*. (19) Burchard Documentation. (20) The
first securely datable landscape is the Royal Collection *S. George and the
Dragon*, of 1629/30, see the catalogue of the exhibition of *The King's Pictures*,
Royal Academy, 1946/7, no. 288. Rubens drew a *View of the Escorial* while
he was in Spain in the previous year, see M. Rooses & Ch. Ruelens (†) *Correspondance de Rubens* etc., 1909, VI, pp. 255–85. The *Landscape with a View of the
Palatine Hills* (Louvre, no. 2119, see Glück, *op. cit.*, no. 11) was engraved by
Schelte à Bolswert; the inscription on the final state, which states that the
prototype was executed by Rubens in Rome, should be treated with caution,
landscape drawings ascribed to Rubens in the same period (see M. Jaffé, *Oud
Holland,* 1957, pp. 1 ff.), notwithstanding. (21) For the inventory, see R. Davies,

The Burlington Magazine, 1906/7, X, pp. 379 ff., where a sunset and sunrise are listed. Philippe Rubens in his Mémoire to de Piles of 1676, stated that Buckingham's pictures were executed before 1626, see the *Rubens-Bulletijn*, 1883, II, p. 166. **(22)** The engraving is F. van den Wijngaert, *Inventaris der Rubeniaasche Prentkunst*, 1940, no. 557 (17). Two sheets are claimed to be the prototype by Rubens: Devonshire collection, pen and pencil, $12\frac{1}{2} \times 20\frac{1}{4}$ (0·318 × 0·515), accepted by L. Burchard and R. A. d'Hulst, catalogue of *Tekeningen van P. P. Rubens*, Antwerp, 1956, no. 82; and British Museum, Department of Prints and Drawings, pen and sepia, $13\frac{3}{8} \times 20\frac{1}{2}$ (0·34 × 0·522), see A. M. Hind, *Catalogue of Drawings . . . in the British Museum*, 1923, II, no. 118, which J. S. Held, *Rubens Selected Drawings*, 1959, p. 12 and p. 133, under no. 88, inclines to accept. Recently Michael Jaffé, see note 6a under no. 2924, has rejected the attribution of both drawings to Rubens, claiming that the Chatsworth drawing is by van Dyck, and that Rubens made use of it in the Munich landscape. But this seems improbable. **(23)** *Loc. cit.* **(24)** See Glück, *op. cit.*, no. 6 and rep. **(25)** See Glück, *op. cit.*, no. 7 and rep. **(26)** See Glück, *op. cit.*, no. 1 and rep. **(27)** See L. Burchard and R. A. d'Hulst, *Rubens Drawings*, 1963, p. 166 under no. 101. **(28)** *Loc. cit.* **(29)** *Loc. cit.* **(30)** Rep. by Glück, *op. cit.*, no. 44; see also *Catalogue of the Paintings and Drawings . . . in the Barber Institute of Fine Arts*, 1952, pp. 88–9. Information concerning the relevant state is derived from photographs in the R.K.D. **(31)** See for instance, J. Hayes, *Apollo*, 1963, pp. 89–90. **(32)** The entry for the lot states: ' . . . It has been, from the circumstance of cattle drinking in the Stream, and a Horseman refreshing his Steed, called 'The Watering Place', and is evidently the counterpart or first thought for the same subject in the possession of the Dutchess [*sic*] Dowager of Buccleuch' (see under *Provenance*). Smith was sceptical about the claimed connection between this sketch and no. 4815; see the ms. of his *Catalogue Raisonné*, II, p. 382 (Victoria and Albert Museum Library). **(33)** See C. G. Voorhelm Schneevoogt, *Catalogue des Estampes Gravés d'après P. P. Rubens*, 1873, p. 236, no. 54 (2). The first state is signed on the plate: *Lucas van Uden*; the second and third states are inscribed: *Lucas van Uden pixit et excudit*; the fourth state is inscribed: *Pet. Paul. Rubenius pinxit Lucas van Uden fecit. Franciscus van den Wyngaerde excudit.* Burchard Documentation suggested that the etching was made by van Uden after a copy he had made of no. 4815; see also Gregory Martin, *Apollo*, 1968, pp. 210–211. Herrmann, *op. cit.*, p. 70, note 36, states that there are two separate prints by van Uden, one after no. 4815 and the other after the so-called sketch in the Hart Davis sale, for which see above, which he considered was the picture later with the dealer Leger and Son, for which see below. **(34)** See Schneevoogt, *loc. cit.*; he states that Browne also made a second print after no. 4815; the first is rep. by Rooses, *op. cit.*, pl. 344. **(35)** See Schneevoogt, *loc. cit.*, for the date of the print see under Rooses, *op. cit.*, no. 1196. **(36)** A photograph and details were kindly supplied by Miss Ludmilla Evgrafova, of the Perm Art Gallery, (letter in N.G. archives, 1966). **(37)** Ex Sir Francis Sharp Powell sale, Sotheby's, 27 November, 1929 (10). Glück, *op. cit.*, stated that the support bore the brand of the coat of arms of the city of Antwerp, and thought that it was perhaps identifiable with the so-called Hart Davis sketch (see above). **(38)** When exh. at *An Exhibition of Sixty Paintings . . . by . . . Rubens*, Detroit Institute of Fine Arts, 1936 (59). It is probably identical with the picture in the T. F. Egerton (not Cave as stated by Glück, *loc. cit.*) sale, Sotheby's, 17 December, 1931 (64) and the picture recorded in the possession of A. L. Nicholson in 1934, where measurements, as given by Burchard Documentation, correspond. **(39)** See Burchard Documentation, where it is also recorded that it was ex coll. the dealer J. M. A. Kockox, Antwerp, and that it may be identical with the copy sold at the Palais des Beaux-Arts, Brussels, 16 March, 1954 (152) for which below and, note 42. **(40)** Photograph in the R.K.D. **(41)** Ex Lord Harcourt sale, Christie's, 11 June, 1948 (178) and Anon. sale, Christie's, 2 June, 1950 (105). Burchard Documentation's view on the status of this picture is not clear; two copies are there noted of what at one stage was called the 'Harcourt version': coll. Hugo Engel,

Vienna, 1930; coll. dealer Herman Abels, Cologne, 1932. A photograph of the
latter is in the R.K.D., where it is stated that it remained in Abel's possession
until at least 1935, and that it measured $33\frac{1}{16} \times 25\frac{9}{16}$ (0·84 × 0·65). Burchard
Documentation also lists the picture in the possession of Leger and Son (see
above) in the same category. (**42**) Ex Anon. sale, Palais des Beaux-Arts, Brussels,
16 March, 1954 (152); information kindly provided by Miss M. Korpershoek
of the R.K.D. (**43**) Letter and photograph from Señor Escoda in the N.G.
archives. (**44**) Photograph in the Witt Library. (**45**) See Glück, cited under
General References. (**46**) See the *Mémoire, Estats et Règlements de droits dans la
famille du feu sieur Évrard Jabach et de dame Anne-Maire de Groot, sa veuve, du
17 July 1696*, no. 574 'Paisage avec des vaches', un homme qui
menne [*sic*] boire deux chevaux, après Rubens, 30 liv', in *Mémoires de la Société
de l'Histoire de Paris*, 1894, p. 278. (**47**) Described as: 'Rubens An Undoubted
. . . Landscape . . . from the cabinet of the Duke de Tallard'. No. 4815 was the
only landscape in the Tallard sale, but was by this time coll. the Duke of
Montagu (see under *Provenance*); unless the provenance given for the Langford
picture is wrong, the only explanation is that it was a copy of no. 4815. (**48**) See
P. J. Mariette, *Abecedario*, ed. Ph. de Chennevières and A. de Montaiglon, 1858–
9, V, p. 139, and the Tallard sale catalogue, note 24. (**49**) The exact identity of
this d'Armagnac 'Grand Ecuier' is not known, as no d'Armagnac sales or inventories have been published. There are three possible candidates, of which the
last seems the most likely: Henry de Lorraine, Comte d'Harcourt, d'Armagnac
etc. († 1666), Grand Ecuyer from 1643; his son, Louis de Lorraine, Comte
d'Armagnac (1641–1718), Grand Ecuyer from 1658, see P. Anselme etc.,
Histoire Genéalogique et Chronologique de la Maison Royale de France, 1733 (3rd
ed.), pp. 509–810; or the latter's son, Charles, Comte d'Armagnac (1684–1753),
Grand Ecuyer from 1712, who died without heirs, see A. de la Chenaye-Dubois &
Badier, *Dictionnaire de la Noblesse*, XII, 1868, col. 434. (**50**) See note 48. (**51**) See
J. B. Descamps, *La Vie des Peintres Flamands*, 1753, I, p. 316. (**52**) As 'Un Paisage d'une belle & riche composition . . . Sur le devant paroissent plusiers Figures
& Animaux, on y voit une vache engagée dans un marais, qui est tirée de l'eau
par un Paisan . . . sur bois de 37 pouces de haut, sur 49 pouces de large [= *ca.*
$39\frac{3}{8} \times 52\frac{1}{8}$]. Il a été gravé par L. Van Uden, & vient du Cabinet de M. d'Armagnac, grand Ecuier'. (**53**) See note 48; reference also from the marked catalogue in the N.G. library. (**54**) Previous writers, see, for instance, Glück, cited
under *General References*, have stated that no. 4815 was in this sale. For a description of the lot and the price, see C. Blanc, *Trésor de la Curiosité*, 1852, I,
p. 114. The description fits no. 4815 very well; but it is probable that it was
a copy, because: (1) the size given (2 pieds 11 pouces × 3 pieds 9 pouces)
is for a slightly smaller picture; (2) the price was much lower than
that fetched by no. 4815 at the Tallard sale; (3) Mariette, in his account of no. 4815, see note 48, does not mentioned the Peilhon sale,
and records that Remy said that no. 4815 'étoit pour l'Angleterre'; (4)
no. 4930 of this Gallery was also in the Tallard sale and then coll. the Duke
of Montagu without any known intervening owners, see N. MacLaren, *National
Gallery Catalogues, The Dutch School*, 1960, p. 334 and note 21, p. 335. The
Peilhon sale catalogue gives a provenance from the late Duc de Valentinois
(= Jacques-François-Léonor de Goyon, Duc de Valentinois (1689–1751)), but
as S. Villarem, archiviste adjoint of the Archives du Palais de Monaco, has
kindly informed the compiler, no such picture is recorded in the Valentinois
inventories of the first half of the eighteenth century, which are referred to by
L. H. Labande, *Inventaires du Palais de Monaco*, 1918, p. CXXVI, note 3.
(**55**) See the letter from Thomas Gainsborough to Garrick in *The Letters of
Thomas Gainsborough*, ed. Mary Woodall, 1963, p. 67, which Miss Woodall,
p. 66, thinks was probably written in the summer of 1768: 'I could wish you to
call *upon any pretence* . . . at the Duke of Montagu, not as if you thought
anything of mine worth that trouble, only to see his Grace's landskip of Rubens
and the four Vandykes [*sic*] . . .' No. 4815 was engraved in 1770 as in the collection of the Duke of Montagu (see under *Engravings*). (**56**) Lent by the Duchess

of Buccleuch. (57) Lent by the Duchess of Buccleuch's second son, Walter, 5th Duke of Buccleuch (1806–1884).

6379 PARIS AWARDS THE GOLDEN APPLE TO VENUS (THE JUDGMENT OF PARIS)

Mercury hails Venus, who stands with her son Cupid at her side between Juno and Minerva, as Paris hands her the golden apple and *putti* descend to award her a victor's crowns and palms.

Oil on oak, $52\frac{11}{16} \times 68\frac{11}{16}$ ($1\cdot339 \times 1\cdot745$).

For the make up of the support, see Appendix I; rebates have been gauged at the sides of the reverse of the support.

In fairly good condition. The paint extends to the top and bottom edges; it has been removed with the ground, at the sides to create a border *ca.* $\frac{9}{16}$ ($0\cdot015$). There is a certain amount of wearing, now re-touched, particularly in the head, body and left arm of Juno, in the head and body of Cupid, and in the right leg and foot of Venus. The river god and nymph are also worn, as are, but to a lesser extent, the *putti* and satyrs. There are some small paint losses where two of the joins have opened and along two cracks in the support. Cleaned, 1967.

There are several *pentimenti*, some visible to the naked eye, others in infra-red photography and X-radiographs. Mercury first leant closer to Paris, and his left arm was lower; the outline of Paris' face sloped farther back; Cupid's head was first pressed against Venus' leg and he looked back towards Paris; the right arm of the lowest *putto* was first placed just to the left of the crown he holds, and a leg has been sup-pressed just to the right of his head; Minerva's left leg was first placed in front of her right, seen from the side and bent at the knee.[1] There are also minor *pentimenti* in the outline of Paris' left shoulder and in his left foot.

Mercury is identifiable by his winged helmet and caduceus, Juno by her patterned robe,[2] Cupid by his wings and quiver, and Minerva by her helmet and shield; a *putto* holds Venus' doves on a leash.[3] For the sub-ject of the *Judgment of Paris*, see under no. 194.

No. 6379 came to light in the summer of 1966; its attribution to Rubens was soon advanced, and has more recently been elaborated in a special exhibition at the National Gallery, followed by an article by Michael Jaffé.[4] No. 6379 is not documented in any way; but it is closely related in handling and colour range to the *Vision of S. Helena* by Rubens at Grasse;[5] further, two drawings, now generally accepted as by Rubens, and an oil sketch, damaged, but also considered to be by Rubens, are closely related to no. 6379 (see below). Taking these factors into account, the compiler sees no reason to doubt the attribution of no. 6379 to Rubens.

No. 6379 was probably executed soon after (or perhaps just before) Rubens' arrival in Italy in 1600. This dating is suggested by the con-tinued influence of Otho van Veen—his last master in Antwerp—in the execution of the *putti*,[6] and by the connection in handling with that in his *Vision of S. Helena*, commissioned in 1601 and completed by the following January.[7]

The *pentimenti* in Cupid's head and Minerva's left leg in no. 6379 confirm that the three related works by Rubens are preparatory to it. Both the *pentimenti* and the preparatory works show that Rubens' first idea in no. 6379, was to show Paris undecided as to which of the goddesses he should award the golden apple. The three preparatory works are the pen drawings on a cut down sheet in the Louvre,[8] which shows Paris, his dog, part of Juno and the wings of Cupid, the pen drawing of Paris on a sheet in the Metropolitan Museum of Art,[9] and the damaged oil sketch of the five main figures in the Akademie der bildenden Künste at Vienna.[10] As the pose of Paris in the oil sketch is closest to that in the Louvre drawing, the likely order of execution is the Louvre drawing, the Vienna sketch, then the Metropolitan Museum drawing. There is a *pentimento* in Paris' right arm in the Louvre drawing, which was first bent round in front of his body to hold the staff. Rubens then straightened the arm. The pose was repeated in the oil sketch, in which the poses of Mercury, Cupid and the legs of Minerva correspond more closely with the *pentimenti* in no. 6379 than with the final ideas expressed there. The drawing in the Metropolitan shows a further development in the pose of Paris, who now holds the golden apple in his right hand, while his left arm was placed behind him, ready to hold his stick. The tilt of Paris' head to some extent corresponds with the *pentimento* in no. 6379.

No major *pentimenti* are evident in the pose of Paris in no. 6379; therefore it seems likely that Rubens changed his mind concerning which moment of the story to depict, after he had begun to execute the goddesses.

The composition of no. 6379 is inspired by Raphael's design of the *Judgment of Paris*, engraved by Marcantonio Raimondi.[11] More specifically, the disposition of the main figures, the river bank setting, the presence of a river god and nymph, the placing of Minerva's shield and helmet, and the pose of Juno derive from the print. The top half of the pose of Paris and part of the pose of Venus may have been inspired by the print of *Adam and Eve* engraved by Sadeler after Martin de Vos,[12] where the suppressed profile of Adam agrees with the *pentimento* in Paris' head in no. 6379. Jaffé has suggested that the muscular back of Paris in no. 6379, may have been inspired by the *Belvedere Torso*.[13] The pose as a whole may derive from Frans Floris.[14] The final pose of Minerva derives directly from the *Juno*, designed by Rosso and engraved by Caraglio;[15] while the pose of Cupid is variant in reverse of that of the *putto* before Psyche in Raphael's *Council of the Gods* in the Farnesina.[16] The river god and nymph may derive from antique types.

DRAWINGS: Study (cut down) for Paris, the dog, part of June and Cupid, Louvre, pen and ink, $7\frac{9}{16} \times 8\frac{3}{16}$ (0·193 × 0·208;[17] study for Paris, Metropolitan Museum of Art, pen and ink, $10\frac{1}{4} \times 13\frac{3}{4}$ (0·26 × 0·35).[18]

SKETCH: Akademie der bildenden Künste, Vienna, copper, $12\frac{3}{4} \times 17\frac{1}{8}$ (0·325 × 0·435).[19]

PROVENANCE: Probably Anon. sale (consigned from Italy by Henry Tresham (†)) Christie's, 3 June (= 2nd day), 1815 (27)⁴/₄ bt. in for 1,500 gns.²⁰ Bt.
between 1934–1940 by A. Coulter of York and sold to Robert Savage of Northampton;²¹ Anon. [= Mrs. Savage] sale, Christie's, July, 1966 (183) withdrawn;
Mrs. Savage sale, Christie's, 25 November, 1966 (49) bt. in; bought, through
Christie's, from Mrs. Savage, December, 1966.

REPRODUCTION: Michael Jaffé, *The Burlington Magazine*, 1968, fig. 2.

REFERENCE: *General:* Michael Jaffé, *The Burlington Magazine*, 1968,
pp. 174 ff., who incorporates material first published in a special exhibition, 1967,
at the National Gallery.

In text: (1) A photograph of the X-radiograph is reproduced by Jaffé, *op.
cit.*, fig. 11. (2) Juno wears a similar decorated robe in the Prague *Asssembly of
the Gods on Mount Olympus* of 1602, the relevant detail of which is reproduced
by Jaffé, *op. cit.*, fig. 14. (3) See under no. 194. (4) See under *General
Reference*. (5) Rep. by R. Oldenbourg, *Rubens, K. der K.*, [1921], p. 1. (6)
Compare the *putti* in van Veen's *Crucifixion of S. Andrew*, in S. Andrew's
Church, Antwerp, completed in 1598, see J. Müller Hofstede, *Musées Royaux
des Beaux-Arts, Bulletin*, 1957, 6, p. 142. Philippe Rubens in his *Mémoire*, sent
to de Piles in 1676, stated that the paintings executed by Rubens before his
departure for Italy had connections with those by van Veen, see *Rubens-Bulletijn*,
1883, II, p. 166. (7) See M. Rooses, *L'Œuvre de P. P. Rubens*, 1888, II,
no. 444, and under no. 446. This altarpiece is also painted on oak, information
kindly supplied by J. Bourgoin, Monte Carlo. (8) See J. S. Held, *Rubens
Selected Drawings*, 1958, no. 8 *verso*; rep. by Jaffé, *op. cit.*, fig. 9. (9) See Held,
op. cit., no. 6 *verso*; rep. by Jaffé, *op. cit.*, fig. 12. (10) The status of this sketch
has been disputed; for a review of more recent discussion of it, see M. Poch-
Kalous, *Akademie der bildenden Künste in Wien, Katalog der Gemälde Galerie*,
1961, p. 38, no. 39; Jaffé, *op. cit.*, p. 179, and fig. 7, now accepts it as by Rubens
and earlier than no. 6379. See also Held, *op. cit.*, p. 97, under no. 8. (11) Reproduced by Jaffé, *op. cit.*, fig. 3. (12) Rep. by Jaffé, *op. cit.*, fig. 6. (13) *Op. cit.*,
p. 179. (14) Compare the pose of Mars in Floris' *Gods on Olympus*, signed and
dated 1550, in the Koninklijk Museum von schone Kunste, Antwerp, see
the 1958 catalogue, no. 956. (15) Rep by Jaffé, *op. cit.*, fig. 14. (16) Rep.
by G. Gronau, *Raffael, K. der K.*, 1923, p. 163. (17) See note 8. (18) See
note 9. (19) See Poch-Kalous, *loc. cit.* (20) See Jaffé, *op. cit.*, p. 175, and Christie's
marked sale catalogue. (21) Information kindly provided by A. Coulter
in a letter in the N.G. archives. The whereabouts of no. 6379 in the
nineteenth century and until it was acquired by A. Coulter are not known.
Jaffé, *op. cit.*, p. 175, considers that it may have been in a house in Yorkshire in
the early part of the nineteenth century; this is possible, but the fact that Mr.
Coulter's premises were in York and the connection (if any) between no. 6379 and
the *Judgment of Paris* by Etty at Port Sunlight are not convincing pieces of
evidence to support this. When no. 6379 first appeared at Christie's and until
it was acquired by the Gallery, it had stuck on the front, a small, modern,
printed label showing the number '80', which presumably refers to a previous
auction sale; and it bore on the reverse, a label with 'Ballen' written on it in a
nineteenth(?)-century hand.

Ascribed to RUBENS

948 A WAGON FORDING A STREAM

Black chalk and oil on paper, stuck on canvas, $18\frac{5}{16}/\frac{1}{2} \times 27\frac{9}{16}/\frac{3}{4}$
$(0{\cdot}465/{\cdot}47 \times 0{\cdot}70/{\cdot}705)$.

The edges of the support are ragged; there is a substantial repair in
the top left-hand corner and a smaller repair in the bottom left-hand

corner. There is a line of nail holes along the bottom edge and perhaps one or two along the top. There are a few creases resulting from a faulty marouflage.

The paint is in fairly good condition. There is some wearing round the wagon and in the bottom left-hand corner. The paper is discoloured as a result of having absorbed varnish; but some brown areas in the sky are due to a wash put on before the white of the sky. Cleaned, 1961.

No. 948 is not finished, as two areas of foliage have not been filled in. In the more finished areas the foliage goes over the sky. The trees (except those at both edges) along the stream and path, the banks (except at the right) and bushes were first drawn in black chalk.

The status of no. 948 has been questioned. The view is the same as that in a landscape by Rubens in the Boymans-van Beuningen Museum,[1] but taken from farther away. No. 948 does not repeat every detail of this landscape; it does not, for instance, include the two trees on the path which are after-thoughts there, but includes a branch (painted out, but now showing up light, in the tree to the right of the gate)[2] and introduces the tree, which has fallen into the stream. Thus Rooses'[3] view that no. 948 is a copy, and Glück's view[4] (followed by the authors of the catalogue *Olieverfschetsen van Rubens*[5]) that it is an enlarged replica or a copy of this picture are not strictly correct. The 1929 catalogue ascribed no. 948 to the School of Rubens, while it was ascribed to the Style of Rubens in the 1958 *Summary Catalogue*. Recently, however, Burchard/d'Hulst[6] and Jaffé[7] have accepted the earlier attribution to Rubens himself, which had previously been revived by Hermann.[8]

Burchard/d'Hulst compared no. 948 with a drawing at Leningrad,[9] about which Held[10] has expressed reservations. Judging from a photograph, there is a certain similarity in technique between the two works— that at Leningrad having been drawn in black chalk, worked up in body colour and tempera, and then 'touched up with black chalk'.[11] However what can be made out of the drawing in no. 948 does not compare in quality with that in, for instance, the drawing in the Ashmolean, considered by Burchard/d'Hulst[12] to date from the same time, while the handling of paint does not compare with that acceptably by Rubens, when working on canvas or panel at about the same time as the Ashmolean drawing.[13] More comparable is the unsatisfactory landscape in oil on paper at Boston.[14] This being the case, the compiler prefers to catalogue no. 948 as ascribed to Rubens.

PROVENANCE: Earl of Mulgrave (†) sale, Christie's, 12 May, 1832 (18) bt. Swaby for £43;[15] John Swaby (†) sale, Phillips, 13 March [=8 day] 1860 (927)[16] sold for £21.[17] Wynn Ellis Bequest, 1876; lent to the Free Library and Museum, Bootle, 1904–1929, and to the City Art Gallery, Wakefield, 1934–5.

REPRODUCTION: *National Gallery Illustrations, Continental Schools (excluding Italian)*, 1950, p. 317 top.

REFERENCES: (1) Panel, $19\frac{1}{2} \times 21\frac{1}{2}$ (0·495 × 0·547), see G. Glück, *Die Landschaften von Peter Paul Rubens*, 1940/5, no. 32 and pl. (2) This branch is also evident in a copy in the A. de Ridder sale, 2 June, 1924 (58); rep. in catalogue. (3) See M. Rooses, *L'Œuvre de P. P. Rubens*, 1890, IV, under no. 1205. (4) See

Glück, *loc. cit.* (5) See the catalogue *Olieverfschetsen van Rubens*, Rotterdam, 1953, under no. 94. (6) L. Burchard and R. A. d'Hulst, *Rubens Drawings*, 1963, p. 332, under no. 208. (7) See M. Jaffé, *The Burlington Magazine*, 1965, p. 381, under no. 200. (8) H. Hermann, *Untersuchungen über die Landschaftsgemälde des P. P. Rubens*, 1936, p. 84, no. 162. (9) See Burchard/d'Hulst, *op. cit.*, no. 208. (10) See J. S. Held, *Rubens Selected Drawings*, 1959, p. 147, under no. 136. (11) See Burchard/d'Hulst, *loc. cit.* (12) *Op. cit.*, no. 207; not to mention the British Museum drawing of a *Landscape with a Wattle Fence*, for which see Held, *op. cit.*, no. 136. (13) For instance no. 66 *q.v.* (14) Paper on panel, 22 × 28¼ (0·56 × 0·72), see *Summary Catalogue of European Paintings* etc., Museum of Fine Arts, Boston, 1955, p. 57; and Glück, *op. cit.*, no. 23 (and pl.). (15) J. Smith, *A Catalogue Raisonné* etc., 1832, II, no. 909, gives the support as paper and measurements as 1 ft. 10 × 2 ft. 2. These measurements fit neither no. 948 nor the Boymans-van Beuningen picture, which has also been identified with the picture in this sale. The fact that Smith gives the support as paper lends weight to the identification of no. 948 with the picture in the sale, as does the identity of the buyer for which see the marked catalogue in the National Gallery library. (16) Described as 'Rubens, A wooded Landscape, with a waggon descending a hill'. (17) See the marked catalogue in the Victoria and Albert Museum library. According to Lugt, there is no extant marked catalogue giving the buyer's names.

Studio of RUBENS

853 DRUNKEN SILENUS SUPPORTED BY SATYRS

Silenus in the centre is helped on his way by two satyrs; on either side are other followers of Bacchus.

Oil on relined canvas, *ca.* 52$\frac{9}{16}$ × 77$\frac{9}{16}$ (1·335 × 1·97).

In good condition. There are small, painted additions all round the composition. The left-hand edge has probably been cut down, but the other edges are probably approximately true.[1] There are a few scattered losses, all retouched, but none is of serious consequence. The underpaint shows up here and there especially round the edges of the figures. Some areas are not as fully worked up as others: the dress of the old Bacchante is only roughly brushed in, and the lower part of the satyr supporting Silenus' back is merely suggested; the heads of the two satyrs are not as highly finished as those of Silenus and the young Bacchante. Cleaned, 1946/7.[2]

Some leaves have been suppressed above Silenus' head; and the drapery on the young Bacchante's arm is an after-thought.

Silenus was the teacher and companion of Bacchus; he is often depicted in Bacchus' train riding an ass (see, for instance, Titian's *Bacchus & Ariadne*, no. 35 of this collection), or, as here, supported on his way by satyrs because he was old and drunk.[3]

Various attributions have been made concerning the authorship of no. 853. It was traditionally thought to be by Rubens.[4] Rooses,[5] however, considered that the fruit and landscape were by an assistant. Burchard then attributed the figures to van Dyck and the rest (?) to Snijders, perhaps working after a design by Rubens.[6] Glück[7] accepted his attribution, confined Sndijers' role to the execution of the fruit, and

seems to have assumed that the design was by Rubens. Evers[8] also
accepted this attribution; he believed that no. 853 was a copy by van
Dyck after a lost original by Rubens. The majority of these views were
accepted in the catalogue of *An Exhibition of Cleaned Pictures* of 1947,[9]
which suggested that no. 853 was executed in Rubens' studio by van
Dyck, perhaps after a design by the master, the fruit being added by
Snijders and the sky and landscape by another hand.

The least that can be said for no. 853 is that it is Rubensian, both in
the types portrayed and composition (see below). Evers[10] has suggested
that no. 853 derives from a picture by Rubens which was evolved in two
stages in a manner similar to the evolution of *The March of Silenus* at
Munich.[11] He argued that the original may first have consisted in the
group surrounding Silenus and then expanded to the right to include
the two children and the satyr embracing the elderly Bacchante. His
theory that the original was the picture engraved by de Launay[12] is not
convincing; but a certain lack of spontaneity in no. 853, and the fact
that the underpaint shows up here and there near the edges of the figures
suggests that the design was executed by a hand following a prototype
or *modello* which may or may not have been evolved in the way Evers
suggested. The sky and much of the flesh show every sign of having
been re-worked. The foliage and fruit were then added, and finally
alterations were made in the area round Silenus' head, where some
leaves have been suppressed and some drapery added to the Bacchante's
left arm. The extent and degree of re-working varies; the two most
highly finished areas appear to have been the young Bacchante and the
head and chest of Silenus.

There can be little doubt that no. 853 was executed in Rubens'
studio *ca.* 1620 (for the dating see below). The sky and landscape is
similar to that in *The Rape of the Daughters of Leucippus* at Munich of
about this time,[13] and is executed in a style comparable to that of Jan
Wildens.[14] The foliage and fruit are clearly executed in a manner
reminiscent of Frans Snijders, and may well be by him, as Burchard
was the first to suggest. Snijders is certainly known to have collaborated
with Rubens at about this time,[15] and Wildens may have done so also.[16]
The quality of execution of the figures varies according to the degree of
finish: the handling of the children compares with that in the *Children
bearing a Swag of Flowers and Fruit* at Munich.[17] No one has suggested
that van Dyck was responsible for these; and so whether he was responsible for the most highly finished or rather for all the figures in
no. 853, as has been suggested, seems at the least open to question.

Van Dyck is known to have collaborated, and to have been in close
association, with Rubens during at least much of the summer of 1620.[18]
But, with the destruction of the ceiling paintings of the Jesuit Church,
was also destroyed the only certainly identifiable paintings showing
van Dyck's style when working in collaboration with the Rubens at this
time.[19] A drawing by van Dyck in the British Museum[20] shows that he
knew Rubens' *March of Silenus* at Munich, which is also borne out by
van Dyck's pictures at Brussels and Dresden of the same subject.[21]

Further the model of the satyr on the left of no. 853 recurs in several works by van Dyck, executed before *ca.* 1620, as Burchard has pointed out.[22] But these observations do not establish that van Dyck was responsible for the figures in no. 853. The areas of flesh, not fully worked up, seem to be worthy of neither van Dyck nor Rubens. Those, which are fully worked up, show little of van Dyck's fascination for surface articulation;[23] rather they suggest Rubens' interest in weight and solidity. For these reasons it seems nearly as fruitful to look for Rubens' hand in the re-working,[24] as van Dyck's, painting, at the most, in imitation of him. Indeed, no. 853 seems, as a whole, comparable with the *Cimon and Iphigenia* at Vienna,[25] which was probably executed a little later. For these reasons, it seems sensible to attribute no. 853 to the studio of Rubens.

The reason for the failure fully to work up the lower part of the satyr who supports the back of Silenus, the dress of the old Bacchante and the (weakly executed) cantharus is uncertain. But the facts that this area are supposed to be in the shade and that no. 853 was basically a studio product should be borne in mind in this respect.

There are no extant preparatory works by Rubens which can be associated uniquely with no. 853 (but see below, under *Copies*). The pose of Silenus with his head thrown back, and supported by two satyrs, appears to be a development from that of Hercules supported by satyrs in the *Drunken Hercules* at Dresden.[26] The pose of Silenus relates more directly with that of Bacchus in the design by Rubens engraved by Suyderhof,[27] where the poses of the satyrs are also similar, but more complicated. This design was developed by Rubens into the composition recorded in the picture at Leningrad,[28] where Silenus' head lolls forward. A study of, or drawing connected with,[29] this new pose for Silenus shows him supported by a satyr on the left in a pose apparently quite similar to that of the satyr on the left in no. 853. The same sheet also has a study, executed later, for the Silenus in the *March of Silenus* at Munich; both studies show Silenus three-quarter length, which corresponds with the field of the first state of the Munich picture[30] and of no. 853.

No. 853 corresponds to the description, given by de Piles,[31] of a picture by Rubens then in the collection of the Duc de Richelieu. According to de Piles this picture was commissioned by Lucas van Uffel from Rubens in competition with Domenichino, Reni, Guercino, Albani, Poussin, van Dyck and Rembrandt. If no. 853 is the picture described by de Piles and if his story is correct, no. 853 would have to have been executed not earlier than *ca.* 1625. However, de Piles' story is not corroborated and is clearly fantastic;[32] and although Rooses dated no. 853 *ca.* 1627,[33] this and the date *ca.* 1625 is too late, judging from the style. The Dresden picture is normally dated *ca.* 1615;[34] Evers has dated the design engraved by Suyderhof *ca.* 1611 which seems too early; both this design and that recorded in the Leningrad picture probably date from shortly after 1615.[35] The Munich picture is normally dated *ca.* 1618;[36] the first state of the painting (pace Evers) from which no.

853 derives was probably executed about the same time. No. 853 itself
may have been executed *ca.* 1620 as Oldenbourg[37] suggested.

The model for the old Bacchante occurs often in Rubens' work and
features on the sheet of drawings by him, engraved by Pontius.[38] The
idea of the satyr embracing the old Bacchante appears to be paraphrase
of the satyr embracing a nymph in the Dresden *Diana returning from
the Chase.*[39] A comparable motif appears in what is possibly a lost Rubens
composition, engraved by Sibelius, of the *Drunkenness of Bacchus.*[40]
The models for the two children occur in pictures by Rubens, normally
dated in the second half of the second decade.[41] The child on the right
derives directly from a drawing in the Albertina, as Glück pointed out;[42]
the identification of the sitter as Albert Rubens, Rubens' eldest son
(born in 1614), is normally accepted (with qualification by Held[43]).
The model of the young Bacchante in no. 853 also occurs, in *inter alia*,
the *Virgin and Child adored by Saints*, the *'Coup de Lance'* and the
Raising of Lazarus.[44] As Burchard has pointed out, the model of the
satyr on the left was the subject of an oil sketch, given to van Dyck;[45]
he features in several works executed by van Dyck during his first
Antwerp period,[46] but may also be the model for the huntsman on the
left in the Munich *Lion Hunt* by Rubens.[47]

Evers[48] has compared what he considered to be the first state of the
lost original from which no. 853 derives (that is the main group without
the two children and the embracing couple) with the picture of Silenus,
satyr and Bacchante at Genoa, published by Kieser.[49] This picture may
or may not be the work of Rubens; but the general disposition of the
three heads is comparable. However, it seems more likely that the design
of no. 853 evolved out of that recorded in Suyderhof's print, as suggested above, as did in a simpler way the lost picture recorded in the
print by Sibelius.

Kieser has shown that the *Drunken Hercules* at Dresden derives
from the antique.[50] Another source, which may have inspired Rubens
in the design of no. 853, is the print by Raimondi after the antique,
where torch bearers also feature in Silenus' retinue.[51] The pipe
player in no. 853 may have been inspired by that in the print by
Mantegna.[52]

Evers[53] considered that the first state of the original from which no.
853 derives, revolved round the relationship of the Bacchante and
Silenus, and illustrated a couplet from Ovid's *Fasti*. In more general
terms he considered that it illustrated drunkenness and lascivity. No.
853 rather illustrates the effects of drunkenness; the composition may be
compared with that in Cartari,[54] which features Bacchus rather than
Silenus, of this subject. In so far as the design recorded in Suyderhof's
print is relevant to no. 853 so is the couplet beneath it: 'Visus Hebet,
fumant Artús, Cerebrumq Rotatúr, | Nec facit Officiúm Pes, Animú sue
suum.'

The gesture of the young Bacchante squeezing grapes over Silenus
recalls the gesture of Aegle described by Virgil in the sixth Eclogue
(20–22).[55]

ENGRAVINGS: By Pistrucci;[56] Giovanni Folo (1764–1836).[57]

COPIES: National Trust, Knole;[58] the prototype engraved by N. de Launay († 1792);[59] Stroganoff collection, St. Petersburg, 1807;[60] Cremer collection, Dortmund, 1914;[61] coll. A. Shaban, 1966;[62] drawing: coll. Delacre, 1930.[63]

DERIVATION (?): *The Triumph of Silenus* by Watteau.[64]

PROVENANCE: Probably coll. Lucas van Uffel († 1637), Venice,[65] and perhaps sold with other pictures in his collection, Amsterdam, in 1637 or ca. 9 April, 1639.[66] Perhaps coll. Arnold Horebeek, Antwerp,[67] from whom bought, through the agency of the dealers Picart and Musson, by the Duc de Richelieu, 1676.[68] Probably the coll. the Duc de Richelieu, Paris, ca. 1676.[69] Perhaps coll. the Duc d'Orléans († 1723), Paris, who gave it away.[70] Probably coll. Dutartre, Paris, 1780[71] or 1784;[72] Dutartre (†) sale, Paris, 19 March, 1804 (16)[73] bt. Maurice[74] for 15,000 francs.[75] Coll. Lucien Bonaparte, by 1812;[76] Prince Lucien Buonaparte sale by private contract, Buchanan, 6 ff. February, 1815 (95) not sold;[77] Lucien Buonaparte sale, Stanley, 14 May, 1816 (62) bt. Stanley for 950 gns.[78] sold to 'some gentlemen in Paris'.[79] Coll. Chevalier Bonnemaison, Paris, by 1824;[80] Chevalier Féréol Bonnemaison (†) sale, Paris, 2 ff. April, 1827 (72) for 21,000 francs.[81] Sold by John Smith to the Rt. Hon. Robert Peel (later Sir Robert Peel, Bart.) for £1,100, 23 June, 1827;[82] exh. B.I., 1831 (47); bought with the Peel Collection, 1871; exh. *An Exhibition of Cleaned Pictures*, The National Gallery, 1947 (no. 56).

REPRODUCTION: *National Gallery Illustrations, Continental Schools* (*excluding Italian*), 1950, p. 311.

REFERENCES: *General:* J. Smith, *A Catalogue Raisonné* etc., 1830, II, no. 564 and Supplement, 1842, Rubens, no. 224; M. Rooses, *L'Œuvre de P. P. Rubens*, 1890, III, no. 680; R. Oldenbourg, *Rubens, K. der K.*, [1921], p. 218.

In text: (1) Concave strains in the canvas are visible in X-ray photographs of the top, right and bottom edges. This is an indication that these edges are old, if not original, the strains being caused by fixing the canvas to the stretcher. It should be noted that the copy at Knole (see below under *Copies*), shows more at the top, and that an engraving by de Launay (see below under *Copies*) shows more at the top than the copy at Knole, and more to the left and a little more to the bottom. (2) The top half of Silenus' loin cloth was found to be a later addition and was removed during cleaning, see the catalogue of *An Exhibition of Cleaned Pictures* (*1936–1947*), The National Gallery, 1947 (56). As a result of cleaning the design of no. 853 corresponds with the engraving by Pistrucci (see below under *Engravings*). (3) See, for instance, V. Cartari, *Imagini de gli Dei delli Antichi*, 1626 (ed.), p. 343. (4) See Smith, under *General References*; and, for instance, G. F. Waagen, *Treasures of Art in Great Britain*, I, 1854, p. 399, no. 2; Oldenbourg, under *General References*, is the last authority to accept the traditional attribution. (5) See under *General References*. (6) See L. Burchard, *Jahrbuch der preuszischen Kunstsammlungen*, 1928, p. 63; and Burchard Documentation. (7) See G. Glück, *Van Dyck, K. der K.*, [1931], p. 21, and note to p. 21 on pp. 519–520. (8) See H. G. Evers, *Rubens und sein Werk*, I, 1944, pp. 246–247. (9) *Loc. cit.* (10) *Op. cit.*, pp. 245–246. (11) Rep. Oldenbourg, *op. cit.*, p. 177. The evolution of this picture in two stages was first described by E. Kieser, *Münchner Jahrbuch der bildenden Kunst*, 1938–39, pp. 185 ff. (12) See below, under *Copies*. (13) Rep. Oldenbourg, *op. cit.*, p. 131. (14) Compare the landscape at Antwerp, signed and dated 1631, see *Musée Royal des Beaux-Arts, Anvers, Catalogue Maîtres Anciens*, 1958, p. 242, no. 987. (15) See, for instance, Rubens' description of the first picture in the list of those offered for sale to Carleton on 28 April, 1618, in M. Rooses and Ch. Ruelens (†), *Correspondance de Rubens*, 1898, II, p. 136. (16) See under the biography of Wildens. (17) Rep. by Oldenbourg, *op. cit.*, p. 132. (18) See under the biography of van Dyck. (19) W. Bode has claimed to find van Dyck's hand present in a number of large paintings, executed in Ruben's studio at about this time, see *Great Masters of*

Dutch and Flemish Paintings, trans. M. Clarke, 1911 (ed.), pp. 321–4; and for instance under no. 1865. (20) See A. Hind, *Catalogue of Drawings by Dutch and Flemish Artists* . . . *in the British Museum*, 1923, II, p. 58, no. 22; and H. Vey, *Die Zeichnungen Anton van Dycks*, 1962, pp. 95–6, no. 24, by whom also connected with no. 853, which he considered to be by van Dyck. (21) Rep. Glück, *op. cit.*, pp. 6 and 67; the condition of the Brussels picture seems problematic and suspect. (22) See Glück, *op. cit.*, p. 520, note to p. 21. (23) As is evident, for instance, in no. 50, or in the *S. Jerome* at Stockholm, rep. Glück, *op. cit.*, p. 57, probably executed *ca.* 1620. (24) His practice of re-working paintings, executed by studio assistants, is amply demonstrated by his comments on the list of pictures for sale, which he sent to Carleton on 28 April, 1618, see Rooses and Ruelens (†), *op. cit.*, pp. 136–7. (25) Rep. Oldenbourg, *op. cit.*, p. 133, by whom dated *ca.* 1617, which is probably too early. The model for the child sleeping on the left was Rubens' son Albert, born in 1614, who probably occurs in no. 853 (see below). He seems to be about just under ten in the Vienna picture. The Vienna picture is probably identical with that catalogued as by Rubens in the York House inventory of the collection of the Duke of Buckingham († 1628), see R. Davies, *The Burlington Magazine*, 1906/7, X, p. 381; and M. Rooses, *L'Œuvre de P. P. Rubens*, 1890, 4, no. 871. (26) Rep. Oldenbourg, *op. cit.*, p. 122; itself a version, as recalled by J. S. Held, *Rubens Selected Drawings*, 1959, p. 111, under no. 41. (27) Rep. Evers, *op. cit.*, fig. 255a. (28) Rep. Oldenbourg, p. 82. To judge from the reproduction, this work looks not to be original. (29) See Held, *op. cit.*, no. 41 and pl. (30) See Kieser, *loc. cit.* (31) For a transcript of de Piles' text, see B. Teyssèdre, *Gazette des Beaux-Arts*, 1963, p. 262. For a further discussion concerning the identity of the picture in the Duc de Richelieu's collection, see under *Provenance*. (32) The statement is perhaps best seen in the light of the controversy concerning the status of Rubens, which took place in Paris *ca.* 1676, for which see J. Thuillier, *Archives de l'Art Français*, 1968, pp. 137 ff. (33) See under *General References*. (34) See, for instance, Oldenbourg, *op. cit.*, p. 122. (35) See Evers, *op. cit.*, p. 244. A design, comparable in many respects with that at Leningrad, features in *The Allegory of Sight* by Jan Brueghel I in the Prado, which is dated 1617, see *Museo del Prado, Catálogo de las Pinturas*, 1963, p. 86, no. 1394. (36) See Oldenbourg, *op. cit.*, p. 177. It is perhaps the picture dated 1618 by Phillippe Rubens in his *Mémoire*, sent to de Piles in 1676, see *Rubens-Bulletijn*, 1883, II, p. 166. (37) See under *General References*. (38) See under no. 59; Pontius' print is reproduced in Rooses, *op. cit.*, 1892, V, pl. 352. (39) Rep. in Oldenbourg, *op. cit.*, p. 123. (40) See Rooses, *op. cit.*, 1890, III, no. 575. (41) The blond, curly headed child occurs three times in the Munich *Virgin and Child and Angels* (Oldenbourg, *op. cit.*, p. 138), as Christ in the Thyssen *Holy Family* and in the Dijon *Virgin showing the Infant Christ to S. Francis* of 1618, rep. Oldenbourg, *op. cit.*, p. 168. The straight, brown haired child occurs twice in the Munich *Virgin and Child with Angels, Children bearing a Swag of Fruit & Flowers* (Oldenbourg, *op. cit.*, p. 132), *March of Silenus* (Oldenbourg, *op. cit.*, p. 177), and in the ex Dahlem variant of it, in the Pitti *Holy Family* (Oldenbourg, *op. cit.*, p. 99) as Christ, and in the Cassel *Virgin and Child adored by Saints* (Oldenbourg, *op. cit.*, p. 129), as S. John the Baptist, and in the *Cimon & Iphigenia* at Vienna. (42) *Op. cit.*, note to p. 21 on pp. 519–520. The drawing in the Albertina is G. Glück and F. M. Halberditzl, *Die Handzeichnungen von Peter Paul Rubens*, 1928, no. 117; Held, *op. cit.*, p. 135 under no. 98, believes this drawing to be wholly by Rubens, contrary to the view of Glück and Halberditzl. (43) *Loc. cit.* The identity of the blond, curly headed child is not known; the features are not so very different from that of Christ in the Munich *Virgin and Child and Angels*, who may well be Albert despite the colour of the hair; this model also occurs in other works by Rubens of the period. The poses of the children in no. 853 were probably inspired by, or taken from drawings available in Rubens' studio: that of the blond haired child, is similar to that of the second angel from the bottom on the right of the Munich *Virgin and Child with*

Angels, and that of the brown haired child to the pose of S. John the Baptist in the Cassel picture. Burchard Documentation considers that the head of the blond haired child was taken directly from that of Christ in the Dijon picture (see under note 41); it also records a study for the child on paper, $15\frac{1}{2} \times 12\frac{1}{2}$ (0·385 × 0·325) in the Karl Alexander Brendel sale, Berlin, January, 1930. **(44)** Rep. Oldenbourg, *op. cit.*, pp. 129, 216 and 217. **(45)** See G. Glück, *op. cit.*, p. 36 bottom, and page 522, note to p. 21. **(46)** See note 22. **(47)** See Oldenbourg, *op. cit.*, p. 154. The model seems not so very different from that of the main satyr in the Munich *Two Satyrs*, rep. Oldenbourg, *op. cit.*, p. 135 left. **(48)** *Op. cit.*, p. 246. **(49)** *Loc. cit.*; the picture is rep. by H. G. Evers, *Peter Paul Rubens*, trans. by K. Ruyssinck, 1946, fig. 43. **(50)** See E. Kieser, *Münchner Jahrbuch der bildenden Kunst*, 1933, pp. 117–18. The pose of Silenus in the composition recorded in the picture at Leningrad, also derives from the antique, see A. M. Hind, *Catalogue of the Drawings . . . in the British Museum*, 1923, II, no. 51; this classical source does not lie directly behind the pose of no. 853. **(51)** Rep. by M. Jaffé, *Van Dyck's Antwerp Sketchbook*, 1966, I, fig. XCVII; the central group of Silenus is also rep. by Lorenzo Pignoria in his notes to Cartari, see V. Cartari, *Imagini de gli Dei delli Antiqui*, 1626 (ed.)., p. 513. **(52)** Rep. by Jaffé, *op. cit.*, I, fig. LXXXVII. **(53)** *Loc. cit.* **(54)** *Op. cit.*, p. 344; this cut also appeared in the 1615 edition. **(55)** 'Addit se sociam timidisque supervenit Aegle, | Aegle, Naiadum pulcherri ima, iamque videnti | sanguineis frontem moris et tempora pingit'. These lines occur in the passage where Silenus is woken from a drunken sleep by Chromis and Mnasyllos. It was the subject of a sheet of sketches at Windsor, as Burchard and d'Hulst pointed out, for their most recent discussion, see L. Burchard and R. A. d'Hulst, *Rubens Drawings*, 1963, no. 51. **(56)** In *Choix de Gravures . . . d'après Les Peintures . . . de la Galerie de Lucien Bonaparte*, 1812, no. 18. **(57)** See C. G. Voorhelm Schneevoogt, *Catalogue des Estampes gravées d'après P. P. Rubens* etc., 1873, p. 135, no. 143. **(58)** Canvas, 60 × 75 (1·524 × 1·905); there is also a record of a 'crayon study' for the composition, 16 × 12 (0·402 × 0·308) also at Knole. This may be the picture mentioned at Knole by P. G. Patmore, *British Galleries of Art*, 1824, pp. 152–154; (Burchard Documentation). **(59)** The engraving was mentioned in the *Mercure de France*, March, 1777, p. 194 (Burchard Documentation). Reproduced by Rooses, *op. cit.*, III, pl. 209; it shows Silenus' loin cloth with the later addition, which was removed when no. 853 was cleaned, and more to the top, bottom and right-hand side, and a goat's head behind the children. For the status of the prototype see note 72 and the Dutartre sale catalogue of 1804 (below); Burchard Documentation notes a picture directly related with the print in the collection of Leonard Milne, 1946. **(60)** See *Collection d'Estampes d'après quelques Tableaux de la Galerie de . . . Comte A. Stroganoff . . . 1807.* Engraved by E. Scotnicoff. It was still in the collection in 1901, when stated to measure, 48 × 72 (1·22 × 1·83), see *Trésors d'Art en Russie*, 1901, p. 172. It was not in the Stroganoff sale, Berlin, 12/13 May, 1931. Scotnicoff's engraving also shows Silenus' loin cloth with the later addition which was removed when no. 853 was cleaned. **(61)** Canvas, $56\frac{11}{16} \times 79\frac{7}{8}$ (1·44 × 2·03), see *Collection . . . Cremer*, 1914, II, no. 1172, pl. 25; not in the Josef Cremer sale, Berlin, 29 May, 1929. **(62)** 54 × 78 (1·372 × 1·982); information kindly provided by M. Jaffé. **(63)** $10\frac{5}{16} \times 13\frac{7}{8}$ (0·262 × 0·352), see M. Delacre, *Études sur quelques Dessins de P. P. Rubens*, 1930, p. 66 and fig. 4. Delacre considered this to be Rubens' preparatory drawing, but the quality appears to be too low for the attribution to be accepted; noted at the R.K.D. as coll. O. Tschamper, Switzerland, 1951. **(64)** See K. T. Parker and J. Mathey, *Antoine Watteau Catalogue Complet de son Œuvre Dessiné*, 1957, I, no. 259 and fig. The authors consider that the drawing is inspired by no. 853, but the connections are not very close. **(65)** According to de Piles, *Conversations sur la connoissance de la peinture*, 1677, pp. 141/3, reprinted by Teyssèdre, *loc. cit.*, a picture by Rubens answering a description of no. 853 (see note 31), was painted in competition with other artists, the competition was sponsored by van Uffel 'Van-Uflen [*sic*] . . . prit plaisir à faire travailler tous ces Illustres en mesme

temps, pour juger de leur Ouvrages de la maniere [*sic*] du monde la plus sûre . . . je
veux dire par comparaison . . .' Although the story of such a competition is not
corroborated (see above), de Piles' statement at the least suggests that the picture
he was describing may have come from van Uffel's collection. Lucas van Uffel,
a connoisseur of Dutch origin, made his career in Venice from 1616 as a banker
and arms manufacturer; he moved to Amsterdam before his death, see M. Vaes,
Bulletin de l'Institut historique belge de Rome, 1925 (5), pp. 162–164; the same
author, *Bulletin de Institut historique belge de Rome*, 1924 (4), pp. 178–80, gives
a briefer biography, and there states that van Uffel was of Flemish origin. If
van Uffel did own no. 853, it would more or less rule out Smith's thesis, see
under *General References*, that it is to be identified with no. 170 of the catalogue
of pictures owned by Rubens for sale at this house, Antwerp, in 1640, for which
see J. Denucé, *Inventories of the Art Collections in Antwerp* etc., 1932, p. 63.
This was probably not the picture later sold by Philippe Rubens to the Duc de
Richelieu as M. Rooses, *L'Œuvre de P. P. Rubens*, 1890, III, under no. 676,
suggested. (66) For the first sale, see M. Vaes, *Bulletin de l'Institut historique
belge de Rome*, 1925 (5), p. 164; for the second sale, see Vaes, *Bulletin de l'Institut
historique belge de Rome*, 1924 (4), p. 180, and note 1, for Sandrart's mention of
it; see also N. MacLaren, *National Gallery Catalogues, The Dutch School*,
1960, under no. 672, for a reference to Rembrandt's copy of Raphael's *Portrait
of Baldassare Castiglione*, which certainly featured in it. (67) He seems to have
been a dealer, active from at least 1668, see J. Denucé, *Na P. P. Rubens*, 1949,
p. 363; he does not feature in the lists of the Antwerp guild of S. Luke. (68) After
the acquisition by the Duc de Richelieu of Rubens' *Judgment of Paris* (perhaps
no. 194 q.v.), Picart wrote to Musson, on 13 December, 1675, about a pendant
for it, whose subject should be from Ovid or a Bacchanal, see Denucé, *op. cit.*,
p. 424. On 3 January, 1676, he wrote mentioning a '*Silenes*' [*sic*] owned by Mr.
Horenbeke [*sic*], an *Andromeda* and a *Bacchus*, see Denucé, *op. cit.*, p. 428. The
two latter pictures were bought by the Duc de Richelieu, see Denucé, *op. cit.*,
pp. 431 ff, and pp. LXI–LXII. They had belonged to Phillipe Rubens, see
his letter to de Piles of 11 February, 1676, in the *Rubens-Bulletijn*, 1883, II,
pp. 162–3. Richelieu's first collection of Rubens' contained three Bacchanals, one
depicting Bacchus and two, Silenus, see Teyssèdre, *op. cit.*, pp. 261–64. These
have been identified with no. 853 (see below), and the pictures at Munich (see
above and under note 11) and at Leningrad, for which see Oldenbourg, *op. cit.*,
p. 409. Of these, the two latter are different in shape to no. 194 *q.v.*, which may
have been the *Judgment of Paris*, for which a pendant was required, while the
measurements of no. 853 are similar to it, though not the same. In a letter of 10
January, Picart asked Musson to see that Horebeek's picture was not much
smaller than the *Judgment* [*of Paris*], see Denucé, *op. cit.*, p. 430. No letters from
Picart, published by Denucé, show that this picture was sent to Paris; but in his
letter of 10 January, he asked Musson to settle a deal with Horebeek's nephew;
a payment was made to this nephew on 28 February, and another to Horebeek
himself on 17 April, see Denucé, *op. cit.*, pp. 437 and 438. If this identification is
correct, it can be added that the pendant (i.e. no. 853) could not have been said
to have been painted in the style of Titian or Giorgione, a requirement set out
by Picart in his letter of 13 December, 1675. This might explain why no. 853
did not remain in the Duc de Richelieu's collection (see below). (69) See de
Piles' description in the *Conversations* etc., of 1677, printed by Teyssèdre, *loc.
cit.*: 'La Seconde [Bacchanale] | Fait voir le Pere [*sic*] Silene [*sic*] dans une
yvresse [*sic*] gaye [*sic*]: il ne sçauroit porter le poids de sa grasse panse, et se lais-
sant aller en arriere [*sic*] sur les Satires qui l'accompagnent, il acheve [*sic*] les
ceremonies [*sic*] de sa marche au son des flustes [*sic*], dont un Satire joüe
pendant qu' une Baccante se retourne . . . pour arrouser ce bon vieillard du jus
des raisins qu'elle presse . . .' It has been generally accepted that this description is of a picture that is to be identified with no. 853. The picture described in the 1677 *Conversations* does not feature in de Piles' later catalogues
of the Duc de Richelieu collection, see Teyssèdre, *op. cit.*, p. 244; according to de
Piles', p. 5 *recto*, of the *Epistre* to the *Dissertation sur les Ouvrages des plus Fameux*

Peintres [1681], Richelieu had 'rejetté des choses de lui [=Rubens] qu'on auroit pû opposer aux plus forts Ouvrages de meilleurs Peintres: & vous [=Richelieu] n'avez garder que ceux que cét [*sic*] Homme incomparable a laissez [*sic*] à la postérité pour immortaliser son Nom'. (70) See the Dutartre sale catalogue of 1804, note 77; other pictures also passed from the collection of the Duc de Richelieu to that of the Duc d'Orléans, but no picture corresponding with no. 853 features in the published catalogues of the Orléans collection, for which see under no. 194. (71) See Duchesne the Elder, *Musée de Peinture* etc., 1828, I, no. 8. (72) See Thiéry, *Guide des Amateurs* . . . *à Paris* etc., I, 1787, p. 584: 'L'hôtel *de la Tour du Pin*, est occupé par M. *du Tartre* [*sic*] . . . On y remarque cinq tableaux de *Rubens* . . . la second contenant sept figures de grandeur naturelle, offre Sylène reconduit au son des instruments. Ce tableau annoncé par M. de Pille [*sic*] . . . à ete gravé, mais malheureusement sur une médiocre copie' (see above under *Copies*). For some details concerning Dutarte, see under no. 157. (73) The catalogue entry by Paillet gives the support as wood and the measurements as 50×70 pouces ($=ca.\ 53\frac{1}{4} \times 74\frac{5}{8}$); it also states that the satyr with the elderly Bacchante are on the left of Silenus. A comparable mistake was made in the description of lot 21, see under no. 157. (74) See C. Blanc, *Le Trésor de la Curiosité*, 1858, II, p. 225. (75) See Smith, under *General References*; Blanc, *loc. cit.*, gives the price as 1,500 francs, which probably resulted from a misreading. (76) When engraved, see note 56. (77) See W. Buchanan, *Memoirs of Painting* etc., II, 1824, p. 286; Buchanan also gives an extract of the catalogue, in which no. 853 bears the number 89, see p. 274. The picture was stated to be ex coll. de Tartre [*sic*]. (78) For the buyer and price, see Smith under *General References*. Buchanan, *op. cit.*, p. 287, states that no. 853 was not sold at the sale; presumably the buyer, Stanley, is identical with the auctioneer. (79) See Buchanan, *loc. cit.* (80) *Ibid.* (81) Stated in the catalogue to be ex coll. the Duc de Richelieu and Lucien Bonaparte. For the price, see Smith under *General References*. (82) See Smith and Successors, *Stockbook*, XII, no. 499 (ms., Victoria and Albert Museum Library); Peel's note in the Goulburn mss., Surrey County Record Office; and Wilkie's letter to Peel of 18 August, 1827, in A. Cunningham, *The Life of Sir David Wilkie* etc., II, 1843, p. 441.

Ascribed to the Studio of RUBENS

67 THE HOLY FAMILY WITH SAINTS IN A LANDSCAPE

On the left are S. George and the princess, with a female Saint; on the right, the Infant S. John the Baptist, aided by two angels, pulls the lamb towards the sleeping Christ; in the distance S. Joseph asleep and the ass.

Oil on relined canvas, *ca.* $46\frac{7}{8} \times 62\frac{3}{8}$ ($1 \cdot 19 \times 1 \cdot 585$).

In fairly good condition. There are several scattered losses in the landscape, architecture and the bottom of the princess's dress. The edge of the painted surface is irregular. Cleaned, 1951/2.

The subject is usually thought to be the *Rest on the Flight into Egypt*, but the presence of the Saints makes this improbable.[1]

No. 67 was considered by the National Gallery in the nineteenth century to be the work of Rubens, but was rejected by Waagen[2] and then Rooses[3]; it was then ascribed in the National Gallery catalogue of 1913 to the School of Rubens and in the 1958 *Summary Catalogue* to the Studio of Rubens. Burchard/d'Hulst[4] considered an attribution to Watteau, which is plainly wrong. The standard of execution of no. 67

is not high, and Rubens evidently had no part in it; but this is not to say that it was not executed during his lifetime (see below).

The composition is closely connected with that by Rubens in the Prado,[5] which was probably executed in the first half of the 1630's. The same composition, but without the Saints and princess, was made into a woodcut by Christoffel Jegher, working under Rubens' supervision.[6] No. 67 does not faithfully follow either the Prado picture, or the woodcut (or the *modello* for it). The right-hand part of no. 67 corresponds with a copy by Watteau of the Infant S. John the Baptist, angels and the landscape behind,[7] except for some details of the landscape.

Burchard/d'Hulst[8] have suggested that no. 67 is a copy after Rubens' first rendering of the composition. They argue that Rubens evolved the composition in this, lost picture; the stages of its evolution are recorded in chronological order by no. 67, the *modello* for the woodcut, the woodcut, and finally the Prado picture.

In the absence of X-radiographs of the Prado picture, it is not possible to accept the whole of their thesis without reservations. The fact that no. 67 agrees far more with the Prado picture than with the woodcut or *modello* for it, does not add weight to their view that the woodcut preceded the Prado picture.[9] However, as no. 67 shares elements of both the woodcut and the Prado picture, and, as one of the areas—the Infant S. John and the angels—where no. 67 does not agree with either, is to some extent authenticated as Rubens' invention by virtue of the copy by Watteau after a lost drawing or painting, it seems probable that no. 67 records a stage in the evolution of the Prado picture. On the other hand no. 67 could rather derive from a copy.[10] Certainly the artist responsible betrays the intention and weakness of a copyist, although he seems to have had a good knowledge of Rubens' manner. Thus it seems best to catalogue no. 67 as ascribed to the studio of Rubens.

COPIES: Coll. J. Jagger, Leeds;[11] Anon. sale, Christie's, 12 June, 1964 (16).[12]

PROVENANCE: Purchased from a clergyman by J. J. Angerstein;[13] purchased with the Angerstein collection, 1824; lent, through the Arts Council, to the City Art Gallery, Manchester, 1958–63.

REPRODUCTION: *National Gallery Illustrations, Continental Schools* (*excluding Italian*), 1950, p. 316, top.

REFERENCES *in text:* (1) See Mrs. Jameson, *Legends of the Madonna*, 1879, pp. 238 ff. (2) See G. F. Waagen, *Treasures of Art* etc., I, 1854, p. 351; no. 67 does not feature in Smith's catalogue raisonné of the work of Rubens of 1830. (3) See M. Rooses, *L'Œuvre de P. P. Rubens*, 1886, I, no. 180; his attribution of the landscape to van Uden is not likely. (4) See L. Burchard and R. A. d'Hulst, *Rubens Drawings*, I, 1963, under no. 179. (5) See *Museo del Prado, Catálogo de las Pinturas*, 1963, p. 573, no. 1640; Rooses, *op. cit.*, no. 179; and R. Oldenbourg, *Rubens, K. der K.*, [1921], p. 345. (6) The woodcut is F. van den Wijngaert, *Inventaris der Rubeniaansche Prenthunst*, 1940, no. 315. Rubens' *modello* is in the National Museum, Poznan, see Burchard/d'Hulst, *loc. cit.* (7) Ex Berlin, see K. T. Parker and J. Matthey, *Antoine Watteau Catalogue Complet de son Œuvre dessiné*, 1957, I, no. 276; and Burchard/d'Hulst, *loc. cit.* (8) *Loc. cit.* (9) It seems more likely that the woodcut was designed simultaneously with the execution of the Prado picture. It is not clear whether Burchard/d'Hulst believe that this picture is the 'fair copy' they suggest that

Rubens made; at all events it cannot be the picture recorded in Rubens' inventory and sold to Philip IV, which was on canvas, see J. Denucé, *Inventories of the Art-Collections in Antwerp*, 1932, pp. 60 & 74–5. (10) Burchard/d'Hulst, *loc. cit.*, suggest that Watteau made his copy from a contemporary repetition. (11) Photo in Witt Library. (12) Canvas, 28 × 36 (0·711 × 0·915); the pose of the legs of the Infant Christ is different. (13) See Young's ms. notes (in the N.G. Library) for his catalogue of the Angerstein collection.

3818   PORTRAIT OF THE ARCHDUKE ALBERT

Oil on relined canvas, 48 × 35 (1·22 × 0·89). The original canvas is bent over the stretcher by as much as $\frac{3}{4}$ (0·020) at the left and top edges.

In good condition. The canvas edge at the top and left is very ragged, but the canvas has not been significantly cut down. The paint round the edges, particularly at the bottom, is damaged and retouched; there is a small area of damage, also retouched in the background.

Infra-red photography reveals *pentimenti* in the plumage of the hat and to the outline of the costume.

The Archduke Albert of Austria (1559–1621), the sixth son of Emperor Maximillan II, was appointed Governor of the Netherlands in 1595, and, from 1598, became joint Sovereign of the Seventeen Provinces with his wife to be, the Infanta Isabella, whom he married in that year. After some early military successes against the rebellious northern provinces, he concluded the twelve years truce with them in 1609.[1] He was made a knight of the Order of the Golden Fleece in 1599, and is depicted wearing the badge of the Order.

Although thought by Rooses[2] to have a good claim to be regarded as the work of Rubens, and catalogued as by him in the 1925 and 1929 catalogues, no. 3818 is clearly not an autograph work. Glück,[3] followed by Burchard,[4] considered it to be a workshop repetition after a lost prototype by Rubens,[5] known through Jan Müller's engraving of 1615.[6] Apart from the jewel carrying the Fleece and the fact that the face looks less aged in the painting, the main differences between no. 3818 and the print result from *pentimenti*. But although both are in the same direction, it seems improbable that no. 3818 should have been copied from the print rather than from the prototype from which the print derived.

There is no reason to suppose that no. 3818 is not a work of the seventeenth century. Glück's attribution to the studio of Rubens is perhaps more attractive than the looser category of 'after Rubens', adopted in the 1958 *Summary Catalogue*. But bearing in mind the (apparently) unusual ground (see Appendix II), Glück's view is followed here only with considerable hesitation.

Rubens was appointed 'paintre de nostre hostel' (court painter) by Albert and Isabella in 1609;[7] the Archduke was apparently on fairly close terms with Rubens.[8]

COPY:[9] Anon sale, Sotheby's, 19 February, 1964 (134).[10]

PROVENANCE: See below, under no. 3819.

REPRODUCTION: *National Gallery Illustrations, Continental Schools (excluding Italian)*, 1950, p. 315, left.

REFERENCES *in text:* (**1**) For a full biography see the *Biographie Nationale . . . de Belgique*, 1866, I, col. 184 ff. (**2**) See M. Rooses, *Rubens*, trans. by H. Child, I, 1904, p. 203; he was judging from a photograph. No. 3818 was then in the collection of R. C. Jackson, see under *Provenance.* (**3**) See G. Glück, *Rubens, van Dyck und ihr Kreis*, 1933, p. 47; and in *The Burlington Magazine*, 1940, I, p. 177. (**4**) See G. Glück, *Rubens, van Dyck und ihr Kreis*, 1933, p. 380. (**5**) See under no. 3819. (**6**) Reproduced (without the inscription) in M. Rooses, *L'Œuvre de P. P. Rubens*, 1890, IV, pl. 279; the inscription is given in *ibid.*, under no. 875. (**7**) The patent is printed by M. Rooses and Ch. Ruelens (†), *Correspondance de Rubens*, 1898, II, pp. 6–7; see also M. de Maeyer, *Albrecht en Isabella en de Schilderkunst*, 1955, pp. 93–8. (**8**) See de Maeyer, *op. cit.*, pp. 98–101; and under no. 57. (**9**) A number of pictures connected with Müller's print are recorded; but as no. 3818 is itself probably only a copy, they are not listed here as *Versions.* (**10**) Canvas, $46\frac{1}{2} \times 37\frac{1}{2}$ (1·181 × 0·952); ex Anon. sale, Sotheby's, 11 July, 1962 (40B).

3819 PORTRAIT OF THE INFANTA ISABELLA

Oil on relined canvas, $47\frac{7}{16} \times 34\frac{15}{16}$ (1·205 × 0·888). The original canvas is bent over the stretcher by as much as $\frac{1}{2}$ (0·013) on the left, $\frac{3}{4}$ (0·002) at the top and $\frac{9}{16}$ (0·015) on the right.

In good condition. The left- and right-hand edges are very ragged, but the canvas has not been significantly cut down. There are some retouched losses along the edges and a few small losses in the background, also retouched. The eyebrows have been strengthened.

Isabella Clara Eugenia (1566–1633), Infanta of Spain, Archduchess of Austria, was the daughter of Philip II, by whom she was made joint Sovereign of the Seventeen Provinces with her husband to be, the Archduke Albert, in 1598. She did not play an active part in politics until after her husband's death in 1621, when she was confirmed in her prerogatives of sovereignty by Philip IV. Henceforth her role was important, and she strove ineffectually to bring to an end the fighting in the Netherlands, which had been resumed after the expiry of the twelve years truce.[1] According to her chaplain, Philippe Chifflet, she was 'la plus savante princesse et la plus accomplie de son temps, fût-ce pour commander avec une douce souveraineté, fût-ce pour obéir sans répugnance.'[2] After the Archduke's death, Rubens retained his position as court painter, and became a trusted adviser of the Archduchess.[3]

Although thought by Rooses[4] to have a good claim to be regarded as the work of Rubens, no. 3819 was considered by Glück,[5] and later Burchard,[6] to be a studio repetition after a lost portrait by Rubens, known from Jan Müller's engraving of 1615.[7] His view was accepted in the case of no. 3819, as opposed to no. 3818 (see above) in the 1925 and 1929 National Gallery catalogues. No. 3819 shows less at the bottom, but more at the left and top than does Müller's engraving, in which the sitter has fewer curls. Nevertheless it seems unlikely that no. 3819 was copied from the engraving rather than the prototype from which the engraving was made. While, as with no. 3818, there is no reason to suppose that no. 3819 is not a work of the seventeenth century, a precise definition of its status is difficult. It shares with no. 3818 an (apparently) unusual ground (see Appendix II); thus Glück's attribution to

the studio of Rubens is only accepted here with considerable hesitation.
The date of Müller's engravings—1615—provides a *terminus ante quem* for the date of execution of the lost portraits, executed as pendants, from which the engravings derive. The portraits could have been executed some two years previously.[8] There may have been a fairly constant demand for copies.[9]

PROVENANCE: Bonomi-Cereda sale, Milan, 14 December, 1896 (89–90).[10] Anon. (= Duncan) sale, Christie's, 10 July, 1897 (75–76)[11] bt. Levy (= bt. in)[12] for £714; coll. Dr. Duncan, London, 1900.[13] Coll. Richard J. Jackson, Camberwell, by 1901;[14] for sale by private contract, Sotheby's, 1912, not sold;[15] bequeathed by Richard J. Jackson, 1923; on loan to the Ministry of Works 1938–41, and to the Ministry of Public Buildings and Works from 1953.

REPRODUCTION: *National Gallery Illustrations, Continental Schools (excluding Italian)*, 1950, p. 315, right.

REFERENCES *in text:* (**1**) For a full biography see the *Biographie Nationale . . . de Belgique*, 1888–9, 10, col. 12 ff. (**2**) See M. de Villermont, *L'infante Isabelle, gouvernante de Pays-Bas*, I, 1912, p. 42, ref. from P. F. Callaey, *Bulletin de l'Institut historique belge de Rome*, 1924 (3), p. 34. (**3**) See M. de Maeyer, *Albrecht en Isabella en de Schilderkunst*, 1955, pp. 101–109; and under no. 46. (**4**) See M. Rooses, *Rubens*, trans. by H. Child, I, 1904, p. 203; he was judging from a photograph. (**5**) See G. Glück, *Rubens, van Dyck und ihr Kreis*, 1940, I, p. 177. (**6**) See G. Glück, *Rubens, van Dyck und ihr Kreis*, 1933, p. 380. (**7**) Reproduced (without the inscription) in M. Rooses, *L'Œuvre de P. P. Rubens*, 1890, IV, pl. 297; the inscription is given in *ibid.*, under no. 967. (**8**) L. Burchard, catalogue of *A Loan Exhibition of Works by Peter Paul Rubens Kt.*, Wildenstein's (London), 1950, under no. 31, has argued that the portraits by Rubens from which Müller made his prints were not the result of *ad vivum* studies, but were rather an elaboration of the two portraits at Vienna (see *Kunsthistorische Museum, Katalog der Gemäldegalerie*, II, 1958, nos. 298–399) which he, and Glück, *op. cit.*, pp. 50–55, dated to 1609. Further elaboration took place, *pace* Glück, *The Burlington Magazine*, 1940, I, p. 177, and Burchard, *loc. cit.*, in the full length portrait of the Archduke, now at the São Paulo Museum of Art. Both authorities identify this full length, with that for which Rubens was paid, along with a lost full length portrait of the Archduchess, on 13 October, 1615. The dating (and perhaps even the status) of the two Vienna portraits is problematic; it is difficult to see them executed at the same time as the *Double Portrait of Rubens and Isabella Brant* (Munich, Alte Pinakothek, 1958, *Catalogue*, p. 89, no. 334) usually dated 1609–10, see, for instance, R. Oldenbourg, *Rubens, K. der K.*, [1921], p. 35. And at all events, Müller's prints differ to an extent that does not rule out that the prototypes were executed *ad vivum*, perhaps a year or two earlier than the date of publication of the prints, to judge from the difference in the face of the Archduchess in the print and in the portrait, thought to have been executed in 1616, see J. A. Goris and J. S. Held, *Rubens in America*, [1947], p. 27, no. 7. (**9**) See M. Rooses, *Rubens*, trans. H. Child, I, 1904, p. 203. A number of portraits of the Archduchess are known, which connect with Muller's print; these are not listed here as *Versions*, as no. 3819 is itself probably only a copy. (**10**) Canvas, $46\frac{1}{16} \times 38\frac{3}{16}$ ($1\cdot17 \times 0\cdot87$), as by C. de Vos. According to Genolini's introduction to the sale catalogue, the collection was formed in the first half of the nineteenth century by Luigi Bonomi and passed by inheritance to the Cereda family. (**11**) As ex coll. Bononi [*sic*] Cereda. (**12**) Note in National Gallery archives. (**13**) See M. Rooses, *Rubens-Bulletijn*, 1910, V, pp. 312–13. (**14**) *Ibid.* (**15**) Note in National Gallery archives.

After RUBENS

279 AN ALLEGORY SHOWING THE EFFECTS OF WAR
('THE HORRORS OF WAR')

Mars, the god of war, is dragged forward from the Temple of Janus by the Fury, Alecto, while Venus, attended by *putti*, attempts to restrain him. Behind Venus is a woman personifying unhappy Europe, with a genius bearing her emblem. On the ground, a caduceus, a broken bundle of arrows, a sculpted bust of a man, an open book and a piece of paper. To the right of Alecto, two monsters personifying Plague and Famine. Beneath Alecto, and falling away from Mars, three figures, a woman with a broken lute personifying Harmony, a woman and child personifying Fecundity, Maternity and Charity, and an architect with a compass and capital. In the distance, a battle and a burning town.

Oil on relined paper, stuck on canvas, *ca.* $18\frac{3}{4} \times 30$ (0.476×0.762).

In fair condition. Losses to the edges of the support have been made good and reconstructed: at the top and bottom left-hand corners, and to the right of the architect. There is much wearing, now mostly retouched. Cleaned, 1947 and 1949.[1]

There are minor *pentimenti* in the fingers of Mars' left hand.

Since no. 279 first came to the attention of connoisseurs (see below under *Provenance*), it has been accepted as by Rubens; only Burchard Documentation has doubted that it was his *modello* for the picture in the Palazzo Pitti,[2] with which it agrees in all essentials. However, despite the only fair state of preservation of no. 279, and the lack of any detailed physical analysis of the Pitti picture, there are strong reasons for questioning the traditional view.

There are some differences between no. 279 and the Pitti picture, not all of which can be explained by the condition of no. 279. In no. 279, the heads of Venus and Mars are closer together, and Venus' head is in less deep foreshortening; the fury, Alecto, stares at Mars and Venus, rather than above them; the face of the personification of Harmony is turned more to the left; and the architect is placed further from the bottom edge of the support. Both the drawing of *The Three Graces* on the sheet of paper in the centre of the Pitti picture,[3] and the music notes on the opened book of scores, held by the personification of Harmony, are absent in no. 279. The Pitti picture has a discoloured, yellow varnish, but its colour range is more brilliant and sharply contrasting; no. 279 lacks the strong, blue sky with dark orange streaked clouds behind Venus. These differences combine to make no. 279 less intense and compelling than the Pitti picture.

The lack of major *pentimenti* in no. 279 and the nature of its support do not in themselves disprove the accepted view concerning its status. The apparent lack of major *pentimenti* in the Pitti picture suggests that it was executed from a *modello*.[4] There are, however, *pentimenti* evident in the left feet of Venus and the *putto* next to her; in both cases no. 279 corresponds with the positions finally adopted in the Pitti picture. Further the modelling of the areas of flesh in no. 279, even where well preserved, lacks vigour, and some areas of drapery, notably the folds of Mars' cloak above his left arm, are misunderstood. These observations, combined with the general lack of spontaneity in no. 279, suggest that it is a copy after the Pitti picture.

The handling in no. 279 is certainly very Rubensian; it is no more than possible that it was executed while the Pitti picture was still in Rubens' studio. The latter was probably executed between the end of 1637 and early in 1638; it was certainly finished before 12 March, 1638, when Rubens wrote from Antwerp to Justus Suttermans in Florence, saying that it was already on its way there.[5] No. 279 was probably not available to Rubens then, as his description of the allegory (see below) includes a detail that is absent in both pictures.

The allegory expressed in no. 279 is one of the few by Rubens for which a detailed explanation by him has survived. In his letter to Suttermans, referred to above, Rubens stated: ' . . . In quanto al soggetto della pittura . . . La principal figura è Marte, che lasciando il tempio di Jano aperto (il quale in tempo di pace, secondo gli costumi romani, stava serrato) va collo scudo e la spada însanguinata minacciando ai popoli qualche gran ruina, curandosi poco di Venere sua dama, che si sforza con carezze ed abbracciamenti a ritenerlo, accompagnata dalli suoi Amori e Cupidini. Dall'altra banda Marte vien tirato dalla furia Aletto, con un face in mano. Mostri acconto, che significano la Peste e la Fame, compagni inseparabili della Guerra. Nel suolo giace rivolta una donna con un liuto rotto, che denota l'armonia, laquale è in-compatibile colla discordia della guerra; siccome ancora una madre col bambino in braccio, dimonstrando che la fecondita, generazione e carità vengono traversate dalla guerra, che corrompe e distrugge ogni cosa. Ci è di più un architetto sottosopra colli suoi strumenti in mano, per dire, che ciò che in tempo di pace vien fabbricato per la commodita e ornamento delle citta, si manda in ruina e gettasí per terra per la violenza dell'armi. Credo, sebben mi ricordo, che V. S. trovera ancora nel suolo, di sotto i piedi Marte, un libro, e qualche disegno in carta, per inferire che egli calca le belle lettere ed altre galanterie. Vi deve esser di più un mazzo di frezze o saette col laccio, che le stringeva insieme, sciolto; che, era stando unite, l'emblema della Concordia, siccome ancora il caduceo e l'ulivo, simbolo della pace, che finsi giacerli a canto. Quella matrona lugubre, vestita di negro e col velo stracciato, e spogliata delle sue gioie e d'ogni sorte d'ornamenti, è l'infelice Europa . . . La sua marca è quel globo, sostenuto da un angeletto o genio, con la croce in cima, che denota l'orbe cristiano . . .' Neither no. 279 not the Pitti picture has an olive branch near the caduceus; no mention is made of the castle on Europe's head,[6] the battle in the distance, the capital beside the lute, and the sculpted bust of a man.

The Pitti picture is a development and combination of motifs, previously used by Rubens.[7] His train of thought may have begun with the poses of Minerva and Mars in no. 46 q.v.;[8] these were developed in the Boymans-van Beuningen sketch,[9] and then elaborated in the Louvre gouache sketch[10] and the oil sketch recently on the London art market.[11]

The figures to the right of Mars are suggested in the Louvre sketch, which as Held[12] has suggested, may represent a stage in the development of the Pitti picture; both a pair of dividers and lute appear in the oil sketch. Rubens, however, abandoned both Minerva and Hercules who feature in these sketches, and developed the motif of Venus and Mars, first used in the *Government of the Queen* in the Marie de Médicis series, executed between 1621–25.[13] Rubens had also depicted in 1634–35, Mars (blindfolded) leaving the temple of Janus, as a decoration for one of the triumphal arches for the entry of the Cardinal Infant Ferdinand into Antwerp;[14] but the pose in the Pitti picture differs considerably and may have been inspired by Polidoro da Caravaggio.[15] The pose of the architect resembles that of one of the Israelites in no. 59 *q.v.*, and thus derives ultimately from Michelangelo.[16] The pose of unhappy Europe recalls that of the mother in the centre of the Munich *Massacre of the Innocents*, probably executed some two or three years earlier.[17]

COPIES: Several copies, deriving from the Pitti picture are recorded; only those which seem to follow no. 279, are recorded here: by Lord Leighton, Anon. sale, Sotheby's, 18 November, 1953 (131), 8 × 12¾ (0·203 × 0·324);[18] Musée des Beaux-Arts, Rennes, oil on oak, 16$\frac{15}{16}$ × 25$\frac{9}{16}$ (0·43 × 0·65); Anon. [= Champernowne family] sale, Christie's, 16 June (17) bt. Piazzetta for 13 gns.; coll. M. and Mme Paul Chévrier-Marcille, Paris, 1937, oil on paper, 19$\frac{5}{16}$ × 29¼ (0·49 × 0·75);[19] A. Gerson sale, Sotheby's, 1 May, 1963 (16);[20] drawing by Wilkins, Anon. sale, Christie's, 30 June (= 2nd day), 1820 (124).

PROVENANCE: Apparently first noted in a Genoese collection by Irvine, 1803;[21] bought by Irvine for Buchanan and Champernowne;[22] perhaps in an Anon. [= John Parke] sale, by private contract, 1804 (33)[23]; perhaps in the John Parke sale, Coxe, 8 May, 1812 (18), 45 gns.;[24] perhaps exh. B.I. 1815 (3) lent by A. Champernowne;[25] Arthur Champernowne (†) sale, Christie's, 30 June (= 2nd day), 1820 (20) £162 15sh. bt. Rogers (= Samuel Rogers 1763–1855);[26] exh. B.I. 1832 (12), 1835 (117); Samuel Rogers sale, Christie's, 2 May (= 5th day), 1856 (608) £210 bt. Bentley for the National Gallery; exh. *An Exhibition of Cleaned Pictures*, The National Gallery, 1947/8 (no. 7).

REPRODUCTION: *National Gallery Illustrations, Continental Schools (excluding Italian)*, 1950, p. 308, bottom.

REFERENCES: *General:* J. Smith, *A Catalogue Raisonné* etc., 1830, II, no. 524; J. Rooses, *L'Œuvre de P. P. Rubens*, 1890, IV, no. 827[1]; R. Oldenbourg, *Rubens K. der K.*, [1921], note to p. 428.

In text: (1) Two areas were cleaned in 1947 for the *Cleaned Pictures Exhibition*, The National Gallery, 1947/8. Cleaning was completed in 1949. (2) See for instance previous National Gallery catalogues and the authors quoted under *General References*. No record of the commission has so far been discovered; according to Baldinucci, the Pitti picture was executed by Rubens for Suttermans, and was thence obtained by the Archduke Ferdinand (for whom see under no. 89), see F. Baldinucci, *Notizie dei Professori del Disegno* etc., ed. F. Ranalli, 1846, 4, p. 492. (3) The presence of the drawing of *The Three Graces* was first noted by J. S. Held, *Rubens Selected Drawings*, I, 1959, p. 15, note 2. (4) The *modello* could have been the picture in the Pieter Leender [*sic*] de Neufville collection 1752 (whose sale of 1765 is Lugt, no. 1470): 'Een zinnebeeld door dezelve [= Rubens] verbeeldende de Mizerien van den Oorlog daar Mars te Veld trekt en al de Konste vertreeden werd & die de aarde beweent, 2 v. 7 d. × 3 v. 8½ d.,' see G. Hoet, *Catalogus* etc., 1752, II, p. 513; or the picture in the Anon. and Charles Oglivie sale, Christie's, 7 March (= 2nd day), 1778 (82) 'Mars destroying the arts and sciences, is prevented by Venus, a *finished model* for the great picture in the Florentine Collection'.

(5) See M. Rooses & Ch. Ruelens (†), *Correspondance de Rubens* etc., 1909, VI, pp. 209–10. (6) Not previously used by Rubens in this sense, see for instance, Rooses, *op. cit.*, 1892, V, nos. 1276, 1281, and 1287; but see G. de Tervarent, *Attributs et Symboles dans l'Art Profane* etc., 1958, col. 130. (7) Held has drawn attention to the connection with emblem 190 in Otho van Veen's *Horatiana Emblemata*, see, I, Jost, *Netherlands Yearbook for the History of Art*, 1964, pp. 213–14, and note 98; the connection is not close. (8) For best discussion, see Held, *op. cit.*, under no. 66. (9) Reproduced by Held, *op. cit.*, fig. 4. (10) For which, see Held, *op. cit.*, no. 66; and L. Burchard and R. A. d'Hulst, *Rubens Drawing*, 1963, no. 169. (11) See *Paintings by Old Masters*, Colnaghi, 1963, no. 13 and plate IX. (12) *Loc. cit.* (13) Reproduced by Oldenbourg, *op. cit.*, p. 254. The theme was taken up again in a sketch, given to Rubens, exhibited in *Olieverschetsen van Rubens*, Rotterdam, 1953 (no. 71) and reproduced in the catalogue, pl. 60, where dated 1625–28. (14) Reproduced by Oldenbourg, *op. cit.*, p. 372. (15) Compare the soldier in the centre of a copy, retouched by Rubens, after Polidoro in the Louvre, for which see F. Lugt, *Musée du Louvre, Inventaire Général des Dessins* etc., II, 1949, no. 1074 and pl. XLV. (16) See under no. 59 (17) Reproduced by Oldenbourg, *op. cit.*, p. 378. (18) Ex Sir Harold Wernher sale, Christie's, 8 December, 1950 (65). (19) Exhibited *Esquisses de Rubens*, Brussels, 1937 (48); see also M. Rooses, *L'Œuvre de P. P. Rubens*, 1890, IV, under no. 827[1], where stated to be ex colls. Calvière, Dubois and Brulé, and described as a 'seconde exemplaire' of no. 279. (20) Perhaps identical with the picture in an Anon. sale, Christie's, 4 August, 1944 (68), 16 × 25 (0·406 × 0·635), where stated to be ex coll. Lord Northwick, and thus probably in the Lord Northwick sale, 26 July (= 18th day), 1859 (1814). (21) See W. Buchanan, *Memoirs of Painting*, II, 1824, p. 129. In the same collection was a *S. Jerome* by Garofalo and a sketch by Reni for his *Holy Trinity* in S. Trinità dei Pellegrini, Rome. The British Institution list of 1832 and the Rogers sale catalogue (see above) both state that no. 279 came from the Palazzo Balbi; but there seems to be no good reason for believing this. (21) See Buchanan, *op. cit.*, pp. 133 and 135. No. 279 and a sketch by 'Guido' from the same collection cost '8,000 livres or nearly £285 sterling'. (23) As 'The Horrors of War'. The National gallery copy of the sale catalogue is unmarked. (24) 'The Horrors of War; a most spirited Sketch for the great picture in the Louvre'. The Pitti picture was exhibited in the Louvre from 1801–15, see Mlle M.-L. Blumer, *Bulletin de la Société de l'Histoire de l'Art Français*, 1936, p. 330, no. 445. The National Gallery copy of the sale catalogue is unmarked. If no. 279 did appear in these two sales, Parke was presumably acting unsuccessfully for Champernowne. (25) The list described Champernowne's picture simply as 'An Allegory'. It is not recorded at Champernowne's house, Dartington Hall, in 1809 see J. Britton and E. W. Brayley, *The Beauties of England & Wales* etc., 1809, IV, p. 120, but was there sometime post 1805/6, according to notes from a typescript kindly communicated by Miss Mary Spender, a relative of Champernowne, in 1954. (26) As 'The Horrors of War, cabinet size, very spirited and fine'. The price is marked in the National Gallery copy of the sale catalogue; the buyer's name is given in a typescript copy kindly communicated by Miss Mary Spender. Thomas Stothard (1755–1834), painted for Rogers *Peace came upon Earth*, oil on canvas, 20 × 30 (0·50 × 0·76), Tate Gallery, no. 2219, as a companion piece to no. 279, see *Tate Gallery, Catalogue British School*, 1936–37.

MARTEN RIJCKAERT
1587–1631

Landscape painter. Born in Antwerp, the son of the painter David Rijckaert I,[1] on 8 December, 1587.[2] Not listed as a pupil in the Antwerp

guild of S. Luke; he was probably taught by his father. It has been
suggested that he was also taught by Tobias Verhaecht and that he
visited Italy.[3] He was admitted as a master (as one of the 'meester-
sonnen') in the Antwerp guild of S. Luke in 1611.[4] By this time
Rijckaert had lost one arm.[5] He died in Antwerp on 28 October, 1631.[6]

Van Dyck's portrait of Rijckaert was etched for the *Iconography* by
Jacob Neeffs with the inscription: 'Martinus Rychart, Uninamus,
Pictor Ruralium Prospectuum Antverpiae'.[7]

Various spellings of his name are given in the records of the guild
of S. Luke;[8] that used here is de Bie's.[9]

REFERENCES: *In text:* (1) See C. de Bie, *Het Gulden Cabinet* etc., 1661, p. 413.
(2) See, for instance, Th. van Lerius, *Catalogue du Musée d'Anvers*, 1874,
(3rd ed.), p. 322. (3) See, for instance, F. J. van den Branden, *Geschiedenis der
Antwerpsche Schilderschool*, 1883, p. 604. For his supposed relations with
Verhaecht and his journey to Italy, see van Lerius, *op. cit.*, pp. 322–23. (4) See
Ph. Rombouts and Th. van Lerius, *De Liggeren* etc., [1864–76], I, p. 476.
(5) See note 4. (6) See van den Branden, *op. cit.*, p. 605. His mortuary debt was
paid in the year 1631–2, see Rombouts and van Lerius, *op. cit.*, II, p. 32. (7) See
Fr. Wibiral, *L'Iconographie d'Antoine van Dyck*, 1877, p. 119, no. 113. (8) See
Rombouts and van Lerius, *op. cit.*, I, pp. 476 ff., and II, pp. 17 and 32. (9) *Loc.
cit.*

Ascribed to MARTEN RIJCKAERT

1353 LANDSCAPE WITH SATYRS

Oil on oak, $4\frac{1}{16} \times 8$ (0·103 × 0·204).

There is a slit in the support in the top left corner, running just
beneath and parallel to the top edge.

In good condition. There are some very small losses round the edges.

No. 1353 has been attributed to Marten Rijckaert at least since it
entered the collection,[1] and more recently has been accepted as his work
by Bernt.[2] No. 1353 seems to be comparable with the two panels at
Weimar, one of which is signed in monogram and dated 1626.[3] But as
Rijckaert's œuvre is ill defined, it seems best to catalogue no. 1353 as
ascribed to him.

MacLaren[4] has suggested that no. 1353 may originally have been
part of the decoration of a cabinet,[5] thus perhaps explaining the slit
in the support, which is not chamfered.

No. 1353 shows connections with the work of Paul Bril.

PROVENANCE: Anon. [= Mrs. Edgar Disney],[6] sale, Christie's, 3 May, 1884
(110)[7] bt. Cooper for 2 guineas;[8] Richard W. Cooper Bequest, 1892; lent,
through the Arts Council, to Cannon Hall, Barnsley, 1958–63.

REPRODUCTION: *National Gallery Illustrations, Continental Schools (excluding
Italian)*, 1950, p. 330, bottom.

REFERENCES: *In text:* (1) See previous National Gallery catalogues and under
Provenance. On the reverse of no. 1353 is an inscription in ink: *1624. MAER-
KERT* [*sic*]. (2) See W. Bernt, *Die Niederländischen Maler des 17. Jahrhunderts*,
1948–1960, III, no. 710. (3) Both on panel, *ca.* $4\frac{1}{8} \times 10$ (0·105 × 0·25), Weimar,
Staatl. Kunstsammlungen (Schloss), inv. nos. G. 1161 and 1162; photos. in

R. K. D. (4) Ms. notes. (5) Such a cabinet, attributed to Rijckaert, was exh. *Paysage Flamand*, Musée Royal des Beaux-Arts de Belgique, Brussels, 1926 (254), as MacLaren noted. (6) Marked catalogue in the National Gallery library. Christie's stencil mark is on the reverse of no. 1353. (7) as by M. Ryckert [*sic*]. (8) See note 6.

Philippus van SANTVOORT

active from *ca.* 1718

Figure painter. Recorded as the pupil of G. J. van Opstal I in the list of the Antwerp guild of S. Luke for the year 1711/12.[1] Bode has published a picture apparently signed and dated 1718; he assumes from the picture that Santvoort had made a journey to Poland.[2] He became a master in the Antwerp guild of S. Luke in the year 1720/21.[3]

Various spellings of his name occur.[4]

REFERENCES: *In text:* (1) See Ph. Rombouts and Th. van Lerius, *De Liggeren* etc. [1864–1876], II, pp. 676 & 678. (2) See W. van Bode, *Zeitschrift für bildende Kunst*, 1924/5, pp. 149–152. (3) See Rombouts and van Lerius, *op. cit.,* pp. 721–22. (4) See, for instance, notes 1 and 3, and under no. 3404.

3404 THE RAPE OF TAMAR BY AMNON

Oil on oak, $23\frac{9}{16} \times 19\frac{7}{16}$ (0·598 × 0·494).

Signed, *P V: Santvoirt*(?). *fc*(?): *17*(?) (.) (.) (PV and fc(?) in monogram).

Probably in fairly good condition. A thick, discoloured varnish obscures the paint. The flesh may be worn and retouched, and there are some small, scattered losses. The last two letters of the signature are damaged: but enough remains of the last letter to read it as a 't'; the last three digits of the date are damaged; a downstroke only remains of the second digit, which makes it seem likely that it was a '7'. The drapery over Tamar's left breast seems to be a later addition.

For the subject, see II Samuel, XIII, 1–14.

In the 1920–1929 catalogues the signature was read as J. van Santvoirt or Santvoort, and no. 3404 was catalogued as by the Dutch sculptor, Jan van Santvoort, active in Scotland, *ca.* 1688 (*sic*?). The reading of the signature is due to MacLaren;[1] he noted other examples of Santvoort signing his surname in the same way.[2]

The subject was thought to be *Judith and Holofernes*, until Pigler identified it correctly in 1939.[3]

A picture of the same subject by Herman van der Myn (1684–1741)[4] is very similar to no. 3404 in composition, and it is possible, as MacLaren has suggested,[5] that both were inspired by a common source.

PROVENANCE: Presented by Augustine Sargent, 1919.

REPRODUCTION: *National Gallery Illustrations, Continental Schools* (*excluding Italian*), 1950, p. 333, left.

REFERENCES: *In text:* (1) See N. MacLaren, *National Gallery Catalogues, The Dutch School*, 1960, index 2. (2) That is the 2 pictures in an Anon.

sale, Christie's, 6 April, 1955 (142), and the picture in an Anon. sale, Christie's, 2 April, 1954 (49). (3) See A. Pigler, *The Art Bulletin*, 1939, p. 230. For other renderings of the subject see A. Pigler, *Barockthemen*, I, 1956, pp. 154–5. (4) In the L.B [loch] of Vienna sale, Amsterdam, 14 November, 1905 (48) rep. in the sale catalogue; see also J. B. Descamps, *La Vie des Peintres Flamands* etc., 1763, IV, p. 246. (5) Ms. notes.

JOANNES SIBERECHTS
1627–1700 or *ca.* 1703

Landscape painter, active in Antwerp and England, where he died. He was born in Antwerp and baptized there on 29 January, 1627.[1] His father was a sculptor[2]; it is not known who Siberechts' master was.[3] He is recorded as a master in the Antwerp guild of S. Luke in the list for the year 1648/9.[4] It has been suggested that he may previously have visited Italy.[5] He remained in Antwerp, where he married in 1652,[6] until at least 1672.[7] He may have settled in England in this year[8]; he was there certainly by 1676.[9] In 1687 he is known to have been living in London,[10] but identifiable views of English country houses, show that he travelled widely.[11] Buckeridge stated in 1706 that Siberechts had died 'about three years ago in London . . . being seventy-three years old'.[12] The two statements do not tally, as Siberechts would have been 73 in 1700.

In Antwerp he concentrated on landscapes staffed with peasants; in England he also executed a number of topographical views especially of houses[13]; a religious picture and an interior scene by him are also extant.[14]

Vertue records that his portrait was painted by Largillierre.[15]

REFERENCE: *General:* T.-H. Fokker, *Jan Siberechts* etc., 1931.

In text: (1) See Th. van Lerius, *Catalogue du Musée d'Anvers*, 1874, (3rd ed.), p. 339. (2) *Ibid.* (3) See Fokker, cited under *General Reference*, pp. 7–8. (4) See Ph. Rombouts and Th. van Lerius, *De Liggeren* etc. [1864–76], II, pp. 197 and 201. (5) See Fokker, *op. cit.*, pp. 8–10. There is no documentary evidence for this. (6) See van Lerius, *loc. cit.* (7) See F. J. van den Branden, *Geschiedenis der Antwerpsche Schilderschool*, 1883, p. 1065. (8) B. Buckeridge, *An Essay towards an English School of Painters* in Roger de Piles, *The Art of Painting*, trans. R. Graham, (2nd ed.: 1st ed. 1706), p. 416, stated that the Duke of Buckingham brought him over to England having seen several of his works in Antwerp on his return from his embassy to Paris. In fact Buckingham's embassy to Paris took place in 1670; but he was in Antwerp in July, 1672, after treating with William of Orange and Louis XIV in the Netherlands, see *Calendar of State Papers, Venetian* etc., *1671–1672*, ed. A. B. Hinds, 1939, XXXVII, p. 261. Fokker, *op. cit.*, pp. 10, and 104–5, assumes, probably rightly, that the picture at Squerryes Court of 1674 was painted in England. (9) A *View of Longleat* (Coll. Ministry of Public Building and Works) is signed and dated 1676. (10) See van den Branden, *loc. cit.* (11) See Fokker, *op. cit.*, pp. 78, 85–6, 97–9, & 100. (12) *Loc. cit.* He also states that he was buried in 'St. James's Church'; but Fokker, *op. cit.*, p. 11, states that his name does not feature in any burial register of a church by that name in London between 1695–1704. (13) See Fokker, *op. cit.*, pp. 13 ff. (14) *Ibid.*, pp. 80 & 91. (15) See Vertue Note Books, *The Walpole Society*, XXIV, 1935–36, p. 110.

**2130 A COWHERD PASSING A HORSE AND CART
     IN A STREAM**

Oil on relined canvas, *ca.* $25\frac{1}{8} \times 23\frac{3}{8}$ (0·638 × 0·543).
There are additions to the top of *ca.* $\frac{9}{16}$ (0·015) and to the bottom of *ca.* $\frac{3}{4}$ (0·02).
Signed and dated, *J. Siberechts·A·anuers·165*(?)*8*(?).
Generally in good condition. There are some retouchings in the cart and sky. The signature inscription and date are much worn—especially the last two digits of the date. The blue of the cowherd's bonnet is diseased.

No. 2130 is signed by Siberechts (albeit faintly) and is accepted as his work by Fokker[1]; there is no reason to doubt this traditional attribution.[2]

The date has been read as 1665[3]; but although the last two digits are much, if not quite totally, worn away, it can be said that what remains does not support this. That no. 2130 was executed at Antwerp provides a *terminus ante quem* of *ca.* 1672–76, by which last year Siberechts was certainly in England.[4] The reading of the date as 1658 is only very tentatively advanced here.

The cowherd is repeated in a picture bearing Siberechts' signature on the London art market, 1954,[5] and is a variation of that in the picture at Antwerp of 1661[6]; the pose is also to be connected with that of the younger cowherd in the pictures at Hanover of 1664,[9] Budapest of 1667[8] and on the London art market, 1967, of 1662.[9] The landscape is not dissimilar from that in the Cook collection picture of 1690 (?).[10]

PROVENANCE: Dr. Franck (†) sale, Christie's, 25 March, 1843 (70) bt. Farrant for £18 7sh. 6d.[11]; Anon. [= Miss Farrant][12] sale, Christie's, 5 March, 1853 (10) bt. Seguier for £13 12sh. 6d.[13]; F. P. Seguier (†)[14] sale, Christie's, 7 February, 1903 (87) bt. Colnaghi for £58 5sh.[15] Presented by John P. Heseltine, 1907; lent, through the Arts Council, to the Graves Art Gallery, Sheffield, 1951–56; and to the Rhodes National Gallery, Salisbury, Rhodesia, 1959–60.

REPRODUCTION: *National Gallery Illustrations, Continental Schools (excluding Italian)*, 1950, p. 338, left.

REFERENCE: *General:* T.-H. Fokker, *Jan Siberechts* etc., 1931, pp. 96–97, and pl. 10.

In text: (1) See under *General Reference*. (2) See under *Provenance*; and National Gallery catalogues from 1908. (3) By Fokker, *op. cit.*, in the rubric to his plate 10; on p. 96 he reads the inscription and date as '...A..ers.t 16.5.'; no inscription or date is given in previous Gallery catalogues. (4) See above under the biography of Siberechts. (5) 47 × 41 (1·194 × 1·041), Anon. sale, Sotheby's, 10 November, 1954 (117), ex Lord Biddulph sale, Sotheby's, 12 May, 1954 (53). (6) See Fokker, *op. cit.*, p. 80, and pl. 5. (7) See Fokker, *op. cit.*, p. 94 and pl. 7A. (8) See Fokker, *op. cit.*, p. 90, and pl. 7b. (9) Anon. sale, Sotheby's, 19 April, 1967 (14); this picture is Fokker, *op. cit.*, p. 84, and pl. 23. (10) See J. O. Kronig, *A Catalogue of the Paintings in the Collection of Sir Frederick Cook, Bart.*, 1904, II, no. 356 as '1694 or 1690'; and Fokker, *op. cit.*, p. 103, as 1690. (11) Buyer and price in Christie's marked catalogue. (12) Identity of vendor in Christie's marked catalogue. (13) Buyer and price in Christie's marked catalogue. (14) As 'Mostly collected by John Seguier ...' (15) Buyer and price in the National Gallery marked copy of the sale catalogue.

Frans SNIJDERS
1579–1657

Painter of animals, hunts and still life. Active in Antwerp, where he was baptized on 11 November, 1579.[1] He is recorded as the pupil of Peeter Brueghel II in the list of the Antwerp guild of S. Luke for 1593.[2] In 1649 it was stated that he had been the pupil of Hendrick van Balen I (q.v.).[3] He became a master in the guild of S. Luke, Antwerp, in 1602.[4] He travelled to Italy; on 26 September, 1608, Jan Brueghel I wrote from Antwerp to Bianchi in Milan that Snijders was leaving Rome for Milan, stating that he wished Snijders to stay the winter in Milan, and asking that he should be lent some money.[5] Snijders was thus to receive there the patronage of Cardinal Archbishop Borromeo. He had returned to Antwerp by the 4 July, 1609.[6] He married Margaretha, the sister of Cornelis and Paul de Vos, in Antwerp on 23 October, 1611.[7] In 1619 he was made a member of the guild of Romanists, and was elected Dean in 1629.[8] The following year he executed a picture for the City of Antwerp;[9] in 1636/7 he executed a series of pictures for Philip IV of Spain;[10] in 1649 it was stated that he had also worked for the Archduke Leopold-Wilhelm.[11] He died on 19 August, 1657.[12]

Snijders is known to have collaborated with Rubens,[13] who appointed him as one of his executors responsible for the sale of his collection after his death.[14] He also collaborated with other figure painters.[15]

His portrait was painted by van Dyck;[16] it was also etched by him for the *Iconography*; a subsequent state of the print is inscribed: 'Franciscus Snyders, Venationum, Ferarum, Fructuum, et Olerum Pictor Antverpiae'.[17]

Both his christian name and surname seem to have been variously spelt in contemporary documents.[18]

REFERENCES: *In text:* (1) See Th. van Lerius, *Catalogue du Musée d'Anvers*, 1874 (3rd ed.), p. 357. (2) See Ph. Rombouts and Th. van Lerius, *De Liggeren* etc., [1864–1876], I, p. 373. (3) See the inscription beneath his engraved portrait by J. Meyssens after van Dyck, in J. Meyssens, *Images de Divers Hommes d'esprit Sublime* etc., 1649. (4) See Rombouts and van Lerius, *op. cit.*, p. 418. (5) See G. Crivelli, *Giovanni Brueghel* etc., 1868, pp. 110–113. (6) See Crivelli, *op. cit.*, pp. 139–40. (7) See van Lerius, *loc. cit.* (8) *Ibid.* (9) See F. J. van den Branden, *Geschiedenis der Antwerpsche Schilderschool*, 1883, p. 675, note 1. (10) See M. Rooses and Ch. Ruelens (†), *Correspondance de P. P. Rubens*, 1909, VI, pp. 170 ff. (11) See note 3. In the inventory of the Archduke Leopold-Wilhelm is recorded a work executed in collaboration with C. de Vos, see *Jahrbuch der Kunsthistorischen Sammlungen des allerhöchsten Kaiserhauses*, 1883, supplement, p. CXXII; and *Kunsthistorisches Museum, Wien, Katalog der Gemäldegalerie*, 1963, p. 126, no. 357. The Archduchess Isabella († 1633) also probably owned a picture executed in collaboration with Rubens, see M. de Maeyer, *Albrecht en Isabella en de Schilderkunst*, 1955, pp. 171 and 413. (12) See van Lerius, *loc. cit.* (13) See the first item in the list of paintings, drawn up by Rubens, which were available for sale to Sir Dudley Carleton on 28 April, 1618, printed by Rooses and Ruelens (†), *op. cit.*, 1898, II, p. 136; and under note 11. (14) See M. Rooses, *Rubens*, trans. by H. Child, II, 1904, p. 622. (15) See, for instance, A. von. Wurzbach, *Niederländisches Künstler-Lexikon*, 1910, II, p. 634; and under note 11. (16) See G. Glück, *Van Dyck, K. der K.*, (1931), pp. 97–99. (17) See Fr. Wibiral, *L'Iconographie d'Antoine van Dyck*, 1877, pp. 61–2, no. 11. (18) Rombouts and van Lerius, *op. cit.*, *passim*; and for instance, references in notes 3, 5, 9 and 15.

See STUDIO OF RUBENS, no. 853

Follower of FRANS SNIJDERS

1252 STILL LIFE OF FRUIT AND VEGETABLES WITH TWO MONKEYS

Oil on relined canvas, $40\frac{1}{2} \times 53\frac{5}{16}$ ($1 \cdot 029 \times 1 \cdot 355$).

In fair condition. Two tears in the canvas are retouched; varying degrees of wearing overall, much of which is retouched. Cleaned, 1955.

No. 1252 was accepted as the work of Frans Snijders from at least the time it entered the collection until the 1958 *Summary Catalogue*, where it was catalogued as ascribed to him.[1]

In fact the status of no. 1252 is confused, for while the composition seems clearly to derive from Snijders,[2] the manner of execution seems to owe something to Fyt.[3] No. 1252 is probably acceptable as a work painted in the second half of the seventeenth century, but the quality of execution is not high.[4] It is possible that it is a copy after a lost work by Snijders, or rather that it is by an artist working in his style.

PROVENANCE: B. R. Haydon (1786–1846) sale, Crook (London), 11 June, 1823 (127) perhaps bt. Decimus Burton (1800–81);[5] certainly his coll. by 1875 when exh. at the R.A. (224);[6] by the wish of Decimus Burton, presented by his niece, Miss Emily Jane Wood, 1888; lent to the Ministry of Works (now Public Building and Works) 1938–41.

REPRODUCTION: *National Gallery Illustrations, Continental Schools (excluding Italian)*, 1950, p. 339, top.

REFERENCES: *In text:* (1) E. Greindl, *Les Peintres Flamands de la Nature Morte au XVIIᵉ Siècle*, 1956, p. 184, lists no. 1252 among the pictures attributed to Snijders. (2) The pose of the main monkey occurs in *The Table* (Prado, *Catálogo de las Pinturas*, 1963, no. 1767) and in other works associated with Snijders. (3) Compare the rendering of the still life in the signed *Flowers and Fruit in a Landscape* (Brussels, Musées Royaux des Beaux-Arts, *Catalogue de la Peinture Ancienne*, 1957, p. 45, no. 179). (4) It is not clear for instance whether the main still life is on a table; and the area immediately beneath is to all intents illegible. (5) According to MacLaren, ms. notes, an old label on the reverse of no. 1252 stated: 'bought at B. R. Haydon's sale 9 [*sic*] June 1823.' The entry in the copies of the sale catalogue in the British Museum (no other (marked) copies are recorded by Lugt), runs: 'Fine painting of Fruit with monkey, by Caravaggio and Encyare [*sic*]'. A label removed from the old re-lining canvas in 1963 reads: *Fruit Piece with a Monkey | Michael Amerigi Angelo | born at Caravaggio | 1569 | Francis Snyders | born at Antwerp | ...*'. For B. R. Haydon, see *The Autobiography . . . of Benjamin Robert Haydon*, ed. by T. Taylor, 1926. The sale is not mentioned there, but took place when Haydon was in prison for debt, see Taylor, *op. cit.*, pp. 332–338. For Decimus Burton see the entry in the DNB. (6) As by Snijders.

Peeter SNIJERS
1681–1752

Landscape, still life and portrait painter. Active in Antwerp, where he was born 30 March, 1681.[1] Recorded as the pupil of Alexander van Bredael in the list of the guild of S. Luke, Antwerp, for the year 1694/95,[2] and as a master of the guild in 1707/8.[3] He married in 1726[4]; and in 1741 became one of the directors of the Académie Royale, Antwerp.[5] He died on 4 May, 1752.[6] He had a collection of pictures, which was sold after his death.[7]

REFERENCES: *In text:* (1) See Th. van Lerius, *Catalogue du Musée d'Anvers*, 1874 (3rd ed.), p. 357. (2) See Ph. Rombouts and Th. van Lerius, *De Liggeren* etc., [1864–1876], II, p. 575. (3) *Ibid.*, p. 654. (4) See van Lerius, *op. cit.*, p. 359. (5) *Ibid.* (6) *Ibid.* (7) See G. Hoet, *Catalogus* etc., 1770, III, pp. 61–65, and pp. 349–353.

1401 A STILL LIFE WITH FRUIT, VEGETABLES, DEAD CHICKENS AND A LOBSTER

Oil on relined canvas, $46\frac{3}{4} \times 39\frac{1}{4}$ ($1 \cdot 188 \times 0 \cdot 997$).

Signed, *P: Snijers*

Generally in good condition. There are a few scattered losses, some not retouched; some of the artichoke leaves in the top right are worn.

No. 1401 bears Snijers' signature, and there is no reason to doubt its authenticity.

There are not enough known dated works by Snijers to make it possible to propose a date for his execution of no. 1401.

PROVENANCE: Bought from Mr. Richard Stephens for £175 in 1894[1]; on loan to the Royal Family, 1930–54.

REPRODUCTION: *National Gallery Illustrations, Continental Schools* (*excluding Italian*), 1950, p. 339, bottom.

REFERENCE: *In text:* (1) The provenance was incorrectly given in the 1929 and 1958 catalogues.

Hendrick van STEENWYCK II
active by 1604–died 1649

Painter of church interiors and architectural scenes. According to van Mander, the son of Henrick van Steenwyck I.[1] Hendrick van Steenwyck I was enrolled in the Antwerp guild of S. Luke in 1577[2]; according to van Mander, he fled the Netherlands and settled finally at Frankfurt[3]; where he was certainly in 1588[4] and where van Mander thought he died in 1603.[5] He may have returned to Antwerp in the intervening period.[6] The date and place of birth of his son are not known. Van Mander speaks of his son as already active in 1604[7]; from van Mander's description of his art[8] may be inferred that he was taught by his father, which is borne out by close connections in style.[9] A painting by Hendrick van Steenwyck of 'una cheisa al u sante de questa paieso' bought by

Jan Brueghel I by 6 March, 1609,[10] and the influence of Hendrick van Steenwyck II's work on Peeter Neeffs (*q.v.*)[11] may be taken as a slight, but unsatisfactory indication that suggests that he may have been in the southern Netherlands perhaps not for the first time[12] soon after his father's death.

Hendrick van Steenwyck II had settled in London by 15 November 1617[13]; he probably remained there until after 1637.[14] By 1645 he had settled in the northern Netherlands.[15] On 17 November, 1649, his widow (also a painter) was recorded as living in Leyden[16]; there is recorded a signed and dated picture by him of 1649 at Berlin.[17] It thus seems established that Steenwyck died in 1649, probably in the northern Netherlands.[18]

His portrait by van Dyck was engraved for the *Iconography*.[19]

He spelt his name in several ways when signing his pictures: Henri van Steinwick; Henderich v: Steenwick; H. Steenwyck, etc.[20]

REFERENCES: *In text:* (1) See C. van Mander, *Het Schilder-Boeck* etc., 1604, p. 261, *verso*. (2) See Ph. Rombouts and Th. van Lerius, *De Liggeren* etc., [1864–1876], I, p. 263. (3) See van Mander, *loc. cit.* (4) See the inscription on the picture at Dessau, which is signed and dated: 'A Franckfort An. 1588', reference from A. von Wurzbach, *Niederländisches Künstler-Lexikon*, 1910, II, p. 660. (5) *Loc. cit.* (6) See H. Jantzen, *Das Niederländisches Architecturbild*, 1910, p. 43. (7) *Loc. cit.* (8) *Ibid.* (9) See Jantzen, *op. cit.*, pp. 33–4. (10) See G. Crivelli, *Giovanni Brueghel* etc., 1868, p. 119; the picture may well, however, have been by the father, see under no. 1443, note 3. (11) See Jantzen, *op. cit.*, pp. 40–43. (12) On the assumption that he returned to Antwerp with his father *ca.* 1590–1600, *pace* Jantzen, see note 6. (13) See the evidence given in Amsterdam on this date, concerning the sale of two of his pictures, printed by A. Bredius, *Künstler-Inventare* etc., 1921, 7, pp. 166–7. For some evidence concerning his activity in England, see *Abraham van der Doort's Catalogue of the Collection of Charles I*, printed by O. Millar, *The Walpole Society*, 1958–60. (14) Jantzen, *op. cit.*, p. 38, notes a picture of Charles I in a vaulted hall, signed and dated by Steenwyck, 1637; see also, for instance, the *Katalog der Staatliche Gemälde Galerie zu Dresden*, 1930, p. 203, no. 1187. This seems to be his last dated work executed in England. (15) In the 1645 edition of van Dyck's *Iconography*, he is described as 'Pictor Architectonices Hagae Comitis', see Fr. Wibiral, *L'Iconographie d'Antoine van Dyck*, 1877, p. 96, no. 67; for the date of Hendrick's edition, see pp. 14–15. (16) See for instance, Wurzbach, *op. cit.*, 1910, II, p. 661 (under Susanna van Steenwyck). (17) See, for instance, Wurzbach, *op. cit.*, p. 660, not listed in the post-war Museum Dahlem catalogues. (18) There seems to be no evidence that he died in London as is often suggested. Jantzen, *op. cit.*, p. 40, believes the picture at Brunswick, to be falsely signed and dated: 'H.V.S. 1653'. (19) See under note 15. (20) Wurzbach, *op. cit.*, pp. 660–61; and below.

141 A MAN KNEELS BEFORE A WOMAN IN THE COURTYARD OF A RENAISSANCE PALACE

Oil on copper, $15\frac{13}{16} \times 27\frac{1}{2}$ (0·402 × 0·698).

Signed and dated, *H·V·STEINWY(?)CK·1610·*

In fair condition. The architecture is fairly well preserved despite many small, scattered losses, not all of which have been retouched. The figures are worn and/or retouched. Some original paint goes over an incised line that runs parallel to and about $\frac{3}{16}$ (0·005) from the right-hand edge.

There is no reason to doubt that the architecture, landscape and sky is the work of Hendrick van Steenwyck II.[1] The figures are clearly by another hand, once considered to be that of 'Pourbus'.[2] They seem to be executed in a style somewhat reminiscent of Cornelis van Poelenburgh, but their poor state makes it impossible to suggest an attribution for them.

The architecture may have been inspired by a design by Hans Vredeman de Vries.[3] The subject of no. 141 has long[4] been thought to be *Aeneas in the Palace of Dido*, but there is nothing conclusive to justify this.

VARIANT: The Hermitage, Leningrad, copper, $21\frac{7}{16} \times 31\frac{1}{2}$ (0·545 × 0·80), signed and dated 1623.[5]

COPY: With Old Masters Galleries Ltd., 1951, copper 15 × 27 (0·381 × 0·686).

PROVENANCE: Probably Philip van Dijk (1680–1753) sale, The Hague, 13 June, 1753 (52) bt. in 270 glds.[6]; widow of Philip van Dijk sale, The Hague, 26 November, 1763 (4) sold for 260 glds.[7] Coll. William Beckford (1759–1844), Fonthill Abbey, by 1822[8]; Fonthill Abbey sale, Christie's (at Fonthill), 15 October (= 7th day), 1822 (39)[9] bt. with the rest of the estate by John Farquhar (1751–1826)[10]; Fonthill Abbey sale, Phillips (at Fonthill), 10 October [= 24th day], 1823 (66). Lieutenant-Colonel John Harvey Ollney Bequest, 1837; lent to the National Gallery of Ireland from 1862–1926, and to the Corporation Art Gallery and Museum, Bradford, 1931.

REPRODUCTION: *National Gallery Illustrations, Continental Schools (excluding Italian)*, 1950, p. 347, bottom.

REFERENCES: *In text:* (1) First correctly ascribed in the 1915 National Gallery catalogue, before which (until 1862 when it no longer featured, see under *Provenance*) it was considered to be by Hendrick van Steenwyck I. (2) See below under *Provenance*; and note 8. (3) Compare the four pictures at Vienna, two of which are dated 1596, see E.R.V. Engerth, *Kunsthistorische Sammlungen des allerhöchsten Kaiserhauses, Gemälde ... Verzeichniss*, 1884, II, nos. 1376–9. (4) See the Beckford catalogues below and previous National Gallery catalogues. (5) See *Musée de L'Ermitage, Département de l'Art Occidental, Catalogue des Peintures*, 1958, p. 101, no. 432. The figures are by a different hand, and there are differences in the architecture. The architecture in no. 141 is comparable to that in the picture of 1614 by Steenwyck II in the Mauritshuis (no. 171). (6) G. Hoet, *Catalogus* etc., 1770, III, p. 72: 'Een extra fraay Stuk met Romeynse Gebouwen, verwonderlyk uitvoerig en kunstig in perspectif geschildert, met Figuuren, door *Hendrick van Steenwyck* Ao. 1610, op *Koper* ... hoog I *voet* $2\frac{1}{2}$ *dium*, breet 2 *voet* $2\frac{1}{2}$ *dium*'. (7) See G. Hoet, *op. cit.*, p. 354, where stated to have been in the 1753 sale and where an abbreviated, description was used. (8) See J. Rutter, *A Description of Fonthill Abbey* etc., 1822 (2nd ed.), p. 51: 'The Court Yard of a Palace by Steenwyck with figures representing the Interview between Dido and Aeneas, by Pourbus'. (9) As ex coll. the Prince of Hesse Cassel. This claim is not correct, as Dr. Lahusen of the Staatliche Kunstsammlungen, Cassel, has kindly pointed out. The confusion may have arisen from a misreading of Rutter's list, see note 8, in which the picture recorded previously to no. 141 was stated to have this provenance. (10) See, for instance, L. Melville, *The Life and Letters of William Beckford* etc., 1910, pp. 314–15.

4040 INTERIOR OF A GOTHIC CHURCH LOOKING
EAST

Oil on copper, $4\frac{1}{8} \times 6\frac{1}{32}$ (0·105 × 0·153).
The tombstone in the foreground bears the date: *16 09*
In fair condition. There are many, small scattered losses, some re-
touched. The foreground is retouched and the nave of the church is
worn.
There is no reason to doubt that the architecture in no. 4040 is by
Hendrick van Steenwyck II; the figures are very probably by him as
well.
The date on the tombstone—1609—provides a *terminus post quem*
for the date of execution; to judge by the style of the costumes, no. 4040
should date from this year or soon after.
Schwartz[1] has suggested that the scene depicts a wedding.
The church has not been identified.[2]

PROVENANCE: Sir Claude Phillips Bequest, 1924; lent, through the Arts
Council, to the Scarborough Art Gallery, 1952–54.

REPRODUCTION: *National Gallery Illustrations, Continental Schools* (*excluding
Italian*), 1950, p. 349, bottom.

REFERENCES: *In text:* (1) See G. Schwartz, *Simiolus*, 1966–67, p. 85, note
26. (2) A view of a church with a very similar nave, attributed to H. van
Steenwyck II, was with Brian Koetser, London, in the autumn of 1967 (no. 23).

HENDRICK VAN STEENWYCK II

and

JAN BRUEGHEL I

1443 THE INTERIOR OF A GOTHIC CHURCH
LOOKING EAST

A christening party enters on the right; behind, a woman kneels and
two men stand by as a priest performs mass in a side chapel; mourners
sit round a catafalque before the screen in the main aisle; and a group of
ladies leave on the left.
Oil on copper, $14\frac{7}{16} \times 21\frac{5}{8}$ (0·367 × 0·55). The reverse of the support
bears the name *HANS GOYVAERTS* engraved on it.
Signed, on the base of the column in the right foreground, *H·W* |
ST(?)E(?)INWICK:
In fairly good condition. There are a good number of small, scattered
losses especially to the left and round the edges, some of which are
retouched. Some of the vaulting ribs may have been strengthened. The
paint of the wood and/or metal work decorations has grown transparent
with time. The letters of the signature and round the border of the tombstone in the left foreground are worn and some of those in the signature
may not be reliable.
Several *pentimenti* are evident, especially in infra-red photography:
the east wall of the first chapel on the left was first lower and the first

arch on the right was first higher; more, minor alterations in the vaulting ribs and windows towards the east end of the church and in the figures. Infra-red photography also reveals much of the underdrawing, some of which was ruled; this is also visible, here and there, to the naked eye.

The design on the altarpiece in the first chapel on the left has not been continued to the top of its frame.

This altarpiece depicts an *Adoration of the Magi*; that in the next chapel has not been filled in with a design; the subjects of the next three are not sufficiently clearly rendered to be identifiable. The picture on the column in the right foreground shows *The Raising of Lazarus*; not enough shows of the three altarpieces behind it for their subjects to be decipherable. There is a placard bearing a coat of arms on the east wall of the entrance on the right, and one to the right and above *The Raising of Lazarus*, whose frame also includes a coat of arms. There are five coats of arms rendered in stained glass in the window of the chapel on the left. What remains of the inscription on the bottom and right-hand border of the tombstone in the left foreground reads: '*MON COV . . . IOM . . . NFT* | *. . .O YN*'. The tombstone in the foreground, to the right of centre, bears on it the date: *1603*. There may be traces of a date on the tombstone on the right, before the column, which could read: (.) *60*(?)*7*(?).

The lettering of the signature is weak. In spite of this and the rather insipid rendering of the vaulting ribs, there is no reason to doubt that the architecture is by Hendrick van Steenwyck II;[1] and it is likely that the signature is also basically genuine, but damaged and re-touched. The wood or metal work round the first chapel on the left and across the arch leading to the first chapel on the right, the sculpted saints along the aisle, the pulpit, and crucifix above the screen are after-thoughts, probably also by Steenwyck and put in after the altarpieces had been filled in.

The figures are by a different hand; the same hand executed the figures in no. 2204 *q.v.* where some recur.[2] They seem clearly to be the work of Jan Brueghel I; whose activity in this respect is documented by a statement in one of his own letters, written in 1609.[3]

Jantzen took the date 1603 on the tombstone in the foreground, right of centre, to be the date of execution of no. 1443.[4] Leaving aside the possibility that the tombstone on the right in front of the column may have borne the date 1607, the date 1603 can only be taken as a *terminus post quem* for Steenwyck's execution of the architecture. The evolution of his early style remains obscure, but no. 1443 is not as tightly controlled in execution as no. 2204 (*q.v.*) of 1615, or as no. 141 (*q.v.*) of 1610; the handling indeed is similar to that in a picture at Vienna, which according to Engerth is dated 1605.[5] On the other hand, the costumes in nos. 1443 and 2204 are very similar; those in no. 2204 must date from soon after 1615—to judge by the style of the costumes. Thus Steenwyck must have executed no. 1443 after 1603, and before 1615 or even 1610. Jantzen has drawn attention to the relationship between no. 1443 and certain pictures by Hendrick van Steenwyck I,[6] which is a further indication that it is an early work. Steenwyck was never enrolled in the Antwerp guild of S. Luke; it is thus probable that he never worked there for any length of time. Thus a certain passage of time between his completion of the architecture and Brueghel's addition of the figures is quite feasible. The name Hans Goyvaerts, which is engraved on the back of no. 1443, may have been that of the Antwerp art dealer from whom Brueghel bought the picture before adding the figures. He was admitted to the Antwerp guild of S. Luke in 1600 and was probably still alive in 1616 when his wife died.[7]

The identity of the church is not known. The nave is comparable to that in the Vienna picture of 1605; there are some resemblances in architecture and standpoint with that in a picture given to Hendrick van Steenwyck II in the Greve sale of 1909,[8] and more closely so with that in a picture at Dresden of 1609.[9] This suggests that the view in no. 1443 may have been at least partly imaginary.

PROVENANCE: Perhaps coll. the dealer Hans Goyvaerts († after 1616), Antwerp;[10] coll. Jan Brueghel I, Antwerp, ca. 1615. G. A. Morland sale, Christie's, 9 May, 1863 (92)[11] bt. Cox for £34. 13sh.[12] Bequeathed by George Mitchell to the South Kensington (now Victoria and Albert) Museum, 1878; lent to the National Gallery, 1895; lent to the Ministry of Works (now Public Building and Works), 1951; and, through the Arts Council, to Cannon Hall, Barnsley, 1958–63.

REPRODUCTION: *National Gallery Illustrations, Continental Schools (excluding Italian)*, 1950, p. 348, bottom.

REFERENCES: *In text:* (1) No doubts have been raised about his authorship of no. 1443. (2) Some of the figures are also repeated in a picture said to be signed and dated by Neeffs in 1636, see under no. 2204. (3) See G. Crivelli, *Giovanni Brueghel* etc., 1868, p. 119, who prints Brueghel's letter of 6 March, 1609 to Cardinal Borromeo ' . . . Ancho ho comparato un quadrettin de Hendric Van Steenlbyck: una cheisa al u sante de questa paieso ben fatte. Io farra in detto quadret alcun figurini, et comme sone da poca pesa, facilmente potra inuiarle a Vs. Ill.m . . .'. Crivelli identified the picture with that in the Ambrosiana (no. 13, p. 15 of the 1937 catalogue); A. von Wurzbach, *Niederländisches Künstler-Lexikon*, II, 1910, p. 660, states that it is dated 1585; if so, it is thus (probably) the work of the father. This date cannot be seen on a photograph. For comparisons with signed works by Jan Brueghel I, see under no. 2204. (4) See Hans Jantzen, *Das Niederländische Architekturbild*, 1910, p. 33. (5) See E. R. V. Engerth, *Kunsthistorische Sammlungen des allerhöchsten Kaiserhauses, Gemälde . . . Verzeichniss*, 1884, II, p. 401, no. 1273. (6) See Jantzen, *op. cit.*, p. 33. (7) See Ph. Rombouts and Th. van Lerius, *De Liggeren* etc., [1864–76], I, pp. 411 and 532–33. (8) H. B. Greve sale, Lepke (Berlin), 13/14 October, 1909 (68) (rep. in the sale catalogue), copper, ca. 13¾ × 17¼ (0·35 × 0·45); judging from this reproduction, it could be by Hendrick van Steenwyck I. (9) Signed and dated by Steenwyck; see *Picture Gallery Dresden Old Masters*, 1962, p. 98, no. 1184; rep. by Jantzen, *op. cit.*, fig. 9. Jantzen, *op. cit.*, p. 34, calls the Dresden picture a repetition of no. 1443; but it is more than a variant. (10) See above. (11) The Christie's stencil mark for this sale is on the reverse of no. 1443. There are no grounds for identifying no. 1443 with no. 342 of the Beckford sale, 13 October, 1823, as was attempted in the 1929 catalogue. It is possible that no. 1443 was in one or more of the following sales: Petronella dela Court sale, Amsterdam, 19 October, 1707 (35)—as 'Een Binne Kerk, van Steenwyck . . . dor Fluweele Breugel Gestoffert' sold for 430 glds., see G. Hoet, *Catalogus* etc., 1752, I, p. 106; Anon. sale, Amsterdam,

21 October, 1739 (27)—as 'Een voornaame Kerk tot Antwerpen, door Steen-wyck . . . gestoffert door den Fluweelen Breugel, h. l v. 2 en een half d. br. 1 v. 6 en een half d. [=ca. 15⅜ × 19¾]', sold for 100 glds., see Hoet, *op. cit.*, p. 610; Count van Wassenaar Obdam sale, The Hague, 19 August, 1750 (101)—as 'Een Roomsche Kerk, met Beeldjes, door den Fluweelen Breugel, 14 d. × 22 d. [=ca. 15 × 23⅜]' sold for 365 glds., see Hoet, *op. cit.*, II, p. 297, according to C. Blanc, *Le Trésor de la Curiosité*, I, 1857, p. 58, the architecture in this picture was by H. van Steenwyck. (12) See Christie's marked catalogue.

2204   THE INTERIOR OF A GOTHIC CHURCH LOOKING EAST

A christening party enters on the right; behind a priest says mass; a funeral procession enters before the screen and proceeds to the high altar; a group of ladies leave the church on the left.

Oil on copper, $10\frac{1}{16} \times 15\frac{3}{16}$ (0·256 × 0·402).

Signed and dated, *H. V. STEEĪN | 1615*

In good condition. There are some losses round the edges and a few in the centre. A margin is scored $\frac{3}{16}$ (0·005) from the top and ⅛ (0·003) from the right, left and bottom edges.

There are three placards bearing coats of arms in the first column on the right; the altarpiece against the second pillar on the right shows *The Walk to Emmaus*(?); the shutters of the next are closed, and the subject of the fourth altarpiece is not clearly decipherable. The picture hung beneath the placard bearing a coat of arms on the first column on the left depicts *Christ and the Woman of Samaria*.

There is no reason to doubt the signature and date on no. 2204, which is clearly an autograph work by Hendrick van Steenwyck II.[1] The figures are by a different hand, some recur in no. 1443, others in a picture at Budapest[2]; and they seem clearly to be by Jan Brueghel I, being comparable, for instance, with those in the signed *Village by a River* of 1614 at Vienna[3] and the *Travellers in a Landscape* of 1616 in the Wellington Museum, Apsley House.[4] The style of the costumes is also acceptable for the period ca. 1615, and they were no doubt added not long after Steenwyck's execution of the architecture.

The church has not been identified.[5]

The funeral and baptismal processions are repeated with some varia-tion in a *Church Interior*, which is said to be signed by Neeffs and dated 1636.[6]

PROVENANCE: Coll. Jan Brueghel I, Antwerp, ca. 1615.[7] Perhaps in the Reverend Edward Balme (†) sale, Christie's, 1 March, 1823 (73) bt. Crawford for 15 gns.[8] Christopher Beckett Denison (†) sale, Christie's, 6 June, 1885 (84) bt. Brunning for £162 15sh.[9]; Henry Calcott Brunning Bequest, 1907; lent, through the Arts Council, to the Art Gallery, Southampton, 1951–1963.

REPRODUCTION: *National Gallery Illustrations, Continental Schools* (*excluding Italian*), 1950, p. 349, top.

REFERENCES: *In text:* (1) See H. Jantzen, *Das Niederländische Architektur-bild*, 1910, no. 458, p. 170. (2) Where the architecture is by Hendrick van Steenwyck I, signed and dated 1583, see the 1937 catalogue of the Budapest Museum, p. 247, no. 579. (3) See *Kunsthistorisches Museum, Wien, Katalog*

der Gemäldegalerie, II, 1958, p. 23, no. 68. (4) Inventory no. W. M. 1634–
1948. (5) The same church is the subject of a picture at Uppark, ascribed to
H. van Steenwyck, panel, 23¼ × 33½ (0·591 × 0·851). (6) Oak, 26¾ × 34⅝
(0·68 × 0·88), Anon. sale, Lempertz (Cologne), April, 1961 (464), apparently
signed and dated *Petrus Nefs 1636*, rep. in cat. (7) When he added the figures,
see above. (8) As 'Inside of a Church with a Funeral Procession' by Hendrick
van Steenwyck I; buyer and price from Christie's marked catalogue. No. 2204
might be identified with the church interior by Hendrick van Steenwyck, on
copper and measuring 9½ × 15 *duimen*, which was in the Pieter Leendert de
Neufville sale, Amsterdam, 10 June, 1765 (94), see G. Hoet, *Catalogus* etc.,
1770, III, p. 475. (9) Marked catalogue in the National Gallery library.

HENDRICK VAN STEENWYCK I
and a follower of
JAN BRUEGHEL I

1132 CROESUS AND SOLON
Solon converses with King Croesus in his palace at Sardis.
Oil on copper, 12¼ × 9 (0·311 × 0·229).
Generally in good condition. There are some losses round the edges
and probably some strengthening of the blacks. The figures and some of
the ornaments have become somewhat transparent with time.

The story of the visit of the Athenian legislator, Solon, to King
Croesus at Sardis is related by Herodotus and Plutarch.[1] Croesus con-
sidered himself the happiest of men because of his great wealth, but
Solon disabused him.

There is no reason to suppose that no. 1132 is not the work of
Hendrick van Steenwyck II. The figures (and flowers?) are by a different
hand (once incorrectly considered to be one of the Francken's)[2] whose
style is close to that of Jan Brueghel I.[3] But although they have suffered
with time, they still do not appear to be of a sufficiently high quality
to be attributed to him. The ornaments may be the work of a third hand.

Jantzen[4] thought that Steenwyck executed no. 1132 not much later
than his picture in the Louvre of 1620,[5] to which Cornelis van Poelenburgh added the figures of Christ, Mary and Martha etc. It should,
however, be pointed out that the rendering of the architecture is not very
dissimilar from that in no. 141 *q.v.* of 1610.

The subject of no. 1132 was identified by MacLaren.[6]

PROVENANCE: 12th Duke of Hamilton (1845–95) sale,[7] Christie's, 8 July
(= 10th day) 1882 (1019) bt. by the National Gallery for £204 15sh. (with the aid
of the Clarke Fund); lent, through the Arts Council, to the Scarborough Art
Gallery, 1952–4, and to the Hatton Art Gallery, Newcastle-upon-Tyne, 1958–
1963.

REPRODUCTION: *National Gallery Illustrations, Continental Schools (excluding
Italian)*, 1950, p. 348, top.

REFERENCES: *In text:* (1) See *Herodotus*, trans. by J. Enoch Powell, I, 1949,
pp. 13 ff.; and *Plutarch's Lives*, with an introduction by A. H. Clough, I, 1910,
pp. 139 ff. (2) In the Christie's sale catalogue, see below under *Provenance*.
(3) Compare the figures in no. 3547 by Jan Brueghel I. (4) H. Jantzen,

Das Niederländische Architekturbild, 1910, p. 38. (5) Inv. no. 2581. Signed and dated 1620. (6) Ms. notes. (7) No. 1132 is not identifiable with certainty in any of the Hamilton inventories (ms. coll. the Duke of Hamilton, Lennoxlove); it is not one of the Beckford pictures which passed into the Hamilton Collection.

Imitator of Hendrick van STEENWYCK II

2205 INTERIOR OF A CHURCH AT NIGHT

Oil on oak, $18\frac{9}{16} \times 25\frac{1}{8}$ (0·471 × 0·657).

The tombstone, centre, bears the inscription: *632 | HIER LEYT BEGRAVEN HENRY STEENWYCK*

Apparently in good condition. There are some losses along a horizontal join in the support. There is a little wearing in the lettering on the tombstone, and a thick, tinted varnish.

The pictures, whose subjects are decipherable, are reading from the left: *Christ carrying the Cross*; *The Virgin and Child*, *The Crucifixion* (in the chapel on the far left), and *S. Jerome*. There are three placards bearing coats of arms. The object in the centre is a font crane supporting a font-cover.[1]

No. 2205 has been attributed both to Hendrick van Steenwyck II[2] and, since it entered the collection, to Peeter Neeffs I; the latter attribution being accepted by Jantzen.[3] The inscription on the tombstone, which seems contemporary with the rest, is a puzzle. The numbers 632 are presumably the last three digits of the date 1632 (the 6 is written at the bottom edge of the support which, however, need not have been cut down); and thus, if the inscription refers to the occupant of the tomb, neither Hendrick van Steenwyck I or II can be intended.[4] It seems more probable that it was intended as the signature of the latter.

The handling of the architecture seems comparable to that in a picture at Vienna, which is said to be signed by Steenwyck and dated 1604.[5] However, no. 2205 is not well executed; it seems rather to be the work of an imitator. The costumes approximate to those fashionable in the 1630's; but no. 2205 may well have been executed later.

The view of the church, which may be imaginary, is taken from the east end.

PROVENANCE: Perhaps in the Fonthill Abbey (= John Farquhar) sale, Phillips, 15 October (= 27th day), 1823 (342).[6] Sir William W. Knighton, Bart.[7] (†) sale, Christie's, 23 May (= 3rd day),[8] 1885 (494) bt. Brunning for £52 10sh.[9]; H. Calcott Brunning Bequest, 1907; lent to the Central Museum and Art Gallery, Northampton, 1929; the Public Library and Art Gallery, Harrogate, 1930; The Corporation Art Gallery and Museum, Bradford, 1931; and, through the Arts Council, to the Laing Art Gallery, Newcastle-upon-Tyne, 1951–63.

REPRODUCTION: *National Gallery Illustrations, Continental Schools (excluding Italian)*, 1950, p. 242, bottom.

REFERENCES: *In text:* (1) According to C. Blair, of the Victoria and Albert Museum, who kindly identified the object, such a crane should date from the second half of the sixteenth or the early seventeenth century. (2) At the Knighton sale, see below under *Provenance*. (**3**) See H. Jantzen, *Das Niederländische Architecturbild*, 1910, p. 166, no. 310. (**4**) The 1929 catalogue took the inscription to be that of Hendrick van Steenwyck I's tomb. (**5**) See E. R. V. Engerth, *Kunsthistorische Sammlungen des allerhöchsten Kaiserhauses, Gemälde . . . Verzeichniss*, 1884, II, p. 460, no. 1271; first recorded in 1783. (**6**) As suggested in the 1929 catalogue, described as by Steenwyck: 'A Church Piece, an Interior with several Figures . . . The *name* of the artist is written on the tomb-stone'; apparently not in the Fonthill Abbey sale, Christie's, 8 ff. October, 1822, which sale did not take place, as the whole estate was bought by John Farquhar (1751–1826), who inserted some items in the subsequent sale, see L. Melville, *The Life and Letters of William Beckford* etc., 1910, pp. 314–15. (**7**) For the Knighton collection, see under no. 2206. (**8**) As by Steenwyck, said to be signed, and to measure, $18\frac{1}{2} \times 25\frac{1}{2}$. (**9**) National Gallery's marked sale catalogue.

ALFRED STEVENS
1823–1906

Born in Brussels, 11 May, 1823. Taught by F. J. Navez at Brussels and by C. Roqueplan at Paris. Worked in both Paris and Brussels. Died on 24 August, 1906 at Paris.

REFERENCE: *General:* Thieme-Becker, *Künstler-Lexikon*, 1938, XXXII, pp. 25–26.

3966   EFFET D'ORAGE À HONFLEUR
Oil on canvas, $26 \times 31\frac{7}{8}/32$ ($0·66 \times 0·81/3$).
Signed, *A Stevens*. (AS in monogram).
In good condition.

The authenticity of no. 3966 need not be doubted.[1] No. 3966 is the subject of a note, written in 1955, by Gaston van Camp.[2] On the basis of a comparison with a picture by Stevens of the same view, signed and dated 1891,[3] he suggested that no. 3966 was executed in 1890 or 1891.

He identified the view in no. 3966 on the same basis. Photographs of both pictures were in a collection owned by Stevens himself in 1893; a note in this collection gave the subject of the latter as 'Mauvais temps à Honfleur'. The title of no. 3966 used here is that given in the sale catalogue of Félix Gérard in 1905[4]; he was stated to be the owner of the picture in a note in the collection of photographs referred to above.

PROVENANCE: Coll. Félix Gérard by 1893[5]; Félix Gérard (père) sale, Drouot (Paris), 1905 (112). Purchased from R. Middleton by the Tate Gallery 1924; transferred to the National Gallery, 1956.

REPRODUCTION: National Gallery photographs available.

REFERENCES: *In text:* (**1**) See for instance E. Van Zype, *Les Frères Stevens*, 1936, no. 96. (**2**) In the National Gallery archives. (**3**) In the Lazare Weiller sale, Drouot (Paris), 1901 (48). (**4**) See under *Provenance*. (**5**) See above.

3270   LE CADEAU
Oil on canvas, $14\frac{7}{8} \times 18\frac{1}{4}$ ($0·37 \times 0·46$).[1]
Signed, *A. Stevens*
On the *verso* are the initials *AS* (in monogram).

The authenticity of no. 3270 need not be doubted.[2]

Van Zype[3] considered that no. 3270 was exhibited at Brussels in 1866, which van Camp thinks unlikely.[4] Four other versions of this subject by Stevens are known,[5] one was exhibited in 1866. No. 3270 was exhibited in London in 1871, and was probably executed after 1866.

Van Camp believes that no. 3270 was entitled 'Le Cadeau' by Stevens himself.[7]

DERIVATIVE: *Fantaisie en folie* by Robert Brough, Tate Gallery, no. 1956.[8]

PROVENANCE: Coll. J. Staats Forbes by 1871, when exh. The French Gallery, London, (80)[9]; exh. Grafton Galleries, London, 1896 (158); The International Society, London, 1899 (210a); Leinster Hall, Dublin, 1899 (69); École des Beaux-Arts, Paris, 1900 (5); coll. the Executors of J. S. Forbes by 1904 when exh. at the Royal Hibernian Academy, Dublin, (5); bt. by Sir Hugh Lane, 1904; exh. National Museum of Ireland 1905 (19); Dublin Municipal Gallery, 1908–1913; exh. The International Society of Painters etc., 1909 (155); Sir Hugh Lane Bequest, 1917; transferred from the Tate Gallery to the National Gallery, 1956; on loan to the Municipal Gallery, Dublin, for five years from 1966.

REPRODUCTION: G. van Zype, *Les Frères Stevens*, 1936, p. 27. National Gallery photographs available.

REFERENCES: *In text:* (1) The measurements are by Ronald Alley, of the Tate Gallery, who has kindly communicated his notes on no. 3270. These notes form the basis of this entry unless otherwise stated. (2) See E. van Zype, *Les Frères Stevens*, 1936, no. 8. (3) *Ibid.* (4) Note in National Gallery archives. (5) As pointed out by van Camp, in his note referred to above: these are van Zype, *op. cit.*, no. 125, no. 34, and the two pictures mentioned under no. 34. (6) See under *Provenance.* (7) See note 4. (8) Oral information from Martin Butlin of the Tate Gallery. Brough's picture was apparently exh. at the Grafton Galleries, 1896, and the R.A., 1897. (9) Mentioned in a review of the exhibition in the *Art Journal*, 1871, p. 145.

JUSTUS SUTTERMANS
1597–1681

Portrait and figure painter. Active chiefly in Florence. Born in Antwerp, where he was baptized on 28 September, 1597.[1] He is recorded as a pupil of W. de Vos in the list of the Antwerp guild of S. Luke for 1609.[2] *Ca.* 1616 he left Antwerp for Paris, where he joined the studio of Frans Pourbus II; he stayed in Paris for between three and three and a half years.[3] He then set out for Italy; he may have reached Florence in 1619 or 1620[4]; at all events he was appointed painter to the Grand Duke of Tuscany, Cosimo II († 28 February, 1621)[5]; he was to remain in the service of the Grand Dukes of Tuscany until his death. He was, however, called to work in Vienna, from 1623–24 by the Emperor Ferdinand II,[6] and in Innsbruck from 1653–54 by Anna Maria de' Medici, wife of the Archduke Ferdinand of Austria.[7] He also worked in several capitals in Italy and may have visited Spain in 1649.[8] He was in Rome in 1627 and 1645[9]; in Parma, Piacenza and Milan in 1640[10]; in Ferrara in 1645[11]; in Genoa in 1649[12]; in Modena in 1649(?), 1650, 1653 and 1656.[13]

He was granted a patent of nobility by the Emperor in 1624.[14] He married three times,[15] and died in Florence on 23 April, 1681.[16]

His portrait was etched by van Dyck for the *Iconography*; a subsequent state of the print was inscribed: 'Judocus Citermans Antverpiensis Pictor Magnis Duci Florentini'.[17]

Several spellings of his names occur in contemporary documents[18]; that adopted here was used by the artist in 1658.[19]

REFERENCES: *General:* F. Baldinucci, *Notizie dei Professori del Disegno* etc., ed. F. Ranalli, 1846, V, pp. 473–511; P. Bautier, *Juste Suttermans* etc., 1912 (see also his article in the *Biographie Nationale ... de Belgique*, 1926–29, 24, cols. 343 ff.).

In text: (1) See Baldinucci, *op. cit.*, p. 476. (2) *Ibid.*, p. 477; see also Ph. Rombouts and Th. van Lerius, *De Liggeren* etc., [1864–1876], I, p. 457. (3) Bautier, *op. cit.*, p. 2, states that he left Antwerp after 7 years of apprenticeship and worked under Pourbus for three years; Baldinucci, *loc. cit.*, states that he worked for two years with Pourbus and for one and a half years independently. (4) Bautier, *op. cit.*, p. 3, gives 1620 as the date; G. Hoogewerff, *Onze Kunst* 1915, I, infers 1619. (5) See Baldinucci, *op. cit.*, pp. 478–79. (6) See Baldinucci, *op. cit.*, p. 479 and 482–83; Bautier, *op. cit.*, p. 59, gives the year of his departure as 1622. (7) See Baldinucci, *op. cit.*, p. 500, gives the date as 1652/3; he says he worked for the Emperor in Germany before going to Innsbruck; see Bautier, *op. cit.*, p. 75. (8) See Baldinucci, *op. cit.*, p. 499; this is denied by Bautier, *op. cit.*, pp. 34–5. (9) See Baldinucci, *op. cit.*, pp. 483–89, and 498–99. (10) See Baldinucci, *op. cit.*, pp. 496–98. (11) See Bautier, *op. cit.*, p. 73. (12) See Baldinucci, *op. cit.*, p. 499. (13) *Ibid.*, pp. 499–500; see also Bautier, *op. cit.*, pp. 66–71. (14) See Baldinucci, *op. cit.*, p. 483. (15) See Bautier, *op. cit.*, p. 98. (16) See Baldinucci, *op. cit.*, p. 510. (17) See Fr. Wibiral, *L'Iconographie d'Antoine van Dyck*, 1877, p. 62, no. 12. (18) See Bautier, *op. cit.*, p. 1; and A. von Wurzbach, *Niederländisches Künstler-Lexikon*, 1910, II, p. 675. (19) See Bautier, *loc. cit.*

89 DOUBLE PORTRAIT OF THE GRAND DUKE FERDINAND II OF TUSCANY AND HIS WIFE VITTORIA DELLA ROVERE

The Grand Duke wears armour and a commander's (blue) sash; he holds a commander's baton, which rests on a table before a coronet and helmet.

Oil on relined canvas, *ca.* $63\frac{3}{8} \times 57\frac{7}{8}$ (1·61 × 1·47). The edge of the support is masked by binding paper.

In fair condition. There are many areas of small, scattered losses, now retouched, notably in the flesh, and particularly in the hands. There is very little modelling in the black dress of the Grand Duchess, which may have suffered considerably in the past; the Grand Duke's blue sash is also worn in places. Cleaned, 1961.

There are several *pentimenti*, chiefly evident in X-radiographs: the Grand Duke's head was first placed more to the left and the curtain on the right was close to it; the Grand Duchess's head was first a little higher. There are some minor alterations in the cuffs.

Ferdinand II de' Medici (1610–1670) was the son of Cosimo II, and succeeded his father as Grand Duke of Tuscany in 1621, assuming power in 1627. He wears the cross of the military Order of S. Stefano, founded by his great-grandfather, Cosimo de' Medici, in 1561 (see under no. 670 of this collection). He married in 1634 Vittoria della Rovere (1621–1694).

In the first half of the last century no. 89 was considered to be by Velazquez[1]; the attribution to Suttermans was first advanced in the 1859 Gallery catalogue and was accepted by Bautier.[2] The level of quality in no. 89 varies; some parts are weak (notably the area of paint immediately above and to the right of the Grand Duke's left arm, which may be a misunderstood reference to his sash); this may be due both to damage and to studio participation in its execution. The attribution of no. 89 to Suttermans is here accepted, although the participation of a studio hand is possible.

The identification of the sitters as Ferdinand de' Medici and Vittoria della Rovere seems first to have been advanced in 1830,[3] and has been confirmed by Bautier.[4]

Bautier has suggested that no. 89 was executed ca. 1655[5]; but the costumes suggest a date in the 1660's. As Bautier has pointed out, the poses in no. 89 correspond to those in two single portraits of the same sitters by Suttermans in the Uffizi[6]; that of the Grand Duke may have been the prototype of the print by Spierre, published—according to Baldinucci[7]—in 1666. There may well have been a time gap of some years between the execution of the painting and the print. The costumes in no. 89 differ from those in the Uffizi portraits. The faces, however, do not appear to be more aged[8]; so it seems likely that earlier drawings were used for the design of no. 89, and that it was probably not executed *ad vivum*.

ENGRAVINGS: By H. F. Rose (etching)[9]; W. Holl[10]; Starling (etching)[11]; Schuler (etching).[12]

PROVENANCE: Bought from F. L. J. Laborde-Méréville (1761–1802) by J. J. Angerstein[13]; purchased with the Angerstein collection, 1824; on loan to the National Gallery of Ireland, 1862–1926.

REPRODUCTION: *National Gallery Illustrations, Continental Schools (excluding Italian)*, 1950, p. 351, right.

REFERENCES: *In text:* (1) See John Young, *Catalogue of the Celebrated Collection of Pictures of the late John Julius Angerstein Esq.*, 1823, no. 27; and, *inter alia*, Gallery catalogues until 1859. (2) See P. Bautier, *Juste Suttermans Peintre des Médicis*, 1912, p. 23 and p. 124 (as belonging to the National Gallery of Ireland). The earlier attribution was also rejected by C. B. Curtis, *Velazquez and Murillo*, 1883, p. 62, no. 150a. (3) See *A Catalogue of Pictures in the National Gallery* etc., 1830, p. 8, no. 38. Young, *loc. cit.*, considered the sitters to be 'Philip IV of Spain and his Queen, Donna Maria Ana (*sic*) Austria'. (4) See P. Bautier, *loc. cit.*; and *Annales de la Société d'Archéologie de Bruxelles*, 1912, pp. 192–94. (5) *Op. cit.*, p. 194. (6) *Ibid.*; for the Uffizi pictures see his figs. 2 and 3. (7) See F. Baldinucci, *Notizie dei Professori del Disegno* etc., ed. F. Ranalli, 1847, V, p. 564; for Suttermans' alterations to the prototype, see *ibid.*, and, IV (1846), p. 500; the print is rep. by Bautier, *Juste Suttermans* etc., 1912, opp. p. 24; Bautier, *op. cit.*, p. 24, dates the print 1659. (8) The Grand Duchess seems younger in no. 89 than she does in Suttermans's renderings of her as *S. Margaret* and *S. Helena* of ca. 1665 and 1669 respectively, for which see G. J. Hooge-werff, *Onze Kunst*, 1915, pp. 37 ff. (9) In Young, *op. cit.*, for no. 27. (10)

In Jones' *National Gallery of Pictures* etc., [1838], I, for no. 24. **(11)** See Curtis, *loc. cit.* **(12)** *Ibid.* **(13)** The ms. notes (National Gallery library) connected with Young's *Catalogue of the Angerstein Collection*, no. 21, advance two theories concerning its earlier provenance: (i) that it was sent as a present from Philip IV to Louis XIV and that it was removed from Versailles on the orders of Robespierre; (ii) that it came from the Orléans collection. No. 89 has not been traced in either the French Royal collection or in the Duc d'Orléans collection. For M. Laborde-Méréville, see under no. 38.

Ascribed to SUTTERMANS

3227 PORTRAIT OF A MAN
Oil on relined canvas, *ca.* $47\frac{1}{4} \times 36\frac{13}{16}$ ($1 \cdot 20 \times 0 \cdot 935$).
The top and left-hand edges have been made up to a border.
Apparently in fairly good condition. The reds and flesh seem fairly well preserved, although both may have been flattened by ironing. There are retouchings in the hair and background. Yellow varnish.

No. 3227 has been catalogued as the work of Suttermans since it entered the collection, and is accepted by Bautier.[1] The yellow varnish makes it difficult properly to assess no. 3227; the handling seems, however, to be hard and the quality of execution not high. What may be a better version was on the Vienna art market in 1968 (see under *Version*). It is possible that no. 3227 is an old copy after Suttermans; at all events it seems best at this stage to catalogue it as ascribed to him.

The sitter in no. 3227 has been described as a Florentine nobleman.[2] The red costume, however, suggests that he may have been Genoese and have held office in the government of that Republic. Suttermans worked in Genoa in 1649.[3]

VERSION: Anon. sale, Dorotheum (Vienna), 17 September, 1968 (122).[4]

PROVENANCE: Bequeathed by W. W. Aston († 1917) with a life interest to his widow, 1919; lent to the Ministry of Works (now Public Building and Works) 1934–35, and, through the Arts Council, to the Corporation Art Gallery, Bradford, 1958–63.

REPRODUCTION: *National Gallery Illustrations, Continental Schools (excluding Italian)*, 1950, p. 351, left.

REFERENCES: *In text:* **(1)** See P. Bautier, in *Biographie Nationale ... de Belgique*, 1926–29, 24, col. 319. **(2)** See Bautier, *loc. cit.*, and N.G. catalogues, 1920–29. **(3)** See the biography above. **(4)** Canvas, $44\frac{1}{2} \times 34\frac{1}{4}$ ($1 \cdot 13 \times 0 \cdot 87$); rep. in cat.

David TENIERS II
1610–1690

Landscape, genre painter and etcher. Active first in Antwerp and then in Brussels. Born in Antwerp and baptized there on 15 December, 1610.[1] He is not listed as a pupil in the lists of the Antwerp guild of S. Luke; in 1649 it was stated that he had been taught by his father, David Teniers I.[2] He was received as a master ('wynmeester') in the Antwerp guild of S. Luke in the year 1632/3.[3] He was Dean of the guild for the

year 1645/6.[4] In 1649, it was stated that he had worked for the King of
Spain, Prince William of Orange and the Archduke Leopold-Wilhelm,[5]
Governor of the Netherlands from 1646–May 1656. By early 1651, he
may have settled in Brussels,[6] and entered the service of the Archduke
as his painter and *ayuda de camera*; the earliest printed references to
him in these capacities is in 1653[7] and 1660[8] respectively. He held the
same posts under the Archduke's successor, Don Juan of Austria,
Governor from 1653–59[9]; in 1683, Teniers still referred to himself as
'Schilder en ayuda de camera van Hare Hoogheden'.[10] He visited
England between 1650–55 to buy pictures for the Count of Fuensaldana.[11]
In 1662 he bought a country house at Perck from J. B. van Brouchoven,
Count of Bergeijck, the second husband of Helena Fourment.[12] In 1662,
he was also one of the prime movers in obtaining the establishment of the
Académie Royale, Antwerp, finally achieved in the following year.[13]
His long drawn out effort to obtain a patent of nobility succeeded in
1680.[14] He died at Brussels on 25 April, 1690.[15]

He was married twice: first in 1637 to Anna (1620–1656), the daughter
of Jan Brueghel I *q.v.*; and second in 1656 to Isabella de Fren.[16] His
eldest son (1638–85), David, was also a painter.[17]

David Teniers II's *Self Portrait* was engraved by P. de Jode.[18]

REFERENCES: *In text:* (1) See, for instance, Th. van Lerius, *Catalogue du
Musée d'Anvers*, 1874 (3rd ed.), p. 383. (2) See the inscription on the print by
P. de Jode after a *Self Portrait* by Teniers in J. Meyssens, *Images de Divers
Hommes d'esprit Sublime* etc., 1649; reprinted by C. de Bie, *Het Gulden Cabinet*
etc., 1661, p. 335. (3) See Ph. Rombouts and Th. van Lerius, *De Liggeren* etc.,
[1864–1876], II, p. 35. (4) *Ibid.*, p. 165. (5) See note 2; for his work in the 1640's
for the Bishop of Ghent and the Archduke, see H. Vlieghe, *Gentse Bijdragen*,
1961–66, pp. 124–25. (6) See Musson's note of 4 February, 1651, referring to
Teniers in Brussels, printed by J. Denucé, *Na P. P. Rubens*, 1949, p. 90. He
bought a property in Brussels in 1656, see Vlieghe, *op. cit.*, p. 128. (7) See his
letter to Musson of 16 December, 1653, in Denucé, *op. cit.*, p. 133. (8) See
Vlieghe, *op. cit.*, pp. 129–30. (9) See, for instance, N. de Pauw, *Bulletin de la
Commission Royale d'Histoire*, 1909, pp. 31 and 34. (10) See L. Galesloot,
Messager des Sciences Historiques de Belgique, 1868, p. 264; P. Saintenoy,
Mémoires, Académie Royale de Belgique, 1935, VI, p. 122, records a payment
made to Teniers in 1669/70 for work undertaken for the then Governor.
(11) See de Bie, *op. cit.*, p. 338; and Sidney, 16th Earl of Pembroke, *A Catalogue
of the Paintings and Drawings . . . at Wilton* etc., 1968, p. 3. (12) For the date of
Teniers' purchase of De Drij Toren, see Z. V. M. in Thieme-Becker; see
also J. Vermoelen, *Journal des Beaux Arts*, 1865, p. 19. (13) See, for instance,
Vermoelen, *op. cit.*, 1864, p. 188. It actually opened its doors in 1664. (14)
See, for instance, Vermoelen, *op. cit.*, 1865, p. 10. (15) See J. B. Descamps,
La Vie des Peintres Flamands etc., 1754, II, p. 157; and, for instance, L. Galesloot, *Annales de l'Académie d'Archéologie de Belgique*, 1867, p. 356. (16) See,
for instance, van Lerius, *op. cit.*, pp. 384–86. (17) See Vermoelen, *op. cit.*,
1864, pp. 53–4; and, for instance, the entry by Z. V. M. on David Teniers III
in Thieme-Becker. (18) See under note 2; and under no. 817.

155 THE COVETOUS MAN

An old man holding a money bag stares towards the light, while an
old woman weighs gold before a table on which are sacks of coins, deeds
and an hour glass.

Oil on relined canvas, $24\frac{5}{8} \times 33\frac{7}{16}$ (0·625 × 0·85). The canvas edge is masked by binding paper.

Signed, *DAVID·TENIERS*

In fair condition. There are some areas of wearing: notably in the old woman's cloak and left sleeve, the objects on the shelf, the objects hanging below it and the wall. The signature is not above dispute, as some of the letters appear to be above pockets of discoloured varnish. Cleaned, 1957.

The subject is taken from Luke XII, 20–21: 'But God said unto him, Thou fool, this night thy soul shall be required of thee: then whose shall those things be, which thou hast provided? So is he that layeth up treasure for himself, and is not rich toward God'. These verses appear on a print by van den Steen after a similar (lost ?) picture by D. Teniers II.[1] No. 155 connects with Massys' *Money Changers* (Louvre), which was in Antwerp in the seventeenth century, when its frame bore a quotation from Leviticus, XIX, 36: 'Statera justa, et aequa sint pondera'.[2]

In spite of the questionable status of the signature, no. 155 is acceptable as the work of David Teniers II. The same models were used in the Vienna *Soldiers Plundering a Village* of 1648.[3] And it is probable that no. 155 was painted about this time or a little earlier.[4]

The writing on the deeds is difficult to decipher: that immediately in front of the money bags seems to be inscribed: 'Lan...ge...geheeten'; that beneath: 'Loquor'.[5]

VARIANTS: Engraved by F. van den Steen[6]; Comte de Vence sale, Paris, 9 ff. February, 1761 (69).[7]

ENGRAVING: By C. W. Sharpe.[8]

COPY: At Christie's October–December, 1963, but not apparently in any sale.

PROVENANCE: Perhaps Anon. sale, Christie's, 28 June, 1814 (81) bt. Gray for 102 gns.[9] In the collection of the Rt. Hon. C. Long (later Lord Farnborough) by 1819, when exh. at the B.I. (77)[10]; Lord Farnborough Bequest, 1838; lent to the Corporation Art Gallery, Bradford, 1935.

REPRODUCTION: *National Gallery Illustrations, Continental Schools (excluding Italian)*, 1950, p. 353, bottom.

REFERENCE: *General:* J. Smith, *A Catalogue Raisonné* etc., 1831, III, Teniers, no. 505.

In text: (1) Published by Abraham Teniers. Smith, cited under *General Reference*, states wrongly that the engraving is after no. 155. The engraving does not show the window in no. 155; in it the old man looks down, and a skeleton with an hour glass appears at a window above him. (2) See *Le Siècle de Bruegel*, Musées Royaux des Beaux-Arts de Belgique, 1963 (167). For the possible symbolism of the carafe, see I. Bergstrom, *The Burlington Magazine*, 1955, p. 346. (3) Canvas, $30\frac{5}{16} \times 44\frac{7}{8}$ (0·77 × 1·14), see *Kunsthistorisches Museum, Katalog der Gemäldegalerie*, 1938, pp. 167–68, no. 1157. (4) A. Rosenberg, *Teniers der Jüngere*, 1895, p. 7, wrongly considered that no. 155 belonged to the 'ersten Zeit' of the master. (5) The compiler wishes to thank Professor J. G. van Gelder and C. van Hasselt for their help in reading the inscriptions. (6) See note 1. Teniers is referred to as 'Serenissimi Archid. Leopoldi Pictoris'—a position which he had from perhaps early in the first half of the 1650's. A print designed and published by Teniers, but engraved by Coryn Boel, and one by van den Brugghen after Teniers, show two different renderings of the same theme. Another

rendering of the same theme by Teniers, measuring 31 × 40 (0·786 × 1·017), was
in the Lord Cadogan sale, 22 February (= 2nd day), 1726/7, see the sale catalogue in the British Museum. (7) Panel, 7 p. 9 l. × 6 p. (= 8¼ × 6⅜); engraved
by F. Basan. The print corresponds (in reverse) to no. 155, but for the presence
of an alcove, with a glass in it, in the wall above the old man. (8) See R. N.
Wornum, *Descriptive and Historical Catalogue of the Pictures in the National
Gallery*, 1858, p. 206. (9) Called 'The Gold Weighers'; buyer's name and price
from Christie's marked catalogue. Smith, *loc. cit.*, referred to an Anon. sale of
1814. (10) Called 'The Misers'.

**158   A MAN HOLDING A GLASS AND AN OLD
       WOMAN LIGHTING A PIPE**
An interior scene with a peasant holding a glass; an old peasant
woman lights a pipe, watched by a third peasant; in the corner a peasant
rouses another, who is sleeping by a fire.

Oil on oak, 9⅜ × 13½ (0·238 × 0·343).

Signed, *D·TENIERS·F*

In fairly good condition. There are some losses along three horizontal
cracks towards the right-hand edge. There is a small loss on the old
peasant woman's jaw, which is retouched; the paint of her dress is
apparently diseased and in poor condition. Two vertical battens on the
reverse and old additions to the support at the top and bottom were
removed, 1949/50. Yellow varnish.

The signature on no. 158 seems old, but is rather weakly written and
not above suspicion; nevertheless, the overall quality is sufficiently high
for the traditional attribution to David Teniers II to be accepted.

No. 158 is comparable in handling to, and probably a little later than,
the Wallace Collection *Boors Carousing* of 1644.[1]

The composition connects with an etching by David Teniers II[2]; and
such scenes were popular with him.[3] They were probably inspired by
Brouwer; the pose of the peasant holding the glass may also ultimately derive from him.[4]

PROVENANCE: Perhaps in the Jacomo de Wit sale, Antwerp, 15 May, 1741
(109), 185 glds.[5] In a French collection as a pendant to a 'Chemist' (by Teniers)
by 1742.[6] Perhaps in another French collection.[7] Coll. the Rt. Hon. C. Long
(later Lord Farnborough) by 1818, when exh. at the B.I. (93); Lord Farnborough Bequest, 1838.

REPRODUCTION: *National Gallery Illustrations, Continental Schools* (*excluding
Italian*), 1950, p. 354, top.

REFERENCE: *General:* J. Smith, *A Catalogue Raisonné* etc., 1831, III, Teniers,
no. 504.

In text: (1) Copper, 13¾ × 18½ (0·35 × 0·47), see *Wallace Collection Catalogues,
Pictures & Drawings*, 1928, no. 227, p. 283. (2) Ch. Le Blanc, *Manuel de l'Amateur d'Estampes*, 1889, IV, p. 17, no. 2. (3) A late rendering (to judge from a
photograph) of the same subject is at Munich, Bayer. Staatsgemäldesammlungen,
no. 819, panel, 6¼ × 9 1/16 (0·16 × 0·23), signed. (4) Compare the Rijksmuseum
Smoker, rep. by G. Knuttel, *Adriaen Brouwer*, 1962, fig. 92. (5) See G. Hoet,
Catalogus etc., 1752, II, p. 40; this picture of boors smoking and drinking
measured 9 d. × 1 v.2 d., which nearly corresponds to the size of no. 158. (6)
According to an ms. label in ink, once on back of no. 158, that reads: *Beau
tenier [sic] pendans | au Chimiste fig[uré?] du Luy | ... et donne [sic] en 1742.*

(7) There were remains of a second, printed, label on the back of no. 158; of which all that can be read is '*DU CABINE* . . .', the rest having been rubbed through.

817   A VIEW OF HET STERCKSHOF NEAR ANTWERP

An elderly peasant offers a fish to a man and two women accompanied by a page, while six peasants, standing in a moat, draw in a net, before a house.

Signed, *D·TENIERS·F*

Oil on relined canvas, $32\frac{1}{4} \times 46\frac{9}{16}$ (0·82 × 1·18).

There is a later addition $1\frac{1}{4}$ (0·032) wide along the bottom edge.

Generally in good condition. There is some wearing in the sky. Cleaned, 1958.

There is no reason to doubt the authenticity of no. 817.

The handling in no. 817 resembles that in the Hermitage *Village Fête* of 1646[1] and in the Duke of Bedford's *Village Fête* (?) of the same year (for which see under no. 952). The costumes also closely resemble those worn in the two latter pictures. It is reasonable to assume that no. 817 is contemporary with them; and a date *ca.* 1646 is therefore acceptable for it.

The house was traditionally thought to be Teniers' house De Drij Toren, at Perck, which he bought in 1662.[2] This identification is not correct.[3] The view is that of the back of Het Sterckshof at Deurne, near Antwerp.[4]

The gentleman in the foreground has on several occasions been identified as Teniers himself; various identifications have been made of the page and two women.[5] There is a resemblance between the boy, gentleman and lady facing outwards in no. 817 and the eldest boy, lady and gentleman, playing the *viola da gamba*, in the *Group Portrait* (Dahlem) by David Teniers II, which was perhaps executed a little later than no. 817.[6] The gentleman in no. 817 does not in fact strikingly resemble Teniers as he lacks his hooked nose; but this is not to rule out the identification, or to say that the gentlefolk in no. 817 were not intended as portraits.[7] But at this stage it seems best to suggest that the three figures in no. 817 are perhaps reminiscences of Teniers himself, his wife, Anna Brueghel (1620–1656), and eldest son, David, born in 1638 (see above under Teniers' biography).

The peasant who offers the fish is perhaps paying a seignorial due. It is thus logical to suppose that the lady to whom the fish is offered is the owner or wife of the owner of the house. But against this is the recurrence of the lady in other compositions by Teniers, notably in no. 952. The owner of Het Sterckshof, *ca.* 1646, was Jacob Edelheer (1599–1657), who in 1644 married its heiress, Isabella van Lemens († 1650).[8]

PROVENANCE : Perhaps Anon. (= Séréville) sale, Paris, 22 January, 1812 (12)[9] bt. Lafontaine for 2410 francs.[10] Probably Anon. (= Lafontaine *et al.*) sale, Christie's, 8 May, 1813 (70) £240 bt. in.[11] Anon.[12] sale, Christie's, 29 June (= 2nd day), 1814 (75) bt. Sir George Warrender for 165 gns.[13] The Rt. Hon. Sir

George Warrender sale, Christie's, 3 June, 1837 (18) bt. Farrer for £362 5s.[14]
Coll. the Rev. F. Leicester by 1855 when exh. at the B.I. (13); exh. *Manchester Art Treasures*, 1857 (no. 532 of the definitive catalogue); the Rev. F. Leicester sale, Christie's, 19 May (= 2nd day), 1860 (160)[15] bt. Nieuwenhuys for £415[16]; from whom bought for £1,000, 1871; lent to the City Art Gallery, Manchester, 1957–58.

REPRODUCTION: *National Gallery Illustrations, Continental Schools (excluding Italian)*, 1950, p. 355, bottom.

REFERENCES: *General:* J. Smith, *A Catalogue Raisonné* etc. 1831, III, Teniers, no. 422.

In text: (1) See *Musée de l'Ermitage, Département de l'Art Occidental, Catalogue des Peintures*, II, 1958, p. 103, no. 594 and rep. no. 97, p. 106. (2) See, for instance, Smith, cited under *General Reference*; and National Gallery catalogues, 1871–1929; for the date of Teniers' purchase of De Drij Toren, see, for instance, Z. V. M.'s entry on Teniers in Thieme-Becker. (3) A. Wauters, *Histoire des Environs de Bruxelles*, II, 1852, p. 705, described what then remained of Teniers' house at Perck: only a few buildings of little importance, and 'la porte d'entrée avec son petit pavillon, surmonté d'un pignon rustique'. For a view of the house, see *Les Belges Illustres, Panthéon Nationale*, 1844, II, p. 32. (4) See Gregory Martin, *The Burlington Magazine*, 1968, pp. 574–7; and fig. 56, for a reproduction of a print showing a view from the house taken from the road approaching the main entrance in J. le Roy, *Notitia Marchionatus*, 1678, opp. p. 94 (the same print occurs in J. le Roy, *Castella & Praetoria Nobilium Brabantiae*, 1699, p. 100). (5) See Smith, *loc. cit.* The cataloguer of the Manchester Art Treasures Exhibition (see below) considered the sitters to be Teniers with three of his children. The National Gallery catalogues from 1871 identified the sitters as Teniers, his wife and son and another lady; the 1929 catalogue considered them to be the artist, his son and two unidentified ladies. (6) See *Verzeichnis der Gemälde im Museum Dahlem*, 1963, no. 857, p. 107. Compare P. de Jode's engraving after a Self Portrait by Teniers in J. Meyssens, *Images de Divers Hommes d'esprit Sublime* etc., 1649, and in C. de Bie, *He-Gulden Cabinet* etc., 1661, p. 335; L. Vorsterman the Younger's engraving after Peter Thijs' portrait of Teniers of 1654 in *Theatrum Pictorum Davidis Teniers* etc. (1658); and Teniers' self-portrait in *The Archduke Leopold-Willhelm in his Picture Gallery*, Vienna, Kunsthistorisches Museum, *Katalog der Gemälde-galerie*, II, 1958, no. 378, pp. 134–36. Another (earlier) self portrait was recorded in the Earl of Normanton's *The Artist's Studio*, rep. in S. Speth-Holterhof, *Les Peintres Flamands de Cabinet d'Amateurs* etc., 1957, fig. 54. (7) The gentlefolk depicted in country scenes by Teniers may well have been intended as portraits. But the differing combinations of the same models suggest that, while they may have been inspired by actual people, Teniers may have intended nothing more than the introduction of an upper or middle class element in peasant gatherings or country scenes. (8) See Martin, *loc. cit.* (9) See Smith, *loc. cit.*; called 'Teniers en promenade dans les environs de sa campagne'; the description and size do not tally exactly. Smith wrongly thought that no. 817 was in the Chevalier Lambert (and Mons. du P [orail]) sale, Paris, 27 ff. March, 1787—in which the only possible candidate—lot 53—does not tally. (10) See the British Museum copy of the sale catalogue. The identity of the buyer gives some weight to Smith's view. (11) See Smith, *loc. cit.* Ms. notes on Christie's copy of the sale catalogue make it clear that lots 69–75 were Lafontaine's and that they were bought in. The catalogue states that the pictures were recently consigned from the continent. (12) An ms. inscription on the National Gallery copy of the sale catalogue states that the seller was the Prince of Wales; Oliver Millar, letter in National Gallery archives, considers that only a few lots belonged to the Prince of which no. 75 was not one. He considered that the pictures mostly belonged to Nieuwenhuys. (13) See Christie's marked catalogue. (14) Ms. note on the National Gallery copy gives the buyer's name and price; and also states: 'from the P. Regents [*sic*] col. cost 165 gns'. This is a reference to the 1814 sale. (15) As ex coll. Warrender. (16) See Christie's marked catalogue.

857 SPRING

A gardener carries a potted tree in a garden.

Oil on copper, $8\frac{11}{16} \times 6\frac{1}{2}$ (0·221 × 0·165); the top and left-hand edges irregularly cut.

Signed, *DT·F* (DT in monogram).

In good condition. There are some losses along the edges.

For commentary and provenance, see below under no. 860.

858 SUMMER

A young peasant holds a sheaf of corn before a corn field that is being harvested.

Oil on copper, $8\frac{5}{8} \times 6\frac{7}{16}$ (0·219 × 0·16); the top and left-hand edges irregularly cut.

Signed, *DT·F* (DT in monogram).

In good condition. There are some losses round the edges.

For commentary and provenance, see below under no. 860.

859 AUTUMN

A man holds a jug and glass of wine before an outhouse where wine is being made.

Oil on copper, $8\frac{11}{16} \times 6\frac{7}{16}$ (0·221 × 0·164); the left-hand edge irregularly cut.

Signed, *DT·F* (DT in monogram).

In good condition. There are some losses round the edges.

For commentary and provenance, see below under no. 860.

860 WINTER

An old man sits before a table warming his hands over charcoal in a bowl, while people sport on the ice in the background.

Oil on copper, $8\frac{3}{4} \times 6\frac{3}{8}$ (0·222 × 0·162); the left-hand edge irregularly cut.

Signed, *DT* (in monogram).

Generally in good condition. There are some losses in the sky. The background details are scratched in with the end of the brush.

Nos. 857–860 are all about the same size and on copper; and it is obviously correct to suppose that they were painted as a series.

Nos. 857–860 are clearly by David Teniers II (although the form of signature varies), and are works of high quality. J. P. B. Lebrun[1] convincingly suggested that they are comparable in date to the Louvre *Prodigal Son* of 1644.[2]

At least four other comparable series attributed to D. Teniers II are known; none follows nos. 857–860 exactly; although two scenes from one set are obviously variants of their counterparts in the National Gallery series.[3]

Teniers may have been inspired by J. Matham's set of engravings of personifications of the Four Seasons.[4] *Winter* in this series walks (as he does in Teniers' other renderings of *Winter*); a set of engravings of the *Four Seasons* by A. Tempesta[5] shows personifications of the Seasons seated on chariots and *Winter* as an old man seated warming his hands.

ENGRAVINGS: By P. L. Surugue, 1749 (in reverse)[6]; after nos. 857 and 858: by Morin, 1751[7] (in reverse); after no. 860 by P. Angier.[8]

COPIES OR REPLICAS: A series on copper, of approximately the same size as nos. 857–860, private collection, Eardisley, 1966; a number of series of *The Four Seasons*, or individual personifications are noted in nineteenth-century sale catalogues.

PROVENANCE: Perhaps La Comtesse de Verrue sale, Paris, 27–28 March, 1737 (49 or 50) sold for 290 francs.[9] No. 857, and probably the whole series, coll. or ex coll. Mr. L'Abbé de Majinville by 1749.[10] Perhaps Martin Robyns sale, Brussels, 22 May, 1758 (46), sold for 146 glds.[11] Villers sale, Paris (Lebrun), 30 March, 1812 (27) 1,800 francs bt. in.[12] Prince Talleyrand sale, Paris, 7–8 July, 1817 (34–37) bt. Buchanan.[13] Coll. G. Watson Taylor by 1822, when exh. at the B.I. (102–105); G. Watson Taylor sale, Christie's, 13 June, 1823 (45)[14] bt. the Rt. Hon. Robert Peel (later Sir Robert Peel, Bart.) for £189[15]; purchased with the Peel Collection, 1871; lent, through the Arts Council, to the City Art Gallery, Manchester, 1951–1963.

REPRODUCTIONS: *National Gallery Illustrations, Continental Schools* (*excluding Italian*), 1950, p. 356.

REFERENCE: *General:* J. Smith, *A Catalogue Raisonné* etc., 1831, III, Teniers, no. 48 (wrong sizes given).

In text: (1) In the Villers sale catalogue of 1812, for which see below. (2) Copper, $26\frac{3}{4} \times 34\frac{5}{8}$ (0·68 × 0·88), signed and dated 1644, see F. Villot, *Notice des Tableaux ... du Louvre*, 2nd part, 1854, pp. 272–3. (3) The four series are: 1) the set engraved by Le Vasseur when coll. La Prade and sold, according to Smith, cited under *General Reference*, in the La Prade sale, Paris, 1776; according to information on the engravings each figure measured 4 p. 6 l.; the supports were of wood and measured 4 l. × 4 p. 6 l. ($=ca. \ 6\frac{5}{8} \times 4\frac{3}{4}$); 2) the set which featured in the Blondel de Gagny sale, Paris, 10 ff. December, 1776 (98), panel, 6 p. 9 l. × 4 p. 6 l. ($=ca. \ 7\frac{1}{8} \times 4\frac{3}{4}$), and fully described in the catalogue; 3) the set which featured in the Gros sale, Paris, 13 ff. April, 1778 (6), of which G. de St. Aubin made sketches, see *Catalogues de Ventes ... illustrés par Gabriel de Saint-Aubin*, introd. by E. Dacier, VII, 1913, p. 8; these were on wood and measured 6 p. 6 l. × 5 p. ($=ca. \ 6\frac{3}{8} \times 5\frac{1}{4}$); a similar set was in an Anon. sale, Sotheby's, 26 April, 1950 (115), panel, $7 \times 5\frac{1}{4}$ (0·18 × 0·13); later coll. P. de Boer, Amsterdam, 1957 (photos. in R.K.D.); variants of *Autumn* were in a Fiévez sale, 8 April, 1930 (14), panel, $9\frac{7}{16} \times 7\frac{1}{2}$ (0·24 × 0·19), and of *Summer* in the Staehelin–Paravicini sale, Geneva, 23–25 March, 1939 (43), panel, $7\frac{1}{16} \times 6\frac{1}{16}$ (0·18 × 0·155); 4) the set in the Sedelemeyer sale, Paris, 1907 (65–68) (rep.), panel, $5\frac{11}{16} \times 4\frac{5}{16}$ (0·145 × 0·11) ex coll. Sir W. A. Fraser (perhaps after Teniers). Of these the *Spring* and *Summer* of the Gros series may be said to be variants of nos. 857–8; (?) variants of nos. 858–859, with D. Katz, (n.d.), panel, $8\frac{3}{4} \times 6\frac{11}{16}$ (0·22 × 0·17), photo. in R.K.D. (4) See A. Bartsch, *Le Peintre Graveur*, 1804, IV, p. 144, nos. 51–54. These may have been inspired by designs by Goltzius which Matham also engraved, see Bartsch, *op. cit.*, 1803, III, pp. 166–167, nos. 140–143. Matham's inventions are more classical in spirit than those of Teniers, who was theoretically wrong to transform *Spring* into a bearded gardener—Matham's *Spring* is a youth carrying a pot of flowers. (5) See Bartsch *op. cit.*, 1818, XVII, pp. 152–3, no. 807. An early personification of *Winter* as an old man is made by Ovid, *Metamorphoses*, II, 36. (6) That after no. 857 bears the inscription 'du cabinet de Mr l'Abbé de Majinville . . .'. Madamoiselle Hébert of the Cabinet des Estampes, Bibliothèque Nationale has kindly confirmed that P. L. Surugue engraved the series, and supplied information concerning the prints. Smith, *loc. cit.*, wrongly states that nos. 857–860 were engraved by Le Vasseur, for whose engravings, see under note 3. (7) Published by P. Angier; that after no. 858 is not dated. (8) Not dated. (9) See Smith, *loc. cit.*; the entries in the ms. copies of the Verrue sale catalogue at the R.K.D. are not specific enough for certain identification: they state that each picture had only one [main?] figure, which would rule out the Blondel de Gagny set (see under note 3). Copies of the sale catalogue in the R.K.D. give either 49 or 50 as the lot number; the price given here is taken from the ms. copies in the R.K.D. (10) When engraved by Surugue, see above. (11) See G. Hoet, *Catalogus* etc., 1770, III, p. 188; the entry reads: 'Vier Getyden des Jaars 8 × 6 du.', which nearly corresponds to the sizes of nos. 857–860. Apart from the correspondence of the sizes there is no other ground for associating the pictures in this sale with nos. 857–860. (12) The catalogue states wrongly that the set was engraved by Le Bas; information concerning the fate of the lot kindly provided by J. Nieuwstraten of the R.K.D. This is probably the sale referred to by Smith, *loc. cit.*; Smith wrongly stated that nos. 857–860 were in a) the La Prade and Blondel de Gagny sales, see note 3; b) the Nourri sale, Paris, 24 February, 1785, but no such series was in this sale, information given by J. Nieuwstraten of the R.K.D.; c) the Destouches sale, 1794 = Destouches sale, Paris, 21 ff. March, 1794 (79) bt. Le Brun the Elder for 1,401 francs; no sizes are given in the catalogue, which states that the support was wood; but the lot entry is too brief for certain identification. N.G. nos. 857–860 were backed with wood (they still are) by the time of the Talleyrand sale of 1817 (see above), but Lebrun correctly described them as on copper in the Villers sale of 1812. (13) This sale never took place— the whole collection being bought by Buchanan, see W. Buchanan, *Memoirs of Painting*, II, 1824, pp. 304–308. The Talleyrand sale catalogue is printed by Buchanan, *op. cit.*, pp. 308 ff; lots 34–37, on p. 339. With the exception of one other lot, these are the only lots that Buchanan did not give details concerning the then owners. (14) As ex coll. Prince Talleyrand. (15) Buyer and price given in the National Gallery marked catalogue.

861 A COTTAGE BEFORE A RIVER WITH A DISTANT
         VIEW OF A CASTLE

A young peasant woman scouring a pot turns to an old peasant wheeling a barrow outside a cottage; on the bank of a river, a cowherd talks to a fisherman; in the distance, a castle set among trees.

Oil on oak (marouflaged), $19\frac{1}{4} \times 26\frac{1}{4}$ (0·489 × 0·667).

Signed, *D·TENIERS·F:*

Generally in good condition. There are some paint losses round the edges and particularly in the top right-hand corner where the support has been repaired. The foliage in the two nearest trees is worn as are probably some areas of browns in the foreground. Spotty, discoloured varnish.

The signature seems to be rather weakly written; but despite this, there is no reason to doubt the traditional[1] attribution of no. 861 to David Teniers II.

No. 861 was probably executed *ca.* 1650.[2]

The castle has not been identified[3]; but the view is, almost certainly, not imaginary.

PROVENANCE: Bought at an Amsterdam sale by the dealers Remy and Hele by 1751 when sold to M. Paignon Dijonval[4]; inherited by his grandson, Le Vicomte de Morel Vindé,[5] by whom sold, Paillet and Bénard (Paris), 17 December, 1821 (107)[6] bt. Emmerson[7] for 3,890 francs[8]; by whom sold to the Rt. Hon. Robert Peel (later Sir Robert Peel, Bart.) for 250 gns. in the spring of 1822[9]; purchased with the Peel Collection, 1871; lent to the Ministry of Works (now Public Building and Works) 1938–41, and, through the Arts Council, to the Art Gallery, Southampton, 1958–63.

REPRODUCTION: *National Gallery Illustrations, Continental Schools (excluding Italian)*, 1950, p. 357, top.

REFERENCES: *In text:* (1) See under *Provenance*. No. 861 is not included by Smith in his catalogue raisonné of Teniers' work, published in 1831. (2) That is probably slightly earlier than the signed and dated picture at Madrid of 1654, (*Catálogo de las Pinturas*, 1963, p. 664, no. 1794, where date not noted) and the picture bearing the same date in the Dr. Axel Wenner-Gren (†) sale, Sotheby's, 24 March, 1965 (50). (3) The suggestion that the castle was Teniers' own, made in the Morel Vindé sale, see below, and by Mrs. Jameson, *Companion to the most celebrated Private Galleries* etc., 1844, p. 364, no. 44, is clearly wrong, see under no. 817. (4) See a note in National Gallery library of a copy of a memorandum of letters to Sir Robert Peel in the possession of A. N. L. Mundy, 1946, being an extract of an ms. catalogue written by the Vicomte de Morel Vindé. (5) According to p. 2 of the *Avertissement* to the catalogue of the Paignon Dijonval/de Morel Vindé sale (see below), de Morel Vindé was the grandson and sole heir of M. Paignon Dijonval. (6) Described as by Teniers 'Vue du château de Téniers: on l'aperçoit dans le milieu d'un bois . . . le point du vue en est d'une ferme . . .' panel, 18 × 24 pouces. (7) See Peel's note in the Goulburn mss., Surrey County Record Office. There has been some confusion over the fate of the Paignon Dijonval/Morel Vindé sale. W. Buchanan, *Memoirs of Painting*, II, 1824, pp. 372–373, stated that he secured 'the collection and transferred his purchase of it to Mr. Phillips of Bond-street . . . A fine Landscape and a Temptation of St. Anthony by David Teniers were sold to the Right Honourable R. Peel . . .' However, J. Smith, *A Catalogue Raisonné* etc., 1829, I, under, *inter alia*, Dou no. 99, states that the collection was sold *en bloc* to Mr. Emmerson (see also under no. 863); finally, a ms. note on the *Feuille de Vacations* of the sale in the National Gallery library states that Buchanan bought the collection of drawings and engravings, but that the paintings were knocked down to bidders; the notes on the *Feuille de Vacations* confirm that the majority seem to have been sold. See also N. MacLaren, *National Gallery Catalogues, The Dutch School*, 1960, pp. 59–60, notes 3 and 4 under no. 208. (8) *Feuille de Vacations* of the sale in the National Gallery library. (9) See note 7.

862   AN OLD PEASANT CARESSES A KITCHEN MAID IN A STABLE ('LA SURPRISE FÂCHEUSE')

An old peasant caresses a kitchen maid, as she scours an earthenware pot; in the background an old woman beckons to a cat from a door.

Oil on oak, $17 \times 25\frac{9}{16}$ (0·432 × 0·649). The city of Antwerp coat of arms is branded on the reverse.

Signed, *D·TENIERS·F*

The foreground is in good condition; the state of the background is only fair and appears to be a good deal retouched. The legs of the cat have been altered. Yellow varnish.

Even taking into account the difference in condition between the foreground and background, it seems evident that the background was never worked up to the same degree of finish. Despite the unsubtle colouring and hard quality of handling of the main figures and objects, it would be unreasonable to suggest that they are not the work of David Teniers II. It is possible that the background was filled in by a studio assistant or that Teniers never worked it up. But in the absence of any definite evidence, it is wisest to accept the traditional view that no. 862 is wholly by David Teniers II, although its quality is not of the highest standard that he was capable of achieving.

The foreground figures are rendered in a manner somewhat similar to those in no. 861 *q.v.*; the presence of the Antwerp brand on the reverse suggests that no. 862 was executed there. Teniers left Antwerp to settle in Brussels perhaps early in 1651.[1] A date towards the very end of Teniers' Antwerp period seems therefore likely for no. 862. The handling is not very comparable to that in no. 155 (*q.v.*) of *ca.* 1648; it shows, however, the same tendency towards a delicate finish that is realized in the so-called *Marriage of the Artist* of 1651.[2]

The title *La Surprise Fâcheuse* seems to date from the early nineteenth century (see below); in fact, in no. 862's present state, the old woman's attention seems to be directed at the cat rather than at the couple in the foregound. Pictures of a similar subject by Teniers are at Petworth,[3] Madrid,[4] Vienna[5] and Basel.[6]

Several of the elements of the still life in the left foreground appear in the Carlsruhe picture of an *Evening Meal in a Stable* of 1634.[7] The furniture in the background occurs in no. 805 (*q.v.*) and in a *Stable Interior* at Vienna.[8]

COPIES: Prado, Madrid, no. 1800, copper, $19\frac{1}{4} \times 25\frac{3}{16}$ (0·49 × 0·64)[9]; of the two main figures only: Goeschl sale, Munich, 29 March, 1897, panel, $17\frac{1}{8} \times 25\frac{5}{8}$ (0·435 × 0·60).[10]

PROVENANCE: Coll. Landgraf Wilhelm VIII (1682–1760) of Hesse at Cassel by 1749[11]; looted from Cassel by General Lagrange and taken to Mainz, October, 1806.[12] Given by Napoleon to the Empress Joséphine († 1814), and perhaps recorded at Malmaison, 1811.[13] Varoc (= Lafontaine)[14] sale, Lebrun (Paris), 28 May–2 June, 1821 (86)[15] 4,000 francs[16] bt. in; Varoc (= Lafontaine) sale, Phillips, 22 March, 1822 (85)[17] bt. by the Rt. Hon. Robert Peel (later Sir Robert Peel, Bart.) for £200[18]; exh. B.I. 1822 (89); purchased with the Peel collection 1871; lent, through the Arts Council, to Leeds City Art Gallery, 1958–63.

REPRODUCTION: *National Gallery Illustrations, Continental Schools (excluding Italian)*, 1950, p. 357, bottom.

REFERENCE: *General: J.* Smith, *A Catalogue Raisonné* etc., 1831, III, Teniers, no. 478.

In text: (1) See H. Vlieghe, *Gentse Bijdragen*, 1961–66, pp. 126–28. (2) Signed and dated, 1651; coll. Lionel de Rothschild, exh. R.A., 1938 (112). (3) See C. H. Collins Baker, *Catalogue of the Petworth Collection of Pictures* etc., 1920, p. 120, no. 633. (4) See *Museo del Prado, Catálogo* etc., 1963, p. 665, no. 1799. The picture of an old man caressing a kitchen maid (without being interrupted) in a stable, coll. Casa de Alba, Madrid, exh. *L'Art Flamand dans les Collections Espagnoles*, Bruges, 1958 (108) seems to be by a follower of D. Teniers II. Smith, *loc. cit.*, no. 174, has not been traced; he refers there to his nos. 24 and 74, now coll. Lord Crawford. In the latter picture the couple are drinking; the earliest rendering of this variation of the theme of no. 862 appears to be the picture, apparently signed and dated 1635, in a Sedelemeyer sale, 3 ff. June,

1907 (73). (5) Canvas, $17\frac{13}{16} \times 20\frac{5}{16}$ (0·45 × 0·72), see E. v. Engerth, *Kunsthistorische Sammlungen des allerhöchsten Kaiserhauses, Gemälde . . . Verzeichniss*, II, 1884, pp. 477–8, no. 1292. (6) Panel, $24\frac{7}{8} \times 29\frac{7}{8}$ (0·61 × 0·86), see *Öffentliche Kunstammlungen Basel, Katalog*, 1926, p. 119, no. 607; the two main figures are variants of those in the Vienna picture. (7) See *Flämische Meister aus der Staatlichen Kunsthalle*, Karlsruhe, 1961, no. 18 and rep. The still life in the Carlsruhe picture seems to have certain affinities with that in *The Stable Interior* of 1634 by Herman Saftleven at Brussels, for which see *Musées Royaux des Beaux-Arts de Belgique, Catalogue de la Peinture Ancienne*, 1957, p. 90, no. 407. There is no evidence that the two artists were ever in direct contact; and the affinity may be due to an influence in common—perhaps that of Cornelis Saftleven who was in Antwerp in the early 1630's, see B. J. A. Renckens, *Bulletin, Museum Boymans-van Beuningen*, 1962, pp. 69 ff. (8) Panel, $27\frac{1}{8} \times 38\frac{9}{16}$ (0·69 × 0·98), see Engerth, *op. cit.*, p. 482, no. 1296. (9) See *Museo del Prado, Catálogo* etc., 1963, p. 666. (10) Lot number not known; photo. in Witt Library. (11) It is no. 59 of the 1749 inventory: 'Teniers David. Ein Haushalt, worinnen ein alter Mann die Magd caressiert auf Holtz . . . Höhe: 1 Schuh 5 Zoll, Breit: 2 Schuh 1 Zoll' (= 17 × 25). Information kindly supplied by Dr. J. Pilz of the Staatliche Kunstsammlungen at Cassel. For Landgraf Wilhelm VIII as a collector, see W. V. Both and Hans Vogel, *Landgraf Wilhelm VIII von Hessen-Kassel*, 1964, pp. 130–147. (12) See G. Gronau, *Internationale Monatschrift . . . für Wissenschaft Kunst* etc., 1917, cols. 1195 and 1203. (13) M. de Lescure, *Le Château de la Malmaison*, 1867, pp. 271–282, reprints the *Catalogue des Tableaux de Sa Majesté l'impératrice Joséphine dans . . . son palais de Malmaison*, 1811; no. 130 is 'Teniers . . . Intérieur de Cuisine Bois)', which is part of the title given to no. 862 in the Varoc sale (see note 14). (14) Varoc, or Varroc, was a bankrupt, and, as the introduction to the sale catalogue makes clear, the pictures had been deposited with him by Lafontaine, who after a lawsuit by Varoc's debtors had agreed to sell them. (15) Described as 'Intérieur de Cuisine, ou la surprise fâcheuse, panel, 16 p. × 24 p.' (16) See the marked copy of the sale catalogue in the British Museum. (17) Described as 'La Surprise Facheuse [*sic*], The Interior of a Dutch Kitchen . . .'. This is the sale referred to by Smith, *loc. cit.* (18) See Peel's note in the Goulburn mss., Surrey County Record Office. (19) Smith, *loc. cit.*, mistakenly states that no. 862 was exhibited at the B.I. in 1823.

863 THE RICH MAN BEING LED TO HELL
        (LE MAUVAIS RICHE)

The rich man stands at the entrance to Hell, surrounded by demons.

Oil on oak, *ca.* 19 × $24\frac{1}{4}$ (0·48 × 0·69).

The top and left-hand edges of the support are irregular. The Antwerp coat of arms is branded (faintly and perhaps twice) on the reverse.

Signed, *D TENIERS·F*

Apparently in very good condition. There is, however, a thick yellow varnish.

The subject is from Luke, XVI, 19–23.

There is no reason to doubt the traditional attribution of no. 863 to David Teniers II.[1]

The handling seems to have been influenced by that of Cornelis Saftleven[2]; and the monsters may also have been inspired by the work of this artist,[3] although ultimately they derive from those of Bosch. Similar monsters appear in David Teniers II's renderings of *The Temptation of S. Anthony*; and no. 863 was probably executed *ca.* 1647, the date of a picture recorded at Berlin of this subject.[4]

The Viscount de Morel Vindé thought that there was a pendant to no. 863, showing the rich man at table, in the collection of the Grand Duke at Florence [5]; but no such picture is recorded in the Pitti or Uffizi. The rich man feasting and being led to Hell are the subjects of two oval paintings, given to David Teniers II, in the Le Boeuf sale of 1783.[6]

ENGRAVING (?): Mezzotint in reverse by R. Earlom (ca. 1742/3–1822).[7]

COPY: Lille Museum, panel, $20\frac{7}{8} \times 28\frac{3}{4}$ (0·53 × 0·73).[8]

DERIVATION (?): Anon. sale, Sotheby's, 6 February, 1957 (113), metal, $19\frac{3}{4} \times 23\frac{3}{4}$ (0·502 × 0·603).[9]

PROVENANCE: Le Comte de Merle sale, Paillet (Paris), 1 ff. March, 1784 (48), bt. Sauset (?) for 3,499 livres.[10] Destouches sale, Lebrun and Jueliot (Paris), 21 ff. March, 1794 (76), bt. Galant for 3,801 livres.[11] Le Vicomte Morel Vindé sale, Paillet and Bénard (Paris), 18 December (= 2nd day), 1821 (109)[12] bt. Emmerson[13]; by whom sold in exchange for a picture by Teniers valued at £100, and £200 to the Rt. Hon. Robert Peel[14] (later Sir Robert Peel, Bart.) in the spring of 1822[15]; probably exh. B.I. 1835 (112)[16]; purchased with the Peel collection, 1871; lent to the Corporation Art Gallery, Bradford, 1935, and, through the Arts Council, to the City of Leicester Museum and Art Gallery, 1958–62.

REPRODUCTION: *National Gallery Illustrations, Continental Schools (excluding Italian)*, 1950, p. 358, top.

REFERENCE: *General:* J. Smith, *A Catalogue Raisonné* etc., 1831, III, Teniers, no. 264.

In text: (1) See under *Provenance* and *General Reference*. (2) Compare Saftleven's rendering of the same subject of 1631 in the National Museum, Warsaw, rep. by B. J. A. Renckens, *Bulletin, Museum Boymans-van Beuningen*, 1962, p. 65, fig. 18. (3) Compare the drawing of 1630 rep. by Renckens, *op. cit.*, p. 64, fig. 17. Renckens, p. 62, draws attention to the description of Saftleven's art in the inscription under his portrait in van Dyck's *Iconography*: 'Hollandus pictor noctium phantasmatum', and, p. 72, discusses his relationship with David Teniers II. (4) Canvas, $31\frac{7}{8} \times 56\frac{1}{16}$ (0·81 × 1·17), see the Kaiser Friedrich Museum catalogue, 1931, p. 418, no. 849; not in the post-war catalogues of the Dahlem Museum. (5) See extracts of an ms. catalogue by de Morel Vindé in an album of letters to Sir Robert Peel, in the possession of A. N. L. Mundy, 1946, who kindly communicated the contents. (6) Anon. [= Le Boeuf] sale, Le Brun (Paris), 8 ff. April, 1783 (33), copper, $21 \times 24\frac{1}{2}$ pouces; see Smith, *op. cit.*, Teniers, nos. 260–261. They may have been the two ovals of the same subject in the John Knight sale, Phillips, 17 March (1821) (27) (where not stated as being ovals) bt. in; John Knight sale, Phillips, 24 May, 1839 (13–14); and later in the Anon. [= Heusch] sale, Christie's, 24 May, 1845 (56–57) as ex coll. John Knight. The Knight pictures are Smith, *op. cit.*, Teniers, no. 452. (7) This print does not exactly follow no. 863; the copy in the British Museum is an early state with no rubric. (8) See *Musée de Lille, Catalogue des Tableaux*, 1893, p. 266, no. 761, where ascribed to David Teniers I. (9) This may be a copy of the ex Le Boeuf picture, see above. A drawing of this subject, given to David Teniers II, was in the Anon. [= L'Empereur] sale, Paris, 24 ff. May, 1773 (338). (10) Panel, 17 pouces, 6 lignes × 25 pouces 6 lignes (= ca. $18\frac{1}{2} \times 27\frac{1}{4}$). The price and buyer in the marked catalogue in the National Gallery library. The measurements in C. Blanc, *Le Trésor de la Curiosité*, 1858, II, p. 92, are not correct. (11) Panel, 18 p. × 18 p. 6 l. (= $19\frac{1}{8} \times 19\frac{5}{8}$), these measurements are incorrect; they do not correspond, but the description given does. See also note 12. For the price and buyer, see the copy of the sale catalogue in the British Museum. The collection of M. Destouches, 'Intendant-général de la Maison & Finances de Madame Comtesse d'Artois,' was noted by Thiéry,

Guide des Amateurs etc., I, 1787, pp. 142–3. (12) Panel, 25 pouces × 18½ pouces (*ca.* 26½ × 19⅜); the sizes have been inverted; as ex the Destouches sale. According to p. 2 of the *Avertissement* to the sale catalogue, de Morel Vindé the grandson and heir of Paignon Dijonval, added to the collection by buying, *inter alia.,* from the Destouches sale, see also nos. 192 and 208 of this collection. (13) See the note by Peel in the Goulburn mss., Surrey County Record Office. There is some confusion of the fate of this sale, see under no. 861, note 6. (14) See note 13; Smith, under *General Reference*, gave the price as 350 gns. (15) See note 13. (16) No. 863 may have been the picture by David Teniers II called 'An Incantation', lent by Sir Robert Peel.

950 A VIEW OF A VILLAGE WITH THREE PEASANTS TALKING IN THE FOREGROUND

Oil on relined canvas, *ca.* 44¼ × 65⅝ (1·125 × 1·667).

Signed, *DT·F* (DT in monogram).

In fairly good condition. There are some large areas of retouchings over losses in the sky; retouchings, presumably over damage, are present on the two small tree trunks behind the greyhound, across the belly of the greyhound and on the wall of the cottage beneath the roof. There are scattered areas of wearing in the cottages, trees and banks. The paint of the foliage of the tree on the left is diseased.

There is a *pentimento* in the nearside bank of the stream, in the centre, where a gate or some wooden construction has been suppressed.

No. 950 was first catalogued at the National Gallery as the work of David Teniers I[1]; there is no reason, however, to doubt its re-attribution to David Teniers II made in the 1915 catalogue.

No. 950 was probably executed about the middle of the 1640's.

The view has not been identified; the same village occurs in a picture said to be signed by David Teniers II, in a Sedelmeyer sale of 1901[2]; the foreground figures recur in a picture, also said to be signed by David Teniers II, in the Baron H. V. Mecklenberg sale, Vienna, 1872.[3]

ENGRAVINGS: By A. Laurent, 1742[4]; of the left half: by 'Jorma'.[5]

COPIES: Anon. sale, Christie's, 31 May, 1963 (21), canvas 39 × 49½ (0·99 × 1·57); of the left-hand half: on The Hague art market, 1964[6]; of the three main figures: tapestry woven by P. van der Borcht, at Petworth.[7]

PROVENANCE: Coll. the dealer Remy, Paris, 1742.[8] Coll. the Marquess of Buckingham (1753–1813) at Stowe by 1801[9]; 2nd Duke of Buckingham sale, Stowe, 15 September (= 24th day), 1848 (428) bt. T. B. Brown for £252.[10] Probably acquired by Wynn Ellis after 1850/1[11]; Wynn Ellis Bequest, 1876; lent to the Ministry of Works (now Public Building and Works), 1934–41.

REPRODUCTION: *National Gallery Illustrations, Continental Schools (excluding Italian)*, 1950, p. 358, bottom.

REFERENCES: *In text:* (1) See the National Gallery catalogues from 1877–1913. (2) Lot 46; rep. in catalogue. (3) Baron H. V. Mecklenberg sale, Vienna, 11 November, 1872 (61), engraved in the catalogue by W. Unger. (4) Called 'La Conversation'; see J. Smith, *A Catalogue Raisonné* etc., 1831, III, Teniers, no. 367. (5) See also Smith, *op. cit.,* Teniers, no. 234. Called 'La Nouvelle du Jour'. According to Ch. Le Blanc, *Manuel de l'Amateur d'Estampes,* 1856–1888, II, p. 591, 'Jorma' was the signature used by P. J. Basan (1727–1797) when copying the work of Thomas Major (1714–1799); but the entry in Thieme-Becker for Major states that he himself sometimes used 'Jorma' as a signature. **(6)** Photo in R.K.D. **(7)** See the Marillier ms. at the Victoria and Albert Museum. **(8)** When engraved by Laurent. No. 950 did not feature in the Anon. [= Remy] sale, Paris, 30 June 1772. **(9)** See J. Britton and E. Wedlake Brayley, *The Beauties of England and Wales* etc., 1801, I, p. 304: 'A large landscape, with an Alehouse, and a group of three Figures resting on their staffs: D. Teniers' as in the State Drawing Room. **(10)** See H. R. Forster, *The Stowe Catalogue Priced and Annotated*, 1848, p. 194. **(11)** No. 950 was not noted in the Wynn Ellis collection by G. F. Waagen, *Treasures of Art in Great Britain*, II, 1854, pp. 293 ff., which Waagen revisited in 1850 or 1851; nor was it in the T. B. Brown sale of 1856. The 1915–1929 Gallery catalogues suggested that no. 950 was in the Thomas Turton (†), Lord Bishop of Ely, sale, Christie's, 14 April, 1864 (9)—'Teniers. A village scene, with three peasants and a dog before a cottage'; this picture was sold for £8 to Permain (?) (see Christie's marked catalogue).

951 PEASANTS PLAYING BOWLS OUTSIDE A
        VILLAGE INN

Three onlookers stand by while a young peasant runs to join his partner at the target, as their opponent is about to play; the opponent's partner awaits his turn. A serving woman brings drinks from an inn, whose sign is a crescent moon.

Oil on relined canvas, $48\frac{1}{8} \times 75\frac{3}{16}$ (1·202 × 1·91).

Signed, *DTf* (DT in monogram).

Generally in good condition. There are some small losses in the sky. Cleaned, 1951.

Wornum wrongly considered no. 951 to be the work of David Teniers I[1]; his attribution was retained until the 1915 Gallery catalogue, where no. 951 was attributed to David Teniers II. It seems uncertain whether the figures and landscape are by the same hand. But the landscape is clearly and acceptably by David Teniers II; the figures are also close to his in style. Until, however, more is known of the personalities working in the circle of David Teniers II, it would be premature to suggest that he was not responsible for at least some of the figures in no. 951.

The treatment of the landscape appears to be comparable to that in the *Peasant's dancing outside an Inn* at Cassel.[2] The figures are also comparable to those in the Cassel picture; they also relate closely to those in paintings bearing David Teniers II's signature and date *ca.* 1660.[3] A date *ca.* 1660 is thus acceptable for the execution of no. 951.

The three foreground figures are very similar to those in the *Landscape with Peasants bowling* at Los Angeles[4]—a work in the same vein as no. 951. A church similar to that set on the hill in no. 951, but with different houses nearby, appears in an engraving of *Peasants outside an Inn* of 1812 by Klauber after D. Teniers II.[5]

COPIES: Niesewand sale, Cologne, November, 1906 (27), panel, $26\frac{3}{4} \times 38\frac{9}{16}$ (0·68 × 0·98); of some of the main figures: tapestry by J. de Vos.[6]

PROVENANCE: Perhaps[7] in the one or some of the following sales: Dr. Bearcroft sale, Langford, 12 February (= 2nd day), 1762 (24); Robert Ansell sale, Walsh, 25 March (= 2nd day), 1775 (81); Robert Heathcote sale, Phillips, 5

April, 1805 (34) £170 bt. Dormer.[8] Probably in the John Humble sale, Christie's, 11 April, 1812 (33) bt. Hannytoe for £144.[9] Anon. (= Lafontaine) sale, Christie's, 8 May, 1813 (74) £680 10 sh. bt. in[10]; Varoc (= Lafontaine) sale, Lebrun (Paris), 28 ff. May, 1821 (81)[11]; Varoc (= Lafontaine) sale, Phillips, 29 June (= 2nd day), 1822 (160).[12] Probably coll. the Chevalier Sebastian Erard, 1831[13]; his sale, 7–14 August, 1832 (144) 4,990 francs (?) bt. in[14]; his (†) sale, Christie's, 22 June, 1833 (19) bt. Taylor for £152.[15] Wynn Ellis Bequest 1876[16]; lent to the City Art Gallery, Leeds, 1934, and to the Graves Art Gallery, Sheffield, 1937.

REPRODUCTION: *National Gallery Illustrations, Continental Schools (excluding Italian)*, 1950, p. 359, top.

REFERENCE: *General:* J. Smith, *A Catalogue Raisonné* etc., 1831, III, Teniers, no. 541. The description is reversed; there is no engraving by Le Bas after no. 951, as Smith states.

In text: (1) See R. N. Wornum, *Catalogue of the Pictures in the National Gallery* etc., 1877; the attribution is accepted by M. H. Witt, *The German and Flemish Masters in the National Gallery*, 1904, pp. 201–202. For David Teniers I's style, see under no. 949; and note 4 under no. 1287. (2) See the *Katalog der Staatlichen Gemäldegalerie zu Kassel*, 1958, p. 148, no. 148. (3) Compare those in the *Card Players in an Inn*, Anon. sale, Christie's, 15 March, 1929 (70) of 1658; and the picture of 1660 at Luxembourg, Museum Piscatore, no. 65 of the 1872 catalogue. (4) See *A Catalogue of Flemish, German, Dutch and English Paintings*, Los Angeles County Museum, 1954, p. 27, no. 23 and rep. (5) The engraving is reproduced in the Duval sale catalogue, Phillips, 12–13 May, 1846, between pp. 22–23; the picture is lot 103 of the sale. The same picture, or a similar one, was in the Rittmann-Ulrech sale, Cologne, 30 April, 1912 (116); coll. Dr. Hüllmann, Wiesbaden, *ca.* 1925; and with Schulthess, Basel, 1962 (note in R.K.D.). (6) See Marillier ms. at the Victoria and Albert Museum. (7) The descriptions are too short for any definite identification. (8) Price given in the National Gallery's copy of the sale catalogue; buyer's name given by G. Redford, *Art Sales* etc. (9) The description in the Humble sale catalogue closely corresponds to no. 951; for the price and buyer's name, see Christie's marked catalogue. (10) For the identity of the seller see under no. 817 (*q.v.*). As ex coll. the Duke Albert. This may refer to the Duc de D'Alberg whose collection was put up for sale at Christie's 13/14 June, 1817; according to the introduction to the catalogue by T. Francillon, the collection was formed over the previous 20 years. The description in the 1813 sale catalogue reasonably corresponds to no. 951; the Duke's ownership of no. 951 either before the Humble sale or (most improbably) between 1812–13 cannot be established. Fate of the lot given by A. Graves, *Art Sales* etc., who wrongly gave the year of the sale as 1812. (11) For the identity of the seller see under no. 863. This is presumably the sale referred to by Smith, *loc. cit.* The measurements are given as 44 × 68 p. (= 46¾ × 72½) and the entry is similar to that which was later used in the Erard sale catalogue (see note 14). (12) As ex coll. the Duc d'Alberg (*sic*). (13) See Smith, *loc. cit.* (14) The sale catalogue is dated 1831; the introduction does not specify a date for the sale because of the political situation. The sale was put off from the 23 April, 1832, see Lugt, no. 12962. The price is given in the marked copy of the sale catalogue in the National Gallery library where not specified as withdrawn. The description does not exactly tally with no. 951 with regard to the foreground figures, two of whom are stated to have already played and to be waiting 'au but', for the throws of their opponents. The picture is stated to be ex coll. 'du gouverneur du Pays-Bas'—presumably a mistaken identification of the Duc de D'Alberg. (15) The description given here is shorter and in one detail inaccurate—for the shepherd and flock in the middle distance of no. 951 are stated to be in the foreground. It is likely that this is the same picture which had been in the previous Erard sale. Buyer's name and price from Christie's marked catalogue. (16)

No. 951 is not noted by Waagen in Wynn Ellis' collection in 1850/51, see
G. F. Waagen, *Treasures of Art* etc., II, 1854, p. 295.

2600 TWO MEN PLAYING CARDS IN THE KITCHEN
OF AN INN

A man deals cards to his opponent, watched by two men and a boy;
a woman looks down from an opening in the wall, above; in the corner
a man urinating; in the background four men and a woman, who is
cooking with a frying pan over an open fire.

Oil on oak, $21\frac{7}{8} \times 30\frac{1}{8}$ (0·555 × 0·765).

The reverse of the support bears the brand of the coat of arms of the
city of Antwerp and the incised initials, *MV* (in monogram).

Signed, *DAVID TENIERS F*

Generally in fairly good condition. The figures are quite well preserved
except in the darks, but the extent of wearing is difficult to establish
because of the old varnish.

The signature is not above suspicion,[1] but there is no reason to
doubt the authenticity of no. 2600.

The panel bears the monogram of, and was therefore made by,
Michiel Vriendt, who died 1636/7.[2] The date of death of the panel
maker can be taken as an approximate guide for the date of Teniers'
execution of no. 2600. No. 2600 is clearly more advanced than Teniers'
earliest rendering of card players of 1633 at Leipzig.[3] The composition
is indeed closely related to the Louvre *Card Players* of 1645, where the
same model was used for the card player on the right.[4] However, the
treatment of the figures in no. 2600 is less refined and the tonality is
darker. The seated onlooker and the dealer in no. 2600 occur in the
Duke of Sutherland's *Card Players* of ca. 1636,[5] and the dealer appears
as the model for the patient in the Budapest *Foot Operation*[6] of that
year. The composition of no. 2600 is more ambitious than that in either
of these pictures. For these reasons, and bearing in mind the presence of
Vriendt's monogram on the support, a date towards the end of the
1630's seems acceptable for no. 2600.

ENGRAVING: By Bernard Lépicié, 1747 (in reverse), as *Les Francs Maçons
Flamands en Loge*.[7]

COPY: Of the main fore and middle ground figures, set outside an inn and in
reverse, Berlin Art Market (n.d.).[8]

PROVENANCE: Perhaps Anon. sale, Amsterdam, 21 October, 1739 (29)
300 glds.[9] Coll. M. Bellanger, Substitut de M. le Procureur du Roi, by 1747
when engraved[10]; M. Bellanger (†), Doyen de M. M. Substituts de M. le
Procureur du Roi, sale, Paris, 18 July, 1789 (4), not sold[11]; M. Bellanger (†),
sale, Hôtel de Bullion, Paris, 18 February, 1790 (4).[12] Perhaps Anon. sale (of
pictures lately consigned from Paris), Christie's, 5 March (= 2nd day), 1791 (40)[13]
bt. Pope for 185 gns.[14] Perhaps Anon. sale, Christie's, 4 May, 1805 (72)[15]
bt. Benlick (?) for £173 5sh.[16] Perhaps General Craig (†) sale, Christie's,
18 April, 1812 (69)[17] bt. Rickards for 185 gns.[18] Coll. Sir Simon Clarke by
1831[19]; Sir Simon Clarke sale, Christie's, 9 May (= 2nd day), 1840 (107)
bt. Dunford for Cope (?) 230 gns.[20]; exh. R.A. 1872 (178) lent by Mrs. Charles
Cope; Charles Cope (†) sale, Christie's, 8 June, 1872 (55)[21] bt. Agnew for £1,500[22]
by whom sold to Louis Huth.[23] Coll. George Salting by 1883[24]; perhaps exh.

The Collection of Pictures and Drawings of the late George Salting, 1910 (169)[25];
Salting Bequest, 1910; lent to the Usher Art Gallery, Lincoln, 1929; Art
Gallery and Museum, Doncaster, 1929; Public Library and Art Gallery,
Harrogate, 1930; Corporation Art Gallery, Bradford, 1931; and, through the
Arts Council, to the Bowes Museum, 1951–63.

REPRODUCTION: *National Gallery Illustrations, Continental Schools (excluding
Italian)*, 1950, p. 361, top.

REFERENCE: *General:* J. Smith, *A Catalogue Raisonné* etc., 1831, III, Teniers,
no. 568.

In text: (1) No signature appears in the engraving of 1747 (see below under
Engraving). (2) See G. Gepts, *Jaarboek, Koninklijk Museum voor Schone Kunsten,
Antwerp*, 1954–1960, p. 87. (3) $9\frac{5}{8} \times 12\frac{3}{4}$ (0·245 × 0·325); no. 1066 of the 1929
catalogue. No. 139 at Cassel is not dated 1633 or 1635 and is probably after
D. Teniers II, this contrary to the *Katalog der Staatlichen Gemäldegalerie zu
Kassel*, 1958, p. 147. (4) Canvas, $22\frac{7}{16} \times 30\frac{11}{16}$ (0·57 × 0·78), for which see
Louis Demonts, *Catalogue des Peintures, Musée National du Louvre*, 1922,
III, p. 32, no. 2162A. One of the seated onlookers occurs in a picture
at Leningrad, by David Teniers II, see *Musée de l'Hermitage, Catalogue
des Peintures*, II, 1958, p. 107, no. 577. (5) Panel, $10\frac{1}{2} \times 13\frac{1}{4}$ (0·267 ×
0·337), see J. Smith, *A Catalogue Raisonné* etc., 1831, III, p. 393, no. 502. This
picture appears to be comparable with, but later than, the *Le Roi Boit*, dated
1635, in an Anon. sale, Sotheby, 10 July, 1963 (42), panel, 19 × 28 (0·483 × 0·712)
ex coll. Edward Betts. (6) Panel, $18\frac{1}{8} \times 24\frac{3}{4}$ (0·46 × 0·63), see the catalogue of
the *Országas Magyar Szépmüveszti Muzeum*, Budapest, I, 1937, pp. 253–4,
no. 565, and rep. in vol. II; he also occurs in a picture at the Musée Fabre, Montpellier, see A. Joubin, *Catalogue des Peintures . . . du Musée Fabre* etc., 1926,
pp. 91–2, no. 298. (7) As in coll. of M. Bellanger, Substitut de M. le Procureur
du Roi. There are no grounds to substantiate the fanciful title given by Lépicié.
(8) A reproduction from a catalogue (of perhaps before 1914 as kindly suggested
by Dr. Gudlaugsson) of the Berlin dealer Weustenberg is in the R.K.D.
The foreground figures probably derive from the engraving by Lépicié. A
similar picture was in coll. C. E. Fritze, Stockholm, 1919 (photo. in the Witt
Library, where the measurements are given as 26 × 33¾ (0·66 × 0·86)). (9) See
G. Hoet, *Catalogus* etc., 1752, I, p. 610: 'Een Binnenhuys, door David Teniers,
vol Beelden en Kaartspeelders. h 2v. 2d., br 2 v. 8d.', which is slightly larger
than no. 2600. (10) There is a seal on the reverse of no. 2600 which nearly
accords with coat of arms of the Bellanger family of Paris, given by A. de la
Chenaye—Dubois & Badier, *Dictionnaire de la Noblesse*, 2, 1863, col. 853: 'de
gueules au lion d'argent; au chef cousu d'azur, chargé de deux molettes
d'épernon d'or, et soustenu d'une trangle, aussi d'or'. (11) M. Sjoberg of the
Cabinet d'Estampes, Bibliothèque Nationale, has kindly given details
of the sale and the lot number (letter in Gallery archives). He states
that the sale, which did not take place, was to be held in the house
of the deceased, 'rue des Marmouzets, près le Cloître Notre Dame'.
The description of lot 4 corresponds with no. 2600, the size was given
as '20 p. 6 l. × 27 p. 6 l.', and Lépicié's engraving is referred to. (12) See M. Sjoberg's letter referred to in note 12; the catalogue was the same as that for the
1789 sale. (13) Described as 'Boors at cards . . .' by 'D. Teniers'. (14) See
Christie's marked catalogue. (15) Described as 'Dutch boors playing at Cards'.
The National Gallery catalogue of 1929 states that no. 2600 was in an Anon.
sale of 1807 '"from Dundas Coll" (1794)'. This sale has not been traced;
no. 2600 was certainly not in the Sir Lawrence Dundas sale of 1794. (16) See
Christie's marked catalogue. (17) Described as 'An interior with card players'
by Teniers. The seller was General Sir James Henry Craig (1748–1812). (18)
See Christie's marked catalogue. (19) See Smith, cited under *General
Reference*. (20) Buyer and price from Christie's marked catalogue. J. Smith,
Supplement to the Catalogue Raisonné etc., 1842, p. 420, no. 205, states that
Cope was the buyer at the sale. (21) The Christie stencil for the Cope sale is

on the reverse of no. 2600. (22) Marked catalogue in the National Gallery library. (23) Information kindly provided by Mr. Julian Agnew. (24) Salting's notebooks in the National Gallery Library. (25) Perhaps to be identified with the picture by Teniers called the 'Tric-Trac Players'.

5851 PEASANTS AT ARCHERY

Oil on relined canvas, 47 × 114 (1·194 × 2·896).
Signed, *D: TENIERS·F*
In fairly good condition. The sky is worn and retouched, notably in the rain clouds. The rainstorm behind the seated man is very unreliable. The same must be said for the distant landscape beneath the rainstorm, part of the tree behind the bank and the left-hand turret of the castle. There are some small areas of wearing; for instance in the foliage, which is very thinly painted. A dirty varnish remains in the declivities of the paint surface.

There is no reason to doubt the traditional view that no. 5851 is the work of David Teniers II.

It was probably executed about the same time as no. 950, but probably after the picture of the same subject in the Baron Oppenheim sale, 1914, of 1645.[1] Two of the poses in this picture are repeated in no. 5851, and four others are similar.

The view has not been identified.[2]

PROVENANCE: Coll. James, 2nd Earl of Bandon (1785–1856) by 1831 when exh. at the B.I. (113); the Rt. Hon. the Earl of Bandon (=James, 4th Earl (1850–1924)) sale,[3] Christie's, 10 July (=2nd day) 1886 (204) bt. Colnaghi for £477 15sh.[4] Perhaps sold by Colnaghi to Arthur James[5]; certainly coll. Arthur James by 1909[6]; Arthur James collection, bequeathed by Mrs. M. V. James, 1948; on loan to the Ministry of Public Building and Works, from 1967.

REPRODUCTION: National Gallery photographs available.

REFERENCE: *General:* J. Smith, *Supplement to the Catalogue Raisonné* etc., 1842, IX, Teniers, no. 140.
In text: (1) Baron Oppenheim sale, Lepke, 27 October, 1914 (38), copper 13⅜ × 24¼ (0·34 × 0·54); rep. in catalogue. See also J. Smith, *A Catalogue Raisonné* etc., 1831, III, Teniers, no. 528; and E. Molinier, *Collection du Baron Albert Oppenheim*, 1904, p. 17, no. 40, and pl. XXXVI. (2) Wrongly identified as Teniers' 'château' in the Christie's sale catalogue of 1886, see under *Provenance*. For Teniers' country house, see under no. 817. (3) Pictures removed from Castle Bernard, nr. Bandon, County Cork. (4) See Christie's marked sale catalogue. (5) Letter of 1949 from Mrs. James's nephew, Mr. V. Cavendish-Bentinck, in the Gallery archives. (6) *Ibid.*

Ascribed to DAVID TENIERS II

154 PEASANTS MAKING MUSIC IN AN INN

Oil on oak, 10 9/16 × 13 13/16 (0·269 × 0·351). Additions all round the support, make the overall measurements, 11 7/16 × 14¼ (0·291 × 0·362). On the reverse of the support are the stamped initials, *F | DB*
Signed, *D·TENIERS·F·*

In fairly good condition. Two cracks across the support are retouched. The additions to the sides have been reduced. Cleaned,
1960–1.[1]

The man plays a lute; the book (of songs) is inscribed: *BASO* [*sic*].
The owl on the window ledge may be a reference to uncleanliness or to
sinners.[1]

No. 154 has been generally accepted as the work of David Teniers
II[2]; and it is executed in a manner obviously reminiscent of him. The
fact that the signature is rather feebly written and apparently contemporary with the rest is not necessarily significant; but there are
evident weaknesses in handling. The initials on the reverse of the support
may well be those of the panel maker[3]—probably to be identified as
François de Bout, who became a master in the Antwerp guild of S. Luke
in the year 1637/8.[4] If this identification is accepted, the year of de Bout's
admission as a master in the guild provides a *terminus post quem* for the
date of execution of no. 154. And it is probable that no. 154 was executed
not very long afterwards, as no. 154 relates to David Teniers II's style
of the mid 1630's.[5] But the handling is inferior to that in, for instance,
no. 2600, executed not later than towards the end of the 1630's. It thus
seems possible that no. 154 is the work of a follower or imitator, perhaps
copying a lost original; one such copyist is known to have been active
by 1645.[6] However, bearing in mind the traditional view concerning
no. 154, it seems best at this stage to catalogue it as ascribed to David
Teniers II.

The subject of no. 154 was fairly popular with David Teniers II; and
no. 154 connects with an etching by him.[7] The *Lute Player* by Brouwer[8]
may be cited as a possible influence on the composition, although the
pose of the lute player in no. 154 also suggests a Caravaggesque influence.

ENGRAVING: Mezzotint by W. Pether, published by T. Bradford, 1764.[9]

COPIES AND/OR VERSIONS: Rotterdam, Boymans-van Beuningen Museum,
panel (oval), $15\frac{9}{16} \times 20\frac{7}{8}$ (0·395 × 0·53)[10]; Sibiu, Brukenthal Museum, $7\frac{7}{8} \times 11$
(0·20 × 0·28)[11]; Anon. sale, Lempertz (Cologne), 10 March, 1925 (143) panel,
11 × 14⅛ (0·28 × 0·36) as by Brouwer[12]; Bukowski sale, Stockholm, 15 March,
1932 (79), panel, $12\frac{3}{16} \times 15\frac{3}{4}$ (0·31 × 0·40) as by Abraham Teniers[13]; with the
dealer M. Wolff, Amsterdam, before 1938, canvas, $8\frac{1}{4} \times 10\frac{1}{4}$ (0·21 × 0·26)[14];
Dr. Z. Brucke sale, Kende Gallery (New York), 5 June, 1940 (19), 10 × 14
(0·254 × 0·355)[15]; Anon. sale, Sotheby's, 27 October, 1948 (139), panel, 10 × 14
(0·254 × 0·355); Anon. sale Christie's, 20 December, 1963, (65) panel (?), 10 × 14
(0·254 × 0·355)[16]; Anon. coll. Curaçao, 1965, canvas[17]; Anon. sale, Sotheby's, 18
January, 1967 (174), panel, $9\frac{1}{2} \times 14\frac{1}{2}$ (0·242 × 0·368); Anon. coll., Lewes, 1967,
canvas, $11\frac{1}{8} \times 14\frac{1}{8}$ (0·28 × 0·359); of the three main figures, Laan sale, Geneva,
9 June, 1934, panel, $8\frac{1}{4} \times 9\frac{13}{16}$ (0·21 × 0·25)[18]; variant of the two main figures, coll.
E. A. Assheton Bennett, panel (?), 11 × 14½ (0·28 × 0·369).[19]

PROVENANCE: Perhaps in the W. van Huls (†) sale, London, 6 ff. August, 1722
(114) bt. Sir I. Eyles for £44 2sh.[20] Coll. T. Bradford by 1764, when engraved[21];
Thomas Bradford sale, Hobbs, 7 February (= 2nd day), 1765 (33).[22] Perhaps in
one or some of the following sales[23]: Dewick sale, Burnsall, 3 March, 1766 (20/
21)[24]; Robert Ansell sale, Walsh, 24 March, 1775 (45)[25]; Robert Heathcote sale,
Phillips, 6 April (= 2nd day), 1805 (72) £50[26]; or Anon. sale, Christie's, 4 May,

1805 (59) bt. Churchill £23 2sh.[27]; Anon. sale, Phillips, 27 June, 1807 (62)[28]; Anon. (= Delahante and others), Phillips, 3 March, 1810 (62).[29] Coll. the Rt. Hon. C. Long (later Lord Farnborough) by 1818, when lent to the B.I. (107); exh. B.I. 1835 (31); Lord Farnbourgh Bequest 1838; lent to the City Art Gallery, Leeds, 1934; and, through the Arts Council, to the Municipal Art Gallery and Museum, Wolverhampton, 1952–4.

REPRODUCTION: *National Gallery Illustrations, Continental Schools (excluding Italian)*, 1950, p. 353, top.

REFERENCE: *General:* J. Smith, *A Catalogue Raisonné* etc., 1831, II, Teniers, no. 503.

In text: (1) See W. H. Janson, *Apes and Ape Lore*, 1952, p. 178, and p. 196, note 91; and L. Brand Philip, *The Art Bulletin*, 1953, pp. 275–6, note 43. (2) See Smith, cited under *General Reference*, and previous National Gallery catalogues. (3) The same initials have been noted on the reverse of the following: *The Stable Interior* by David Teniers II at Basle (no. 207), *The Physician* by (or perhaps after) David Teniers II at Carlsruhe, Staatliche Kunsthalle (no. 194 of 1966 catalogue); *The Peasants Dance* after Rubens, Vienna, Akademie, see R. Eigenberger, *Die Gemäldegalerie der Akademie der bildenden Künste in Wien*, 1927, p. 359, no. 645; a copy after *The Stable Scene*, by David Teniers II at the Wellington Museum, Apsley House, in an Anon. sale, Sotheby's, 14 February, 1968 (31); and two *Church Interiors*, signed *Neeffs*, in the Miss F. G. Alston and Mrs. P. Williams sale, Christie's, 1 November, 1968 (61). (4) See Ph. Rombouts and Th. van Lerius, *De Liggeren* etc., [1864–1876], II, p. 91. He was still alive in 1661/2, when his wife died, see Rombouts and van Lerius, *op. cit.*, p. 331. (5) Compare with, for instance, the *Le Roi Boit* of 1635, see note 5 under no. 2600. (6) In this year Jan Brueghel II paid Diric van den Bos for a copy after picture by Teniers, see his day book, published by J. Denucé, *Letters and Documents concerning Jan Bruegel I and II*, 1934, p. 158. (7) See Ch. Le Blanc, *Manuel de l'Amateur d'Estampes*, 1889, 4, p. 17, no. 5. (8) Rep. by G. Knuttel, *Adriaen Brouwer* etc., 1962, pl. 77. (9) As in the collection of Mr. Bradford. (10) See M. D. Henkel, *Zeitschrift für bildende Kunst*, 1910, p. 214, and fig. 15, who records that the picture had been doubted. (11) No. 1107 of the 1909 catalogue. (12) Photo. in R.K.D. (13) Rep. pl. 16 of the sale catalogue; photo. in R.K.D. (14) *Ibid.* (15) *Ibid.* (16) Ex Anon. sale, Christie's, 19 July, 1963 (126). (17) Photo. in R.K.D. (18) Rep. pl. XXXIX of the sale catalogue. (19) Photo. in R.K.D. (20) As by Teniers, described as 'A Man with a Fiddle &c.'; for buyer and price, see the marked ms. catalogue in the Victoria and Albert Museum Library. The picture was not in the Sir Joseph Eyles sale of 1741. (21) When mezzotinted, see note 9. (22) No marked catalogue is listed by Lugt. (23) On the back of no. 154 is written 'No. 75'; MacLaren, ms. notes, also records the number 111, written in chalk partly over the ink. (24) By Teniers, described as a 'Musical Conversation'. (25) *Ibid.* (26) By Teniers, described as a 'Musical Conversation' the catalogue claimed that the pictures came from several continental collections. (27) By Teniers, described as 'An Interior with Figures and a Man playing the Guitar'. Buyer's name and price given in Christie's marked catalogue. The collection was stated to have been purchased on the continent. (28) By Teniers, described as 'The Guitar Player'; the pictures were claimed to have been consigned from Holland. (29) *Ibid.*

242 BACKGAMMON PLAYERS

An old man is about to throw the dice as his younger opponent moves a chip, watched by two men.

Oil on oak, $14\frac{3}{4} \times 22\frac{5}{16}$ (0·375 × 0·567).

The reverse of the support bears the brand of the coat of arms of the city of Antwerp.

Signed, ·D·TENIERS·F

Probably in fairly good condition. The state of preservation is obscured by a yellow varnish. There are retouched cracks $1\frac{1}{2}$ (0·04) long from the left-hand edge and 1 (0·025) long from the right.

No. 242 was accepted by both Smith[1] and Waagen[2] as the work of David Teniers II. The signature seems to be rather weakly written. No. 242 is not as highly finished as comparable works by Teniers; indeed it seems that the younger gambler was intended to wear a hat or beret, but that it has been omitted. The lack of finish and discoloured varnish may partly explain the fact that the quality of execution in no. 242 is not of the highest that he could achieve. But it seems best, at this stage, to catalogue no. 242 as ascribed to David Teniers II.

The composition of no. 242 is closely related to the *Backgammon Players* (ex Berlin)[3] which was dated 1641. It is probable that no. 242 was also executed in the early 1640's.

The model for the younger gambler in no. 242 recurs in the ex Berlin picture; while the poses of the two players recur in the *Backgammon Players* at Polesden Lacy[4] and with some variation in the Budapest Museum *Backgammon Players*.[5]

COPY: Anon. sale, Sotheby's, 13 November, 1963 (22).[6]

PROVENANCE: Coll. N. W. Ridley Colborne (later Lord Colborne) by 1838 when lent to the B.I. (58)[7]; exh. B.I. 1848 (65); Lord Colborne Bequest, 1854.

REPRODUCTION: *National Gallery Illustrations, Continental Schools (excluding Italian)*, 1950, p. 354, bottom.

REFERENCE: *General:* J. Smith, *Supplement to the Catalogue Raisonné*, 1842, IX, Teniers, no. 117.

In text: (1) See under *General Reference.* (2) See G. F. Waagen, *Treasures of Art in Great Britain*, II, 1854, p. 240. (3) See *Staatl. Museen zu Berlin, Beschreibendes Verzeichnis der Gemälde*, 1931 (ed.), p. 467, no. 856; this picture was destroyed in 1945. (4) Panel, $18\frac{1}{2} \times 22\frac{1}{2}$ (0·47 × 0·572), see the catalogue of *Flemish Art, 1300–1700*, The Royal Academy, 1953/4, no. 415. (5) Panel, $9\frac{13}{16} \times 13\frac{3}{4}$ (0·25 × 0·35) see the 1954 catalogue, p. 557, no. 4309. (6) $13\frac{1}{2} \times 22\frac{1}{2}$ (0·343 × 0·572); no details of the support given. (7) Described as an 'Interior with Dutch Boors'.

949 A GIPSY TELLING A PEASANT HIS FORTUNE IN A HILLY LANDSCAPE

Oil on relined canvas, $64\frac{1}{4} \times 84\frac{3}{4}$ (1·632 × 2·153).

Signed, *DT* (in monogram).

In fairly good condition. Paint loss, caused by a tear about 24 (0·61) in the left middle ground has been made good. There is a fair amount of wearing overall, especially in the sky. Cleaned, 1960.

The status of no. 949 is problematic. Certainly the treatment of the figures bears no resemblance to that of David Teniers I[1] (so far as it is known),[2] to whom no. 949 has previously been attributed.[3] The monogram is old,[4] but weakly written, and is thus not necessarily reliable. The figures are painted over the landscape, but seem not to be by another hand.

No. 949 is to be associated with David Teniers II. The foreground figures recur, in reverse and with others, in a tapestry woven by J. van de Borcht after a design by David Teniers II.[5] Puyvelde has suggested that a picture, similar to no. 949, in the Prado,[6] is a tapestry cartoon by him; but no tapestry corresponding to no. 949 has been traced. The Prado picture apart, there is a group of other pictures, also by, or thought to be by, D. Teniers II, that are comparable with no. 949.

The landscape in no. 949 and in the comparable works, shows the influence of David Teniers I[7] and of Joos de Momper II, whose style seems also to have influenced David Teniers II in the 1630's.[8] Of the comparable works, the picture at Leningrad is signed and dated 1640.[9] It is probable that others in the group, including no. 949, are also by David Teniers II, working under the inspiration of pictures executed by de Momper in collaboration with Jan Brueghel I. But it seems wisest, at this stage, to catalogue no. 949 as ascribed to David Teniers II.

PROVENANCE: Perhaps[10] in the Richard Morgan (†) sale, Christie's, 9 March, 1850 (16)[11] bt. Watson for 11 gns.[12] Wynn Ellis Bequest, 1876; lent, through the Arts Council to the Municipal Art Gallery and Museum, Wolverhampton, 1958–60; and to the Ministry of Works (now Public Buildings and Works), from 1961.

REPRODUCTION: *National Gallery Illustrations, Continental Schools (excluding Italian)*, 1950, p. 352, bottom.

REFERENCES: *In text:* (1) Compare also the figures in the series, signed and dated 1638, at Vienna, for which see E. R. V. Engerth, *Kunsthistorische Samm-lungen des allerhöchsten Kaiserhauses Gemälde ... Verzeichniss*, 1884, II, nos. 1281–1284. (2) See J. G. can Gelder and I. Jost, *Simiolus*, 1966–7, I, pp. 147–51. (3) See R. N. Wornum, *A Catalogue of the Pictures in the National Gallery*, 1876, p. 309; and subsequent Gallery catalogues. No. 949 was ascribed to David Teniers I in the 1958 *Summary Catalogue*. (4) It resisted the solvent used during cleaning in 1960. (5) See H. C. Marillier, *Handbook to the Teniers Tapestries*, 1932, p. 9, no. 6, when coll. the Earl of Iveagh, Marillier (ms. notes, the Victoria and Albert Museum) records that one of this set was signed: 'D. TENIERS SERENISSI[MO] | LEOPOLDI ARCHIDUCI | JOANNI AUSTRIACO | PICTOR FA[M]ILIARIS . . . PINX'; he also notes a similar tapestry by J. Le Clerc, which was owned by the Crown Prince Ruprecht, Brussels, 1693. (6) Canvas, $69\frac{11}{16} \times 94\frac{1}{16}$ (1.77×2.39), signed, *Museo del Prado, Catálogo de las Pinturas*, 1963, p. 671, no. 1818. (7) Compare the landscape in *The Rest on the Flight into Egypt*, by David Teniers I, signed and dated 1620, published and reproduced by O. Granberg, *Svenska Kontsamlingarnas Historia* etc., 1930, II, p. 131, and pl. 50. (8) Compare for instance the *S. Mary Mag-dalen in a Cave*, Dulwich College, panel, $12 \times 20\frac{5}{8}$ (0.305×0.525) signed and dated, *D. Tenier [sic] Iv. 1634*, usually considered to be by David Teniers I, see for instance the catalogue of the exhibition of *Flemish Art*, The Royal Academy, 1953/4 (403). (9) See *Musée de l'Ermitage ... Catalogue des Peintures*, II, 1958, no. 580 and fig. 93. (10) The 'large and capital landscape, a View of the Alps with Gypsies and Peasants...' by Teniers in the Earl of Bessborough sale, Christie's, 6 February (= 2nd day), 1801 (90) might also be mentioned; the catalogue states that it was ex coll. Sir Luke Schaub, but no comparable picture features in his sale, Langford, 26 ff. April, 1758. Christie's marked catalogue of the Bessborough sale gives the buyer as Earl Temple, but no comparable picture features in the Duke of Buckingham sales at Stowe or Avington in 1848 or at Christie's in 1849. (11) Described as 'A romantic land-scape with a river, a gypsey [sic] telling a man's fortune in the foreground' by Teniers and van Uden. (12) Buyer and price in Christie's marked catalogue.

After David TENIERS II

952 A COUNTRY FESTIVAL NEAR ANTWERP

Gentlefolk stand by as peasants assemble to receive food and drink, that is being prepared. A festooned, carved Cross with the *Virgin and Child* (?) at the top of a column in the right middle ground.

Oil on relined canvas, $35\frac{5}{16} \times 49\frac{3}{16}$ (0.897×1.25).

Later additions to the support account for $1\frac{7}{16}$ (0.037) to the height and $1\frac{3}{4}$ (0.045) to the width.

Falsely signed and dated, *D·TENE(?)I(?)RS·F. 1643:*

Generally in good condition. There are a few, scattered losses; there is a thin incision in the paint above the Cross and some small areas of wearing. Yellow varnish.

The city on the horizon is Antwerp.[1]

The status of no. 952 is complicated by the existence of an almost identical picture by David Teniers II in the collection of the Duke of Bedford that is signed and dated 1646.[2] This picture corresponds with the amount shown in no. 952 without the additions. The colours agree except for the doublet and trousers of the page, the feathers in the hat and the skirt of the lady in centre of the group in the left foreground.

Wornum considered no. 952 to be a replica of the Bedford picture[3]; the 1929 National Gallery catalogue reversed the position. The evident falseness of the signature[4] and date on no. 952 removes all the ground for considering it to be earlier than the Bedford picture.[5] The Bedford picture is of higher quality, and the quality of execution in some details of no. 952 is somewhat coarse.[6] It is probable therefore that no. 952 is a replica of the Bedford picture. No. 952, however, bears many characteristics of Teniers' handling; and it is possible that it was executed in his studio. Waagen[7] suggested that Teniers himself painted this copy; but this is unlikely.

The group in the left foreground is traditionally thought to represent Teniers and his family.[8] The blonde haired woman, the man in the red cloak and (probably) the page seem to recur in no. 817 (*q.v.*); and it is thus possible that they are reminiscences of Teniers himself, his first wife and eldest son, although it should be pointed out that the man in no. 952 is without a moustache. The woman seen from the back also recurs in no. 817; and the lady in no. 952 with the black shawl occurs in the *Village Fête* of 1646 at Leningrad.[9]

The name and nature of the festival depicted in no. 952 is not known; it may be the subject of Sebastian Vrancx's picture at Munich of 1622.[10]

PROVENANCE: Perhaps in the D. Potter sale, The Hague, 19 May, 1723 (48) sold for 665 glds.[11] Coll. Bourchier Cleeve (1715–1760),[12] but apparently only recorded for the first time at his house, Foots Cray Place, Kent, in 1761[13]; inherited as part of the contents of Foots Cray Place by his daughter, Ann, and passed to her husband Sir George Yonge Bt. when they married in 1765[14]; Sir George Yonge Bt.[15] sale, White (London), 25 (= 2nd day) March, 1806 (84) bt. Philip Metcalfe for 425 gns.[16] Probably coll. Wynn Ellis when put up for sale anonymously, Christie's, 26 May, 1836 (91) bt. in at 87 gns.[17]; certainly coll. Wynn Ellis by 1851[18]; exh. B.I. 1863 (5); Wynn Ellis Bequest, 1876.

REPRODUCTION: *National Gallery Illustrations, Continental Schools (excluding Italian),* 1950, p. 359, bottom.

REFERENCE: *In text:* (1) The tower of the Onze Lieve Vrouwekerk, stands out distinctly. (2) Canvas, 23 × 47 (0·838 × 1·194); exh. at the R.A. 1953/4 (423). (3) See *Descriptive and Historical Catalogue of the Pictures in the National Gallery,* 1877, p. 313. The difficulty presented by the later date of the Bedford picture was apparently not recognized. (4) This mis-spelling of Teniers' name occasionally appears in the *MS. English Sale Catalogues, 1711–1759,* in the Victoria and Albert Museum Library. (5) The handling is not typical of pictures by David Teniers II of 1643. (6) For instance the faces of the children with the flags and of the gentlefolk in the left foreground. (7) See *Treasures of Art* etc., II, 1854, p. 295; he also stated that the Wynn Ellis picture 'was not equal to the Bedford picture in delicacy'. (8) As for instance in the Yonge sale catalogue (see above). This group in the Bedford picture has been similarly identified; as, for instance, by J. Smith, *A Catalogue Raisonné* etc., 1831, III, Teniers, no. 137; and most recently in the R.A. catalogue of 1953/4 (see note 2). The National Gallery catalogues from 1877–1929 identified the group as 'Teniers and his party.' (9) See note 1 under no. 817. (10) *Alte Pinakothek München, Katalog 1, Deutsche und Niederländische Malerei zwischen Renaissance und Barock,* 1963, p. 64, no. 2058. (11) See G. Hoet, *Catalogus* etc., 1752, I, p. 293: 'Een Boere Kermis . . .; the size is given as '2 v. 9 d. × 4 v.' (=*ca.* 33 × 48), which is close to that of no. 952; there is no other evidence for associating no. 952 with this lot. (12) See the entry in the D.N.B. According to the Yonge sale catalogue of 1806 (see above), Cleeve's collection 'was formed in the early part of the last century. The greater part . . . were [*sic*] collected abroad.' (13) See *London and its Environs,* published by R. & J. Dodsley, II, 1761, p. 315: Bouchier (*sic*) Cleeve coll. at Foots Cray Place as a 'Country Wake, Teniers'. No. 952 is also recorded at Foots Cray Place in *The English Connoisseur,* 1766, I, p. 60; and in *The Ambulator,* 1774, p. 59. (14) See note 12. (15) As ex Bouchier (*sic*) Cleeve. The size is given as 28 × 40; this was 'the size of the pictures taken within the frames', which however does not well explain the discrepancies. (16) See the *Marked Catalogue, . . . of the . . . Collection . . . of Sir George Yonge,* 1806. (17) As 'A village festival, with many figures . . .' by Teniers; the marked catalogue at Christie's as the initial 'E' by the lot, the same initial occurs by other lots—one, 82, was bought in by Ellis. Certainly no. 952 was not among Philip Metcalfe's pictures, which passed to Henry Metcalfe and were sold 15 June, 1850 at Christie's. (18) See note 7; Waagen revisited England in 1850 and 1851.

Follower of DAVID TENIERS II

805 AN OLD WOMAN PEELING PEARS

An old woman in a barn sits peeling pears; behind her, a still life with cauliflowers, and earthenware and brass pots; beside her a greyhound; in the background, a milk churn and two pieces of furniture.

Oil on relined canvas, $19\frac{1}{8} \times 26\frac{3}{16}$ (0·486 × 0·665).

Falsely signed, *D. TENIERS·F*

Inscribed on the wall above the carafe: *XXVIIII*

In fair condition. There are paint losses round the edges and scattered losses overall, many of which are retouched. The floor and ceiling appear to be retouched in places, as is the bottom right-hand corner in the area of the signature. The woman's apron is worn. There is a tear (retouched) across the canvas. Yellow varnish.

Previously catalogued as by David Teniers II [1]; but, although no. 805 has many characteristics of Teniers' style, the quality of execution is not of a sufficiently high standard for the old attribution to be retained. Although the condition of no. 805 is not good, it is evident that it is a work of the seventeenth century and possible that it was executed in the studio of David Teniers II, or more probably by a follower, working in imitation of him. Judging from a photograph, the style is reminiscent of that of Juliaen Teniers II (1616–ca. 1676),[2] the brother of David Teniers II, by whom there is a signed work at Copenhagen [3]; this is of the same subject as no. 805, and is related to it in composition.[4]

The dating of no. 805 is problematic: it is different from David Teniers II's only dated rendering of this theme—the Mauritshuis picture of 1644.[5] It is more comparable to the *Old Woman peeling Turnips* (Royal Collection),[6] and it is probable that no. 805 was inspired by David Teniers' style of the 1640's. It may be worth noting that Juliaen Teniers II became a master in Antwerp guild of S. Luke in 1635/6.[7]

The furniture at the back of the barn in no. 805 recurs in no. 862 *q.v.*

COPIES: Anon. sale, Lek (Amsterdam), 31 March, 1925 (93); coll. Mr. Mazure, 1957.[9]

VERSION (?): An *An Old Woman peeling Pears* by David Teniers II was listed in the Royal Palace, Madrid, 1772.[10]

PROVENANCE: Perhaps coll. Count d'Astorg (1787–1853), from whom purchased by G. H. Phillips[11]; purchased from G. H. Phillips by the National Gallery, 1870; lent to the Art Galleries at Northampton, 1929, Burton on Trent, 1930, and Bradford, 1931, and to the Ministry of Works (now Public Buildings and Works), 1938–1941.

REPRODUCTION: *National Gallery Illustrations, Continental Schools (excluding Italian)*, 1950, p. 355, top.

REFERENCES: *In text:* (1) See R. Wornum, *Descriptive and Historical Catalogue of the Pictures in the National Gallery*, 1870, and subsequent Gallery catalogues. (2) See Z. v. M's entry in Thieme-Becker. (3) Panel, $9\frac{7}{16} \times 13\frac{5}{8}$ (0·24 × 0·345), Copenhagen Museum, no. 697. (4) Other works are related to no. 805 and the Copenhagen picture: Fitzwilliam Museum, no. 72, see H. Gerson and J. W. Goodison, *Fitzwilliam Museum, Catalogue of Paintings*, 1960, I, p. 128, no. 72 and fig., panel, $14 \times 18\frac{1}{4}$ (0·356 × 0·464), where given to David Teniers II; and the *Old Woman sorting Onions*, panel, $13 \times 18\frac{1}{4}$ (0·33 × 0·47), ex colls. George Salting and the Earl of Haddington. (5) Copper, $22\frac{7}{16} \times 30\frac{5}{8}$ (0·57 × 0·778), see the *Abridged Catalogue of the Pictures . . . Royal Picture Gallery, Mauritshuis*, 1959, no. 260. (6) Panel, 20×28 (0·508 × 0·712), exh. R.A., 1953/4, no. 278. (7) See note 2. (8) Photo. in R.K.D. (9) Canvas stuck on panel, $18\frac{7}{8} \times 25\frac{3}{4}$ (0·48 × 0·65); note in the Gallery archives. (10) See the 1772 inventory (coll. the Duke of Wellington) of the Royal Palace, Madrid: 'Otra [pintura] en tabla, de una vieja sentada junto á un horno, mondando peras de tres cuartas de largo, y mas de media vara de caida [=ca. 15 × 25], de le mismo autor [= David Teniers II]'. (11) See a letter from G. H. Phillips of, 1 January, 1870 in the Gallery archives. He refers there to the Prince d'Astorg, but no such person existed. For Alexandre-Eugène-Louis-François-Saturnin, Count d'Astorg, see *Dictionnaire de Biographie Française*, ed. J. Balteau, 1939, III, cols. 1362–4; it is also possible that Phillips bought it from his son Charles (b. 1819, married 1853). Phillips also states, in his letter, that no. 805 was taken from the Hesse-Cassel collection by Jérôme Bonaparte (1784–1860) and presented by him to his *aide de camp*, General Myot, whence it passed into the family of the Prince (*sic*) d'Astorg. A General Myot has not been traced; and Dr. J. Pilz of the Staatliche Kunstsammlungen, Cassel, has kindly informed the compiler that no picture corresponding to no. 805 features in the eighteenth-century inventories of the Hesse-Cassel collection. Phillips' letter formed the basis for the provenance of no. 805 given in the National Gallery catalogues from 1870–1929.

Imitator of DAVID TENIERS II

953   PERSONIFICATION OF AUTUMN (?)

Oil on oak, *ca.* $6\frac{7}{16} \times 4\frac{7}{8}$ (0·164 × 0·124).
Falsely signed, *DT* (in monogram).
In fairly good condition. The shape of the support is irregular; only its left-hand edge is chamfered. Yellow varnish.

The quality of execution of no. 953 is not sufficiently high to justify the attribution to David Teniers II, made since it entered the collection. It seems rather to be the work of an imitator.

No. 953 has borne the title 'The Toper', but it may well have been intended to represent the Personification of Autumn, and it could derive from no. 859 (*q.v.*), to which it relates more directly than to any other known renderings of this subject by Teniers.

PROVENANCE: Not certainly identifiable[2] before its bequest by Wynn Ellis, 1876; lent through the Arts Council, to the Laing Art Gallery and Museum, Newcastle upon Tyne, 1951–6, and to the Cooper Art Gallery, Barnsley, 1958–63.

REPRODUCTION: *National Gallery Illustrations, Continental Schools (excluding Italian)*, 1950, p. 360, top.

REFERENCES: *In text:* (1) See the National Gallery catalogues from 1877–1958. (2) National Gallery catalogues from 1915–1929 wrongly suggested that no. 953 featured in an Anon. sale, Christie's, 8 May, 1824, and that it was in the Wynn Ellis collection by 1838.

2599   A DOCTOR TENDING A PATIENT'S FOOT IN HIS SURGERY

A doctor tends a patient's foot, watched by an old lady, while his assistant warms a plaster and an old man leaves the surgery carrying a jug.

Oil on oak, $15\frac{3}{8} \times 24\frac{1}{16}$ (0·39 × 0·611).
Bears signature: *D TENIERS F*, and the remains of a date on the drawing on the wall: *16*
Apparently in fair condition. A yellow varnish obscures the paint surface, which appears to be much retouched especially in the darks, and on the floor and walls. Markings on the wall above the assistant have been painted over. The signature appears to be over areas of retouching[1]; infra-red photography suggests that it once may have read: *PD* (in monogram) *TENIERS F*

This subject was several times painted by David Teniers II, who appears to have been directly inspired by Adriaen Brouwer's renderings of such scenes—for example the pictures at Munich[2] and Aachen.[3]

No. 2599 has much in common with other renderings of this subject by or ascribed to David Teniers II. The poses of the patient, doctor and lady onlooker follow those in a picture in the Budapest Museum[4] of 1636, which is probably Teniers' first essay in the subject. The faces of the doctor and patient, and the former's costume in no. 2599 are also similar to those in the Budapest picture. The placing of the boy assistant follows (not precisely) that in a composition recorded in a picture at Amiens.[5] The same assistant in the same pose and position occurs in the Prado *Surgical Operation*,[6] which also has a man leaving the surgery from a similarly placed door.

The composition of no. 2599 is noticeably less compact than in other renderings of foot operations by David Teniers II.[7] Although previously catalogued as by him, its execution appears to be too poor for this to be accepted.[8] There are good reasons for doubting the authenticity of the signature (see above). The remains of a date (also referred to above) do not appear to be written in a seventeenth-century hand.[9] And it seems not necessary to believe that no. 2599 was executed in his lifetime.

The existence of other versions (?), see below, of no. 2599 might be taken to suggest that it is a copy after a lost original.

ENGRAVING: Etching by A. P. Martial, 1873.[10]

COPIES OR VERSIONS: Verrier sale, Brussels, 8/9 December, 1924 (154)[11]; Anon. sale, Cologne, 14 June, 1941 (89)[12]; Anon. sale, Giroux (Brussels), 15/16 May, 1953 (194).[13]

PROVENANCE: Possibly in the Willem Lormier sale, The Hague, 4 July 1763 (279) bt. Palthe (?) for 150 glds.[14] Probably in the following sales: Walsh Porter sale, Christie's, 14 April, 1810 (25) £250 bt. N. Baily for £252[15]; Anon. sale, Christie's, 8 May, 1824, 2nd part, (2), 139 gns. bt. in[16]; Anon. sale, Christie's, 6 May (=2nd day) 1826 (25) bt. N. Baillie for 114 gns.[17] Certainly in the Anon. (=Thomas Tomkinson) sale, Phillips, 6 May, 1830 (65) 79 gns. bt. in[18]; recorded in the T. Tomkinson coll., 1831[19]; and perhaps exhibited by him at Suffolk St., 1834 (81). Recorded in the [Desiré] van den Schrieck coll., Louvain, 1842[20]; Desiré van den Schrieck (†) sale, Louvain, Le Roy, 8 ff. April, 1861 (113).[21] Marquis de la Rocheb . . . (=Anon.)[22] sale, Paris, 5/6 May, 1873 (94)[23] bt. Milbank (=H. V. Millbank) for 1200 francs.[24] Anon. (=C. J. Wertheimer) sale, Christie's, 13 May, 1899 (39) £378 bt. Lesser.[25] Coll. George Salting[26]; exh. *The Collection of Pictures and Drawings of the late George Salting*, Agnew's, 1910 (8); Salting Bequest, 1910; lent, through the Arts Council, to the Walker Art Gallery, Liverpool, 1951–63.

REPRODUCTION: *National Gallery Illustrations, Continental Schools (excluding, Italian)*, 1950, p. 360, bottom.

REFERENCES: *In text*: (1) The falseness of the signature was first pointed out in the *Summary Catalogue*, 1958. See also note 10. (2) See C. Hofstede de Groot, *A Catalogue Raisonné* etc., 1910, III, p. 573, no. 37; rep. in G. Knuttel, *Adriaen Brouwer*, 1962, pl. VII. (3) See Hofstede de Groot, *op. cit.*, pp. 572–3, no. 36; engraved in reverse by C. Visscher, the fourth state bears an inscription 'Ure, feca, purga, cura, Chirurge! dolori. Sentiat, id patiens est medicina dolor'. (4) See the 1937 Budapest catalogue, I, pp. 253–4, no. 565, and rep. vol. II. (5) *Ville d'Amiens, Catalogue . . . Musée de Picardie*, 1911, p. 79, no. 342, panel, $18\frac{1}{2} \times 24$ (0·47 × 0·61), ascribed to David Teniers I, but perhaps only a copy after a lost work by the son. (6) See *Museo del Prado, Catálogo de las Pinturas*, 1963, p. 666, no. 1802. (7) Among which can be noted the picture at Cassel, signed, panel, $25\frac{5}{8} \times 27\frac{1}{2}$ (0·555 × 0·693) acquired 1738, see the *Katalog der Staalichen Gemäldegalerie zu Kassel*, 1958, p. 148, no. 147 with rep.; the picture engraved by J. Daullé, 1760, as *Le Chirurgien Flamand*, when in coll. Peilhon, Paris; a similar picture was on the London art market, 1960, panel, $14\frac{3}{4} \times 20$ (0·375 × 0·508); a related composition was engraved by Mayor in 1747; Glasgow Art Gallery, signed, panel, $14\frac{1}{2} \times 10\frac{3}{4}$ (0·37 × 0·27), see *Catalogue Dutch and Flemish . . . Paintings, Glasgow Art Gallery*, I, 1961, p. 134, no. 13, and rep. in vol. II, p. 24, where the provenance is claimed to be ex Lormier, but see note 14. The Glasgow picture is closely related to the picture ascribed to Brouwer recorded in the J. G. Johnson Coll. Philadelphia, for which see Hofstede de Groot, *op. cit.*, p. 573, no. 38. (8) See also MacLaren ms. notes. (9) By someone who preferred not to commit himself to the 2 essential digits. (10) Published in the *Gazette des Beaux-Arts*, 1873, I, between pp. 366 and 367; no signature or date appear on it. (11) Panel, $19\frac{1}{4} \times 25\frac{3}{16}$ (0·49 × 0·64); said to be signed and dated. (12) Panel, $19\frac{1}{4} \times 25$ (0·49 × 0·64), signed, rep. in cat.; information kindly supplied by W. L. van de Watering of the R.K.D. (13) Panel, $19\frac{1}{4} \times 25\frac{3}{16}$ (0·49 × 0·64), said to be signed. Judging by the reproduction in the Witt Library, not identical with the Verrier sale picture. (14) This according to the van den Schrieck sale catalogue see above and note 21. For the Lormier sale, see G. Hoet, *Catalogus* etc., 1770, III, p. 332, which gives the lot number as 278. The size given is IV. $2\frac{1}{2}$d. × IV. $11\frac{1}{2}$d. = *ca.* $15\frac{3}{8} \times 25$. The buyer and price given in the National Gallery copy of the sale catalogue (lot no. 279). J. B. Descamps, *La Vie des Peintres* etc., 1754, II, p. 168, records the picture as in the Lormier collection. It is tempting to propose that no. 2599 was in the Greenwood sale (of pictures imported from abroad), Christie's, 18 February, 1774 (50); but the description does not include the old man, and the size is given as 15 × 21. 'A Surgeon dressing his Patient' by Teniers was in an Anon. sale (of pictures imported from abroad), Prestage, 13 February (= 2nd day), 1766 (14). (15) The description in the Walsh Porter catalogue is slightly ambiguous; it also states that the picture was engraved, which no. 2599 had not been, and that it was ex coll. Le Chevalier de Venée [? = Le Comte de Vence]. No such picture appears in the Comte de Vence sale, Paris, 9 ff. February, 1761. This fact throws doubt on the claimed provenance, while the description of the 1826 sale does fit no. 2599 (see notes 17 and 18). For the buyer and price, see Christie's marked catalogue. (16) As engraved and ex coll. the Chevalier Venée. For the fate of the lot, see Christie's marked catalogue. (17) Described as 'Interior of a village Surgeon's Shop: the Surgeon kneeling in the centre of the Picture, is raising a plaster from the foot of an elderly Man, his patient, while his assistant is warming another over a chafing dish; an elderly woman in the centre is looking on, and a boor with a jug in his hand, is going out of the door at the farther end of the Chamber . . . It was formerly in the collection of Walsh Porter Esq.' Buyer and price from Christie's marked catalogue. (18) See J. Smith, *A Catalogue Raisonné* etc., 1831, III, p. 369, no. 420. Smith gave its provenance as ex coll. Walsh Porter, 1810 and Thomson Martin, 1830, bt. in. The size tallies with no. 2599. The 1830 sale to which Smith referred did contain pictures owned by the late Thomson Martin; but no. 2599 was in a separate property, which, according to a ms. note on the R.K.D. copy of the sale catalogue, was that of Tomkinson. Fate of lot given in the marked catalogue of the R.K.D. (19) See Smith, *loc. cit.* (20) See J. Smith, *Supplement to the Catalogue Raisonné*, 1842, p. 437, no. 96, and note 22. (21) The relevant excerpt from this sale catalogue is stuck on the back of no. 2599. The catalogue repeats the provenance given by Smith in 1832 and adds the Lormier sale. (22) H. Mireur, *Dictionnaire des Ventes* etc., 1912, VII, p. 152 gives the seller's name as Rochebousseau. Lugt, no. 33985, states that the name is fictitious. H. Perrier, *Gazette des Beaux-Arts*, I, 1873, p. 376 identifies this picture with

Smith, *A Catalogue Raisonné* etc., 1831, III, no. 420. (23) Stated to be ex colls. Lormier, Walsh Porter, Thomson Martin and Thomas Tomkinson and to be Smith, *op. cit.*, no. 420. Information kindly provided by R. L. van de Watering of the R.K.D. (24) See marked catalogue in R.K.D.; information kindly provided by R. L. van de Watering of the R.K.D. (25) Provenance is given as ex Walsh Porter and H. V. Millbank. Buyer and price in the National Gallery marked catalogue. (26) The picture is not mentioned in either of Salting's notebooks (the second of *ca.* 1900) in the National Gallery library; no. 2599 was thus probably bought by Salting towards the very end of his life.

2601   AN OLD WOMAN READING

Oil on oak, $7 \times 5\frac{5}{8}$ (0·178 × 0·143).
Bears initials, $DT \cdot$ (in monogram).
Apparently in good condition.

The initials seem to be suspect; and it seems right to continue the demotion in status of no. 2601 since it entered the collection.[1] No. 2601 is probably only an old imitation in David Teniers II's manner; the imitator was perhaps 'inspired' by Rembrandt.[2]

PROVENANCE: Acquired by George Salting after 1900[3]; exh. the *Collection of Pictures and Drawings of the late George Salting*, Agnew's, 1910 (266); Salting Bequest, 1910; lent through the Arts Council, to the Municipal Art Gallery and Museum, Wolverhampton, 1952–4.

REPRODUCTION: *National Gallery Illustrations, Continental Schools (excluding Italian)*, 1950, p. 361, bottom.

REFERENCES: *In text:* (1) From 1911–1921 catalogued as by D. Teniers II; from 1922 catalogued as by the school of D. Teniers II; from 1958 (*Summary Catalogue*) as by a follower. (2) Compare Rembrandt's *Portrait of his Mother*, Rijksmuseum, *Catalogue of Paintings*, 1960, p. 260, no. 2024A1. (3) No. 260, does not feature in his notebooks (the last of which was begun in 1900) in the National Gallery library. There are two unidentified seals on the reverse: one bearing the initials JD (in monogram), and the other showing a satyr, with pipes, running to the left.

CHARLES-PHILOGÈNE TSCHAGGENY
1815–1894

Figure, animal painter and engraver. Born in Brussels, 26 May, 1815. Taught by E. Verboeckhoven. He was in England in 1848–1849 (–?1850).[1] He exhibited at Brussels, London, Paris, Oporto and Vienna; his paintings were bought by several museums and crowned heads of Europe. He died on 12 June, 1894 at St.-Joost-ten-Node (near Brussels).

REFERENCE: *General:* P. Lambotte, *Biographie Nationale ... de Belgique*, 1930–32, 25, cols. 703–5; Thieme-Becker, *Künstler-Lexikon*, 1939, 33, p. 458.

In text: (1) He exhibited at the Royal Academy in this year, see under no. 738.

738   AN EPISODE OF THE FIELD OF BATTLE

Oil on relined canvas, *ca.* $57\frac{1}{4} \times 76\frac{3}{4}$ (1·455 × 1·95).
Signed and dated, *Ch^s. TSCHAGGENY. 1848*
In good condition. A tear in the sky is retouched.

Presumably painted in England; it was exhibited two years later at

the Royal Academy, with the title given above. The costume approximates to mid-seventeenth century types; Ronald Alley suggests that the
battle is between Roundheads and Cavaliers.[1]

PROVENANCE: Exh. R.A., 1850 (322). Johann Moritz Oppenheim Bequest,
1864; hung at South Kensington; on loan to the Corporation Art Gallery,
Oldham, 1884–1929, when transferred to the jurisdiction of the Tate Gallery;
returned to the National Gallery, 1956.

REPRODUCTION: National Gallery photographs available.

REFERENCE: *In text:* (1) Ms. notes.

LUCAS VAN UDEN
1595–1672

Landscape painter and etcher. Active mainly in Antwerp where he was
born on 18 October, 1595,[1] the son of Artus van Uden († 1627/8) and
Joanna Tranoy.[2] His name does not appear as a pupil in the lists of the
Antwerp guild of S. Luke; thus it is likely that he was taught by his
father.[3] Rooses has suggested that he was the young landscape painter
at Antwerp, described by Gage in a letter to Carleton on 14 March, 1617,
as having lived long in Italy[4]; but there seems to be no evidence to
support this. He was admitted as a master ('wynmeester') to the Antwerp
guild of S. Luke in the year of his father's death.[5] He married Anna van
Woelput on 14 February, 1627, by whom he had eight children.[6]
A pupil was enrolled in his studio at Antwerp in the year 1641/2.[7] In
March 1644, he obtained a passport to travel[8] and made his way,
according to Delevoy, up the valley of the Rhine.[9] He was in Antwerp
for a few months after July, 1646,[10] but may have departed once again.
On 31 December, 1649 he was registered as a 'buytenpoorter' at Antwerp,
by which he retained, for one year, his rights as a citizen during his
absence.[11] He may have spent this year in Brussels.[12] De Bie in 1661[13]
refers to him as living in Antwerp, where he died on 4 November,
1672.[14]

It has been suggested that van Uden worked in Rubens' studio[15];
this is possible[16] but there is no definite proof of it. He certainly admired
Rubens' landscapes.[17] Collaborators occasionally executed the staffage
in his landscapes.[18]

His portrait by van Dyck was engraved by Vorsterman for the
Iconography; a subsequent state is inscribed: 'Pictor Ruralium Prospectuum Antverpiae'.[19]

REFERENCES: *In text:* (1) See C. de Bie, *Het Gulden Cabinet* etc., 1661, p. 240.
He was baptized on the 21 October, see Th. van Lerius, *Catalogue du Musée
d'Anvers*, 1874 (3rd ed.), p. 508. (2) See van Lerius, *loc. cit.*, and pp. 510–11.
His parents both died in the year 1627/8, see Ph. Rombouts and Th. van Lerius,
De Liggeren etc., [1864–1876], p. 652. E. Quellinus noted on his copy of de Bie,
see T. Levin, *Zeitschrift für bildende Kunst*, 1888, p. 136, that Artus had been
a painter to Queen Elizabeth of England. (3) F. J. van den Branden, *Geschiedenis
der Antwerpsche Schilderschool*, 1883, p. 688, believed that he worked as a
young man for his father, but that he was self taught. (4) See M. Rooses

and Ch. Ruelens (†), *Correspondance de Rubens*, 1898, II, pp. 104–106.
(5) See Rombouts and van Lerius, *op. cit.*, p. 638. (6) See van den Branden, *op. cit.*, p. 689. He also had two bastard children. (7) See Rombouts and van Lerius, *op. cit.*, II, p. 133. (8) See R. Delevoy, *Belgisch Tijdschrift voor Oudheidkunde en Kunstgeschiedenis*, 1940, p. 47. (9) *Ibid.* (10) *Ibid.*, p. 48. (11) See van Lerius, *op. cit.*, p. 509; and Delevoy, *loc. cit.* (12) See A. Wauters, *Le Tapisseries Bruxelloises*, 1878, p. 245; and Delevoy, *loc. cit.* (13) *Loc. cit.* (14) See van den Branden, *op. cit.*, p. 690. (15) See for instance M. Rooses, *Rubens*, trans. H. Child, I, 1904, p. 210; and van den Branden, *op. cit.*, p. 688. (16) See Gregory Martin, *Apollo*, 1968, pp. 210–11; a copy by van Uden of a landscape (by ? Rubens) was in Rubens' estate, see J. Denucé, *The Antwerp Art Galleries, Inventories of the Art-Collections in Antwerp* etc., 1932, p. 79. (17) See note 16. (18) See, for instance, A. von Wurzbach, *Niederländisches Künstler-Lexikon*, 1910, II, pp. 725–6; and no. 5866, below. (19) See Fr. Wibiral, *L'Iconographie d'Antoine van Dyck*, 1877, p. 111, no. 94.

LUCAS VAN UDEN and DAVID TENIERS II

5866 PEASANTS MERRYMAKING BEFORE A COUNTRY HOUSE

Oil on relined canvas, *ca.* 70¼ × 104 (1·785 × 2·642). The top and left-hand edges of the support are ragged; the two other edges are masked by binding paper.

Signed, *D TENIERS*

In fair condition. There are many, small losses in the sky, now retouched; there are also losses down the right-hand edge; much of the rest is worn and to some extent retouched. The signature is worn and faint. Cleaned, 1949.

No. 5866 was ascribed to David Teniers II in the 1958 *Summary Catalogue*. The signature is not necessarily reliable, but the peasants (and the table on the right) although somewhat coarsely rendered, are probably his work. The landscape is acceptably by Lucas van Uden,[1] and is to be compared with van Uden's *Watermill* at Antwerp.[2] There are other examples of collaboration between van Uden and Teniers.[3]

The execution of the figures suggests that they were added by Teniers *ca.* 1650[4]; the landscape was probably executed not long before.

The country house has not been identified; the coat of arms to the left of the entrance is no longer legible.

PROVENANCE: Probably coll. John Skipp (1742–1811) at Overbury[5]; passed to his sister, Penelope, widow of James Martin; coll. John Martin by 1841, when exh. at the B.I. (65)[6]; by descent to John Hanbury Martin, by whom presented to the National Gallery, 1948.

REPRODUCTION: National Gallery photographs available.

REFERENCES: *In text:* (1) As also recognized by MacLaren, ms. notes. (2) Dr. Wolfgang Adler kindly drew the compiler's attention to the similarity between no. 5886 and a picture at Antwerp, which is no. 476 of the Koninklijk Museum voor schone Kunsten: canvas, 62¾₁₆ × 71¼ (1·58 × 1·81). (3) For instance, no. 475 of the Musées Royaux des Beaux-Arts de Belgique, Brussels; and Berlin, no. 678A, see, for instance, the 1921 catalogue of the Kaiser Friedrich Museum, not in the post war catalogues of the Dahlem Museum. (4) Compare, with, for instance, *The Wedding Feast*, 1650, in the Hermitage (see *Musée de l'Ermitage* ... *Catalogue des Peintures*, 11, 1958, p. 103, no. 1719). The motif of a peasant pulling a woman from the ground to dance occurs in the earlier picture of *Peasants dancing outside an Inn* by David Teniers II in the Royal Collection; while the bagpipe player first (?) occurs in a picture in the Prado (no. 1788) of 1637. (5) In the parlour at Overbury as a 'Dutch Wake with Teniers [sic] House' by Teniers, reference from the original ms. catalogue in the collection of Skipp's descendant, John Hanbury Martin. (6) As a 'Château in Flanders, Merry-making'.

Jan WILDENS
1586–1653

Landscape painter. Active mostly in Antwerp, where he was born; no baptismal record has been traced, but in 1613 he stated that he was 27.[1] He is recorded as the pupil of Peeter Verhult in the list of the Antwerp guild of S. Luke for the year 1596.[2] He became a master in the guild in 1604.[3] In 1613 he made a journey to the south (perhaps to Italy).[4] He had certainly returned to Antwerp by 26 October, 1619, when his marriage contract with Maria Stappaert was drawn up[5]; one of the witnesses was Rubens—'zijnen goeden vriendt'.[6] He became related through his wife's family to Rubens, when the latter married Helena Fourment in 1630;[7] and was one of the three executors responsible for the sale of Rubens' collection in 1640.[8] Wildens had two sons, one of whom became a painter.[9] He died on 16 October, 1653.[10]

Wildens certainly collaborated with Rubens, by providing the landscape on one occasion[11]; it is thought that he did this fairly regularly.[12]

Van Dyck's portrait of Wildens was engraved by Pontius for the *Iconography*; a subsequent state is inscribed: 'Pictor Ruralium Prospectuum Antwerpiae'.[13]

His christian name is variously spelt in contemporary documents, Jan,[14] Hans[15] and Joannes.[16]

REFERENCE: *General:* M. Manneback in Thieme-Becker, *Künstler-Lexikon*, 1942, XXXV, pp. 562–4.

In text: (1) See F. J. van den Branden, *Geschiedenis der Antwerpsche Schilderschool*, 1883, p. 684. (2) See Ph. Rombouts and Th. van Lerius, *De Liggeren* etc., [1864–1876], I, p. 394. (3) *Ibid.*, p. 425. (4) See note 1; it should be pointed out that Wildens does not seem to have been enrolled as a member of the Antwerp guild of Romanists after his return, which suggests that he may not have visited or worked in Rome. (5) See van den Branden, *loc. cit.* It is possible that Wildens is the 'yong [sic] man [at Antwerp] who hath lived long in Italy, who I think is the rarest man living in Lantscape [sic]', thus described by Gage in a letter to Sir Dudley Carleton of 14 March 1617, see M. Rooses and Ch. Ruelens (†), *Correspondance de Rubens*, 1898, II, p. 104; but these authors consider, p. 106, that Lucas van Uden (*q.v.*) is a more likely candidate. (6) See van den Branden, *loc. cit.* (7) *Ibid.* Rubens painted Wildens' portrait and that of his mother or mother-in-law (probably the latter), see the inventory of his son Jeremias' pictures, taken after his death (also in 1653) in J. Denucé, *The Antwerp Art Galleries, Inventories of the Art-Collections in Antwerp* etc., 1932, pp. 159 and

165. (8) See M. Rooses, *Rubens*, trans. H. Child, II, 1904, p. 622. (9) See van den Branden, *op. cit.*, pp. 686–687. (10) See, for instance, Th. van Lerius, *Catalogue du Musée d'Anvers*, 1874 (3rd ed.), p. 541. (11) See no. 139 of the inventory of pictures owned by Wildens' son Jeremias taken after his death, in Denucé, *op. cit.*, p. 157: 'Een Pan ende Seringa van Rubens, het Lantschap van den ouden Wildens'. (12) See, for instance, Rooses, *op. cit.*, I, p. 210. Wildens can be associated in this respect with Rubens' remark in a letter to Carleton of 26 May, 1618: 'Ho preso secondo il mio solito un valentuo-mo nel suo mestiere a finire li paesaggi . . .', see M. Rooses and Ch. Ruelens (†), *op. cit.*, p. 170. It is not certain that Wildens had returned to Antwerp by this date, see above; but the close relationship between Rubens and Wildens makes it seem likely that he may have been called on to collaborate fairly frequently. (13) See Fr. Wibiral, *L'Iconographie d'Antoine van Dyck*, 1877, pp. 97–8, no. 70. (14) As he signed a picture at Dresden, see A. von Wurzbach, *Niederländsches Künstler-Lexikon*, 1910, II, p. 882; see also Rombouts and van Lerius, *op. cit.*, II, p. 255. (15) As occasionally spelt in the lists of the Antwerp guild of S. Luke, see Rombouts and van Lerius, cited, for instance, in notes 2 and 3. (16) See note 13.

See STUDIO OF RUBENS, no. 853.

Franchoys WOUTERS
1612–1659 or 1660

Landscape and figure painter. Active in Antwerp, Vienna and England. Born at Lierre, and baptized there on 12 (?) October, 1612.[1] Recorded as the pupil of Peeter van Avont in the lists of the Antwerp guild of S. Luke for 1628/9.[2] On the death of his father in 1634, he deserted his master for Rubens[3]; but he is then recorded as a master in the guild in the list for the year 1634/5.[4] Appointed painter to the Emperor Ferdinand II († 15 February, 1637)[5]; and travelled in the retinue of the Emperor's ambassador to Charles I, Clement Radolti, who arrived in England 31 April, 1636.[6] He decided to remain in England on hearing the news of the death of the Emperor, which reached England, *ca.* 13 March, 1637[7]; and is recorded (in 1649) as having been painter to the Prince of Wales.[8] He had returned to Antwerp, where he was to remain for the rest of his life, by 26 August, 1641, when he is noted as having taken part in the winding up of Rubens' estate.[9] In 1644, he married the wealthy daughter of Balthazar Doncker († 1640), once treasurer of the City of Antwerp.[10] In 1648, paintings and *objets d'art*, belonging to the 2nd Duke of Buckingham, were pawned to him and another dealer for 30,000 guilders.[11] He was Dean of the Antwerp guild of S. Luke for the year 1649/50.[12] By 8 April, 1653, he had bought the right to the title of Drossaard (baillif) of the fief of Ballaar[13]; by 29 May, 1658 he laid claims to other fiefs.[14] On this date he is also referred to as 'Ayuda de camara [*sic*]' of the King of England[15] (i.e. the future Charles II) to whom he had lent money.[16] He died after 16 October, 1659 and before 26 January, 1660,[17] probably at the end of 1659, as the result of a pistol shot.[18]

A *Self Portrait* (lost) was engraved by P. de Jode II.[19]

The spelling of his christian name used here is that used in his record of baptism[20]; other spellings also occur; Franchoijs,[21] Franchois,[22] Francis,[23] Frans,[24] etc.

REFERENCE: *General:* F. J. van den Branden, *Annales de l'Académie d'Archéologie de Belgique*, 1872, pp. 196 ff.

In text: (1) The record of his baptism is printed by F. J. van den Branden, cited under *General Reference*, p. 223, who states, p. 147, that he was baptized on 2 October; Th. van Lerius, *Catalogue du Musée d'Anvers*, 1874 (3rd ed.), p. 361, note 1, gives the date as 3 October, 1612. (2) See Ph. Rombouts and Th. van Lerius, *De Liggeren* etc., [1864–1872], I, p. 662. The contract concerning the terms of his apprenticeship, made between his father and Peeter van Avont was drawn up on 4 December, 1629, see van den Branden, *op. cit.*, p. 199 and 223. The list of the Antwerp guild was for the year 18 September, 1628–18 September, 1629. (3) See van den Branden, *op. cit.*, pp. 200–1, and pp. 223–4; and the same author, *Geschiedenis der Antwerpsche Schilderschool*, 1883, pp. 805–6. (4) See Rombouts and van Lerius, *op. cit.*, II, p. 59. (5) See the inscription of the print by P. de Jode after Wouters' *Self Portrait* (lost) in J. Meyssens, *Images de divers Hommes d'esprit Sublime* etc., 1649, reprinted by C. de Bie, *Het Gulden Cabinet* etc., 1661, p. 175. (6) See *Calendar of State Papers, Venetian* etc., *1632–1636*, ed. A. B. Hinds, 1921, XXIII, p. 554. Wouters wrote from London, 28 May, 1636, to Forchoudt in Antwerp describing his life there, see J. Denucé, *Art-Export in the 17th Century in Antwerp, The Firm of Forchoudt*, 1931, pp. 23–4. (7) See the report of the Venetian Ambassador in London in *Calendar of State Papers, Venetian* etc., *1636–9*, ed. A. B. Hinds, 1923, XXIV, p. 161. On 20 March, 1637, Radolti was reported to have left 'last week', see the report of the Venetian Ambassador, *ibid.*, p. 168. (8) See note 5. (9) See, for instance, J. Denucé, *The Antwerp Art Galleries, Inventories of the Art-Collections in Antwerp* etc., 1932, p. 81. (10) See van den Branden, cited under *General Reference*, pp. 213–215; and for the contract and deed, pp. 225–228; he himself also owned land near Lierre. (11) *Ibid.*, p. 217. (12) See Rombouts and van Lerius, *op. cit.*, p. 215. (13) See van den Branden, *op. cit.*, p. 219. (14) *Ibid.* (15) *Ibid.* (16) After his death, his widow went to England to obtain repayment of loans made to the English exiles during the Interregnum, see van den Branden, *op. cit.*, pp. 220 and 232–233. (17) *Ibid.*, pp. 220–221. (18) See de Bie, *op. cit.*, pp. 174 and 177. (19) See note 5. (20) See note 1. (21) As he signed himself in 1636, see under note 6. (22) Thus, for instance, spelt in the deposition made by P. van Avont in 1634, see note 3. (23) He thus signed himself on his print, reproduced by G. Glück, *Rubens, van Dyck und ihr Kreis*, 1933, fig. 240. (24) See reference in note 12.

1871 NYMPHS SURPRISED BY SATYRS

Oil on oak, *ca.* $17\frac{1}{16} \times 22\frac{7}{8}$ (0·433 × 0·581).
Signed with initials, *WF*

The reverse of the support bears the stamp of the coat of arms of the city of Antwerp, and the incised initials, *NV* (in monogram).

In fairly good condition. There are some losses round the edges of the support and some discoloured repaint in the sky. The darks of the foreground and the lake are worn.

The initials probably stand for 'Wouters fecit'; and there seems to be no reason to doubt that no. 1871 is the work of Franchoys Wouters.

No. 1871 is comparable to pictures by him at Vienna and Copenhagen,[1] which Glück believes were executed in the last decade of his life.[2]

The composition may have been inspired by such a work as *Diana*

and her Nymphs surprised by Satyrs by Rubens and Jan Brueghel I at
Schleissheim.[3] The pose of the nymph seen from the front recalls (in
reverse) that of Psyche in van Dyck's *Cupid and Psyche* (Royal Collection).[4]

The monogram on the reverse of the support may well be that of the
panel maker, Nicolaes Vrints, recorded as a master in the Antwerp
guild of S. Luke in the year 1637/8, when active as a frame maker; and
listed as a panel maker in the year 1640/1; he died in the year 1676/77.[5]

PROVENANCE: Presented by M. Forster, 1845; first catalogued, 1929.

REPRODUCTION: *National Gallery Illustrations, Continental Schools (excluding Italian)*, 1950, p. 406, top.

REFERENCES: *In text:* (1) Rep. by G. Glück, *Rubens, van Dyck und ihr Kreis*, 1933, figs. 123 and 133. (2) *Op. cit.*, p. 241. (3) Rep. by A. Rosenberg, *Rubens, K. der K.*, 1905, p. 212. (4) Rep. by G. Glück, *Van Dyck, K. der K.*, [1931], p. 362; see also O. Millar, *The Tudor, Stuart, and Early Georgian Pictures in the collection of . . . The Queen*, 1963, no. 166. (5) See Ph. Rombouts and Th. van Lerius, *De Liggeren* etc., [1864–1876], II, pp. 92, 125 and 456.

Appendix I

The Supports of Pictures by or associated with Rubens

Diagrams of some of the more simply constructed supports have not been included below. Nos. 59, 67, 853, 2968, 3818–9, all have canvas supports made up of a single piece; the support of no. 948 is a single sheet of paper. The oak supports of nos. 1865 and 2598 are made up out of two members joined vertically. The widths of the three pieces of paper that make up the support of no. 680 are given in the relevant entry.

Key to diagrams (the reproductions are not to scale)

The full, white lines represent joins in the supports.
As a general rule the grain of the wood in panel supports runs parallel with the length of the individual planks of which the support is composed. In the rare exceptions to this rule the direction of the wood grain is indicated by a white arrow.
The shaded areas in no. 66 indicate panel members, the thickness of which is made up of two layers of wood laminated together.
The dotted, white lines in no. 278 indicate the joins in the canvas support, the full white lines the joins in the panel support beneath.

No. 38

No. 46

No. 57

No. 66

No. 157

No. 187

No. 194

No. 278

No. 853P

No. 852

No. 1195

No. 2924

No. 4815

No. 6379

APPENDIX II

THE GROUNDS FOR PICTURES BY OR ASSOCIATED WITH RUBENS

N.G. No.	Support*	Type of ground
38	P	White ground of chalk (plus a trace of calcium sulphate) in glue medium; similar preparation on reverse of panel (subsequently covered with brown paint).
46	C	Orange-brown ground of a mixture of red lead, red ochre and lead white in oil medium.
57	P	White ground of chalk in glue medium.
59	C	Cream-coloured ground of lead white, slightly tinted with yellow ochre, in oil medium.
66	P	White ground of a mixture of chalk and gypsum in glue medium.
157	P	White ground of chalk in glue medium.
187	P	White ground of chalk and a small proportion of gypsum in glue medium (coating on reverse of panel is similar).
194	P	White ground of gypsum with a trace of chalk in glue medium.
278	C on P	Light brown ground of a mixture of lead white and brown ochre in oil medium.
279	Paper on C	Cream-coloured ground of lead white tinted with a little yellow ochre and in oil medium.
680	Paper on P	No ground; paper merely sized with glue preparatory to painting.
852	P	White ground of chalk in glue medium.
853p	P	White ground of chalk in glue medium.
1195	P	White ground of chalk with a comparatively high proportion of gypsum, in glue medium.
1865	P	White ground of chalk in glue medium.
2598	P	White ground of chalk in glue medium.
2924	P	White ground of chalk in glue medium.
2968	C	Orange-brown ground of a mixture of red lead, red ochre and lead white in oil medium; the ground is closely similar to that of no. 46.
4815	P	White ground of chalk, with a comparatively high gypsum content, in glue medium.
6379	P	White ground of chalk in glue medium.

N.G. No.	Support*	Type of ground
948	Paper on C	Light brown ground of lead white tinted with yellow-brown ochre and a little red lead in oil medium.
853	C	Whitish ground of chalk in glue medium.
67	C	Cream-coloured ground of lead white slightly tinted with red lead and ochre in oil medium.
3818	C	Thick white gesso ground of gypsum in glue medium.
3819	C	Thick white gesso ground of gypsum in glue medium.
279	Paper on C	Cream-coloured ground of lead white, tinted with a little yellow ochre, in oil medium.

*P = Panel   C = Canvas

Joyce Plesters

LIST OF CHANGED ATTRIBUTIONS

Attribution of 1958 *Summary Catalogue*	*Inventory number*	*Present Catalogue*
A. van Dyck	49	After (?) van Dyck
Studio of Rubens	59	Rubens
Studio of Rubens	67	Ascribed to the Studio of Rubens
D. Teniers II	154	Ascribed to D. Teniers II
Ascribed to van Dyck	156	Imitator of A. van Dyck
D. Teniers II	242	Ascribed to D. Teniers II
Rubens	279	After Rubens
Flemish School, XVII Century	659	Hendrick van Balen I and a follower of Jan Brueghel I
Ascribed to Rubens	680	Rubens
D. Teniers II	805	Follower of D. Teniers II
A. van Dyck	853	Studio of Rubens
Style of Rubens	948	Ascribed to Rubens
Ascribed to D. Teniers I	949	Ascribed to D. Teniers II
D. Teniers II	952	After D. Teniers II
D. Teniers II	953	Imitator of D. Teniers II
C. Huysmans	954	Ascribed to J.-B. Huysmans
Flemish School (?), XVII Century	1012	Ascribed to Peeter Franchoys
Flemish School, XVII Century	1017	Follower of Joos de Momper II
Coques	1118	After Coques
Ascribed to F. Snijders	1252	Follower of F. Snijders
Marten Rijckaert	1353	Ascribed to Marten Rijckaert
Hendrick van Steenwyck II	1443	Hendrick van Steenwyck II and Jan Brueghel I
Ascribed to Duchâtel	1810	Flemish School, XVII Century
A. van Dyck	1865	Rubens
P. Boel	1903	D. de Coninck
Flemish School (?), XVII Century	2104	To to catalogued in the Italian XVII Century School volume
Flemish School (?), XVII Century	2105	To be catalogued in the Italian XVII Century School volume
A van Dyck	2127	Ascribed to A. van Dyck
A. van Dyck	2144	Ascribed to A. van Dyck
Hendrick van Steenwyck II	2204	Hendrick van Steenwyck II and Jan Brueghel I
P. Neeffs the Elder	2205	Imitator of Hendrick van Steenwyck II
P. Neeffs the Elder	2206	P. Neeffs I and Bonaventura Peeters I
Ascribed to Brouwer	2569	Style of Brouwer
D. Teniers II	2599	Imitator of D. Teniers II
Follower of D. Teniers II	2601	Imitator of D. Teniers II
Flemish School, XVII Century	3132	Style of van Dyck
J. Suttermans	3227	Ascribed to J. Suttermans
Ascribed to Jan van Santvort	3404	Philippus van Santvoort
A. van Dyck	3605	Style of A. van Dyck

Attribution of 1958 Summary Catalogue	*Inventory number*	*Present Catalogue*
J. van Oost	3649	Ascribed to J. van Oost
After Rubens	3818–9	Ascribed to the Studio of Rubens
Ascribed to P. Brill	4029	To be catalogued in the Italian XVII Century School volume
Flemish School, XVII Century	5631	Ascribed to the Flemish School, XVII Century
Ascribed to David Teniers II	5866	Lucas van Uden and David Teniers II
Ascribed to Coques	6160	Imitator of Coques
J. Fyt	6335	Ascribed to J. Fyt

INDEX OF WORKS BY FLEMISH ARTISTS (a) VESTED IN THE TRUSTEES OF THE NATIONAL GALLERY AND/OR (b) INCLUDED IN THE 1929 CATALOGUE, NOT INCLUDED IN THIS CATALOGUE

Attribution	*Inv. no.*	
(a)		
After A. van Dyck	877	On loan to the Trustees of the National Portrait Gallery.
Studio of A. van Dyck	6363	On loan to the Trustees of the National Portrait Gallery.
Studio of A. van Dyck	6364	On loan to the Trustees of the National Portrait Gallery.
P. P. Rubens	853A–O	On loan to the Trustees of the British Museum (Department of Prints and Drawings).
(b)		
Attributed to J. Brueghel I	1881	Returned to the Victoria and Albert Museum
D. Teniers II	1869	Returned to the Victoria and Albert Museum.

SUBJECT INDEX (1)

Religious Subjects

(Scenes from the Bible and lives of the Saints, Biblical personages and Saints.)

Adoration of the Kings, The, nos. 3547, 1287*, 1443*
S. Agletrude (?), no. 57
S. Amand, no. 57
S. Ambrosius, no. 50
Amnon, no. 3404
S. Anthony of Padua (?), no. 203

S. Bavo, no. 57
Bathsheba, no. 1287*
S. Begga, no. 57
Betrayal of Christ, no. 1287*

Christ carrying the Cross, no. 2205*
Covetous Man, The, no. 155
Crucifixion, The, nos. 1865, 2205*

Eleazar, no. 59
S. Elizabeth, no. 3215
Emmaus, The Journey to, nos. 1287*, 2204*

Flight into Egypt, The, no. 1287*
S. Floribert, no. 57

S. George, nos. 67, 1287*
S. Gertrude, no. 57
Gideon, no. 3649*

S. Jerome, nos. 1287*, 2205*

S. John the Baptist, nos. 164, 1287*, 3215
S. John the Evangelist, no. 1865
S. Joseph, nos. 67, 164

Lazarus, The Raising of, nos. 1443*, 6384
S. Longinus, no. 1865

S. Mary of Cleophas (?), no. 1865
S. Mary Magdalene, nos. 1865, 2206* (?)
Miraculous Draught of Fishes, The, no. 680
Moses, no. 59

S. Peter, no. 680
S. Peter, The Deliverance of, no. 1287*

Rich Man, Parable of the, no. 863
Ruffinus (?), no. 50

Salome, no. 1287*
Samaria, Christ and the woman of, no. 2204*
Serpent, The Brazen, no. 59

Tamar, no. 3404
Theodosius, The Emperor, no. 50

Virgin, The, no. 1865
Virgin and Child, nos. 67, 164, 1287*, 2205–7*, 3215

Zacharias, no. 3215

*An asterisk indicates that the person or subject is a minor part of the picture.

SUBJECT INDEX (2)

Profane Subjects

(Scenes from classical myth etc. and history; gods and personages, from myth, fiction and history; allegories and personifications.)

Abundance, no. 187*
Alecto, nos. 194, 279
Alexander, no. 1287*
Amphitrite, no. 1195*
Andromeda, no. 1287*
Anger, no. 187
Armida, no. 877B
Aurora, no. 2598

Bacchus, The Triumph of, no. 1287*
Birth of Venus, The, no. 1195

Carlo, no. 877B
Cassiope, Queen, no. 1287*
Cephalus, no. 2598
Cepheus, King, no. 1287*
Ceres, no. 1287*

*An asterisk indicates that the subject or person is a minor part of the picture.

SUBJECT INDEX (3)

Scenes from Everyday Life

*An asterisk indicates that the subject is a minor part of the picture.

INDEX OF SITTERS

*An asterisk indicates that the sitter is only a minor part of the picture.

INDEX OF PREVIOUS OWNERS

Anon. sale, 21 October, 1739 (?), 2600
Anon. sale, 5 March, 1791 (?), 2600
Anon. sale, 4 May, 1805 (?), 2600, 154
Anon. sale, 27 June, 1807 (?), no. 154
Anon. sale, 28 June, 1814, no. 155
Anon. sale, 29 June, 1814, no. 817
Anon. sale, 8 May, 1824 (?), no. 2599
Anon. sale, 6 May, 1826 (?), no. 2599
Anon. sale, 5–6 May, 1873, no. 2599
Anon. = Delahante
Anon. = Mrs. Edgar Disney
Anon. = Duncan
Anon. = Miss Farrant
Anon. = Hart-Davis
Anon. = Lafontaine
Anon. = Parke, J.
Anon. = Séréville
Anon. = T. Tomkinson
Anon. = H. Tresham
Anon. = C. J. Wertheimer
Aertselaer, d' see H. J. Stier
Agnew, nos. 1011, 1195, 2600, 4889
Alford, Lord, no. 3011
Amor, no. 5633
Angerstein, J. J., nos. 38, 49, 50, 52, 67, 89
Ansell, R. (?), nos. 951, 154
Anthoine, J.-B., no. 877B
Aveschoot, Schamp d', no. 1865
Armagnac, d' (=?Charles, Comte), no. 4815
Aston, W. W., no. 3227
Astorg, Comte d', no. 805

Baillie (?), no. 2599
Baillieur, C. de. (?), no. 203
Baily, N. (?), no. 2599
Balbi, Costantino (1676–ca. 1741) (?), no. 278
Balbi, Costantino, no. 66, 278
Balbi, F. M., no. 3011
Balbi, Giacomo, nos. 66, 278
Balme, Rev. E. (?), no. 2204
Bandon, Earls of, no. 5851
Battersea, Constance, Lady, no. 4889
Bavaria, Elector of, see Duke Maximilian II Emanuel
Bearcroft, Dr. (?), no. 951
Beaucousin, E., no. 659
Beaumont, Sir George, no. 66
Beaumont, Lady, no. 66
Beauvau, Prince de, no. 3132
Beckett, J. S., no. 1287
Beckford, W., nos. 141, (?) 2205
Bellanger, no. 2600
Berca, Graf (?), no. 278
Birch, Charles (?), no. 38
Blamire, G. no. 1865

Bonaparte, Prince Lucien, no. 853
Bonnemaison, Chevalier F., no. 853
Bonomi, see Cereda
Bosschaert, Madame la Douarière, no. 38
Bosschaert, J. J. no. 38
Bradford, T., no. 154
Brockedon, no. 278
Brown, T. B., no. 959
Brownlow, Earl (1842–1867), no. 3011
Brownlow, Earl (1844–1921), no. 3011
Brueghel, J., I, nos. 1443, 2204
Brunning, H. C., nos. 2204, 2205, 2206, 2207
Bryan, no. 52
Buccleuch, Dukes of, nos. 4815
Buchanan, W., nos. 46, 57, 59, 66, 278, 279, 857–60
Buckingham, Marquess and Dukes of, no. 950
Bulkeley, Owen, see Owen
Burton, D., no. 1252

Calcott-Brunning, see Brunning
Carelli, Cavaliere R., no. 680
Carlisle, Earls of, nos. 2924, 2968
Carr, see Holwell-Carr
Carrega family, no. 57
Carstairs, Mrs. C. S., no. 6160
Cattaneo family, nos. 2127, 2144
Cereda-Bonomi, nos. 3818–9
Ceulen, Gisbert van, no. 1172
Champernowne, A., nos. 46, 66, 278, 279
Champion, W., no. 59
Chariot (?), no. 659
Charles I, nos. 46, 1172
Churchill (?), no. 154
Clarke, Miss J., no. 600
Clarke, Sir Simon, no. 2600
Cleeve, Bouchier, no. 952
Clerk, J., see Lord Eldin
Colborne, N. W. Ridley (Lord Colborne), no. 242
Colnaghi, nos. 2127, 2130, 2144, 5633, 5851
Cope, C., no. 2600
Cooper, R. W., no. 1353
Coulter, A., no. 6379
Cowper, Dowager Countess, no. 3605
Cox, no. 1443
Craig, General (?), no. 2600
Crawford (?), no. 2204
Cressent, no. 2924

Davis, see Hart-Davis
Decordes, Dr., nos. 1114–8
Delahante, A., nos. 194, 154 (?)
Delmé, Peter, no. 156
Denison, C. B., nos. 1195, 2204

NUMERICAL INDEX

2206	P. Neeffs I and B. Peeters I	3818–9	Ascribed to the Studio of Rubens
2207	P. Neeffs I	3963	Flemish School, later part of XVII Century
2527	G. Coques		
2569	Style of A. Brouwer	3966	A. Stevens
2598	P. P. Rubens	4040	H. van Steenwyck II
2599	Imitator of D. Teniers II	4815	P. P. Rubens
2600	D. Teniers II	4889	A. van Dyck
2601	Imitator of D. Teniers II	4976	Follower of H. Janssens
2924	P. P. Rubens	5631	Ascribed to the Flemish School, 1636
2968	P. P. Rubens		
3011	A. van Dyck	5633	A. van Dyck
3132	Style of A. van Dyck	5851	D. Teniers II
3215	J. Jordaens	5866	L. van Uden and D. Teniers II
3227	Ascribed to J. Sutter-mans		
		6160	Imitator of G. Coques
3270	A. Stevens	6293	J. Jordaens
3404	P. van Santvoort	6335	Ascribed to J. Fyt
3537	After A. van Dyck	6379	P. P. Rubens
3547	J. Brueghel I	6384	Ascribed to the Flemish School, XVII Century
3605	Follower of A. van Dyck		
3649	Ascribed to J. van Oost I		

LIST OF PAINTINGS ACQUIRED
SINCE 1970

Peter Paul RUBENS
1577–1640

6393 PORTRAIT OF LUDOVICUS NONNIUS

Inscribed on the bust: HIPPOCRATES (in Greek letters)
Wood, 124·4 × 92·2 (49 × 39$\frac{1}{4}$)
Purchased, 1970.

6461 SAMSON AND DELILAH

Wood (oak), 185 × 205 (72$\frac{3}{4}$ × 81)
Purchased, 1980.

Anthony van DYCK
1599–1641

6437 LADY ELIZABETH THIMBELBY AND DOROTHY,
VISCOUNTESS ANDOVER

Canvas, 132·1 × 149 (52 × 59)
Purchased by private treaty from Earl Spencer, 1977.

6494 CHARITY

Wood (oak), 148·2 × 107·5 (58$\frac{1}{4}$ × 42$\frac{1}{4}$)
Purchased, 1984.